COUNCIL OF SOCIETIES
FOR THE STUDY OF RELIGION

DIRECTORY

OF DEPARTMENTS AND PROGRAMS
OF RELIGIOUS STUDIES
IN NORTH AMERICA

1999 Edition

David G. Truemper, Editor

Council on the Study of Religion, Inc.
Valparaiso, Indiana
1999

BL
41
.D57
1999

Additional copies of this directory are
available for $40.00 (prepaid) from the
CSSR Executive Office, Valparaiso
University, Valparaiso IN 46383-6493.
Phone: 888-422-2777.
FAX: 219-464-6714
E-mail: cssr@valpo.edu.

An electronic version of this Directory is
available at our Web site: www.cssr.org.

ISBN 1-883135-10-9 (Cloth)

PREFACE

The entries in the main body of the *Directory* represent the responses to a questionnaire mailed in 1999 to four-year schools with departments or programs of religious studies or theology and to theological schools. The statistical data given therefore are, with some exceptions (e.g., from later submissions), those available at the time of completion of the questionnaire. Data on faculty personnel are generally current as of late spring or early summer of 1999.

Each entry supplies the information necessary to contact the department or school or to obtain further information about it. For schools with graduate programs the *Directory* also provides data on degrees offered and granted, on the nature and size of the program, on research facilities, requirements, financial aid, and a profile of the graduate student population.

The *Directory* is thus intended to aid schools with religious studies departments or programs in their day-to-day work as well as to provide them with comparative data for use in self-assessments and long-range planning. Students contemplating the study or teaching of religious studies at the undergraduate or graduate level, and persons counseling them, should also find the *Directory* useful.

All schools that have been identified as meeting the criteria for inclusion are listed in the main section of this book, whether they have chosen to submit a full listing or not. Users therefore may simply turn to the entry for the school for which they seek information, and they will find printed there the extent of information submitted by that institution.

The strong response from participating schools has been both encouraging and a clear indication of the value of the annual publication of this *Directory*.

See also the electronic version of this *Directory* at our web site: **www.cssr.org** for a searchable on-line way to accesss this information.

I wish to thank Pam Gleason, the Council's Office Manager, and Emilie Owens, student aide, for their careful work in the production of this volume.

David G. Truemper
Valparaiso University
Valparaiso, Indiana
December 1999

USER'S GUIDE

Entries are alphabetized according to the key word in the title (University of Michigan appears in the M's, e.g., but Central Michigan University in the C's), except that all the "Saint" schools are grouped under "Saint" and then in alphabetical order according to the name of the saint.

Within a state, **State Colleges** are listed first, then **State Universities, then "University of"** (see the California state schools).

Under **Faculty** the date in parentheses is the year in which the person's highest degree was conferred. The date following the parentheses indicates the year the person was appointed in the department or school. Ecclesiastical titles and initials of ecclesiastical orders are generally not included.

Some information on professional degree programs (e.g., MDiv, DMin) has been provided by theological schools but is generally outside the purview of this *Directory*.

Where expected data are missing from the entry of a school, it generally means they were not supplied by the school.

Appendix A lists theological schools in the U.S. and Canada, including those holding Accredited or Associate status with the Association of Theological Schools as well as schools not related to the ATS.

Appendix B lists schools belonging to the Council on Graduate Studies in Religion.

The **first index** lists all participating schools alphabetically within a state or province. The index thus gives a geographical overview of departments and programs of religious studies, while the main body of the *Directory* lists the schools alphabetically.

The **second index** lists all faculty members reported in the entries of participating schools, indicating on which page(s) information regarding that person is printed.

TABLE OF CONTENTS

Abilene Christian University

ACU Station
Box 29400
Abilene TX 79699-9400

Phone: 915-674-3700
Fax: 915-674-3776
E-mail: reese@bible.acu.edu

TYPE OF INSTITUTION: Private, Churches of Christ

EXECUTIVE OFFICER: Jack R. Reese, Dean

CHAIRPERSONS: David Wray, Undergraduate Bible and ministry; James Thompson, Graduate Bible and ministry; Waymon Hinson, marriage and family

UNDERGRADUATE ENROLLMENT: 4,806

GRADUATE ENROLLMENT: 450

DEGREES OFFERED: BA, BS

UNDERGRADUATE MAJORS: 275

DEGREES CONFERRED: 25

DESCRIPTION OF UNDERGRADUATE PROGRAM: The Department of Undergraduate Bible and Ministry offers the Bachelor of Science Degree and the Bachelor of Arts Degree. A cumulative GPA of 2.25 is required of all degrees in Bible. The department exists for the purpose of educating students for Christian leadership throughout the world. From this central purpose of training Christian leaders, two emphases emerge: 1) training ministers of the Gospel of Christ, including preachers, missionaries, and youth ministers and 2) training students who will become active church leaders and servants in the Lord's kingdom. The department provides instruction and knowledge of the Bible and related studies to help students become intellectually and practically grounded in the Christian faith. It also provides an environment in which the student's faith can be a personal experience to be lived and shared. Specifically, the department seeks: 1) To prepare for, and deepen faith in God, Christ, and the Holy Spirit. 2) To instill in every student a deep commitment to the Bible as the inspired Word of God, and to the church of our Lord. 3) To furnish basic training for sound biblical interpretation. 4) To inspire students to develop a life-long practice of Bible study. 5) To convey an understanding of the history of Christianity and its contemporary expressions. 6) To explore the nature of religion and the contemporary world and to understand how Christianity relates to them; and 7) To teach students to think deeply and to formulate for themselves an integrated and well-grounded Christian world view with clearly defined goals, purposes, and assumptions. The study of the Bible as God's word is at the heart of the curriculum of Abilene Christian University and is the reason for the existence of the university. An education without knowledge of the spiritual is sadly lacking, since only the information and strength derived from the Word of God can furnish the world view and the sense of meaning and purpose so necessary to the happy and useful life. Four-year graduates of the university from all the departments must take two and one-half years of courses in Bible, with two full years in a study of the text itself. The Department of Missions functions as a part of the College of Biblical Studies, administered by a chair under the dean of the college. A BA degree may be obtained with a major in missions. Certificates and minors are also offered. On the graduate level, An MA is offered, along with a program missions "track" in the MDiv program.

GRADUATE PROGRAM

Member of the Council on Graduate Studies in Religion

Graduate Advisor: James Thompson

Graduate Degrees Offered: MA; MS; MDiv; DMin

Degrees Conferred: 11 MA; 59 MS; 16 MDiv

Graduate Students in Residence: 18 MA; 134 Other

Not in Residence: 69 Other

Average No. of New Students Enrolled: 5 MA; 70 Other

Women Students: 3 MA; 21 Other

Minority Students: 3 MA; 31 Other

Foreign Students: 1 MA; 13 Other

Minimum GRE Score Requisite to Admission: 800, verbal and quantative

Minimum GPA Score Requisite to Admission: Yes, 3.0

Foreign Language Proficiency Evaluated: Yes, 550 TOEFL

Financial Aid to First Year Students: 90% MA; 90% Other

Financial Aid to Other Students: 90% MA; 90% Other

Attrition Among Students: 4% MA; 4% Other

Graduates Placed: 95% MA; 95% Other

DESCRIPTION OF GRADUATE PROGRAM AND RESEARCH FACILITIES: Abilene Christian University Graduate School of Theology offers the MA, MS, MMFT, MDiv and DMin degrees. Fields of study are available in Old Testament, New Testament, Greek New Testament, History of Christian Thought, Theology, Marriage and Family Therapy, Missions, Missiology. Master of Arts Religion, 54 hours, possibility of advanced standing. All MA programs are 36 hours including thesis. MS programs are 36 hours with no thesis (MMFT requires more hours). The MMFT is a 60 hour COAMFTE-approved program. The MDiv is an 84 hour program. The DMin is a 30 hour post-MDiv degree. The Graduate departments are Associate Members of the Association of Theological Schools. The ACU library offers excellent research opportunities and is linked to a national inter-library loan system which extends research opportunities far beyond the local library's capacity and is fully computer automated.

ACADEMIC PLAN, ADMISSION REQUIREMENTS, FINANCIAL AID: Abilene Christian University operates on a two-semester, Maymester (three weeks' intensive study), and Summmester (two summer terms, each of five weeks' intensive study) program. Most undergraduate degrees require 128-134 semesters hours' credit for graduation. The university is fully accredited by the Southern Association of Colleges and Schools, and other national accrediting agencies. Preparation for the undergraduate degrees is in the liberal arts fields. The university is divided into three colleges: Business Administration, Arts and Sciences, and Biblical Studies. Adequate scholarship aid on both the undergraduate and graduate levels is available to the students through both federal programs and private scholarship funds.

FACULTY:

Aquino, Frederick, PhD (cand.), Southern Methodist University (1999), 1998, Instructor—theology and philosophy, 915-674-3789

Ash, Anthony L., PhD, University of Southern California (1966), 1985, Professor—biblical studies, 915-674-3788

Ashlock, Rodney, PhD (cand.), Baylor University (1999), Instructor—biblical studies, 915-674-3787

Boglin, Major, MMFT, Abilene Christian University (1995), 1996, Assistant Professor—marriage and family therapy, 915-674-3722, E-mail: boglin@bible.acu.edu

Brecheen, Carl, DRE, Southwestern Baptist Theological Seminary (1965), 1952, Professor—Bible and ministry, 915-674-3750

Childers, Jeff, DPhil, Oxford University, England (1996), Assistant Professor—biblical studies and biblical languages, 915-674-3797

Cukrowski, Ken, PhD, Yale University (1994), Associate Professor—biblical studies, 915-674-3700

Fair, Ian A., PhD, University of Natal (South Africa) (1978), Professor—systematic theology, New Testament, 915-674-3782

Ferguson, Everett, PhD, Harvard University (1960), 1962, Professor—church history, 915-674-3734

Foster, Douglas, PhD, Vanderbilt University (1987), 1991, Associate Professor—church history, 915-674-3795

Guild, Sonny, DMin, Abilene Christian University (1996), Instructor—biblical studies, 915-674-3765

Halstead, Jackie, PhD (cand.), Iowa State University (1999), 1998, Instructor—marriage and family therapy, 915-674-3724, E-mail: halstead@bible.acu.edu

Harris, Randy, PhD (cand.), Syracuse University (1999), Instructor—biblical studies, 915-674-3793

Hinson, Waymon, PhD, University of Mississippi (1982), 1984, Professor—marriage and family therapy, 915-674-3778, E-mail: hinson@bible.acu.edu

Lightfoot, Neil R., PhD, Duke University (1958), 1958, Frank and Della Pack Distinguished Professor in the Chair of New Testament, 915-674-3738

Mathews, Edward F., DMiss, Fuller Theological Seminary (1980), 1980, Professor—missions, 915-674-3758

Milholland, Thomas, PhD, Texas Tech University (1979), 1979, Assistant Provost for Institutional Effectiveness and Professor—marriage and family studies, 915-674-3722, E-mail: milholland@nicanor.acu.edu

Money, Royce, PhD, Baylor University (1975), President of the University, Professor—Bible, 915-674-2412

Oglesby, Robert, Jr., MS, MFT, Abilene Christian University (1982), Instructor—youth and family studies, 915-674-3798

Osburn, Carroll D., PhD, University of St Andrews, Scotland (1974), 1987, Art Carmichael Distinguished Professor—New Testament studies, 915-674-3799

Reese, Jack R., PhD, University of Iowa, School of Religion (1988), 1988, Dean and Professor—Bible, homiletics, 915-674-3700

Sensing, Timothy, PhD, University of North Carolina at Greensboro (1998), Director of Supervised Practice of Ministry—field education, 915-674-3792

Siburt, Charles, DMin, Austin Presbyterian Theological Seminary (1978), 1988, Associate Professor—Director of Doctor of ministry program, 915-674-3732

Thompson, James, PhD, Vanderbilt University (1974), 1992, Professor—biblical studies, biblical languages, 915-674-3730

Van Rheenen, Gailyn, DMiss, Trinity Evangelical Divinity School (1990), 1988, Associate Professor—missions, 915-674-3753

Wallace, David, PhD, Baylor University (1995), 1988, Associate Professor—biblical studies and biblical languages, 915-674-3740

Willis, John T., PhD, Vanderbilt University (1966), 1971, Burton Coffman Distinguished Professor—biblical studies, 915-674-3736

Willis, Wendell, PhD, Southern Methodist University (1981), 1994, Associate Professor—biblical studies and biblical languages, 915-674-3796

Wray, David, DRE, Temple Baptist Seminary (1996), 1990, Chair, undergraduate Bible and ministry, Associate Professor—Christian education, Christian ministry, 915-674-3740

Rabbinical Seminary of Adas Yereim

185 Wilson St, Brooklyn NY 11211

Adelphi University

Garden City NY 11530

Adrian College

Dept of Religion and Philosophy
North Hall
Adrian MI 49221

Phone: 517-265-4401
Fax: 517-264-3100
E-mail: gaichele@adrian.adrian.edu
URL: users.tc3net.com/gaiche

TYPE OF INSTITUTION: Private, United Methodist
EXECUTIVE OFFICER: Stanley Caine, President
CHAIRPERSON: George Aichele
UNDERGRADUATE ENROLLMENT: 1,100

Universidad Adventista De Las Antillas

Box 118, Mayaguez PR 00681

Agape Bible College

920 South Grandview St, Los Angeles CA 90006

Agnes Scott College

Dept of Religion
141 E College Ave
Decatur GA 30030-3797

Phone: 404-638-6000
Fax: 404-638-6177
E-mail: firstinitiallastname@agnesscott.edu

TYPE OF INSTITUTION: Private
EXECUTIVE OFFICER: Mary Brown Bullock, President
CHAIRPERSON: Tina Pippin
UNDERGRADUATE ENROLLMENT: 746
GRADUATE ENROLLMENT: 21

University of Alabama

Dept of Religious Studies, Tuscaloosa AL 35487-0264

Alabama Bible Institute

PO Box 727, Guin AL 35563

University of Alaska

3211 Providence Drive
Anchorage AK 99508

Phone: 907-786-4455
Fax: 907-786-4383
E-mail: afrhk@uaa.alaska.edu

TYPE OF INSTITUTION: Public
EXECUTIVE OFFICER: Theodore L. Kassier, Dean
CHAIRPERSON: Rubert Kuhner

Alaska Bible College

Box 289, Glenn Allen AK 99588

Alaska Pacific University

Dept of Liberal Studies
4101 University Dr
Anchorage AK 99508

Phone: 907-564-8274
Fax: 907-562-4276
E-mail: boiscl@corecom.net
URL: moose.alaskapacific.edu

TYPE OF INSTITUTION: Private, Non-Denominational (Methodist Heritage)
EXECUTIVE OFFICER: Douglas North, PhD, President
COORDINATOR: Regina A. Boislcair, PhD, Religious and Theological Studies, Cardinal Newman Chair of Catholic Thought
UNDERGRADUATE ENROLLMENT: 450
GRADUATE ENROLLMENT: 200

University of Alberta

Religious Studies Program
Dept of Modern Language and
Comparative Studies
200 Old Arts Building
Edmonton, Alberta T6G 2E6 Canada

Phone: 403-492-2174
Fax: 403-492-2715
E-mail: ewaugh@gpu.srv.ualberta.ca

TYPE OF INSTITUTION: Public
CHAIRPERSON: Earle H. Waugh
UNDERGRADUATE ENROLLMENT: 1,600
GRADUATE ENROLLMENT: 15

Albertson College of Idaho

2112 Cleveland Blvd, Caldwell ID 83605

Albertus Magnus College

New Haven CT 06511

Albion College

Department of Religious Studies
Albion MI 49224

Phone: 517-629-0207
Fax: 517-629-0286
E-mail: fsfrick@alpha.albion.edu
URL: www.albion.edu/fac/relg

TYPE OF INSTITUTION: Private, United Methodist
EXECUTIVE OFFICER: Jeff Carrier, Dean of the Faculty
CHAIRPERSON: Frank S. Frick
UNDERGRADUATE ENROLLMENT: 1,600
DEGREES OFFERED: AB
UNDERGRADUATE MAJORS: 20
DEGREES CONFERRED: 4 per year
DESCRIPTION OF UNDERGRADUATE PROGRAM: Our department offers courses in a liberal arts context. Our curriculum includes "standard" courses plus courses concentrating on environmental studies, gender studies, and ethnicity studies.
FACULTY:

Frick, Frank S., PhD, Princeton University (1970), 1969, Stanley S. Kresge Professor and Chair—Hebrew Bible and Judaica, 517-629-0354, Fax: 517-629-0286, E-mail: fsfrick@albion.edu

Gillham, William, PhD, Princeton University (1964), 1961, Professor—theology and ethics, 517-629-0209, Fax: 517-629-0286, E-mail: wgillham@albion.edu

Raj, Selva J., PhD, Chicago (1994), 1995, Assistant Professor—Asian religions, comparative religion, 517-629-0400, Fax: 517-629-0286, E-mail: sraj@albion.edu

Albright College

PO Box 15234, Reading PA 19612-5234

Alderson-Broaddus College

Phillippi WV 26416

Alfred University

Religious Studies Program
Division of Human Studies
Saxon Drive
Alfred NY 14802-1205

Phone: 607-871-2217
Fax: 607-871-2831
E-mail: hustud@bigvax.alfred.edu
URL: www.alfred.edu/college/la/religion.html

TYPE OF INSTITUTION: Private, Non-Denominational
EXECUTIVE OFFICER: William Hall, Dean of College of Liberal Arts and Sciences
CHAIRPERSON: Vicki L. Eaklor
COORDINATOR: Thomas V. Peterson
UNDERGRADUATE ENROLLMENT: 2,000
GRADUATE ENROLLMENT: 500
DEGREES OFFERED: BA Major in Comparative Cultures, BA Minor in Religious Studies

DEGREES CONFERRED: 15

DESCRIPTION OF UNDERGRADUATE PROGRAM: The religious studies program is in the division of Human Studies, which offers majors in philosophy and history. Religious Studies has combined with Anthropology to offer a major in "Comparative Cultures." Field-work projects are required; study abroad is encouraged. Courses in religious studies are also an integral part of the philosophy of religion track of the philosophy major. Because religious beliefs, rituals, and values bear on all aspects of life, a minor in religious studies supplements many majors in the liberal arts college.

FACULTY:

Cassidy, William J., III, PhD, Graduate Theological Union, Berkeley (1985), 1987, Associate Professor—ancient religions, East Asian religions, history of religions, 607-871-2704, E-mail: fcassidy@bigvax.alfred.edu

Peterson, Thomas V., PhD, Stanford (1975), 1975, Professor—ritual studies, history of religions, philosophy of religions, American religions, 607-871-2998, E-mail: fpett@bigvax.alfred.edu

---

Allegheny College

Dept of Religious Studies
Meadville PA 16335

Phone: 814-332-3316
Fax: 814-333-8180
E-mail: gholland@alleg.edu

TYPE OF INSTITUTION: Private, Methodist

EXECUTIVE OFFICER: Bruce Smith, Dean

CHAIRPERSON: Glenn Holland

UNDERGRADUATE ENROLLMENT: 1,800

DEGREES OFFERED: BA

UNDERGRADUATE MAJORS: 10

DEGREES CONFERRED: 2

DESCRIPTION OF UNDERGRADUATE PROGRAM: Religious Studies offers students a wide range of educational experiences through its faculty and curriculum and its cross-cultural and multi-disciplinary approach. The course program in the department enables a student to integrate selected courses into a variety of academic preparations which includes biblical studies, history of religions, ethics, history of the church, and religion and culture.

FACULTY:

Holland, Glenn, PhD, University of Chicago (1985), 1985, Associate Professor and Chairperson—biblical studies, church history, ancient religions, 814-332-3316, Fax: 814-333-8180, E-mail: gholland@alleg.edu

Olson, Carl, PhD, Drew University (1977), 1981, Professor—Hinduism, Buddhism, Islam, tribal religions, comparative philosophy, methodology, 814-332-3313, Fax: 814-333-8180, E-mail: colson@alleg.edu

Russell, Helene, PhD, Claremont Graduate School (1997) 1997, Assistant Professor—theology, ethics, church history, 814-332-3621, Fax: 814-333-8180, E-mail: hrussell@alleg.edu

---

Allegheny Wesleyan College

2161 Woodsdale Rd
Salem OH 44460

Phone: 330-337-6403
Fax: 330-337-6255
E-mail: college@awc.edu

TYPE OF INSTITUTION: Private, Wesleyan Methodist
EXECUTIVE OFFICER: David Phelps, Sr., President
UNDERGRADUATE ENROLLMENT: 100

Allentown College of St Francis de Sales

2755 Station Avenue
Center Valley PA 18034-9568

Phone: 610-282-1100, ext 1464
Fax: 610-282-2254
URL: www4.allencol.edu/~philtheo/

TYPE OF INSTITUTION: Private, Roman Catholic
EXECUTIVE OFFICER: Karen Walton, Vice President for Academic Affairs
CHAIRPERSON: Thomas F. Dailey, OSFS
UNDERGRADUATE ENROLLMENT: 1,700
GRADUATE ENROLLMENT: 400
DEGREES OFFERED: BA
UNDERGRADUATE MAJORS: 14
DEGREES CONFERRED: 1
DESCRIPTION OF UNDERGRADUATE: The study of Theology seeks to fulfill the mission of Allentown College of St Francis by: 1) facilitating within Theology majors the formation of a comprehensive understanding of and appreciation for the Christian vision within the many dimensions of human experience as preparation for further study and/or immediate activity in teaching or pastoral ministry; 2) facilitating within all students the formation of a basic understanding of the central tenets of Roman Catholic Theology and an appreciation of the Christian vision in at least one dimension of human experience so that their faith might be more enlightened and more powerfully present in their lives; 3) encouraging all students and faculty to engage in theological reflection upon their own lived experiences and their own chosen disciplines; and 4) engaging in a continuing dialogue with the institutions of the Lehigh Valley Association of Independent Colleges and the larger community of the Lehigh Valley (PA).
FACULTY:
Chapp, Larry, PhD, Fordham University (1994), 1994, Assistant Professor—systematic theology, 610-282-1100 ext 1264, Fax: 610-282-2254, E-mail: lsc0@email.allencol.edu
Dailey, Thomas F., STD, Pontifical Gregorian University (1993), 1988, Associate Professor and Chairperson—biblical theology, 610-282-1100 ext 1464, Fax: 610-282-2254, E-mail: dailey@faculty_1.allencol.edu
Harvey, John F., STD, Catholic University of America (1951), 1987, Professor (part-time)—sexual ethics, 610-282-3300, Fax: 610-282-2254
Kane, Brian M., PhD, Marquette University (1994), 1992, Associate Professor—moral theology, 610-282-1100 ext 1274, Fax: 610-282-2254, E-mail: kane@faculty_1.allencol.edu
Magnusen Chapp, Carmina, PhD, Duquesne University (1997), 1996, Instructor—liturgical theology, 610-282-1100, Fax: 610-282-2254, E-mail: cmm2@email.allencol.edu
Pocetto, Alexander T., PhD, Université Laval (1970), 1993, Professor—Salesian spirituality, 610-282-1100 ext 1234, Fax: 610-282-2059, E-mail: atp0@email.allencol.edu
Urbine, William F., DMin, Eastern Baptist Theological Seminary (1985), 1979, Adjunct Instructor—pastoral theology, 610-791-3888

Alliance Theological Seminary

350 North Highland Ave, Nyack NY 10960-1416

Alma College

Dept of Religious Studies, Alma MI 48801

Alvernia College

400 Saint Bernardine St
Reading PA 19607

Phone: 610-796-8200
Fax: 610-777-6632
E-mail: www.vignage.alvernia.edu
URL: www.alvernia.edu

TYPE OF INSTITUTION: Denominational: Roman Catholic
EXECUTIVE OFFICER: Lawrence Mazzeno, President
CHAIRPERSON: Gerald S. Vigna
UNDERGRADUATE ENROLLMENT: 1,200
DEGREES OFFERED: BA Theology and Philosophy, BA Theology
UNDERGRADUATE MAJORS: 6
DEGREES CONFERRED: 0
DESCRIPTION OF UNDERGRADUATE PROGRAM: The Department of Theology and Philosophy plays a significant role in the core curriculum of the college. It offers a joint major in Theology and Philosophy designed for those seeking a career in the academic study of religion or in ministry and a 30-credit theology major. There are separate minors available in either discipline. The department seeks to develop in students an awareness of the college's Franciscan tradition and its relevance to contemporary life.
FACULTY:

Godfrey, Kevin, PhD, St Louis University (1996), 1996, Assistant Professor—historical and systematic theology, spirituality, medieval theology, 610-796-8223, Fax: 610-777-6632
Stichler, Richard N., PhD, Georgetown University (1978), 1984, Professor—ethics, social and political philosophy, virtue ethics, Greek philosophy, 610-796-8316, Fax: 610-777-6632, E-mail: rns7@kutztown.edu.
Vigna, Gerald S., PhD, Northwestern University (1980), 1992, Associate Professor—fundamental moral theology; sexual, social, and medical ethics; Christian origins, 610-796-8365, Fax: 610-777-6632, E-mail: www.vignage.alvernia.edu

Alverno College

3401 South 39th Street
PO Box 343922
Milwaukee WI 53234-3922

Phone: 414-382-6364
Fax: 414-382-6354
E-mail: leisd831@aol.com

TYPE OF INSTITUTION: Private, Roman Catholic
CHAIRPERSON: Daniel Leister
UNDERGRADUATE ENROLLMENT: 2,300

Amber University

1700 Eastgate Dr, Garland TX 75041

Rabbinical Seminary of America

92-15 69th Ave, New York NY 11375

American Baptist College

1800 White's Creek Pk
Nashville TN 37207

Phone:
Fax: 615-226-7855

TYPE OF INSTITUTION: Private, National Baptist Convention, USA, Inc.
EXECUTIVE OFFICER: Forrest E. Harris, Sr., President

American Baptist Seminary of the West

2606 Dwight Way
Berkeley CA 94704

Phone: 510-841-1905
Fax: 510-841-2446
E-mail: dschirer@absw.edu
URL: www.absw.edu

TYPE OF INSTITUTION: Private, American Baptist Churches USA
EXECUTIVE OFFICER: Keith A. Russell, President
GRADUATE ENROLLMENT: 81

American Christian Schools of Religion

PO Box 1334
Monroe LA 71201

Phone: 318-323-2666
Fax: 318-322-6833
E-mail: elders@bayou.com

TYPE OF INSTITUTION: Private, Non-Denominational
EXECUTIVE OFFICER: Donald A. De Lukie, President

American Indian College of the Assemblies of God

10020 N 15th Ave
Phoenix AZ 85021

Phone: 602-944-3335
Fax: 602-943-8299
E-mail: compuserve75127,1175

TYPE OF INSTITUTION: Private, Assemblies of God
EXECUTIVE OFFICER: W. Duane Collins DMiss
CHAIRPERSON: J. E. Dempsey
UNDERGRADUATE ENROLLMENT: 120

Amherst College

Religion Dept
Box 2252
Amherst MA 01002

Phone: 413-542-2181
Fax: 413-542-2727
E-mail: name@amherst.edu

TYPE OF INSTITUTION: Private
EXECUTIVE OFFICER: Tom Gerety, President
CHAIRPERSON: Janet Gytso
UNDERGRADUATE ENROLLMENT: 1,600

Anderson College

316 Boulevard
Anderson SC 29621

Phone: 864-231-2000
Fax: 864-231-2004
URL: www.anderson-college.edu

TYPE OF INSTITUTION: Private, Southern Baptist
EXECUTIVE OFFICER: Lee Royce, President
COORDINATOR: Shirley Jacks
UNDERGRADUATE ENROLLMENT: 1,000

Anderson University, School of Theology

1100 East 5th St, Anderson IN 46012

Anderson University

1100 East Fifth Street
Anderson IN 46012

Phone: 317-641-4500
Fax: 317-641-3851
E-mail: anderson.edu

TYPE OF INSTITUTION: Private, Church of God
EXECUTIVE OFFICER: Blake D. Janutolo, Dean, School of Science and Humanities
CHAIRPERSON: Merle D. Strege
UNDERGRADUATE ENROLLMENT: 1,800

Andover Newton Theological School

210 Herrick Road, Newton Centre MA 02159

Andrews University Theological Seminary

Andrews University
Berrien Springs MI 49104-1500

Phone: 616-471-3537
Fax: 616-471-6202
E-mail: seminary@andrews.edu
URL: www.andrews.edu/SEM

TYPE OF INSTITUTION: Private, Seventh-day Adventist

EXECUTIVE OFFICER: Werner Vyhmeister, Dean
GRADUATE ENROLLMENT: 434

Annenberg Research Institute

420 Walnut St, Philadelphia PA 19106

Antioch College

Yellow Springs OH 45387

Apostolic Bible Institute Inc

6944 Hudson Blvd N, Saint Paul MN 55128

Appalachian Bible College

Box ABC, Bradley WV 25818

Appalachian State University

Philosophy and Religion Dept
114 Greer Hall
Boone NC 28608

Phone: 704-262-3089
Fax: 704-262-6619
E-mail: taylorj@appstat.edu
URL: www.acs.appstate.edu/dept/phil-rel/

TYPE OF INSTITUTION: Public
EXECUTIVE OFFICER: Faye Sawyer, Acting Dean College of Arts and Sciences
CHAIRPERSON: Jesse Taylor
UNDERGRADUATE ENROLLMENT: 60

School of Applied Theology

5890 Birch Ct
Oakland CA 94618

Phone: 510-652-1651
Fax: 510-420-0542
E-mail: mcgroddy@gtu.edu

TYPE OF INSTITUTION: Private, Roman Catholic
EXECUTIVE OFFICER: Bernard LoCoco, FSC, President/Dean Graduate Theological Union/
     Berkeley Sabbatical Program
GRADUATE ENROLLMENT: 53

Aquinas College

1607 Robinson Rd SE
Grand Rapids MI 49506

Phone: 616-459-8281
Fax: 616-732-4487
E-mail: @aquinas.edu

TYPE OF INSTITUTION: Private, Roman Catholic
EXECUTIVE OFFICER: Harry Knopke, President
CHAIRPERSON: Amata Fabbro, OP

Aquinas Institute of Theology

3642 Lindell Blvd
St Louis MO 63108

Phone: 314-977-3882
Fax: 314-977-7225
E-mail: aquinas@slu.edu
URL: www.ai.edu

TYPE OF INSTITUTION: Private, Roman Catholic
EXECUTIVE OFFICER: Charles Bouchard, OP, President
GRADUATE ENROLLMENT: 235

University of Arizona

Tucson AZ 85721

Arizona State University

Dept of Religious Studies
Box 873104
Tempe AZ 85287-3104

Phone: 480-965-7145
Fax: 480-965-5139
E-mail: relstudy@asu.edu
URL: www.asu.edu/clas/religious_studies/

TYPE OF INSTITUTION: Public
CHAIRPERSON: Joel Gereboff; James Foard, Interim Chair
UNDERGRADUATE ENROLLMENT: 42,000
GRADUATE ENROLLMENT: 11,000
DEGREES OFFERED: BA
UNDERGRADUATE MAJORS: 121
DEGREES CONFERRED: 18
DESCRIPTION OF UNDERGRADUATE PROGRAM: The Department of Religious Studies at Arizona State University includes 15 full-time faculty, and several faculty associates who offer courses in the cross-cultural, interdisciplinary study of religion. Majors in religious studies are required to take courses in three disciplinary areas: Religion in the Americas, Religion and Asian Cultures, and Religion and Western Cultures. Students may elect to pursue the major in combination with the following emphases: Asian Studies, Jewish Studies, Latin American Studies, Russian and East European Studies, Southeast Asian Studies, and Women's Studies. Arizoa State University's main campus is in Tempe, a city of 156,000 in the Phoenix metropolitan area. There are 42,000 students at ASU in addition to 11,000 who are pursuing graduate studies.
GRADUATE PROGRAM
Member of the Council on Graduate Studies in Religion
Graduate Advisor: Eugene Clay
Graduate Degrees Offered: MA

Degrees Conferred: 24 MA

Graduate Students in Residence: 50 MA

Not in Residence: 9 MA

Average number of New Students Enrolled: 15 MA

Women Students: 17 MA

Minority Students: 9 MA

Foreign Students: 3 MA

Minimum GRE Score Requisite to Admission: No, combined 1600 (V, Q, A)

Minimum GPA Score Requisite to Admission: Yes, 3.0 on a scale 4.0

Foreign Language Proficiency Evaluated: Yes, University Test

Financial Aid to First Year Students: 50% MA

Financial Aid to Other Students: 50% MA

Attrition Among Students: 20% MA

Graduates Placed: 80% MA

DESCRIPTION OF GRADUATE PROGRAM AND RESEARCH FACILITIES: Emphasizing the comparative study of religions, the department seeks to understand the phenomena of religion across a wide spectrum of cultural contexts and historical periods. Reflecting the different interests and areas of expertise of the faculty, the curriculum incorporates a variety of approaches to the subject, including the cultural, historical, literary, sociological, and theological. Primary areas of emphasis include religion in the Americas (African-American, Latin American, Native American, and Euro-American religions); modern western theological and ethical thought; Buddhism, Christianity, East and Southeast Asian religions, Hinduism, Islam, and Judaism. Comparative themes and issues such as religion and gender, religion and society, religion and modernity, mysticism, popular religion, ritual studies, and religion, nationalism, and ethnicity, are central to the curriculum. Although students often concentrate upon a single religious tradition for their thesis work, the program seeks to provide a broadly comparative understanding of religion, not a speciualist's training in a single tradition.

ACADEMIC PLAN, ADMISSIONS REQUIREMENTS, FINANCIAL AID: Regular acceptance normally requires an undergraduate GPA of 3.0, GRE scores of at least 550, or a minimum TOEFL score of 550 for international students. For applicants whose background in religious studies is weak, the acceptance letter may stipulate courses to be taken in addition to the regular MA requirements. The registration and tuition fees for out-of-state students at ASU are $4154 per semester for 12 or more credit hours. In-state fees each semester are $972 for 7 or more credit hours. Graduate assistantships, which are competitively awarded, constitute the main form of financial aid for graduate students. The assistantships provide $5897-$8936 per academic year for 13 hours of work each week. In addition, graduate assistantship awards cover out-of-state tuition, leaving the student responsible for in-state tuition fees. The University also offers Graduate Tuition Scholarships, loan programs, and student employment.

FACULTY:

Cady, Linell E., ThD, Harvard (1981), 1983, Professor—contemporary western religious thought, religion and modernity, religion and American life, 480-965-7255

Clay, Eugene, PhD, University of Chicago (1989), Assistant Professor—Russian religious history, Eastern Orthodoxy, 480-965-1982

Coudert, Allison, PhD, University of London, Warburg Institute (1972), Associate Professor—formation of Christian tradition, Hebrew Bible, 480-727-6112

Damrel, Dave, PhD, Duke University (1991), Lecturer—religions of the world, ritual, symbol, and myth, Western religious traditions, 480-727-61120

Feldhaus, Anne, PhD, University of Pennsylvania (1976), 1981, Professor—religion in South Asia, Hinduism, 480-965-4749

Fessenden, Tracy, PhD, University of Virginia (1993), Assistant Professor—women and religion, ritual, symbol, and myth, 480-965-0662

Foard, James H., PhD, Stanford (1977), 1977, Professor—religion in Japan, Buddhism, 480-965-2067

Gereboff, Joel D., PhD, Brown (1977), 1978, Associate Professor—Judaism, religion and moral issues, 480-965-7738

Leon, Luis D., University of California, Santa Barbara (1997), Assistant Professor—US and Hispanic religious traditions, 480-965-0442

Moore, Moses N., PhD, Union Theological Seminary (1987), 1989, Associate Professor—religion in America, African and Native American religions, 480-965-8671

Morrison, Kenneth M., PhD, University of Maine (1975), 1983, Associate Professor—Native American religions, myth, ritual, and symbol studies, 480-965-7148

Schober, Juliane, PhD, University of Illinois (1989), 1992, Associate Professor—religion and culture in Southeast Asia, Therevada Buddhism, 480-965-7045

Swanson, Tod D., PhD, University of Chicago (1988), 1988, Associate Professor—North and South Native American religions, Christian traditions, 480-965-4057

Umar, Sani, PhD, Northwestern University (1997), 1997, Assistant Professor—Western religious traditions, Islamic civilization, 480-965-2766

Wentz, Richard E., PhD, George Washington University (1971), 1972, Professor—religions in America, religion and culture, 480-965-7145

Woodward, Mark, PhD, University of Illinois (1985), 1985, Associate Professor—religion in Southeast Asia, modernization issues, 480-965-2766

University of Arkansas
Little Rock AR 72204

Arkansas Baptist College
1600 Bishop St, Little Rock AR 72202

Arkansas State University
Main Campus, PO Box 790, State University AR 72467-0790

Arlington Baptist College

3001 W Division
Arlington TX 76012

Phone: 817-461-8741
Fax: 817-274-1138

TYPE OF INSTITUTION: Private, Baptist
EXECUTIVE OFFICER: David Bryant, President
UNDERGRADUATE ENROLLMENT: 212

Armenian Bible College

1605 East Elizabeth St, Pasadena CA 91104

Asbury College

1 Macklem Dr
Wilmore KY 40390

Phone: 606-858-3511
Fax: 606-858-3921
E-mail: robert.moore@asbury.edu

TYPE OF INSTITUTION: Private, Non-Denominational
EXECUTIVE OFFICER: David Gyertson, President
CHAIRPERSON: Robert Moore, Dept of Bible and Theology
UNDERGRADUATE ENROLLMENT: 1,286

Asbury Theological Seminary

204 North Lexington Ave
Wilmore KY 40390

Phone: 606-858-2206
Fax: 606-858-2248

TYPE OF INSTITUTION: Private
EXECUTIVE OFFICER: Maxie D. Dunnam, President
GRADUATE ENROLLMENT: 173

Ashland College

Ashland OH 44805

Ashland Theological Seminary

910 Center St
Ashland OH 44805

Phone: 419-289-5161
Fax: 419-289-5969
E-mail: ats@ashland.edu

TYPE OF INSTITUTION: Private, Brethren (Ashland)
EXECUTIVE OFFICER: Frederick J. Finks, DMin, President
GRADUATE ENROLLMENT: 645

Assemblies of God Theological Seminary

1445 Boonville Ave, Springfield MO 65802

Assumption College

500 Salisbury St, Worcester MA 01609

Assumption College

Mendham NJ 07945

Assumption Seminary

PO Box 28240, San Antonio TX 78284

Athenaeum of Ohio

6616 Beechmont Ave
Cincinnati OH 45230-2091

Phone: 513-231-2223
Fax: 513-231-3254
E-mail: tcallan@mtsm.org
URL: www.mtsm.org

TYPE OF INSTITUTION: Private, Roman Catholic
EXECUTIVE OFFICER: Rev. Gerald R. Haemmerle, President
GRADUATE ENROLLMENT: 130

Athens State College

Beaty St, Athens AL 35611

Atlanta Christian College

2605 Ben Hill Rd, East Point GA 30344

Atlantic Baptist Bible College Inc

500 Baptist Ln, Chester VA 23831-0578

Atlantic School of Theology

640 Francklyn St
Halifax, Nova Scotia B3H 3B5
Canada

Phone: 902-423-6939
Fax: 902-492-4048
E-mail: dmackinnon@astheology.ns.ca
URL: astheology.ns.ca

TYPE OF INSTITUTION: Multi-Denominational (ACC, RCC, UCC)
EXECUTIVE OFFICER: William Close, President
GRADUATE ENROLLMENT: 120

Atlantic Union College

South Lancaster MA 01561

Auburn University

310 Thach Hall
Auburn University AL 36849-5205

Phone: 334-844-4616
E-mail: penasri@mail.auburn.edu

TYPE OF INSTITUTION: Public
COORDINATOR: Richard Penaskovic
UNDERGRADUATE ENROLLMENT: 22

Augsburg College

731 21st Ave S, Minneapolis MN 55454

Augustana College

639 38th St
Rock Island IL 61201

Phone: 309-794-7000

TYPE OF INSTITUTION: Private
EXECUTIVE OFFICER: Thomas Tredway, President
CHAIRPERSON: Eddie Mabry
UNDERGRADUATE ENROLLMENT: 2,200

Augustana College

Sioux Falls SD 57197

Augustana University College

4901-46 Avenue
Camrose, Alberta T4V 2R3
Canada

Phone: 780-679-1100
Fax: 780-679-1590
E-mail: wascj@augustana.ab.ca
URL: www.augustana.ab.ca

TYPE OF INSTITUTION: Private, Lutheran, but open to a diversity of traditions
EXECUTIVE OFFICER: Richard L. Husfloen, President
CHAIRPERSON: Jack Waschenfelder
UNDERGRADUATE ENROLLMENT: 15

Austin College

900 N. Grand Avenue
Sherman TX 75090

Phone: 903-813-3100
Fax: 903-813-2368

TYPE OF INSTITUTION: Private, Presbyterian
EXECUTIVE OFFICER: Oscar Page, President
CHAIRPERSON: Steve Stell
UNDERGRADUATE ENROLLMENT: 1,200

Austin Presbyterian Theological Seminary

100 East 27th St, Austin TX 78705

Averett College

420 West Main St
Danville VA 24541

Phone: 804-791-5707
Fax: 804-799-0658
E-mail: laughlin@averett.edu
URL: www.averett.edu

TYPE OF INSTITUTION: Private, Baptist
EXECUTIVE OFFICER: Frank Campbell, President
CHAIRPERSON: John C. H. Laughlin
UNDERGRADUATE ENROLLMENT: 700
GRADUATE ENROLLMENT: 1,500

Avila College

11901 Wornall Rd, Kansas City MO 64145

Azusa Pacific University

901 E Alosta Ave
Azusa CA 91702-7000

Phone: 818-969-3434
Fax: 818-815-3809
E-mail: yarchin@msmail.apu.edu

TYPE OF INSTITUTION: Private, various Protestant
EXECUTIVE OFFICERS: Richard Felix, President; Les Blank, Dean, School of Theology
CHAIRPERSON: William Yarchin
UNDERGRADUATE ENROLLMENT: 2,470
GRADUATE ENROLLMENT: 350

Azusa Pacific University Graduate and Theological School

901 East Alosta, Azusa CA 91702

Bais Binyomin Academy

132 Prospect St, Stamford CT 06901

Baker University

PO Box 65
Baldwin City KS 66006-0065

Phone: 785-594-8476
Fax: 785-594-6721
E-mail: wiley@harvey.bakeru.edu
URL: www.bakeru.edu

TYPE OF INSTITUTION: Denominational, United Methodist

EXECUTIVE OFFICER: Daniel Lambert, President

CHAIRPERSON: George Wiley

UNDERGRADUATE ENROLLMENT: 750

GRADUATE ENROLLMENT: 1,650

DEGREES OFFERED: BA philosophy, BA religion, BA ph/rel

UNDERGRADUATE MAJORS: 8

DEGREES CONFERRED: 4

DESCRIPTION OF UNDERGRADUATE PROGRAM: The department has played an integral role in Baker's education mission since the College's founding in 1858. The present program emphasizes the relation of traditional Western philosophical and theological inquiry to contemporary issues. Undergraduate research and writing is stressed, along with learning critical thinking skills. The staff includes one full time in religion, two full time in philosophy and about six adjunct instructors.

FACULTY:

Hatcher, Donald L., PhD, University of Kansas (1983), 1978, Professor—ethics, critical thinking, E-mail: hatcher@harvey.bakeru.edu

Peard, Thomas, PhD, University of Colorado (1992), 1997, Assistant Professor—analytic philosophy, philosophy and law, logic, E-mail: peard@harvey.bakeru.edu

Wiley, George B., PhD, Emory University (1978), 1977, Associate Professor—Bible, Christian theology and ethics, E-mail: wiley@harvey.bakeru.edu

Baldwin-Wallace College

Department of Religion
275 Eastland Road
Berea OH 44017-2088

Phone: 440-826-2076
Fax: 440-826-3264
E-mail: rfowler@bw.edu
URL: www.bw.edu/~wwwrel

TYPE OF INSTITUTION: Private, United Methodist

EXECUTIVE OFFICER: Carol Thompson, Acting Dean of College

CHAIRPERSON: Robert M. Fowler

UNDERGRADUATE ENROLLMENT: 4,134

GRADUATE ENROLLMENT: 655

DEGREES OFFERED: BA

UNDERGRADUATE MAJORS: 6

DEGREES CONFERRED: 2

DESCRIPTION OF UNDERGRADUATE PROGRAM: The curriculum of the Department of Religion is designed for the total campus community. Studies offered are an integral part of the Humanities Division of the College and reflect a commitment to a liberal arts education through humanities studies.

FACULTY:

Burtner, Hugh W., PhD, Chicago (1978), 1969, Professor—Christian theology, religion and literature, religion and science, 440-826-2176, Fax: 440-826-3264, E-mail: hburtner@bw.edu

Collier, Mark H., PhD, Kent State (1979), 1974, Professor—Christian theology, religion in America, 440-826-2424, Fax: 440-826-3777, E-mail: mcollier@bw.edu

Fowler, Robert M., PhD, Chicago (1978), 1980, Professor—Bible, 440-826-2173, Fax: 440-826-3264, E-mail: rfowler@bw.edu

Gordon, John W., III, DMin, Lancaster (1992), 1994, Associate Professor—Bible, Christian ethics, 440-826-2175, Fax: 440-826-2075, E-mail: jgordon@bw.edu

Kordas, Edward J., DMin, United Theological Seminary (Dayton) (1988), 1990, Lecturer (part-time)—Roman Catholic studies

Oppenheimer, Michael, MA, Hebrew Union (1967), 1977, Lecturer (part-time)—Judaic studies

Palmer, Greg, MDiv, Duke University (1979), 1995, Lecturer (part-time)—African-American church

---

Ball State University

2000 University Ave, Muncie IN 47306

Bangor Theological Seminary

300 Union Street
Bangor ME 04401

Phone: 207-942-6781
Fax: 207-990-1267
E-mail: sdavies@bts.edu
URL: www.bts.edu

TYPE OF INSTITUTION: Private, United Church of Christ
EXECUTIVE OFFICER: Ansley Cole Throckmorton, President
CHAIRPERSON: Susan E. Davies
UNDERGRADUATE ENROLLMENT: 27
GRADUATE ENROLLMENT: 154

Baptist Bible College

628 E Kearney, Springfield MO 65803

Baptist Bible College

Clarks Summit PA 18411

Baptist Bible College West

8333 Acoma Way, Denver CO 80221

Baptist Fellowship Bible College

505 E Palm Ave, Tampa FL 33602

Baptist Missionary Association of Theology

1410 E Pine St, Jacksonville TX 75766-5414

Baptist Theological Seminary at Richmond

PO Box 9157, Richmond VA 23227-0157

Barat College

Lake Forest IL 60045

Barber-Scotia College

145 Cabarrus Ave
Concord NC 28025

Phone: 704-789-2941
Fax: 704-789-2622
E-mail: jpetteway@ctc.net
URL: www.theology.org/apcu/bsc.htm

TYPE OF INSTITUTION: Private, Presbyterian
EXECUTIVE OFFICER: Sammie Potts, President
UNDERGRADUATE ENROLLMENT: 488

Barclay College

607 N Kingman
PO Box 288
Haviland KS 67059

Phone: 316-862-5252
Fax: 316-862-5403

TYPE OF INSTITUTION: Private, Evangelical Friends (Quaker), Interdenominational
EXECUTIVE OFFICER: Walter E. Moody, President
CHAIRPERSON: Mark Kelly
UNDERGRADUATE ENROLLMENT: 100

Bard College

Annandale-on-Hudson NY 12504

Phone: 914-758-6822
Fax: 914-758-4294
E-mail: brockopp@bard.edu

TYPE OF INSTITUTION: Private
EXECUTIVE OFFICER: Leon Botstein, President
CHAIRPERSON: Bruce Chilton
UNDERGRADUATE ENROLLMENT: 1,000

Barnard College

Department of Religion
3009 Broadway
New York NY 10027-6598

Phone: 212-854-2597
Fax: 212-854-7491
E-mail: true@barnard.columbia.edu
URL: www.barnard.columbia.edu/religion/

TYPE OF INSTITUTION: Private, Non-Denominational

EXECUTIVE OFFICER: Elizabeth S. Boylan, Provost

CHAIRPERSON: Randall Balmer, PhD

UNDERGRADUATE ENROLLMENT: 2,000

DEGREES OFFERED: BA

UNDERGRADUATE MAJORS: 40

DEGREES CONFERRED: 12

DESCRIPTION OF UNDERGRADUATE PROGRAM: The undergraduate program in Religion at Barnard and Columbia is an entirely coordinated venture between the two institutions. In addition, Barnard students have access to certain graduate resources at Columbia and to the resources of Union Theological Seminary and the Jewish Theological Seminary of America, both of which are Columbia's neighbors.

FACULTY:

Balmer, Randall, PhD, Princeton (1985), 1991, Professor—religion and American culture, evangelicalism, 212-854-3292, Fax: 212-854-7491, E-mail: rb281@columbia.edu

Castelli, Elizabeth, PhD, Claremont (1987), 1995, Assistant Professor—New Testament, early Christianity, Gnosticism, Greco-Roman religions, gender and the study of religion in the ancient Mediterranean world, 212-854-8291, Fax: 212-854-7491, E-mail: ec225@columbia.edu

Deutsch, Celia M., PhD, St Michael's College, University of Toronto (1985), 1985, Adjunct Associate Professor—biblical studies, early Christianity, 212-854-6023, Fax: 212-854-7491, E-mail: cdeutsch@barnard.columbia.edu

Hawley, John Stratton, PhD, Harvard (1977), 1986, Professor—Hinduism, comparative religion, 212-854-5292, Fax: 212-854-7491, E-mail: jsh3@columbia.edu

Segal, Alan F., PhD, Yale (1975), 1986, Professor—history of religion with a concentration in Hellenistic religions, early Rabbinic Judaism and Christianity, 212-854-5419, Fax: 212-854-7491, E-mail: afs4@columbia.edu

Weisenfeld, Judith, PhD, Princeton (1992), 1991, Assistant Professor—African-American religious history, religion and American culture, women in American religion, 212-854-5071, Fax: 212-854-7491, E-mail: jw40@columbia.edu

Barry University

11300 NE 2nd Avenue
Miami Shores FL 33161-6695

Phone: 305-899-3469
Fax: 305-899-3385
E-mail: vanmerrien@pcsa01.barry.edu

TYPE OF INSTITUTION: Private

EXECUTIVE OFFICER: Jeanne O'Laughlin, OP, President

CHAIRPERSON: Edward van Merrienboer, OP

UNDERGRADUATE ENROLLMENT: 4,500

GRADUATE ENROLLMENT: 1,600

Bartlesville Wesleyan College

Bartlesville OK 74003

Barton College

PO Box 5000
Wilson NC 27893

Phone: 252-399-6449
Fax: 252-399-6571

TYPE OF INSTITUTION: Private, Christian Church (Disciples of Christ)
EXECUTIVE OFFICER: James B. Hemby, Jr., President
CHAIRPERSON: Coleman C. Markham
UNDERGRADUATE ENROLLMENT: 1,200

Bates College

Dept of Philosophy and Religion
73-75 Campus Ave
Lewiston ME 04240

Phone: 207-786-6310
Fax: 207-786-6123
E-mail: ttracy@bates.edu

TYPE OF INSTITUTION: Private, Non-Denominational
CHAIRPERSON: Thomas F. Tracy
UNDERGRADUATE ENROLLMENT: 1,565

Bayamon Central University

PO Box 1725, Bayamon PR 00960-1725

Baylor University

Department of Religion
P.O. Box 97284
Waco TX 76798-7284

Phone: 254-710-3735
Fax: 254-710-3740
E-mail: randall_obrien@baylor.edu

TYPE OF INSTITUTION: Private, Baptist
EXECUTIVE OFFICER: Wallace L. Daniel, Jr., Dean, College of Arts and Sciences
CHAIRPERSON: J. Randall O'Brien, Acting Chair
COORDINATOR: E. Russell Lester, Undergraduate Studies; William H. Bellinger, Jr., Graduate
    Studies in Religion
UNDERGRADUATE ENROLLMENT: 100
GRADUATE ENROLLMENT: 67

Baylor University

J.M. Dawson Institute of Church-State Studies
PO Box 97308
Waco TX 76798-7308

Phone: 254-710-1510
Fax: 254-710-1571
E-mail: derek_davis@baylor.edu

TYPE OF INSTITUTION: Private, Baptist

EXECUTIVE OFFICER: Robert Sloan, President

DIRECTOR: Derek H. Davis

DEGREES OFFERED: MA, PhD

DEGREES CONFERRED: 16 MA; 19 PhD

DESCRIPTION OF PROGRAM: From its inception the Institute has sought to stimulate intellectual inquiry and encourage research and publicaiton in the broad area of church-state relations. The degree programs offer to a limited number of future college and university teachers, ministers of religion, government leaders, scholars and writers a broad curriculum of interdisciplinary study. The MA degree involves 24 semester hours of course work with a thesis. The Doctor of Philosophy degress requires 36 semester hours of course work, proficiency in one foreign language, preliminary examinations, and a dissertation.

FACULTY:

Davis, Derek H., PhD, University of Texas at Dallas, Director and Professor—political theory, civil religion, intellectual history, E-mail: derek_davis@baylor.edu

Ellis, Marc H., PhD, Marquette University, University Professor—Jewish and American thought, liberation theology, Post-Holocaust theology, E-mail: marc_ellis@baylor.edu

Gvosdev, Nikolas K., PhD, Oxford University, Associate Director—Eastern Orthodoxy, East European politics, Russian history, E-mail: nikolas_gvosdev@baylor.edu

Hankins, Barry G., PhD, Kansas State University, Assistant Professor—American fundamentalism, evangelicalism, religion and culture, E-mail: barry_hankins@baylor.edu

Approximately 25 other Baylor professors who teach relevant courses in religion, philosophy, political science, history, and sociology are also affiliated with the program.

Bay Ridge Christian College

PO Box 726, Kendleton TX 77451

Beaver College

Glenside PA 19038

Be'er Shmuel Talmud Academy

1363 50th St, Brooklyn NY 11219

Beeson School of Divinity

Samford University, Birmingham AL 35229

Belhaven College

1500 Peachtree St
Jackson MS 39202

Phone: 601-968-5916
Fax: 601-968-9998

TYPE OF INSTITUTION: Private, Presbyterian

EXECUTIVE OFFICER: Daniel Carl Fredericks, Provost and Dean of Academic Affairs

CHAIRPERSON: Joseph M. Martin, Biblical Studies and Ministries

UNDERGRADUATE ENROLLMENT: 1,300

Bellarmine College

2000 Norris Pl, Louisville KY 40205

Belleview College

3455 W 83rd Ave
Westminster CO 80030

Phone: 303-427-5461

TYPE OF INSTITUTION: Private, Pillar of Fire
EXECUTIVE OFFICER: Robert B. Dallenback, President

Belmont University

1900 Belmont Blvd
Nashville TN 37212

Phone: 615-460-6405
Fax: 615-460-5684
E-mail: simplers@mail.belmont.edu

TYPE OF INSTITUTION: Private, Baptist
EXECUTIVE OFFICER: Jerry Warren, Interim President
CHAIRPERSON: Steven H. Simpler, Dean
UNDERGRADUATE ENROLLMENT: 2,900
GRADUATE ENROLLMENT: 400
DEGREES OFFERED: BA
UNDERGRADUATE MAJORS: 70
DEGREES CONFERRED: 15

DESCRIPTION OF UNDERGRADUATE PROGRAM: The vision of the School of Religion is to become a premier academic community that nurtures a living faith in God, reflects critically on its discipline, and develops skills for Christian ministry. The School offers a traditional religious studies curriculum with additional work in practical ministry and women's studies in religion.

FACULTY:

Bell, Marty, PhD, Vanderbilt University (1988), 1988, Associate Professor—church history, 615-460-6375, Fax: 615-460-5684, E-mail: bellm@mail.belmont.edu

Byrd, Robert O., ThD, Southern Baptist Theological Seminary (1973), 1973, Professor—Greek, New Testament, 615-460-6312, Fax: 615-460-5684, E-mail: byrdb@mail.belmont.edu

Curtis, Oliver B., PhD, Baylor University (1972), 1974, Professor—spiritual formation, 615-460-6316, Fax: 615-460-5684

Elder, Lloyd, ThD, Southwestern Baptist Theological Seminary (1966), 1991, H. Franklin Paschall Chair of Biblical Studies and Preaching—practical ministry, Anna & Ernest J. Moench Center for Church Leadership—Director and Instructor, 615-460-5580, Fax: 615-460-5582, E-mail: byrdj@mail.belmont.edu

Simpler, Steven H., PhD, Baylor University (1981), 1987, Dean of the School of Religion and Professor—religion and theology, 615-486-6405, Fax: 615-460-5684, E-mail: simplers@mail.belmont.edu

Skeen, Judy, PhD, Southern Baptist Theological Seminary (1988), 1998, Assistant Professor—biblical studies, 615-460-6273, Fax: 615-460-5684, E-mail: skeenj@mail.belmont.edu

Tooley, Michelle, PhD, Southern Baptist Theological Seminary (1994), 1995, Assistant Professor—women's studies, 615-460-5549, Fax: 615-460-5684, E-mail: tooleym@mail.belmont.edu

---

Belmont Abbey College

Dept of Theology
Belmont NC 28012

Phone: 704-825-6850
Fax: 704-825-6670
URL: belmontabbeycollege.edu

TYPE OF INSTITUTION: Private, Roman Catholic
EXECUTIVE OFFICER: Robert Preston, President
CHAIRPERSON: Sr. Jane Russell
UNDERGRADUATE ENROLLMENT: 7

Beloit College

Beloit WI 53511

Belzer Yeshiva-Machzikei Seminary

4814 16th Ave, Brooklyn NY 11204

Bemidji State University

Religious Studies Program
Box 7, Hagg-Sauer Hall
Bemidji MN 56601
TYPE OF INSTITUTION: Public

Phone: 218-755-3985

EXECUTIVE OFFICERS: M. James Bensen, President; Linda Baer, Senior Vice President and Academic Vice President
COORDINATOR: Gerald Michael Schnabel
UNDERGRADUATE ENROLLMENT: 4,000
GRADUATE ENROLLMENT: 400

Benedict College

1600 Harden Street
Columbia SC 29204

Phone: 803-253-5098
Fax: 803-253-5063
URL: www.benedict.edu

TYPE OF INSTITUTION: Private, American Baptist
EXECUTIVE OFFICER: David H. Swinton, President
CHAIRPERSON: Harry Singleton
UNDERGRADUATE ENROLLMENT: 2,500

Benedictine College

1020 North 2nd St
Atchison KS 66004

Phone: 913-367-5340
Fax: 913-367-6230
E-mail: dmeade@raven.benedictine.edu
URL: www.benedictine.edu/

TYPE OF INSTITUTION: Denominational: Roman Catholic

EXECUTIVE OFFICER: Aidan Dunleavy, Vice President for Academic Affairs

CHAIRPERSON: Denis Meade, OSB, JCD

UNDERGRADUATE ENROLLMENT: 750

DEGREES OFFERED: BA, BS

UNDERGRADUATE MAJORS: 35

DEGREES CONFERRED: 4

DESCRIPTION OF UNDERGRADUATE PROGRAM: The program, an integral part of Benedictine College, provides courses for all students completing the three theology courses of the core curriculum. The undergraduate major consists of ten three-credit hour courses distributed between the areas of doctrinal, scriptural, Christian life and ecumenical studies. The department also supervises the 54 credit hour interdisciplinary Youth Ministry major. Collaboration with the Philosophy and other departments prepares students for entry into seminary, graduate school or entry level pastoral positions. There is a strong Catholic emphasis. However, other religious traditions are also studied.

FACULTY:

Brockwell, Molly, OSB, MA (cand.), Catholic Theological Union, Chicago—New Testament studies

Meade, Denis, OSB, STD (cand.), Lateran University (1961), 1982, Professor—moral, church history, 913-367-5340, ext 2565, E-mail: dmeade@raven.benedictine.edu

Sri, Edward, STL, Angelicum University (1997), 1997, systematics, scripture, 913-367-5340, E-mail: tsri@raven.benedictine.edu

White, Richard A., PhD, Marquette University (1995), 1996, Assistant professor—systematics, scripture, ecumenical studies, 913-367-5340, E-mail: rwhite@raven.benedictine.edu

Benedictine University

5700 College Road
Lisle IL 60532

URL: ben.edu

TYPE OF INSTITUTION: Private,Catholic

EXECUTIVE OFFICER: William Carroll, President

UNDERGRADUATE ENROLLMENT: 1,600

GRADUATE ENROLLMENT: 700

Bennett College

Greensboro NC 27420

Berea College

Department of Philosophy and Religion
CPO Box 878
Berea KY 40404

Phone: 606-986-9341
Fax: 606-986-9494

TYPE OF INSTITUTION: Private, Non-Denominational
EXECUTIVE OFFICER: Steve Boyce, Provost and Vice President for Academic Affairs
CHAIRPERSON: Robert W. Hoag
UNDERGRADUATE ENROLLMENT: 1,500

Berean College

1455 Boonville Ave, Springfield MO 65802

Berean Bible College

PO Box 242, Poway CA 92074

Berry College

Mount Berry GA 30149

Phone: 706-232-5374
Fax: 706-236-2248
URL: www.berry.edu

TYPE OF INSTITUTION: Private, Non-Denominational
EXECUTIVE OFFICER: Scott Colley, President
COORDINATOR: Michael B. Smith
UNDERGRADUATE ENROLLMENT: 1,942
GRADUATE ENROLLMENT: 169

Beth Hamedrash Shaarei Yosher Institute

4102 16th Ave, Brooklyn NY 11204

Beth Hatalmud Rabbinical College

2127 82nd St, Brooklyn NY 11241

Beth Jacob Hebrew Teachers College

1213-23 Elm Ave, Brooklyn NY 11230

Beth Joseph Rabbinical Seminary

1427 49th St, Brooklyn NY 11219

Beth Medrash Eeyun Hatalmud

14 Fred Eller Dr, Monsey NY 10952

Beth Medrash Emek Halacha

1763 63rd St, Brooklyn NY 11204

Beth Medrash Govoha

617 6th St, Lakewood NJ 08701

Associated Beth Rivkah Schools

310 Crown St, Brooklyn NY 11225

Beth Rochel Seminary

145 Saddle River Rd, Monsey NY 10952

Rabbinical College of Beth Shraga

PO Box 412, 28 Saddle River Rd, Monsey NY 10952

Bethany College

421 N First St
Lindsborg KS 67456

Phone: 913-227-3311
E-mail: maclennar@bethany.bethanylb.edu

TYPE OF INSTITUTION: Denominational: Evangelical Lutheran Church in America
EXECUTIVE OFFICER: Chris Thomforde, President
CHAIRPERSON: Eugene F. Bales
COORDINATOR: Ron MacLennan

Bethany College

Bethany WV 26032

Bethany College of the Assemblies of God

800 Bethany Dr, Scotts Valley CA 95066

Bethany College of Missions

6820 Auto Club Rd
Suite C
Bloomington MN 55438

Phone: 612-829-2561
Fax: 612-829-2535
E-mail: bcom.admin@bethfel.org
URL: www.bcom.org

TYPE OF INSTITUTION: Non-Denominational
EXECUTIVE OFFICER: Paul F. Hartford, Dean of College
UNDERGRADUATE ENROLLMENT: 175

Bethany Theological Seminary

615 National Road West
Richmond IN 47374-4019

Phone: 765-983-1800
Fax: 765-983-1840
E-mail: bethanysem@aol.com
URL: www.brethern.org/bethany

TYPE OF INSTITUTION: Private, Church of the Brethren
EXECUTIVE OFFICER: Eugene F. Roop, President
GRADUATE ENROLLMENT: 90

Bethel College

1001 W McKinley Avenue
Mishawaka IN 46545

Phone: 219-259-8511
Fax: 219-257-3326
E-mail: admissions@bethel-in.edu
URL: www.bethel-in.edu

TYPE OF INSTITUTION: Private, Missionary Church
EXECUTIVE OFFICER: Norman Bridges, President
CHAIRPERSON: Eugene E. Carpenter, Religion and Philosophy
UNDERGRADUATE ENROLLMENT: 1,650
GRADUATE ENROLLMENT: 60

Bethel College

300 E 27th Street
North Newton KS 67117

Phone: 316-283-2500
Fax: 316-284-5286
E-mail: ps@bethelks.edu
URL: www.bethelks.edu

TYPE OF INSTITUTION: Private, General Conference Mennonite
EXECUTIVE OFFICER: Douglas Penner, President
CHAIRPERSON: Phil Stoltzfus
UNDERGRADUATE ENROLLMENT: 625

Bethel College

3900 Bethel Dr
Saint Paul MN 55112

Phone: 612-638-6350
Fax: 612-638-6001
E-mail: j-herzog@bethel.edu

TYPE OF INSTITUTION: Private, Baptist General Conference
EXECUTIVE OFFICER: James Barnes, Provost
CHAIRPERSON: John Herzog
UNDERGRADUATE ENROLLMENT: 2,200

Bethel College

Cherry St, McKenzie TN 38201

Bethel Theological Seminary

3949 Bethel Dr
Saint Paul MN 55112

Phone: 651-638-6180
Fax: 651-638-6002
E-mail: bethelsem@aol.com
URL: www.bethel.edu

TYPE OF INSTITUTION: Denominational: Baptist General Conference
EXECUTIVE OFFICER: Leland V. Eliason, Executive Vice President and Provost
CHAIRPERSON: Greg Bourgond, Associate Academic Dean
GRADUATE ENROLLMENT: 719

Bethune-Cookman College

Daytona Beach FL 32015

Beulah Heights Bible College

892 Berne St SE
PO Box 18145
Atlanta GA 30316

Phone: 404-627-2681
Fax: 404-627-0702
E-mail: kerscher@bellsouth.net
URL: www.beulah.org

TYPE OF INSTITUTION: Private, International Pentecostal Church of Christ
EXECUTIVE OFFICER: James B. Keiller, Vice President and Dean of Academic Affairs
UNDERGRADUATE ENROLLMENT: 600

Bible Missionary Institute

3501 46th Avenue
Rock Island IL 61202

Phone: 309-788-0491

TYPE OF INSTITUTION: Denominational: Bible Missionary
EXECUTIVE OFFICER: Dale Hayford, Principal

CHAIRPERSON: Anna Rosa, Registrar
UNDERGRADUATE ENROLLMENT: 100

Biblical Theological Seminary

200 N Main St
Hatfield PA 19440

Phone: 215-368-5000
E-mail: admissions@biblical.edu
URL: www.biblical.edu

TYPE OF INSTITUTION: Private, Intedenominational
EXECUTIVE OFFICER: David G. Dunbar, President
GRADUATE ENROLLMENT: 308

Binghamton University

PO Box 6000
Binghamton NY 13902-6000

Phone: 607-777-2735
Fax: 607-777-2734
E-mail: apreus@binghamton.edu
URL: philosophy.binghamton.edu

TYPE OF INSTITUTION: Public
EXECUTIVE OFFICER: Lois DeFleur, President
CHAIRPERSON: Anthony Preus
UNDERGRADUATE ENROLLMENT: 550
GRADUATE ENROLLMENT: 75

Birmingham Southern College

Birmingham AL 35204

Bishops University

Lennoxville, Quebec J1M 1Z7 Canada

Blackburn College

Philosophy and Religion Dept, Carlinville IL 62626

Bloomfield College

Bloomfield NJ 07003

Bloomsburg State College

Bloomsburg PA 17815

Blue Mountain College

Division of Biblical & Associated Studies
201 West Main Street
Blue Mountain MS 38610
TYPE OF INSTITUTION: Private, Baptist
EXECUTIVE OFFICER: E. Harold Fisher, President
CHAIRPERSON: Douglas Bain
UNDERGRADUATE ENROLLMENT: 459
GRADUATE ENROLLMENT: 515

Phone: 601-685-4771
Fax: 601-685-4776

Bluefield College

3000 College Dr
Bluefield VA 24605

Phone: 540-326-4271
Fax: 540-326-4288
E-mail: tcrawford@mail.bluefield.edu
URL: www.bluefield.edu

TYPE OF INSTITUTION: Private, Baptist
EXECUTIVE OFFICER: Daniel Macmillan, President
CHAIRPERSON: Timothy G. Crawford
UNDERGRADUATE ENROLLMENT: 550

Bluefield College of Evangelism

PO Box 830, Bluefield WV 24701-0830

Bluffton College

280 W College Ave
Bluffton OH 45817-1196

Phone: 419-358-3000
Fax: 419-358-3323

TYPE OF INSTITUTION: Private, Mennonite
EXECUTIVE OFFICER: Lee Snyder, President
CHAIRPERSON: J. Denny Weaver
UNDERGRADUATE ENROLLMENT: 1,001
GRADUATE ENROLLMENT: 19

Bob Jones University

Greenville SC 29614

Rabbinical College of Bobover Bnei Zion

1577 48th St, Brooklyn NY 11219

Boise Bible College

8695 Marigold St
Boise ID 83714

Phone: 208-376-7731
Fax: 208-376-7743
URL: www.boibible.edu

TYPE OF INSTITUTION: Private, Christian Church
EXECUTIVE OFFICER: Charles Crane, President
UNDERGRADUATE ENROLLMENT: 100

Booker T. Crenshaw Christian College and School

3134 Franklin Ave, San Diego CA 92113

Boston College

Dept of Theology, Carney 417, Chestnut Hill MA 02167

Boston University

745 Commonwealth Ave
Boston MA 02215

Phone: 617-353-2635
Fax: 617-353-5441
E-mail: juliving@bu.edu
URL: www.bu.edu

TYPE OF INSTITUTION: Private
EXECUTIVE OFFICER: Jon Westling, President
CHAIRPERSON: John Clayton
UNDERGRADUATE ENROLLMENT: 15,496
GRADUATE ENROLLMENT: 11,007
DEGREES OFFERED: BA and BA/MA
UNDERGRADUATE MAJORS: 45
DEGREES CONFERRED: 15
DESCRIPTION OF UNDERGRADUATE PROGRAM: Undergraduates may pursue a general major or minor, or they may major in one of the following concentrations: South and East Asian Religions, Judaism, Christianity, Islam, Religion in America, Religion and Culture. Joint concentrations in Religion and Philosophy or Religion and Classical Studies are also available. The combined BA/MA program makes it possible for qualified candidates to attain master's level competency in one of the above concentrations with only one additional year beyond the BA. Advanced graduate work leading to the PhD is available through the Graduate School, Division of Religious and Theological Studies.
GRADUATE PROGRAM
Member of the Council on Graduate Studies in Religion
Graduate Advisors: John Berthrong, Paula Fredricksen, Ray Hart
Graduate Degrees Offered: MA; PhD
Degrees Conferred: 6 MA; 9 PhD
Graduate Students in Residence: 100
Not in Residence: 27

Average No. of New Students Enrolled: 15

Women Students: 42

Minority Students: 12

Foreign Students: 28

Minimum GRE Score Requisite to Admission: Yes; 1800

Minimum GPA Score Requisite to Admission: Yes; 3.25 out of 4.0

Foreign Language Proficiency Evaluated: Yes

Financial Aid to First Year Students: 75% MA; 75% PhD

Financial Aid to Other Students: 10% MA; 60% PhD

Attrition Among Students: 5% MA; 15% PhD

Graduates Placed: N/A

DESCRIPTION OF GRADUATE PROGRAM AND RESEARCH FACILITIES: The graduate program is a Division of the Graduate School of Arts and Sciences. Students may choose among twelve fields of concentration in three main subject areas, each of which is cross-cultural and multi-disciplinary. Religious Texts and Traditions: Judaic Studies; New Testament and Christian origins; History of Christianity; and Islamic studies. Religion, Philosophy, and Ethics: Philosophy of religion; Science, philosophy, and religion; Theology; and Social ethics. Religion, Culture and Society: Religion and society; Religion and literature; Psychology of religion; and Pastoral psychology. Advisors are chosen from appropriate departments of the Graduate School of Arts and Sciences, the School of Theology, the University Professors Program, and the School of Education. Through the Boston Theological Institute, Division students may also take courses in the consortium of theological institutes which includes Andover-Newton Theological School, Boston College, Gordon-Conwell School of Theology, Harvard Divinity School, St John's Seminary, and Weston School of Theology. In addition to Boston University's extensive libraries, Division students also have access to the libraries of all the schools in the Boston Theological Institute.

ACADEMIC PLAN, ADMISSION REQUIREMENTS, FINANCIAL AID: Academic plan, admission requirements, financial aid: Students enrolled in these specializations take a minimum of thirty-six semester hours (nine courses). MA candidates may write a thesis or present a comprehensive examination. PhD candidates must write and defend a dissertation. The application deadline for fall admission is January 15. There is no spring admission. Financial aid is awarded on the basis of merit; a student applying for financial aid should indicate this on the application form. Applicants may also apply for financial aid, work-study grants, and loans through the Office of Financial Assistance; 881 Commonwealth Avenue; Boston, MA 02215.

FACULTY:

Abimbola, Wande, PhD, University of Lagos, Professor—African religions

Berger, Peter L., PhD, New School for Social Research, University Professor—sociology of religion

Berthrong, John H., PhD, University of Chicago, Assistant Professor—comparative theology and Chinese religions

Bohn, Carole R., EdD, Boston University, Associate Professor—pastoral psychology, developmental psychology, feminist psychology

Burch, Sharon Peebles, PhD, Graduate Theological Union, Assistant Professor—Christian theology, religious education

Cartwright, John H., PhD, Boston University, Professor—ethics, sociology of religion, black religion

Chung, Chai-sik, PhD, Boston University, Professor—East Asian religions, social ethics, sociology of religion

Clayton, John, PhD, Cambridge, Professor—philosophy of religion

Darr, Katheryn Pfisterer, PhD, Vanderbilt, Associate Professor—Hebrew Bible

Doehring, Carrie, PhD, Boston University, Assistant Professor—pastoral psychology

Eckel, M. David, MDiv, Harvard, Associate Professor—comparative religions, South Asian religions

Fredriksen, Paula, PhD, Princeton, Aurelio Professor of the Appreciation of Scripture, Christian Origins and Patristics

Hart, Ray L., PhD, Yale, Professor—religion and literature, philosophical theology

Hill, Geoffrey, MA, Oxford, University Professor—literature and religion

Katz, Steven, PhD, Cambridge, Professor—Judaic studies, philosophy of religion

Klawans, Jonathan, PhD, Columbia, Assistant Professor—Judaic studies

Kohn, Livia, PhD, Bonn, Associate Professor—East Asian religions

Korom, Frank, Assistant Professor—religion and anthropology, South Asian religions, Asian religions in America, folklore and anthropology of religion

Levine, Hillel, PhD, Harvard , Professor—Judaic studies, sociology of religion

Lindberg, Carter, PhD, University of Iowa, Professor—history of the Protestant Reformation

Mason, Herbert, PhD, Harvard , University Professor—Islamic studies, religion and literature

Neville, Robert C., PhD, Yale, Professor—Christian theology, philosophy of religion

Olson, Alan, PhD, Boston University, Professor—philosophy of religion

Parker, Simon, PhD, Johns Hopkins University, Associate Professor—Hebrew Bible

Prothero, Stephen, PhD, Harvard, Assistant Professor—Asian religions in America

Purvis, James, ThD, Harvard, Professor—Hebrew scripture, Jewish sectarianism, archaeology

Robert, Dana L., PhD, Yale, Associate Professor—non-Western church history

Rouner, Leroy S., PhD, Columbia University, Professor—philosophy of religion

Sampley, J. Paul, PhD, Yale University—New Testament and Christian origins

Schlauch, Chris R., PhD, University of Chicago, Assistant Professor—pastoral psychology and psychology of religion

Seligman, Adam, PhD, Hebrew University of Jerusalem—sociology of religion

Swartz, Merlin, PhD, Harvard, Professor—Islamic studies, phenomenology of religion

Wiesel, Elie, MA, Sorbonne, Andrew Mellon Professor in the Humanities—Judaic studies

Wildman, Wesley, PhD, Graduate Theological Union, Assistant Professor—Christian theology, philosophy of religion

Zank, Michael, PhD, Brandeis, Assistant Professor—Judaic studies

---

Boston Theological Institute

210 Herrick Road
Newton Centre MA 02459

Phone: 617-527-4880
Fax: 617-527-1073
E-mail: bti@world.std.com
URL: www.bu.edu/sth/BTI

TYPE OF INSTITUTION: Private, Multi-Denominational: consortium of nine schools, including Roman Catholic, Orthodox, and Protestant branches

EXECUTIVE OFFICER: Rodney L. Petersen

Bowdoin College

Religion Department
7300 College Station
Brunswick ME 04011-8473

Phone: 207-725-3465
Fax: 207-725-3495
E-mail: imakarus@polar.bowdoin.edu
URL: www.bowdoin.edu

TYPE OF INSTITUTION: Private
EXECUTIVE OFFICER: Charles R. Beitz, Dean for Academic Affairs
CHAIRPERSON: Irena S. M. Makarushka
UNDERGRADUATE ENROLLMENT: 1,550

Bowling Green State University

Bowling Green OH 43403

Bradley University

Peoria IL 61625

Brandeis University

Dept of Near Eastern and Judaic Studies
Mailslot 054
Waltham MA 02454-9110

Phone: 781-736-2950
Fax: 781-736-2070
E-mail: judaica@brandeis.edu
URL: www.brandeis.edu/departments/nejs

TYPE OF INSTITUTION: Private
EXECUTIVE OFFICER: Jehuda Reinharz, President
CHAIRPERSON: Jonathan D. Sarna
UNDERGRADUATE ENROLLMENT: 60
GRADUATE ENROLLMENT: 96

Brandon University

Dept of Religion
Brandon, Manitoba R7A 6A9
Canada

Phone: 204-727-7430
Fax: 204-726-0473
E-mail: mahoney@brandonu.ca
URL: www.brandonu.ca/index40.html

TYPE OF INSTITUTION: Public
EXECUTIVE OFFICER: Dennis Anderson, President
CHAIRPERSON: A. Edward Milton
UNDERGRADUATE ENROLLMENT: 2,800
GRADUATE ENROLLMENT: 75
DEGREES OFFERED: BA general, BA specialist
UNDERGRADUATE MAJORS: 8
DEGREES CONFERRED: 4

DESCRIPTION OF UNDERGRADUATE PROGRAM: Although originally established as a Baptist college in 1899, Brandon University is now a fully independent secular institution. The religion program is designed to contribute to a broad liberal arts education by systematically considering religious and ethical issues. The primary emphasis is the study of the major historical faiths, but minor religious movements are also discussed. The approaches of both the humanities and the social sciences are used.

FACULTY:

Brockway, Robert W., PhD, Columbia (1951), 1965, Professor Emeritus

Florida, Robert E., PhD, McMaster (1973), 1969, Professor—religion and society, Eastern religions, mythology, medical ethics, American native religions

Hordern, Peter John C., PhD, McMaster (1972), 1971, Associate Professor—biblical and ancient Near Eastern religions, American native religions, medical ethics, death and dying

Medd, Susan M., MA, Calgary (1988), 1988, Lecturer (part-time)—world religions, myth, psychology of religion, women and religion

Milton, A. Edward, PhD, McMaster (1985), 1984, Associate Professor—biblical studies, Judaism, Christianity, ethics, Hellenistic Greek

---

Brescia University

717 Frederica St
Owensboro KY 42301

Phone: 502-685-3131
Fax: 502-686-4266
E-mail: @brescia.edu

TYPE OF INSTITUTION: Private, Roman Catholic (Ursuline Sisters)
EXECUTIVE OFFICER: Vivian Bowles, OSU, President
COORDINATOR: Cheryl Clemons
UNDERGRADUATE ENROLLMENT: 750
GRADUATE ENROLLMENT: 40

Brewton-Parker College

Highway #280
Mount Vernon GA 30445

Phone: 912-583-2241
Fax: 912-583-4498
E-mail: dhorton@bpc.edu
URL: www.bpc.edu/religion/rel.htm

TYPE OF INSTITUTION: Private, Baptist
EXECUTIVE OFFICER: David Smith, President
CHAIRPERSON: Doug Weaver
UNDERGRADUATE ENROLLMENT: 1,400

Briar Cliff College

3303 Rebecca St
Sioux City IA 51104

Phone: 712-279-1704
E-mail: cooney@briar-cliff.edu
URL: www.briar-cliff.edu

TYPE OF INSTITUTION: Private, Roman Catholic
EXECUTIVE OFFICER: Jack Calareso, President

CHAIRPERSON: William Cooney
UNDERGRADUATE ENROLLMENT: 6

Bridgewater College

402 East College St
Bridgewater VA 22812

Phone: 540-828-8000
Fax: 540-828-5479
URL: www.bridgewater.edu

TYPE OF INSTITUTION: Private, Church of the Brethren
EXECUTIVE OFFICER: Phillip C. Stone, President
CHAIRPERSON: William E. Abshire
UNDERGRADUATE ENROLLMENT: 1,150
DEGREES OFFERED: BA
UNDERGRADUATE MAJORS: 20
DEGREES CONFERRED: 7
DESCRIPTION OF UNDERGRADUATE PROGRAM: The Department of Philosophy and Religion offers an undergraduate major (30 semester hours) with courses required both in philosophy and religion and undergraduate minors (18 semester hours) in philosophy and religion and in peace studies. Biblical studies, comparative religion, and contemporary and historical courses in philosophy and theology are combined in a program emphasizing the scholarly investigation of philosophical and religious thought and committment in a pluralistic culture.
FACULTY:
Abshire, William E., PhD, University of Virginia (1996), 1987, Associate Professor—philosophical theology, philosophy of religion, history of religions, 540-828-5346, Fax: 540-828-5479, E-mail: wabshire@bridgewater.edu
Miller, Robert R., MDiv, Bethany Theological Seminary (1983), 1990, Instructor (part-time)—biblical studies, 540-828-5383, Fax: 540-828-5479, E-mail: rmiller@bridgewater.edu
Scheppard, Carol, PhD, University of Pennsylvania (1997), Assistant Professor—church history, exegesis, biblical studies, 540-828-5725, Fax: 540-828-5479, E-mail: cscheppa@bridgewater.edu
Watson, W. Steve, MDiv, Southeastern Baptist Seminary (1967), 1970, Associate Professor—contemporary philosophy, history of philosophy, philosophy of science, 540-828-5345, Fax: 540-828-5479, E-mail: swatson@bridgewater.edu

---

Brigham Young University

55-220 Kulanui St, Laie HI 96762

Brigham Young University

Religious Education
Joseph Smith Building
Provo UT 84604

Phone: 801-378-2735
Fax: 801-378-5980

TYPE OF INSTITUTION: Denominational: The Church of Jesus Christ of Latter-day Saints
EXECUTIVE OFFICER: Robert L. Millet, Dean

UNDERGRADUATE ENROLLMENT: 22,000

Brite Divinity School

Texas Christian University, Fort Worth TX 76129

University of British Columbia

Dept of Classical, Near Eastern and Religious
Studies
1866 Main Mall Buch C
Vancouver BC V6T 1Z1 Canada

Phone: 604-822-2515
Fax: 604-822-9431
E-mail: cnrs@unixg.ubc.ca
URL: www.arts.ubc.ca/cnrs/index~1.htm

TYPE OF INSTITUTION: Public
CHAIRPERSON: A. A. Barrett

Brown University

Department of Religious Studies
59 George St/PO Box 1927
Providence RI 02912

Phone: 401-863-3104
Fax: 401-863-3109
E-mail: gail_tetreault@brown.edu
URL: www.brown.edu

TYPE OF INSTITUTION: Private, Non-Denominational

EXECUTIVE OFFICER: Gordon Gee, President

CHAIRPERSON: Stanley K. Stowers

COORDINATOR: Susan A. Harvey

UNDERGRADUATE ENROLLMENT: 5,500

GRADUATE ENROLLMENT: 1,300

DEGREES OFFERED: AB Religious Studies

UNDERGRADUATE MAJORS: 65

DEGREES CONFERRED: 27

DESCRIPTION OF UNDERGRADUATE PROGRAM: Undergraduate instruction in the academic study of religion; a concentrator must take 8 courses, studying at least two religious traditions and must take account of more than one approach to the study of religion. Instruction (along with other departments and programs) is offered in Hinduism, Buddhism, the religion of ancient Israel, Judaism, Christianity, Greek and Hellenistic religions, Islam, Taoism, and Confucianism.

GRADUATE PROGRAM

Member of the Council on Graduate Studies in Religion

Graduate Advisor: Susan A. Harvey

Graduate Degrees Offered: MA; PhD

Degrees Conferred: 4 MA; 1 PhD

Graduate Students in Residence: 15 PhD

FACULTY:

Cohen, Shaye J. D., PhD, Columbia University (1975), Samuel Ungerleider, Jr. Professor—Judaism in antiquity

Dietrich, Wendell S., PhD, Yale University (1961), 1958, Professor—late nineteenth-and early twentieth-century Christian thought, its relation to Judaic thought

Gordon, Lewis R., PhD, Yale University (1993), Associate Professor—African-American philosophy, Black theology, existentialism

Harvey, Susan Ashbrook, PhD, University of Birmingham, England (1982), 1987, Associate Professor—Late antique and Byzantine Christianity, Syriac studies, women in early Christianity

Olyan, Saul M., PhD, Harvard University (1985), Associate Professor—history, literature, religion of Ancient Israel

Reeder, John P., Jr., PhD, Yale University (1968), 1971, Professor—philosophical and theological ethics, comparative religious ethics, social ethics

Roth, Harold D., PhD, University of Toronto (1981), 1987, Associate Professor—Chinese religion and philosophy, Buddhism

Stowers, Stanley K., PhD, Yale University (1979), 1981, Professor—history of early Christianity, New Testament studies, Hellenistic philosophy and religion

Twiss, Sumner B., PhD, Yale University (1974), 1971, Professor—comparative moral and religious thought, philosophy and theory of religion, contemporary moral problems (including Biomedical ethics)

Wulff, Donna M., PhD, Harvard University (1978), 1974, Associate Professor—history of religions, Hinduism (classical and medieval), Buddhism

Zaman, Muhammad Q., PhD, McGill University, Canada, (1994), Assistant Professor—Early Islam, Islam in South Asia, modern Islamic thought

---

Brown University

Program in Judaic Studies
Box 1826
Providence RI 02912

Phone: 401-863-3900
Fax: 401-863-3938
E-mail: annette_boulay@brown.edu

CHAIRPERSON: Saul M. Olyan
UNDERGRADUATE ENROLLMENT: 5,400
GRADUATE ENROLLMENT: 1,200
DEGREES OFFERED: AB, AM, PhD
UNDERGRADUATE MAJORS: 10
DEGREES CONFERRED: 2
GRADUATE PROGRAM
Graduate Degrees Offered: PhD; AM
Degrees Conferred: 0 PhD; 0 AM
Graduate Students in Residence: 4 PhD/ThD
Average No. of New Students Enrolled: 1 PhD/ThD
Women Students: 20% PhD/ThD
Minimum GRE Score Requisite to Admission: No
Minimum GPA Score Requisite to Admission: No
Foreign Language Proficiency Evaluated: Yes; GSFLT Score: 525 German; 540 French
Financial Aid to First Year Students: 100% PhD
Financial Aid to Other Students: 100% PhD
Graduates Placed: 100% PhD

DESCRIPTION OF GRADUATE PROGRAM AND RESEARCH FACILITIES: Graduate degrees are offered at both the MA and PhD levels. The MA is intended both as a terminal degree and as preparation for the PhD. Required for the MA: eight semester courses; proficiency in French or German; a thesis. The PhD Program is in Ancient Judaism, and includes training in Hebrew Bible, the history, literature and religion of the Second Temple period, and that of the period 70-500 CE. A descriptive detail of the program is available upon request. Students have access to the more than two million volumes at either the University's or the City of Providence's libraries. The research-level library of Temple Bethel is also available to university students as are the resource of the Boston Area Library Consortium. In addition, students have access to the Computer Center, site of the University's primary computing resource, and to the Watson Building for Computing Information and Technology. The University supports an extensive network of interactive IBM and Apple terminals for use.

ACADEMIC PLAN, ADMISSION REQUIREMENTS, FINANCIAL AID: Brown University operates on the semester system. Applicants for admission must present a baccalaureate degree; GRE (general test); application; transcripts; references. Students are eligible in the first year for support as Fellows, Tuition Scholars, Proctors (College Work Study) and on occasion as Teaching Assistants. Students should request a copy of the Program brochure on Judaic Studies.

FACULTY:

DIRECTOR:

Olyan, Saul M., Dorot Associate Professor—Judaic studies, Hebrew Bible and ancient Judaism

PROFESSORIAL MEMBERS OF THE PROGRAM:

Cohen, Shaye J. D., Samuel Ungerleider Jr. Professor—Judaic studies for Judaism of antiquity

Davidman, Lynn, Associate Professor—Judaic studies and sociology, Jewish sociology and women's studies

Dietrich, Wendell S., Professor—religious studies and Judaic studies, modern Jewish and Christian thought

Goldscheider, Calvin, Dorot Professor—Judaic studies, sociology, Jewish sociological and demographic studies

Hirsch, David, Professor Emeritus—English, Judaic Studies, Jewish literary studies

Jacobson, David, Associate Professor—Judaic studies, modern Hebrew language and literature

FELLOWS OF THE PROGRAM:

Goldstein, Sidney, George Hazard Crooker University Professor]7sociology,Jewish sociological and demographic studies

Harvey, Susan, Associate Professor—religious studies, late antiquity, early Christianity

Kertzer, David, Paul Dupee Jr. University Professor of Social Science—anthropology and history for Jewish anthropological studies

Stowers, Stanley, Professor—religious studies, early Christianity

Vieira, Nelson, Professor—Portuguese, Jewish literature studies in Latin America

---

Bryan College

Dayton TN 37321

Bryn Mawr College

Hebrew and Judaic Studies
Bryn Mawr PA 19010

Phone: 610-526-5077
Fax: 610-526-5331
E-mail: drabeeya@brynmawr.edu

Bucknell University

Dept of Religion
Lewisburg PA 17837

Phone: 570-577-1205
Fax: 570-577-1064
E-mail: ssnyder@bucknell.edu

TYPE OF INSTITUTION: Private

EXECUTIVE OFFICERS: William D. Adams, President; Eugenia P. Gerdes, Dean of College of Arts and Sciences

CHAIRPERSON: John A. Grim

UNDERGRADUATE ENROLLMENT: 3,300

GRADUATE ENROLLMENT: 150

DEGREES OFFERED: BA in Religion

UNDERGRADUATE MAJORS: 26 Majors, 38 Minors

DEGREES CONFERRED: 11

DESCRIPTION OF UNDERGRADUATE PROGRAM: Courses are offered on major religious traditions, East and West. Interdisciplinary studies are stressed—relations of religions to ethics, psychology, politics, literature, science.

FACULTY:

Antonaccio, Maria, PhD, Chicago (1996), 1994, Assistant Professor—Western religions and philosophical ethics, environmental ethics, ethics and literature, 570-577-3530, Fax: 570-577-1064, E-mail: antoncco@bucknell.edu

Grim, John A., PhD, Fordham University (1979), 1989, Professor—Native American Indian religions, religion and ecology, inter-religious dialogue, 570-577-3521, Fax: 570-577-1064, E-mail: grim@bucknell.edu

LaBarge, Joseph A., PhD, Catholic University (1971), 1979, Associate Professor—Roman Catholic studies, bioethics, biblical studies, 570-577-3519, Fax: 570-577-1064, E-mail: labarge@bucknell.edu

Mazur, Eric M., PhD, University of California, Santa Barbara (1997), 1997, Assistant Professor—history of religions, American religions, religion and law, sociology of religion, Judaic studies, 570-577-3525, Fax: 570-577-1064, E-mail: mazur@bucknell.edu

Tucker, Mary Evelyn, PhD, Columbia University (1985), 1989, Professor—Asian religions, Confuciansim in China and Japan, religion and ecology, 570-577-3180, Fax: 570-577-1064, E-mail: mtucker@bucknell.edu

White, Carol Wayne, PhD, Iliff School of Theology-University of Denver (1994), 1992, Associate Professor—philosophy of religion, contemporary religious thought, philosophical hermeneutics, post structuralist philosophy and religion, science and religion, 570-577-3526, Fax: 570-577-1064, E-mail: cwhite@bucknell.edu

Buena Vista College

Storm Lake IA 50588

Butler University

Dept of Philosophy and Religious Studies
4600 Sunset Ave
Indianapolis IN 46208-3485
TYPE OF INSTITUTION: Private, Non-Denominational
EXECUTIVE OFFICER: Geoffrey Bannister, President
CHAIRPERSON: Katharina Dulckeit
UNDERGRADUATE ENROLLMENT: 3,000

Phone: 317-940-9974
Fax: 317-940-9930

Cabrini College

610 King of Prussia Rd
Radnor PA 19087

Phone: 610-902-8331
Fax: 610-902-8285
E-mail: mcguinness@hslc.edu

TYPE OF INSTITUTION: Private, Roman Catholic
EXECUTIVE OFFICER: Antoinette Iadarola, Provost
CHAIRPERSON: Margaret M. McGuinness
UNDERGRADUATE ENROLLMENT: 1,100
GRADUATE ENROLLMENT: 500
DEGREES OFFERED: BA
UNDERGRADUATE MAJORS: 2
DEGREES CONFERRED: 5
DESCRIPTION OF UNDERGRADUATE PROGRAM: Cabrini College is a Catholic, coeducational, residential, undergraduate college offering programs in liberal arts and professional studies. All undergraduates (adult and traditional, full-time and part-time) must complete three credits in Religious Studies. In addition, Religious Studies courses feature prominently in the area of the curriculum dedicated to "Values and Commitments." Courses such as "Search for Meaning," "Faith and Justice," and "Heroes of Conscience" are offered regularly at the College. The curriculum of the Religious Studies Department is designed to deepen one's understanding of the religious dimension of humankind. Sacred texts and traditions are examined and their contemporary implications investigated. The history and doctrine of Roman Catholicism are given special emphasis. The major program prepares students for graduate school and to work in the field of religious education at both the elementary and secondary levels.

FACULTY:

Bloemker, Geraldine, PhD, Widener University (1998), 1983, Instructor (part-time)—religion and education, world religions, 610-902-8310

McGuinness, Margaret, PhD, Union Theological Seminary, New York (1985), 1985, Associate Professor—religion in America, faith and justice, liberation theologies, 610-902-8331, Fax: 610-902-8285, E-mail: margaret.mcguinness@cabrini.edu

Primiano, Leonard Norman, PhD, University of Pennsylvania (1993), 1993, Assistant Professor—American Catholicism, religious folklife, 610-902-8330, Fax: 610-902-8285, E-mail: leonard.primiano@cabrini.edu

Reher, Margaret Mary, PhD, Fordham University (1972), 1973, Professor Emerita—world religions, women and religion, 610-902-8331, Fax: 610-902-8285, E-mail: mmreher@op.net

Caldwell College

Dept of Religious Studies and Philosophy, Caldwell NJ 07006

University of Calgary

Dept of Religious Studies
2500 University Drive NW
Calgary, Alberta T2N 1N4 Canada

Phone: 403-220-5886
Fax: 403-210-0801
E-mail: rels@ucalgary.ca
URL: www.ucalgary.ca/RELS

TYPE OF INSTITUTION: Public

CHAIRPERSON: Eliezer Segal

UNDERGRADUATE ENROLLMENT: 2,100

GRADUATE ENROLLMENT: 25

DEGREES OFFERED: BA Major or Honors, MA, PhD

UNDERGRADUATE MAJORS: 53

DESCRIPTION OF UNDERGRADUATE PROGRAM: The Department of Religious Studies at The University of Calgary is the only Religious Studies department in the province of Alberta. The department came into being in the absence of church colleges or seminaries attached to the University; hence it has served as an academic resource to Calgary and area religious communities. The Religious Studies Department is non-sectarian and aims to foster informed understanding of the wide variety of religious beliefs and practises. Students at the undergraduate and MA levels focus their studies in one of three streams: Eastern Religions, Western Religions, or Nature of Religion. At the PhD level, research is concentrated in three areas: Religious Texts and Commentaries, History of Religious Movements and Institutions, and Interpretations of Religion.

GRADUATE PROGRAM

Member of the Council on Graduate Studies in Religion

Graduate Advisor: Leslie Kawamura

Graduate Degrees Offered: MA; PhD

Degrees Conferred: 62 MA; 4 PhD

Graduate Students in Residence: 13 MA; 10 PhD

Not in Residence: 1 PhD

Average No. of New Students Enrolled: 6 MA; 3 PhD

Women Students: 5 MA; 4 PhD

Foreign Students: 1 MA; 1 PhD

Minimum GPA Score Requisite to Admission: MA: 3.3 on a 4-point scale; PhD: 3.5 on a 4-point scale

Foreign Language Proficiency Evaluated: No

Financial Aid to First Year Students: 50% MA; 100% PhD

Financial Aid to Other Students: 50% MA; 100% PhD

Attrition Among Students: 15% MA; 18% PhD

DESCRIPTION OF GRADUATE PROGRAM AND RESEARCH FACILITIES: The MA degree may be pursued in Western Religions, Eastern Religions, or the Nature of Religion. MA with Thesis: While there is no fixed ratio of thesis research to course work and all programs are based upon the student's interests and preparation, the normal expectation is completion of two full-course equivalents in addition to the thesis. It is expected that at least one half-course will be completed in the two areas of specialization other than the one in which the thesis will be written. The MA degree also may be done in a course-based, non-thesis program, requiring successful completion of five full-course equivalents and a final comprehensive examination.

Doctoral studies may be pursued in three primary areas: Religious Texts and Commentaries, History of Religious Movements and Institutions, and Interpretations of Religion. These research areas encompass the varied research done in the Department and provide students with a sense of the multi- and inter-disciplinary nature of the study of religion.

ACADEMIC PLAN, ADMISSION REQUIREMENTS, FINANCIAL AID: For entrance to the MA programme, the Faculty of Graduate Studies requires a baccalaureate degree from a recognized institution with a minimum GPA of 3.3 in the last two years of full-time study. Two specific criteria must also be met: (1) Given the wide range of themes and traditions involved in undergraduate study in religion, the Department will need to determine that an applicant's preparation is adequate in those areas in which he or she is likely to specialize, and that an appropriate balance exists in the student's preparation. (2) Scholarship in many areas of Religious Studies requires substantial preparation in relevant languages. The Department reserves the right to determine language preparation required for admission, and subsequent program requirements.

For entrance to the PhD programme, applicants should have an MA in Religious Studies or a comparable degree with equivalent balance components of Eastern Religions, Western Religions, and the Nature of Religion, with a minimum GPA of 3.5.

FACULTY:

Barber, Anthony W., PhD, Wisconsin (1984), 1991, Associate Professor, Buddhist Studies—Tathagatagarbha, Chinese Buddhism, Vajrayana, E-mail: abarber@ucalgary.ca

Eslinger, Lyle M., PhD, McMaster (1982), 1984, Professor, Hebrew Bible—Hebrew Bible, biblical narrative, inner-biblical exegesis, Bible and literature, E-mail: eslinger@ucalgary.ca

Hexham, Irving R., PhD, University of Bristol (1975), 1984, Professor, Nature of Religion—new religious movements, African religion and society, Dutch neo-Calvinism, charismatic religions, methods and theory in the study of religion, E-mail: hexham@ucalgary.ca

Hove, Philo, PhD, Edmonton (1998), 1997, Instructor, Eastern Religion—early Indian Buddhism, E-mail: hove@ucalgary.ca

Joy, Morny, PhD, McGill (1981), 1988, Professor, Nature of Religion—hermeneutics, philosophy of religion, postmodernism, women and religion, E-mail: mjoy@ucalgary.ca

Kawamura, Leslie S., PhD, Saskatchewan (1976), 1976, Professor, Buddhism—Yogacara, Indian, Chinese, Tibetan, and Japanese Buddhism, respective languages for these traditions, E-mail: kawamura@ucalgary.ca

McCready, Wayne O., PhD, McMaster (1980), 1979, Associate Professor, Early Christianity—Second Temple Judaism, Qumran Scrolls, origins of Christianity, E- mail: mccready@ucalgary.ca

Moore, Anne, MA, Calgary (1989), 1997, Instructor, Christian Origins/NT—Gospels, biblical intertextuality, rhetorical criticism, E-mail: amoore@ucalgary.ca

Neufeldt, Ronald W., PhD, Iowa (1977), 1977, Professor, Hinduism—history of Indian religions, religion in modern India, methodology, new religions, E-mail: rneufeld@ucalgary.ca

Penelhum, Terence M., BPhil, Oxford (1952), 1963, Professor Emeritus—philosophy of religion, E-mail: penelhum@ucalgary.ca

Rippin, Andrew L., PhD, McGill (1981), 1980, Professor, Arabic and Islamic Studies—Qur'an, Qur'an interpretation, E-mail: arippin@ucalgary.ca

Segal, Eliezer, PhD, Jerusalem (1982), 1986, Associate Professor, Judaism—Jewish exegesis, Judaism, rabbinics, Talmud, E-mail: elsegal@ucalgary.ca

Shantz, Douglas, PhD, Waterloo (1987), 1999, Associate Professor, Christian Thought—radical Reformation studies, German pietism

Tumasz, Virginia, PhD, Temple (1987), 1997, Instructor, Nature of Religion—process thought, history of Christian thought, philosophical theology, E-mail: tumasz@ucalgary.ca

---

University of California/Berkeley

Berkeley CA 94720

Phone: 510-642-2363
Fax: 510-642-4607
URL: ls.berkeley.edu/ugis/religionsstudies

TYPE OF INSTITUTION: Public
EXECUTIVE OFFICER: Robert Berdahl, Chancellor
COORDINATOR: Susanna Elm
GRADUATE ENROLLMENT: 47

University of California/Davis

Department of Religious Studies
One Shields Ave
622 Sproul Hall
Davis CA 95616

Phone: 530-752-4999
Fax: 530-752-4339
E-mail: gjhart@ucdavis.edu
URL: ucdavis.edu/RST/

TYPE OF INSTITUTION: Public
EXECUTIVE OFFICER: Patricia Turner, Dean/Arts, Cultural Studies
CHAIRPERSON: Jacob K. Olupona
DEGREES OFFERED: BA
UNDERGRADUATE MAJORS: 31
DEGREES CONFERRED: 5
DESCRIPTION OF UNDERGRADUATE PROGRAM: Small but intensive and flexible undergraduate program that emphasizes critical analysis and interdisciplinary approaches; majors are required to take an integrative course "Issues and Method" to graduate.

FACULTY:

Albu, Emily, University of California, Berkeley (1975), 1996, Assistant Professor—Spanish and Classics, Classical and Medieval Latin, Byzantine Greek, Old French/Old Provençal

Frankenberg, Ruth, University of California, Santa Cruz (1988), 1993, Associate Professor—American studies, new developments and new syncretisms in religion in the contemporary United States, US religious and spiritual practices outside the institutions, critical study of whiteness and racial formation, cultural studies

Hurst, Lincoln, PhD, Oxford University, England (1982), 1988, Associate Professor—Hellinistic Judaism, Judaism of the Second Temple Period, the epistle to the Hebrews, New Testament Christology, New Testament Theology, Christian origins, patristic period, church history, religious biography

Janowitz, Naomi, PhD, University of Chicago (1984), 1991, Associate Professor—Hellenistic religions, theories of ritual, ancient and post-biblical Judaism

Lai, Whalen, PhD, Harvard University (1975), 1980, Professor—Eastern traditions, Pan-Asian Buddhism, Chinese philosophy, myth and narrative analysis, meaning and identity, ethical discourse

O'Connor, Kathleen, University of Pennsylvania (1994), 1998, Lecturer—Islamic studies, comparative religion

Olupona, Jacob K., PhD, Boston University (1983), Professor—African traditional religion, West African society and culture, African religion in the Americas, Islam in Africa and the Americas

Rosenstock, Bruce, PhD, Princeton University (1979), Lecturer—ancient philosophy, biblical studies, Sabbateanism, modern Jewish philosophy

Schaeffer, Peter, Lic Theol, University of Ottawa (1959), PhD, Princeton University (1971), 1976, Professor of German—scholastic philosophy and theology, reformation history, German and Neo-Latin reformation literature and polemics, theory and practice of biblical translation

University of California/Irvine

Irvine CA 92713

University of California/Los Angeles

Dept of History
PO Box 951473
Los Angeles CA 90095-1473

Phone: 310-825-8948
E-mail: religion@humnet.ucla.edu
URL: www.humnet.ucla.edu/hemnet/religion

TYPE OF INSTITUTION: Public
EXECUTIVE OFFICER: Pauline Ya, Dean
CHAIRPERSON: S. Scott Bartchy
UNDERGRADUATE ENROLLMENT: 23,000
GRADUATE ENROLLMENT: 12,500

University of California/Riverside

Dept of Religious Studies
Riverside CA 92521

Phone: 909-787-3612
Fax: 909-787-3324
URL: www.ucr.edu.religious

TYPE OF INSTITUTION: Public
CHAIRPERSON: Ivan Strenski
UNDERGRADUATE ENROLLMENT: 8,531

University of California/San Diego

Program for the Study of Religion
9500 Gilman Drive
Mail Stop 0410
La Jolla CA 92093-0410

Phone: 858-534-8849
Fax: 858-534-8686
E-mail: religion@ucsd.edu
URL: religion.ucsd.edu

TYPE OF INSTITUTION: Public
FACULTY DIRECTOR: Arthur Droge
DEGREES OFFERED: BA
UNDERGRADUATE MAJORS: 21
DEGREES CONFERRED: 31
DESCRIPTION OF UNDERGRADUATE PROGRAM: The Program engages in the academic study of religious phenomena; and it studies literature, history, and society in relation to religion. Faculty and students associated with the Program give primacy to humanistic and social scientific methods of study that have become established in the academic community during the nineteenth and twentieth centuries. The location of the Program in the Arts and Humanities Division and its use of courses from a variety of departments and divisions imply that neither the study of religion nor its data are the privileged possession of a single discipline. The hallmark of the Program is it interdisciplinary and interdepartmental structure. At UCSD, faculty from the departments of Anthropology, History, Literature, Philosophy, Political Science, Sociology, and Visual Arts provide students with the opportunity to examine religious artifacts, texts, institutions, and communities within a particular cultural and historical

context and in the context of comparable manifestations with the general history of religions. A concentration in the Study of Religion aims at fostering a student's understanding of religion as one of the primary expressions of the human condition and as an historically powerful force in the shaping of human cultures. It also seeks to develop a student's appreciation of the difficulties and possibilities inherent in undertaking a critical, disciplined study of religion. The goal is not to fashion "experts" in religion, but rather to use the study of religion in order to develop critical thinking and a more adequate understanding of history and society. Since the program endorses an interdisciplinary and comparative approach to the study of religious phenomena, lower-division preparation should be wide and varied. Lower-division courses in which religion figures prominently (e.g., The Making of the Modern World or the Revelle College Humanities Program), as well as courses which focus on textual and contextual analysis and employ the analytical tools and conceptual categories of the human sciences, would all be useful in preparing the student for a major in the Study of Religion. The Program strongly encourages foreign language study. The ability to read the languages of original sources and of modern scholarship is highly recommended.

FACULTY:

Caciola, Nancy, PhD, Assistant Professor—history, Medieval European history, popular culture

Cahill, Suzanne, PhD, Berkeley, Adjunct Associate Professor—history, Asian religious traditions, Chinese religions, women in Chinese religion, Buddhism, Taoism

Cohen, Alain J.-J., PhD, UCLA, Professor—literature, comparative literature, psychoanalysis, semiotics, film history and theory

Cohen, Richard S., Assistant Professor—literature, history, Buddhism, South Asian religions, theory in the study of religion

Cox, Stephen, PhD, UCLA, Professor—literature, English literature, New Testament and its literary influence

Droge, Arthur J., PhD, University of Chicago, Professor and Program Director for the Study of Religion—literature, early Christian history and literature (including the New testament); Hellenistic Judaism; Scriptures of Judaism, Christianity, and Islam

duBois, Page A., PhD, Berkeley, Professor—literature, classics and comparative literature

Fitzgerald, William C., PhD, Princeton, Associate Professor—literature, classics and comparative literature

Freedman, David Noel, PhD, Johns Hopkins, Hebrew Biblical Studies Endowed Chair and Professor—history, Bible, archaeology, ancient Near East

Friedman, Richard E., ThD, Harvard, Katzin Chair of Jewish Civilization, Professor—literature, Hebrew and comparative literature

Goodblatt, David, PhD, Brown, Judaic Studies Endowed Chair, Professor—history, ancient Jewish history

Gutierrez, Ramon, PhD, Wisconsin Madison, Professor—ethnic studies, Chicano, Spanish borderlands, colonial Latin America

Houston, Alan, PhD, Harvard, Associate Professor—political science, political theory

Howe, Fanny Q., Stanford, Professor—literature, mysticism, writing

Jolley, S. Nicholas, PhD, Cambridge, Professor—philosophy, 17th and 18th century philosophy, political philosophy

Jordan, David K., PhD, Chicago, Professor—anthropology, anthropology of religion and ideology, sociolinguistics, culture history, Taiwan, Chinese religion and kinship

Jules-Rosette, Bennetta W., PhD, Harvard, Professor—sociology, sociology of religion, knowledge and culture, ethnomethodology, social change, ethnographic film

Kayali, Hasan, PhD, Harvard, Associate Professor—history, modern Middle East history and Islamic studies

Lakoff, Sanford A., PhD, Harvard, Professor—political science, political thought, science and public policy

Lee, Edward N., PhD, Princeton, Professor—philosophy, ancient Greek philosophy, Greek literature and civilization, ancient mythology and religion

Luhrmann, Tanya M., PhD, Cambridge, Professor—anthropology, beliefs and moral concepts, witchcraft

Madsen, Richard P., PhD, Harvard, Professor—sociology, sociology of ideas/culture, theory, political sociology, Chinese society, sociology of religion, moral anthropology

Marino, John A., PhD, Chicago, Associate Professor—history, early modern Europe, Renaissance and Reformation

McDaniel, Timothy, PhD, Professor—sociology, Russia, Islam, social change, religion and society comparatively, revolutions

Meeker, Michael E., PhD, Chicago, Professor—anthropology, politics, religion, oral tradition, social theory, Turkey

Mosshammer, Alden A., PhD, Brown, Professor—history, ancient Greece, Rome, early Christianity

Nodelman, Sheldon A., PhD, Yale, Professor—visual arts, art of antiquity

Propp, William H. C., PhD, Harvard, Professor—history, Hebrew language, biblical studies

Randel, Fred V., PhD, Yale, Associate Professor—literature, English literature

Reynolds, Edward, PhD, London, Professor—history, Africa, West African economic, missionary

Shafir, Gershon, PhD, Berkeley, Professor—sociology, religion and politics in Israeli society, the Israeli-Palestinian conflict, comparative historical sociology, nationalism

Shiffman, Gary, PhD, Assistant Professor—political science, political theory, political philosophy

Spiro, Melford E., PhD, Northwestern, Professor Emeritus—anthropology, psychological anthropology, comparative religion, symbolic systems Southeast Asia, Middle East

Strong, Tracy B., PhD, Harvard, Professor—political science, political theory

Turner, Christena, PhD, Stanford, Associate Professor—sociology, Japanese society, culture, every day life, organizations

Tuzin, Donald F., PhD, Professor—anthropology, social anthropology, psychological anthropology, symbolism, religion, Melanesia, Australia, Indonesia

---

University of California/Santa Barbara

Dept of Religious Studies
Santa Barbara CA 93106

Phone: 805-893-7136
Fax: 805-893-2059
E-mail: lombrozo@humanitas.ucsb.edu
URL: www.religion.ucsb.edu/

TYPE OF INSTITUTION: Public
EXECUTIVE OFFICER: Henry Yang, Chancellor
CHAIRPERSON: Wade Clark Roof
COORDINATOR: Sally Jean Lombrozo
UNDERGRADUATE ENROLLMENT: 130
GRADUATE ENROLLMENT: 80
DEGREES OFFERED: BA

UNDERGRADUATE MAJORS: 130

DEGREES CONFERRED: 75

DESCRIPTION OF UNDERGRADUATE PROGRAM: The Department of Religious Studies at UCSB is unique among California universities, state universities, and colleges. The courses it offers address the critical issues relating to the subject of religion in its many facets: historical, cultural, literary, aesthetic, sociological, experiential, and philosophical. In introductory and advanced courses, its faculty—respected in their fields nationally and internationally—regularly teach about the religions of the world, and about the complex relationship between religion and politics, society, war, and everday life. It is the only such department in the University of California system to offer BA, MA, and PhD degrees.

GRADUATE PROGRAM

Member of the Council on Graduate Studies in Religion

Graduate Advisor: David G. White

Graduate Degrees Offered: MA; PhD

Degrees Conferred: 8 MA; 5 PhD

Graduate Students in Residence: 6 MA; 74 PhD

Not in Residence: 10 PhD

Average No. of New Students Enrolled: 3 MA; 15 PhD

Women Students: 2 MA; 32 PhD

Minority Students: 1 MA; 12 PhD

Foreign Students: 1 MA; 2 PhD

Minimum GRE Score Requisite to Admission: No

Minimum GPA Score Requisite to Admission: Yes, 3.0 on a scale of 4.0

Foreign Language Proficiency Evaluated: No

Financial Aid to First Year Students: 85% PhD

Financial Aid to Other Students: 95% PhD

Attrition Among Students: 10% MA; 10% PhD

Graduates Placed: 99% PhD

DESCRIPTION OF GRADUATE PROGRAM AND RESEARCH FACILITIES: The graduate program in the Department of Religious Studies is designated as cross-cultural and interdisciplinary studies in religion. The cross-cultural aspect of the program is concerned with the comparative study of religious traditions in eastern and western cultures and includes Native American religious traditions. Advanced work in this area emphasizes the study of religious texts and other source materials, requiring philological competence; the study of methodology and hermeneutics; and comparative phenomenological, philosophical, and theological investigation. The interdisciplinary studies aspect of the program concentrates on the relation of religion to the humanistic traditions of thought and expression in both classical and contemporary forms. Students are expected to do advanced work in one of the traditional disciplines—literature, history, history and theory of art, philosophy, sociology—in addition to preparing themselves in the history of western thought and in a general approach to the theory and history of religion.

ACADEMIC PLAN, ADMISSION REQUIREMENTS, FINANCIAL AID: Please contact the Graduate Program Assistant to request our departmental information including a full description of the academic plan, admission requirements, and financial aid possibilities.

FACULTY:

Albanese, Catherine L., PhD, University of Chicago (1972), 1988, Professor—American religious history, religion and American culture, 805-893-3530, E-mail: albanese@humanitas.ucsb.edu

Campo, Juan E., PhD, University of Chicago (1985), 1983, Associate Professor—history of religions (Islam), Arabic, 805-893-3945, E-mail: jcampo@humanitas.ucsb.edu

Campo, Magda, MA, American University in Cairo (1995), 1986, Lecturer—Arabic, 805-893-3585, E-mail:campo@humanitas.ucsb.edu

Carlson, Thomas A., PhD, University of Chicago (1995), 1995, Assistant Professor—Christianity and culture, religion and philosophy, 805-893-7142, E-mail: tcarlson@humanitas.ucsb.edu

Friedland, Roger, PhD, University of Wisconsin (1977), 1998, Professor—sociology and religion, cultural analysis, 805-893-5695, E-mail: friedlan@alishaw.ucsb.edu

Garr, W. Randall, PhD, Yale University (1982), 1987, Associate Professor—Northwest Semitic languages, Hebrew bible, ancient Near East, 805-893-8428, E-mail: wrgarr@humanitas.ucsb.edu

Hammond, Phillip E., PhD, Columbia University (1960), 1979, Professor—sociology of religion, 805-893-2942, E-mail: hammond@humanitas.ucsb.edu

Hecht, Richard D., PhD, University of California, Los Angeles (1976), 1976, Professor—history of religions, Judaic studies, 805-893-4552, E-mail: ariel@humanitas.ucsb.edu

Holdrege, Barbara A., PhD, Harvard University (1987), 1987, Associate Professor—comparative history of religions, South Asian religions, Judaic studies, 805-893-8445, E-mail: holdrege@humanitas.ucsb.edu

Powell, William F., PhD, University of California, Berkeley (1982), 1982, Associate Professor—history of religions, China, 805-893-4455, E-mail: bpowell@humanitas.ucsb.edu

Reynolds, Dwight F., PhD, University of Pennsylvania (1991), 1991, Associate Professor—Arabic languages and literatures, folklore and folklife, 805-893-7143, E-mail: dreynold@humanitas.ucsb.edu

Roof, Wade Clark, PhD, University of North Carolina (1971), 1989, J. F. Rowny Professor of Religion and Society—sociology and psychology of religion, American religion, 805-893-3564, E-mail: wcroof@humanitas.ucsb.edu

Talamantez, Inés M., PhD, University of California, San Diego (1976), 1978, Associate Professor—Native American religions, 805-893-4326

Thomas, Christine M., PhD, Harvard University (1995), 1997, Assistant Professor—Hellenistic religions, early Christianity, archaeology of religions, 805-893-4004, E-mail: thomas@humanitas.ucsb.edu

Wallace, B. Alan, PhD, Stanford University (1995), 1997, Visiting Lecturer—Tibetan, 805-893-3134, E-mail: bwallace@humanitas.ucsb.edu

Wallace, Vesna B., PhD, Stanford University, 1997, Visiting Lecturer—Sanskrit languages and literature, 805-893-3134, E-mail: vwallace@humanitas.ucsb.edu

White, David G., PhD, University of Chicago (1988), 1996, Associate Professor—South Asian religions, 805-893-4627. E-mail: white@humanitas.ucsb.edu

Professors Emeriti:

Comstock, W. Richard, PhD, Union Theological Seminary—religion in western culture

Iyer, Nandini, MA, Oxford University—Sanskrit

Larson, Gerald J., PhD, Columbia University—Sanskrit, philosophy and history of religions (India)

Long, Charles H., PhD. University of Chicago—history of religions, African and African-American religions

Michaelsen, Robert S., PhD, Yale University—religion in America

Panikkar, Raimundo, PhD, University of Madrid—comparative religion and philosophy of religion

Pearson, Birger A., PhD, Harvard University—Christian origins, Hellenistic religions
Smart, Ninian, BPhil, Oxford University—philosophy of religion, comparative religions

California Baptist College

8432 Magnolia Avenue
Riverside CA 92504-3297

Phone: 909-689-5771
Fax: 909-351-1808
E-mail: dannykwilson@juno.com

TYPE OF INSTITUTION: Denominational: Southern Baptist
EXECUTIVE OFFICER: Ronald Ellis, President
CHAIRPERSON: Dan Wilson, Division of Christian Studies
UNDERGRADUATE ENROLLMENT: 2,009

California Christian College

4881 E University Ave, Fresno CA 93703

California Christian Institute

1744 W Katella, Suite 26, Orange CA 92667

California Graduate School of Theology

400 W Freedman Way, Anaheim CA 92802

California Institute of Integral Studies

1453 Mission St
San Francisco CA 94714

Phone: 415-575-6100

California Lutheran University

Dept of Religion
60 W Olsen Rd
Thousand Oaks CA 91360-2787

Phone: 805-493-3238
Fax: 805-493-3013
E-mail: everson@callutheran.edu
URL: robles.clunet.edu

TYPE OF INSTITUTION: Private, Evangelical Lutheran Church in America (ELCA)
EXECUTIVE OFFICER: Luther S. Luedtke, President
CHAIRPERSON: A. Joseph Everson
UNDERGRADUATE ENROLLMENT: 1,800
GRADUATE ENROLLMENT: 1,000

California Missionary Baptist Institute

Box 848, 9246 Rosser St, Bellflower CA 90706

California State University/Bakersfield

9001 Stockdale Hwy
Bakersfield CA 93311-1099

Phone: 805-664-2291
Fax: 805-665-6904
E-mail: bjones@csubak.edu
URL: www.csubak.edu/religiousstudies

TYPE OF INSTITUTION: Public
EXECUTIVE OFFICER: Thomas Arciniega
CHAIRPERSON: Gary E. Kessler
UNDERGRADUATE ENROLLMENT: 12

California State University/Chico

239 Trinity Hall
Chico CA 95929-0740

Phone: 530-898-5661
Fax: 530-898-5468
E-mail: jzimbelman@csuchico.edu
URL: www.csuchico.edu/rs/

TYPE OF INSTITUTION: Public
EXECUTIVE OFFICER: Donald Heinz, Dean College of Humanities and Fine Arts
CHAIRPERSON: Joel Zimbelman
UNDERGRADUATE ENROLLMENT: 13,900
GRADUATE ENROLLMENT: 1,000
DEGREES OFFERED: BA
UNDERGRADUATE MAJORS: 70
DEGREES CONFERRED: 13

DESCRIPTION OF UNDERGRADUATE PROGRAM: The Department (one of seven in the College of Humanities and Fine Arts) approaches the study of religion from the perspectives of history, textual studies of sacred writings, sociology, anthropology, philosophy, and other disciplines. In addition to providing an understanding of the development of the major religious traditions of the world, these approaches also equip students to explore the complex relationship of religion to other aspects of contemporary culture, including law, psychology, gender constructs, literature, the visual arts, and a variety of contemporary social, political, and ethical issues. The cross-cultural and historical study of religions is an integral part of education for citizenship in a pluralistic society. Life in such a society is based on respect for religious liberty and freedom of conscience. Such respect of other religious groups (or those who espouse no religious belief) is difficult to sustain without significant knowledge of the histories, beliefs, and customs of diverse peoples and religious traditions of the world. The discipline of religious studies helps students to understand the complex and ambiguous role of religions in history and society, both as sources of conflict and as spiritual, philosophical, and moral resources in human life.

FACULTY:

Anderson, James Douglas, EdD, Harvard (1990), 1972, Lecturer (part-time)—ethics and education, world religions and global ethics, Asian religions, western religions, 530-898-5662; Fax: 530-898-5468, E-mail: jimanderson@csuchico.edu

Bash, John A., PhD, Yale (1965), 1968, Professor Emeritus—comparative religions, philosophy of religions, 530-898-5661, Fax: 530-898-5468

Caldwell, Sarah L., PhD, UC Berkeley (1995), 1998, Assistant Professor—Hinduism, mysticism, gender and religion, 530-898-4165, Fax: 530-898-5468, E-mail: scaldwell@csuchico.edu

Grelle, Bruce, PhD, University of Chicago (1993), 1989, Associate Professor—comparative religious ethics, religion and society, religion and public education, cross-cultural environmental ethics, 530-898-4739, Fax: 530-898-5468, E-mail: bgrelle@csuchico.edu

Heinz, Donald J., PhD, Graduate Theological Union (1975), 1976, Professor; Dean of College of Humanities and Fine Arts—religion and society, history of Christian thought, religious ethics, dying, death, and afterlife, 530-898-5351, Fax: 530-898-5468, E-mail: dheinz@csuchico.edu

Jeffreys, Derek S., PhD, University of Chicago Divinity School (1999), 1999, Lecturer—religious ethics, philosophy of religion, theology, 530-898-5263, Fax: 530-898-5468, E-mail: djeffreys@csuchico.edu

Kanda, Shigeo H., PhD, Claremont Graduate School (1974), 1970, Professor—Buddhism, Asian religions, Asian American studies, religion and America's ethnic minorities, bible, 530-898-5108, Fax: 530-898-5468, E-mail: skanda@csuchico.edu

McCarthy, Kate, PhD, Graduate Theological Union (1994), 1994, Assistant Professor—women and religion, third world theology, Christianity, interreligious dialogue, 530-898-4485, Fax: 530-898-5468, E-mail: kmccarthy@csuchico.edu

Pike, Sarah M., PhD, Indiana University (1997), 1996, Assistant Professor—American religions, new religious movements, ritual studies, religion and ethnicity, 530-898-6341, Fax: 530-898-5468, E-mail: spike@csuchico.edu

Pinnock, Sarah K., MPhil, Yale University (1996), 1998, Lecturer, part-time—comparative philosophy of religion, theodicy, post-Holocaust theology, women and religion, 530-898-5263, Fax: 530-898-5468, E-mail: spinnock@csuchico.edu

Williams, George Mason, Jr., PhD, The University of Iowa (1972), 1973, Professor Emeritus—history of religions, Hinduism, religion in modern India, religions of the Pacific rim, religion and personality, experiential phenomenology, 530-898-5662, Fax: 530-898-5468, E-mail: gwilliams@csuchico.edu

Wyrick, Jed, PhD, Harvard University (1999), 1999, Assistant Professor—Judaism, Western religions, Bible, ancient Greek religion/literature, 530-898-5860, Fax: 530-898-5468, E-mail: jwrick@csuchico.edu

Zimbelman, Joel Andrew, PhD, University of Virginia (1986), 1987, Professor—history of Christian thought, religious and applied social ethics, religion, ethics, and medicine, humanities, 530-898-4741, Fax: 530-898-5468, E-mail: jzimbelman@csuchico.edu

---

California State University/Dominguez Hills

Dept of Philosophy and Religion, Carson CA 90747

California State University/Fullerton

Dept of Comparative Religion   **Phone: 714-278-2442**
PO Box 6868   **Fax: 714-278-5820**
800 N State College Boulevard   **E-mail: bhubbard@fullerton.edu**
Fullerton CA 92831-3599
TYPE OF INSTITUTION: Public

CHAIRPERSON: Benjamin J Hubbard

UNDERGRADUATE ENROLLMENT: 30

California State University/Long Beach

Religious Studies Dept
1250 Bellflower Blvd
Long Beach CA 90840-2409

Phone: 562-985-5341
Fax: 562-985-5540
URL: www.csulb.edu/dept/relstud/

TYPE OF INSTITUTION: Public

CHAIRPERSON: Peter Lowentrout

UNDERGRADUATE ENROLLMENT: 35

DEGREES OFFERED: BA in Religious Studies

UNDERGRADUATE MAJORS: 35

DEGREES CONFERRED: 13

DESCRIPTION OF UNDERGRADUATE PROGRAM: The department offers both a major and a minor in Religious Studies, each structured to balance both breadth and depth. On the one hand this organization aims toward the goal of understanding a wide variety of the religious traditions in our pluralistic society. On the other it seeks to achieve a professional level of systematic expertise—ethical, imaginative, analytic and interpretive. A certificate program is available, mostly for graduate students. The department participates in a campus wide interdisciplinary program which provides the opportunity to pursue MA degrees in cooperation with other departments.

FACULTY:

Battaglia, Anthony, PhD, Princeton University (1972), 1974, Professor—religious ethics, contemporary religious thoughts, religion in the modern world, E-mail: battagli@csulb.edu

Broughton, Jeffrey, PhD, Columbia University (1975), 1976, Associate Professor—Asian religions, specialty in East Asian religions, E-mail: jbrought@csulb.edu

Eisenman, Robert, PhD, Columbia University (1971), 1973, Professor—Middle East religions and early Christianity

Hibbets, Maria, PhD, Harvard University (1999), 1999, Assistant Professor—South and Southeast Asian religions, E-mail: mhibbets@csulb.edu

Hughes, Edward, PhD, Claremont Graduate School (1984), 1990, Associate Professor—philosophy and history of religion, contemporary and comparative religious thought

Jones, F. Stanley, PhD, Vanderbilt University (1989), 1988, Associate Professor—New Testament, early Christian thought, Hellenistic religions, E-mail: fsjones@csulb.edu

Lowentrout, Peter, PhD, University of Southern California (1983), 1984, Professor—religion and science, religion and literature, E-mail: plowentr@csulb.edu

Piar, Carlos, PhD, University of Southern California (1991), 1990, Associate Professor—theological ethics, Christian ethics, Latin American liberation theology, E-mail: crpiar@csulb.edu

LECTURER:

Hawkins, Bradley, PhD, University of California Santa Barbara (1996), 1995, Lecturer—religions of Southeast and South Asia, E-mail: bhawkins@csulb.edu

California State University/Los Angeles

5151 State University Dr
Los Angeles CA 90032-8223

Phone: 323-343-2046

TYPE OF INSTITUTION: Public

COORDINATOR: Erika Wilson

UNDERGRADUATE ENROLLMENT: 16

GRADUATE ENROLLMENT: 4

California State University/Northridge

18111 Nordhoff Street   **Phone: 818-677-3392**
Northridge CA 91330-8316   **Fax: 818-677-3985**
E-mail: religious.studies@csun.edu
URL: www.csun.edu/religious.studies

TYPE OF INSTITUTION: Public

CHAIRPERSON: Crerar Douglas

DEGREES OFFERED: BA

UNDERGRADUATE MAJORS: 26

DEGREES CONFERRED: 12

DESCRIPTION OF UNDERGRADUATE: The Religious Studies Department is one of eight departments in the School of Humanities. The major is designed to provide 1) a liberal arts education with an emphasis on Religious Studies, 2) a broad background for advanced work in professional and social fields, and 3) preparation for graduate work in Religious Studies and related disciplines. The department's service function to the University's General Education and interdisciplinary programs accounts for a large part of its student enrollments.

FACULTY:

Douglas, Crerar, PhD, Hartford Seminary Foundation (1973), 1971, Professor—history of Christian theology, 818-677-3392, E-mail: crerar.douglas@csun.edu

Goss, James, PhD, Claremont Graduate School (1970), 1969, Professor—religion and literature, New Testament, 818-677-3940, E-mail: james.goss@csun.edu

Happ, Howard J., PhD, Princeton University (1974), 1971, Professor—religion in America, history of Christianity, religion and society, sects and cults, 818-677-2742, E-mail: howard.happ@csun.edu

Herman, Phyllis, PhD, University of California, Los Angeles (1979), 1999, Assistant Professor—Hinduism, women and religion, 818-677-3925, E-mail: phyllis.k.herman@csun.edu

Hussain, Amir, ABD, University of Toronto, 1997, Assistant Professor—Islam, 818-677-2741, E-mail: amir.hussain@csun.edu

Lam-Easton, Linda, PhD, University of Chicago (1980), 1987, Professor—Chinese religions, 818-677-3396, E-mail: linda.lam.easton@csun.edu

Medina, Lara, PhD, Claremont Graduate University, Assistant Professor—religion and US Latinas/os, gender and religion, ethnicity and religion, liberation theologies/spiritualities

Miyuki, Mokusen, PhD, Claremont Graduate School (1965), 1970, Professor—Asian religions, religion and personality, 818-677-2357

Myers, Jody, PhD, UCLA (1984), 1986, Professor—Jewish studies, 818-677-3007, E-mail: jody.myers@csun.edu

Nichelson, Patrick, PhD, University of Southern California (1974), 1970, Professor—ethics, religion and literature, 818-677-2741, E-mail: pat.nichelson@csun.edu

Calumet College of St Joseph

2400 New York Ave
Whiting IN 46394-2146

Phone: 219-473-4252
Fax: 219-473-4259
E-mail: efinnegan@ccsj.edu
URL: www.ccsj.edu

TYPE OF INSTITUTION: Private, Roman Catholic
EXECUTIVE OFFICER: Dennis Rittenmeyer, President
CHAIRPERSON: Eugene Finnegan, STD
UNDERGRADUATE ENROLLMENT: 201

Calvary Baptist School of Theology

Valley Forge and Sumneytown, Lansdale PA 19446

Calvery Bible College

15800 Calvery Rd, Kansas City MO 64147-1341

Calvin College

Dept of Religion and Theology
3201 Burton St SE
Grand Rapids MI 49546

Phone: 616-957-6315
Fax: 616-957-8551
E-mail: psturgeo@calvin.edu
URL: www.calvin.edu/academic/religion

TYPE OF INSTITUTION: Private, Christian Reformed
EXECUTIVE OFFICER: Michael J. Stob, Dean
CHAIRPERSON: Richard J. Plantinga
UNDERGRADUATE ENROLLMENT: 4,100
DEGREES OFFERED: BA
UNDERGRADUATE MAJORS: 60
DEGREES CONFERRED: 20

DESCRIPTION OF UNDERGRADUATE PROGRAM: The department is made up of 13 full-time teachers. The Religion and Theology major provides opportunity for concentration in biblical studies, or systematic/historical studies. Courses are also offered in world religions and missions. A teaching major is also offered. Two minors are offered: missions and general studies.

FACULTY:

Crump, David, PhD, Aberdeen (1988), 1997, Associate Professor—New Testament, 616-957-6319, E-mail: dcrump@calvin.edu

de Groot, Christiana, PhD, Notre Dame (1990), 1988, Professor—Old Testament, 616-957-7042, E-mail: cdegroot@calvin.edu

Griffioen, Arie J., PhD, Marquette (1988), 1992, Associate Professor—historical theology, 616-957-6325, E-mail: grifar@calvin.edu

Harlow, Daniel C., PhD, (1994), 1999, Assistant Professor—New Testament, 616-957-6538, E-mail: dharlow@calvin.edu

Hotz, Kendra G., PhD (cand.), Emory, 1998, Instructor—patristic theology, 616-957-6612, E-mail: khotz@calvin.edu

Lee, Won W., PhD, Claremont (1998), 1996, Assistant Professor—Old Testament, 616-957-6323, E-mail: wlee@calvin.edu

Mathews, Matthew, PhD (cand.), Emory, 1998, Instructor—history of Christianity, 616-957-6641, E-mail: mmathews@calvin.edu

Plantinga, Richard J., PhD, McMaster (1990), 1990, Professor—Christian theology and religious pluralism, 616-957-6316, E-mail: plar@calvin.edu

Pomykala, Kenneth E., PhD, Claremont (1992), 1988, Professor—New Testament, 616-957-6320, E-mail: pomk@calvin.edu

Schneider, John R., PhD, Cambridge (1987), 1986, Professor—systematic theology, 616-957-6718, E-mail: schn@calvin.edu

Smit, Laura, PhD, (1998), 1999, Assistant Professor—history of Christian thought, 616-957-8580, E-mail: lsmit@calvin.edu

Thompson, Thomas R., PhD, Princeton (1996), 1992, Associate Professor—systematic theology, 616-957-6429, E-mail: thomto@calvin.edu

Whitekettle, Richard W., PhD, Yale (1995), 1994, Assistant Professor—Old Testament, 616-957-6517, E-mail: rwhiteke@calvin.edu

---

Calvin Theological Seminary

3233 Burton St SE
Grand Rapids MI 49546

Phone: 616-957-6036
Fax: 616-957-8621
E-mail: ddevadat@calvin.edu
URL: www.calvin.edu/seminary

TYPE OF INSTITUTION: Private, Christian Reformed Church
EXECUTIVE OFFICER: James A. DeJong, President
GRADUATE ENROLLMENT: 290

Cameron University

Lawton OK 73501

Campbell University

PO Box 1029
Buies Creek NC 27506

Phone: 800-334-4111
Fax: 910-893-1878
E-mail: jonas@mailcenter.campbell.edu
URL: www.campbell.edu

TYPE OF INSTITUTION: Private, North Carolina Baptist
EXECUTIVE OFFICER: Norman Adrian Wiggins
CHAIRPERSON: W. Glenn Jonas, Jr.
UNDERGRADUATE ENROLLMENT: 5,800
GRADUATE ENROLLMENT: 600
DEGREES OFFERED: BA in Religion; BA in Religion and Philosophy; BA in Religion and Christian Ministries

UNDERGRADUATE MAJORS: 100

DEGREES CONFERRED: 24

DESCRIPTION OF UNDERGRADUATE PROGRAM: Campbell University is a private, co-educational liberal arts university affiliated with the North Carolina Baptist State Convention. The Department of Religion offers the BA degree with concentration in one of three tracks: Religion, Religion and Philosophy, and Religion and Christian Ministries. A minor in Religion is also offered. Courses in biblical studies, theology, ethics, church history, religion and society, and practical ministries are offered to prepare students for graduate work or to go directly into ministry vocations.

FACULTY:

Ballard, H. Wayne, PhD, The Southern Baptist Theological Seminary (1995), 1997, Assistant Professor—Old Testament studies, biblical Hebrew, 910-893-1680, Fax: 910-893-1878, E-mail: ballard@mailcenter.campbell.edu

Jonas, W. Glenn, Jr., PhD, Baylor University (1990), 1994, Associate Professor and Chair of the Department—church history, practical theology, 910-893-1678, Fax: 910-893-1878, E-mail: jonas@mailcenter.campbell.edu

Martin, Dean M., PhD, Baylor University (1972), 1974, Professor—theology and philosophy, 910-893-1675, Fax: 910-893-1878, E-mail: dmartin@mailcenter.campbell.edu

Penny, Donald N., PhD, Emory University (1979), 1980, Associate Professor—New Testament studies, New Testament Greek, 910-893-1682, Fax: 910-893-1878, E-mail: penny@mailcenter.campbell.edu

Campbellsville University

1 University Drive
Campbellsville KY 42718-2799

Phone: 502-789-5029
E-mail: hurtgenj@campbellsvil.edu
URL: www.campbellsvil.edu

TYPE OF INSTITUTION: Private, Kentucky Baptist Convention

EXECUTIVE OFFICER: Frank Cheatham, Academic Dean

CHAIRPERSON: Walter Jackson

UNDERGRADUATE ENROLLMENT: 90

GRADUATE ENROLLMENT: 12

Canadian Baptist Seminary

See Associated Canadian Theological Schools (ACTS)

Canadian Bible College/Canadian Theological Seminary

4400 Fourth Ave
Regina SK S4T 0H8
Canada

Phone: 306-545-1515
Fax: 306-545-0210
E-mail: intouch@cbccts.sk.ca
URL: www.cbccts.sk.ca

TYPE OF INSTITUTION: Denominational: Christian and Missionary Alliance

EXECUTIVE OFFICER: George Durance, President

UNDERGRADUATE ENROLLMENT: 420

GRADUATE ENROLLMENT: 119

Associated Canadian Theological Schools (ACTS)

Trinity Western University
7600 Glover Rd
Langley, BC V2Y 1Y1
Canada

Phone: 604-513-2044
Fax: 604-513-2045
E-mail: acts@twu.ca
URL: acts.twu.ca

TYPE OF INSTITUTION: Multi-Denominational: Fellowship Baptist of Canada, Baptist General Conference of Canada, Evangelical Free Church of Canada
CONSORTIUM CO-ORDINATOR: Guy Saffold
GRADUATE ENROLLMENT: 250

Candler School of Theology

Emory University
Atlanta GA 30322

Phone: 404-727-6324
Fax: 404-727-3182
E-mail: candler@emory.edu
URL: www.emory.edu/candler/

TYPE OF INSTITUTION: Private, United Methodist affiliation
EXECUTIVE OFFICER: R. Kevin LaGree, Dean
GRADUATE ENROLLMENT: 599

Canisius College

2001 Main
Buffalo NY 14208-1098

Phone: 716-888-2820
Fax: 716-888-2525
E-mail: fiore@canisius.edu
URL: www.canisius.edu

TYPE OF INSTITUTION: Private, Roman Catholic
EXECUTIVE OFFICER: Vincent M. Cooke, SJ, President
CHAIRPERSON: Benjamin Fiore, SJ
UNDERGRADUATE ENROLLMENT: 3,500
GRADUATE ENROLLMENT: 1,300
DEGREES OFFERED: BA
UNDERGRADUATE MAJORS: 12
DEGREES CONFERRED: 5
DESCRIPTION OF UNDERGRADUATE PROGRAM: The Religious Studies Department expresses the religious dimension of the College's founding in the Jesuit and Catholic tradition, and its orientation to serve the community which shares the values of that tradition. The department's specific aims are: 1) to help develop an inquiring mind in matters of religious import by acquainting the student with the role religion has played and is now playing in the total development and life experience of humanity; 2) to provide the student with the methodological tools, both scientific and theological, for the academic study of religion; 3) to aid the students to appreciate the religious viewpoints and values within their own community and in the broader community of humankind. The courses present a scientific and theologi-

cal study and appreciation of the unique approaches of Roman Catholicism, other confessional Christian churches, Jewish religious thought, and other religions. The ecumenical approach also attempts a comparative study of religions and a positive approach to the varieties of non-religion such as atheism.

FACULTY:

Duling, Dennis C., PhD, University of Chicago (1970), 1978, Professor—New Testament, synoptic gospels, sociological/anthropological background, 716-888-2821, Fax: 716-888-2525, E-mail: duling@canisius.edu

Fiore, Benjamin, SJ, PhD, Yale (1982), 1979, Professor—New Testament, New Testament Greek, 716-888-2822, Fax: 716-886-6506, E-mail: fiore@canisius.edu

Goldberg, Martin L., PhD, Pittsburgh (1955), 1967, Adjunct Professor (part-time)—Jewish thought and practice, Bible, history, 716-888-2820

Jamros, Daniel P., SJ, PhD, Vanderbilt (1986), 1985, Associate Professor—systematic theology, philosophical theology, history of theology, 716-888-2827, Fax: 716-886-6506, E-mail: jamros@canisius.edu

Liderbach, Daniel P., SJ, PhD, St Michael's College/University of Toronto (1978), 1983, Professor—systematic theology, sacramental theology, science and religion, 716-888-2288, Fax: 716-886-6506, E-mail: liderbac@canisius.edu

Lynch, Patrick J., SJ, PhD, University of Chicago (1980), 1986, Associate Professor—systematic theology, social ethics, 716-888-2831, Fax: 716-886-6506, E-mail: lynchp@canisius.edu

McDermott, James P., PhD, Princeton (1971), 1977, Professor—comparative religions, Eastern religions, Buddhism, 716-888-2825, Fax: 716-888-2525, E-mail: mcdermot@canisius.edu

McNutt, Paula M., PhD, Vanderbilt (1989), 1987, Associate Professor—Hebrew Bible, anthropology of religion, sociology of Ancient Israel, 716-888-2832, Fax: 716-888-2525, E-mail: mcnutt@canisius.edu

Moleski, Martin X., SJ, PhD, Catholic University of America (1991), 1990, Associate Professor—systematic theology, philosophical theology, 716-888-2383, Fax: 716-886-6506, E-mail: moleski@canisius.edu

Palmere, Mary Ann, MA, Christ the King Seminary (1991), 1999, Adjunct Instructor—introduction to religion, 716-888-2820

Pastizzo, Michael R., SJ, Doctorate in Theology, STD (Spirituality), The Georgian University (Rome, Italy), 1996 , Adjunct professor (half time in ITS), introduction to religion, theology and film, 716-888-3189, Fax: 716-886-6506, E-mail: pastizzm@canisius.edu

Rizzo, Robert F., PhD, Catholic University of America (1971), 1968, Professor—moral theology, spirituality, 716-888-2828, Fax: 716-888-2525

Skretny, Judith, MA, McMaster University, Assistant Professor—theology of death, 716-888-2820, Fax: 716-888-2525, E-mail: skretnyj@canisius.edu

Steller, Paul, MA, Canisius; MA, Catholic University of America—religious education, 716-632-8898

Thompson, Mary Robert, PhD, McMaster University, 1999, Adjunct Professor—women in religion, 716-888-2820

Wadkins, Timothy H., PhD, Graduate Theological Union (Berkeley) (1988), 1992, Associate Professor—church history, historical theology, English history, 716-888-2824, Fax: 716-888-2525, E-mail: wadkins@canisius.edu

Watt, Trevor L., PhD, Union Theological Seminary (1967), 1968, Professor—psychology of religion, systematic theology, 716-888-2823, Fax: 716-888-2525, E-mail: comlib@canisius.edu

Wyrobek, Mary Lou, MA, Christ the King Seminary (1999), 1999, Adjunct Instructor—introduction to religion

---

Capital University

Columbus OH 43209

Capital Bible College

9470 Micron Ave
Sacramento CA 95827

Phone: 916-856-5677
Fax: 916-856-5959
E-mail: cbc@capchrist.edu
URL: www.capchrist.edu

TYPE OF INSTITUTION: Private, Assemblies of God
EXECUTIVE OFFICER: Chris Howard, Executive Vice President
UNDERGRADUATE ENROLLMENT: 110

Cardinal Stritch University

6801 N Yates Rd
Milwaukee WI 53217

Phone: 414-410-4000
Fax: 414-410-4239
URL: www.stritch.edu

TYPE OF INSTITUTION: Denominational, Roman Catholic
EXECUTIVE OFFICER: Mary Lea Schneider, OSF, President
CHAIRPERSON: Angelyn Dries, OSF
UNDERGRADUATE ENROLLMENT: 1,200
GRADUATE ENROLLMENT: 2,000
DEGREES OFFERED: BA in Religious Studies
UNDERGRADUATE MAJORS: 39
DEGREES CONFERRED: 8
DESCRIPTION OF UNDERGRADUATE PROGRAM: Religious Studies offerings are integral to the Liberal Arts Core of the College. Enriched by the Franciscan tradition, students explore the manner in which religious traditions and symbols have provided and continue to provide an interpretation of human life. In addition to courses that probe the Roman Catholic tradition, students may pursue courses in Protestantism, Judaism, Islam, and Eastern Religious Traditions. They study the historical, theoretical and practical aspects of the religious experience in its global setting. With a Religious Studies Major graduates are prepared to work in various Church ministries, to teach, or to pursue graduate studies.
GRADUATE PROGRAM
Graduate Degrees Offered: MA; MEPD in Ministry
Degrees Conferred: 4 MA; 3 MEPD
Average No. of New Students Enrolled: 5 MA; 7 MEPD
Women Students: 16 MA
Minority Students: 6 MA
Minimum GRE Score Requisite to Admission: No
Minimum GPA Score Requisite to Admission: Yes; 2.75 on 4.0 scale

Financial Aid to First Year Students: 50% MA

Financial Aid to Other Students: 50% MA

Graduates Placed: 100% MA

DESCRIPTION OF GRADUATE PROGRAM AND RESEARCH FACILITIES: The Master of Arts in Religious Studies is designed for those who wish to pursue studies leading to a variety of ministries in the Church and who aspire to further graduate studies. In the Master of Education/Professional Development Program, twelve or more credits earned in Religious Studies may serve as an area of concentration in one of the following areas: Adult and Family Ministry, Youth Ministry, Special Needs Ministry, or Urban Ministry.

ACADEMIC PLAN, ADMISSION REQUIREMENTS, FINANCIAL AID: For both MA and MEPD: Courses are selected during the initial professional development seminar designed to assist students to formulate their program. The final culminating project for each 30-credit degree program consists of one of the following: Synthesis Seminar, Thesis, or Supervised Field Placement with research paper. In addition to an undergraduate degree from an accredited college or university and a minimum 2.75 GPA admission to each graduate program requires: 1) Admission application, including statement of goals. 2) two letters of recommendation: e.g., from former instructors or work supervisors; 3) An interview with a member of the Religious Studies Department. Financial aid, including assistantships, is available.

FACULTY:

Alfonso, Meneo, PhD, Marquette University (1990), 1993, Assistant Professor—philosophy, spirituality, ecclesiology, E-mail: mafonso@acs.stritch.edu

Di Domizio, Daniel, STD, Institut Catholique de Paris (1969), 1988, Professor—contemporary Catholicism, social ethics, spirituality, E-mail: ddom@acs.stritch.edu

Dries, Angelyn, PhD, Graduate Theological Union (1989), 1989, Associate Professor—American religions, historical theology, Eastern religions, E-mail: adries@acs.stritch.edu

Dunn, Coletta, PhD, Catholic University of America (1969), 1969, Professor—religious history, ministry studies, nursing ethics, 414-410-4163, E-mail: cdunn@acs.stritch.edu

Klotz, Margaret, OSF, St Michael, Toronto, 1997, Lecturer (part-time)—Franciscan studies

Perry, John, PhD, Marquette University (1970), 1967, Professor—scripture studies, 414-410-4164

Shapiro, Ronald, MA in Hebrew Letters, Hebrew Union College (1981), Lecturer (part-time)—Judaism.

Wenzel, Lorrie, MTS, St Francis School of Pastoral Ministry (1987), 1987, Lecturer (part-time)—scripture studies.

Carey Theological College

5920 Iona Dr
Vancouver, British Columbia V6T 1J6
Canada

Phone: 604-224-4308
Fax: 604-224-5014
E-mail: careytc@interchange.ubc.ca

TYPE OF INSTITUTION: Baptist Union of Western Canada

EXECUTIVE OFFICER: Brian Stelck, Principal

Carleton College

Dept of Religion
One North College St
Northfield MN 55057

Phone: 507-646-4232
Fax: 507-646-4223
E-mail: rcrouter@carleton.edu

TYPE OF INSTITUTION: Private
CHAIRPERSON: Richard E. Crouter
UNDERGRADUATE ENROLLMENT: 1,850

Carleton University

Religion Dept, Ottawa, Ontario K1S 5B6 Canada

Carlow College

Dept of Theology/Ministry, 3333 5th Ave, Pittsburgh PA 15213

Carroll College

1601 N Benton Avenue
Helena MT 59625

Phone: 406-447-4335
Fax: 406-447-5476
E-mail: jhart@carroll.edu
URL: www.carroll.edu

TYPE OF INSTITUTION: Denominational: Catholic
EXECUTIVE OFFICER: James Trudnowski, Academic Dean
CHAIRPERSON: John Hart
UNDERGRADUATE ENROLLMENT: 1,400

Carroll College

100 North East Avenue
Waukesha WI 53186-5593

Phone: 414-547-1211
E-mail: lcope@carroll1.cc.edu
URL: www.cc.edu

TYPE OF INSTITUTION: Private, Presbyterian
EXECUTIVE OFFICER: Frank Falcone, President
CHAIRPERSON: Lamar Cope
UNDERGRADUATE ENROLLMENT: 22

Carson Newman College

Jefferson City TN 37760

Carthage College

Kenosha WI 53140

Carver Bible Institute and College

Po Box 4335, Atlanta GA 30302

Cascade Bible College
13646 NE 24th St, Bellevue WA 98005

Case Western Reserve University
Dept of Religion
Cleveland OH 44106-7112

Phone: 216-368-2210
Fax: 216-368-4681
E-mail: jwf2@po.cwru.edu

TYPE OF INSTITUTION: Private, Non-Denominational
CHAIRPERSON: James W. Flanagan
UNDERGRADUATE ENROLLMENT: 3,700
GRADUATE ENROLLMENT: 6,300

Catawba College
2300 W Innes St, Salisbury NC 28144

Cathedral Bible College
927 Idaho Ave, Escondido CA 92025

Catholic Theological Union at Chicago
5401 S Cornell Avenue
Chicago IL 60615

Phone: 773-324-8000
Fax: 773-324-4360

TYPE OF INSTITUTION: Private, Roman Catholic
EXECUTIVE OFFICER: Donald Senior, President
GRADUATE ENROLLMENT: 348

The Catholic University of America
School of Religious Studies
Caldwell Hall 113
Washington DC 20064

Phone: 202-319-5683
Fax: 202-319-4967
E-mail: cua-deansrs@cua.edu
URL: www.cua.edu/www/srs/

TYPE OF INSTITUTION: Private, Roman Catholic
EXECUTIVE OFFICER: Stephen P. Happel, STD, Acting Dean
UNDERGRADUATE ENROLLMENT: 2,370
GRADUATE ENROLLMENT: 3,777
DEGREES OFFERED: STB, MRE, MDiv, DMin, MA, STL, PhD, STD, JCL, JCD
UNDERGRADUATE MAJORS: 11
DEGREES CONFERRED: 80

GRADUATE PROGRAM

Graduate Degrees Offered: MA; PhD; Other

Degrees Conferred: 19 MA; 10 PhD; 46 Other

Average No. of New Students Enrolled: 50 MA

Women Students: 84 MA

Minority Students: 10 MA

THE SCHOOL OF RELIGIOUS STUDIES: Dean, Raymond F. Collins, Caldwell Hall, Room 113, Catholic University of America, Washington DC 20064. Located on the campus of the Catholic University of America, the School of Religious Studies is made up of five departments and an interdepartmental program in liturgical studies. The Department of Biblical Studies provides students with the training and practice needed to develop skills for effective teaching, research, and publication in the field of biblical literature. Its program involves a critical study of selected books of the Old Testament and New Testament based on the original languages and ancient versions. Prerequisite courses in Semitic languages are offered by the Department of Semitic and Egyptian languages and Literatures. The degraes offered are the MA and PhD. The Department of Canon Law offers the JCL and JCD degrees. It prepares professional administrators for the church and trains students for research, teaching, and publication in the area of church law. The Department of Church History seeks to continue the University's tradition of preparing teachers, researchers, and writers, in the field of ecclesiastical history, principally that of the Roman Catholic Church in Europe and America. Its program of courses and seminars is supplemented by offerings in many other departments of the University, but especially those of History and Theology. Degrees offered are the MA and the PhD. The Department of Religion and Religious Education prepares students for teaching and research in religion in colleges and universities and in other forms of educational ministry. The basic concern of the department is the relationship between religion and culture, both in general and within the Roman Catholic tradition. Degrees offered are the MRE, the MA, and the PhD. Concentrations are available in Roman Catholic studies, religious education, religion and culture, spirituality, and biblical literature. The Department of Theology aims at fostering graduate research in the Roman Catholic tradition as well as providing professional pastoral training required for the ministry (especially the priesthood) in the Roman Catholic Church. Its graduate degree programs lead to the MDiv, STB, MA, DMin, STL, PhD, and STD degrees. Spiritual formation for students preparing for the priesthood is provided by their religious communities or by the Theological College, which is an integral component of the University. The Interdepartmental Program of Liturgical Studies is interdisciplinary in character. Its purpose is twofold: 1) to prepare persons to exercise leadership in liturgical ministry and 2) to offer a graduate curriculum to those who wish to prepare for academic appointments or other research-related positions in the field of liturgical studies.

RESEARCH FACILITIES, FINANCIAL AID: Mullen Library houses more than a million volumes. In Addition, the Library of Congress, the National Archives, and the libraries of the member institutions of the Washington Theological Consortium are available to students for research. Aid is available to qualified full-time students in the form of departmental assistantships and scholarships (University, Board of Trustees, Vincent Pallotti, Women Religious). Admission to a degree program is a precondition for consideration; the deadline for application is February 1. Students should direct inquiries to the Office of the Dean of the School of Religious Studies.

DEPARTMENT OF BIBLICAL STUDIES FACULTY:

Di Lella, Alexander A., PhD, Catholic University of America, The Andrew-Kelly-Ryan Professor of Biblical Studies

Fitzmyer, Joseph A., PhD, Johns Hopkins University, Professor Emeritus and Professorial Lecturer

Gignac, Francis T., DPhil, University of Oxford, Professor and Chairperson
DEPARTMENT OF CANON LAW:
Beal, John P., JCD, Catholic University of America, Associate Professor and Chairperson
Green, Thomas, JCD, Gregorian University, Stephan Kuttner Professor of Canon Law
Kennedy, Robert T., JD, Harvard University, JUD, Lateran, Associate Professor
Lynch, John E., PhD, University of Toronto, Professor
McDermott, Rose, JCD, Catholic University of America, Assistant Professor
McManus, Frederick R., JCD, Catholic University of America, Professor Emeritus
Pfnausch, Edward G., JCD, Catholic University of America, Assistant Professor
Provost, James H., JCD, Lateran University, The O'Brien-O'Connor Professor of Canon Law
DEPARTMENT OF CHURCH HISTORY:
Gres-Gayer, Jacques, STD, Catholic Institute of Paris, Professor
Kauffman, Christopher, PhD, St Louis, The Catholic Daughters of the Americas Professor—American church history
Merdinger, Jane E., PhD, Yale University, Assistant Professor
Minnich, Nelson, PhD, Harvard University, Professor and Chairperson
Trisco, Robert, HistEcclD, Gregorian University, Professor
DEPARTMENT OF RELIGION AND RELIGIOUS EDUCATION:
Barbieri, William, PhD, Yale, Assistant Professor
Beggiani, Seely, STD, Catholic University of America, Adjunct Associate Professor
Cenkner, William, PhD, Fordham University, Professor, Katharine Drexel Professor of Religion
Collins, Mary, PhD, Catholic University of America, Professor
Crysdale, Cynthia S. W., PhD, Toronto School of Theology, Associate Professor
Dinges, William, PhD, University of Kansas, Associate Professor
Dooley, Catherine, PhD, University of Louvain, Associate Professor
Friday, Robert M., STD, Gregorian University, Assistant Professor
Happel, Stephen, PhD, University of Louvain, Associate Professor and Chairperson
Jensen, Joseph, STD, Catholic University of America, Associate Professor
Jones, Charles, PhD, University of Virginia, Assistant Professor
Kelleher, Margaret M., PhD, Catholic University of America, Associate Professor
Komonchak, Joseph, PhD, Union Theological Seminary, John and Gertrude Hubbard Professor of Religious Studies
Loewe, William, PhD, Marquette University, Associate Professor, Associate Dean
Marthaler, Berard, STD, San Bonaventura PhD, University of Minnesota, Emeritus Professor of Religion and Religious Education
Phan, Peter C., PhD, University of London, STD, Salesian Pontifical University, Professor, The Warren Blanding Professor of Religion
Stoeber, Michael, PhD, University of Toronto, Associate Professor
Studzinski, Raymond, PhD, Fordham University, Associate Professor
DEPARTMENT OF THEOLOGY:
Austin, C. Gerard, STD, Catholic Institute of Paris, Associate Professor
Begg, Christopher T., PhD, STD, University of Louvain, Professor
Berkman, John, PhD, Duke University, Assistant Professor
Casarella, Peter J., PhD, Yale University, Associate Professor

Collins, Raymond F., STD, Catholic University of Leuven, Professor and Dean

Danella, Francis W., DMin, Catholic University of America, Clinical Assistant Professor

Ford, John T., STD, Gregorian University, Professor

Galvin, John, DTh, Innsbruck, Associate Professor

Grabowski, John S., PhD, Marquette University, Associate Professor

Granfield, Patrick, PhD, Collegio San Anselmo; STD, Catholic University of America, Professor

Gravenstine, Charles, DMin, Lutheran Theological Southern Seminary; ACPE, Supervisor and Clinical Associate

Heet, Donald J., DMin, Catholic University of America, Clinical Assistant Professor

Hoonhout, Michael A., PhD, Boston College, Assistant Professor

Irwin, Kevin, STD, Collegio San Anselmo, Professor

Kane, Thomas C., STD, Pontifical Faculty of the Immaculate Conception, Assistant Professor

Matera, Frank, PhD, Union Theological Seminary in Virginia, Professor and Chairperson

Power, David, STD, Collegio San Anselmo, The Shakespeare-Caldwell-Duval Professor of Systematic Theology

Wiseman, James, STD, Catholic University, Associate Professor

Young, Robin Darling, PhD, Chicago, Associate Professor

Catholic University of Puerto Rico

Ponce PR 00731

Cedar Crest College

Allentown PA 18104

Cedarville College

Box 601, Cedarville OH 45314

Centenary College

400 Jefferson St, Hackettstown NJ 07840

Centenary College of Louisiana

PO Box 41188
Shreveport LA 71134-1188   **Phone: 318-869-5156**
TYPE OF INSTITUTION: Denominational: United Methodist
EXECUTIVE OFFICER: Robert Bareikis, Provost and Dean
CHAIRPERSON: David Otto
UNDERGRADUATE ENROLLMENT: 800
GRADUATE ENROLLMENT: 210

Central College

Dept of Philosophy and Religion
812 University Street
Pella IA 50219

Phone: 515-628-5112
Fax: 515-628-5316
E-mail: timmerd@central.edu

TYPE OF INSTITUTION: Private, Reformed Church in America
EXECUTIVE OFFICER: William Wiebenga, President
CHAIRPERSON: Benjamin F. Armstrong
UNDERGRADUATE ENROLLMENT: 1,500

Central College

1200 S Main, McPherson KS 67460

Central Baptist College

1501 College Ave
Conway AR 72032

Phone: 501-329-6872
Fax: 501-329-2941
E-mail: cattebery@admin.cbs.edu

TYPE OF INSTITUTION: Private, Baptist
EXECUTIVE OFFICER: Charles Attebery, President
UNDERGRADUATE ENROLLMENT: 350

Central Baptist Theological Seminary

741 N 31st Street
Kansas City KS 66102-3964

Phone: 913-371-5313
Fax: 913-371-8110
E-mail: central@cbts.edu
URL: www.cbts.edu

TYPE OF INSTITUTION: Private, Baptist
EXECUTIVE OFFICER: Thomas E. Clifton, President
CHAIRPERSON: James F. Hines
GRADUATE ENROLLMENT: 158

Central Baptist Theological Seminary

900 Forestview Lane N
Plymouth MN 55441-5934

Phone: 612-417-8250
Fax: 612-417-8258
E-mail: info@centralseminary.edu
URL: www.centralseminary.edu

TYPE OF INSTITUTION: Private, Independent Baptist
EXECUTIVE OFFICER: Douglas R. McLachlan, President
CHAIRPERSONS: Charles A. Hauser, Jr.; Kevin T. Bauder
GRADUATE ENROLLMENT: 112
GRADUATE PROGRAM

Graduate Advisors: Charles A. Hauser, Jr.; Kevin T. Bauder

Graduate Degrees Offered: MA; MDiv; ThM; ThD; DMin

Degrees Conferred: 16

Graduate Students in Residence: 112

Women Students: 21

Minimum GRE Score Requisite to Admission: No; no for MA, yes for ThD

Minimum GPA Score Requisite to Admission: Yes

Financial Aid to First Year Students: 3% MA

Financial Aid to Other Students: 10% MA; 2% ThD

Attrition Among Students: 1% MA

Graduates Placed: 90% MA; 100% ThD

DESCRIPTION OF GRADUATE PROGRAM AND RESEARCH FACILITIES: Central is a private independent Baptist graduate school with emphasis on systematic theology and the Biblical languages. In addition to the MDiv, ThM and DMin programs the school offers the MA in Biblical Studies and in Counseling. The ThD degree has two tracks: Biblical studies or Theological Studies.

ACADEMIC PLAN, ADMISSION REQUIREMENTS, FINANCIAL AID: The MA programs are 32 credit hours in length and require a baccalaureate degree for entrance into the program. The ThD program requires a 3.6 GPA in master level work and is a 32 credit hour program tailored to each individual.

FACULTY:

Bauder, Kevin T., DMin, Trinity Evangelical Divinity School (1991), 1997, Associate Professor—systematic and historical theology, 612-417-8250, Fax: 612-17-8258, E-mail: kbauder@centralseminary.edu

Beacham, Roy E., ThD, Grace Theological Seminary (1991), 1976, Professor—Old Testament, 612-417-8250, Fax: 612-417-8258, E-mail: rebeacham@centralseminary.edu

Buck, C. Raymond, PhD, University of Kansas (1967), 1990, Professor—missions and evangelism, 612-417-8250, Fax: 612-417-8258

Hauser, Charles A., Jr., ThD, Grace Theological Seminary (1962), 1986, Professor—Bible and systematic theology, 612-417-8250, Fax: 612-417-8258, E-mail: chauser@centralseminary.edu

McLachlan, Douglas R., MDiv, Central Baptist Theological Seminary (1970),1994, Professor—practical theology, 612-417-8250, Fax: 612-417-8258, E-mail: dmclachlan@centralseminary.edu

Milliman, Robert W., PhD, Trinity Evangelical Divinity School (1997),1996, Associate Professor—New Testament, 612-417-8250, Fax: 612-417-8258, E-mail: rmilliman@centralseminary.edu

Zempel, Thomas L., DMin, Westminster Theological Seminary (1990), 1994, Assistant Professor—biblical counseling, 612-417-8250, Fax: 612-417-8258, E-mail: tzempel@centralseminary.edu

---

Central Bible College

3000 N Grant
Springfield MO 65802

Phone: 417-833-6269
E-mail: info@cbcag.edu
URL: www.cbcag.edu

TYPE OF INSTITUTION: Private, Assemblies of God

UNDERGRADUATE ENROLLMENT: 1,050

Central Christian College of the Bible

911 Urbandale Drive East
Moberly MO 65270

Phone: 816-263-3900
Fax: 816-263-3936
E-mail: pechawer@ccob.edu
URL: www.cccb.edu

TYPE OF INSTITUTION: Non-Denominational
EXECUTIVE OFFICER: Larry J. Pechawer, Academic Dean
UNDERGRADUATE ENROLLMENT: 150

Central Connecticut State College

Religion Prog and Dept of Philosophy, New Britain CT 06050

Central Methodist College

411 Central Methodist Square, Fayette MO 65248

Central Michigan University

Dept of Philosophy and Religion
Mt Pleasant MI 48859

Phone: 517-774-3444
Fax: 517-774-2426
E-mail: david.l.smith@cmich.edu
URL: www.chsbs.cmich.edu/rel

TYPE OF INSTITUTION: Public
CHAIRPERSON: David L. Smith
UNDERGRADUATE ENROLLMENT: 14,605
GRADUATE ENROLLMENT: 1,992

Central Missouri State University

Martin 118
Warrensburg MO 64093

Phone: 816-543-8674
Fax: 816-543-8006

TYPE OF INSTITUTION: Public
EXECUTIVE OFFICER: Ed Elliott, President
CHAIRPERSON: Marla J. Selvidge
UNDERGRADUATE ENROLLMENT: 160

Central State University

Wilberforce OH 45384

Central Washington University

Philosophy Department
400 E 8th Ave
Ellensburg WA 98926-7555

Phone: 509-963-1818
Fax: 509-963-1822
E-mail: farrellj@cwu.edu
URL: www.cwu.edu\~philo\philosophy.html

TYPE OF INSTITUTION: Public
EXECUTIVE OFFICER: Ivory Nelson, President
CHAIRPERSON: Chenyang, Li
UNDERGRADUATE ENROLLMENT: 8

Central Yeshiva Tomchei Tmimim Lubavit

841-853 Ocean Pkwy, Brooklyn NY 11230

Centre College

600 W Walnut
Danville KY 40422

Phone: 606-238-5522
Fax: 606-236-9610
E-mail: wardj@centre.edu

TYPE OF INSTITUTION: Private, Covenant Relationship with Presbyterian Church, USA
EXECUTIVE OFFICERS: John Roush, President; John Ward, Dean
CHAIRPERSON: Beth Glazier-McDonald
UNDERGRADUATE ENROLLMENT: 1,052
DEGREES OFFERED: BA
UNDERGRADUATE MAJORS: 20
DEGREES CONFERRED: 6
DESCRIPTION OF UNDERGRADUATE PROGRAM: Centre's curriculum is devoted to the liberal arts and sciences. The religion program is part of the Division of Social Studies and includes five full-time faculty members, four of whom also teach some courses in history, integrative studies, philosophy and one of whom also serves as chaplain. All students are required to take either Biblical History and Ideas or History of Christian Thought (both three hour courses) to graduate and may take a second religion course of their choosing to meet a general education requirement in the "context of fundamental questions." All of the faculty members in the program teach some of the general education surveys.
FACULTY:
Axtell, Richard D., PhD, Southern Baptist Theological Seminary (1992), 1995, Assistant Professor and College Chaplain—Christian ethics, biblical studies, theology, 606-238-5245, Fax: 606-236-7925, E-mail: axtellr@centre.edu
Glazier-McDonald, Beth H., PhD, University of Chicago (1983), 1988, Associate Professor—biblical studies, ancient languages, Judaism, 606-238-5252, Fax: 606-236-7925, E-mail: glzrmcd@centre.edu
McCollough, Claude Thomas, PhD, University of Notre Dame (1985), 1980, Professor—ancient Christianity, biblical archaeology, history of Christian thought, medieval Christianity, Reformation, 606-238-5247, Fax: 606-236-7925, E-mail: mccollog@centre.edu

Mount, C. Eric, Jr., PhD, Duke University (1966), 1966, Professor—Christian social ethics, professional ethics, contemporary theology, religion and literature, 606-238-5249, Fax: 606-236-7925, E-mail: mounte@centre.edu

Scarborough, Milton R., Duke University (1972), 1969, Professor—philosophy of religion, science and religion, world religions, Buddhism, 606-238-5235, Fax: 606-236-7925, E-mail: mscarb@centre.edu

Chadron State College

1000 Main Street, Chadron NE 69337

Chaflin College

College Ave NE, Orangeburg SC 29115

Chaminade University of Honolulu

3140 Waialae Avenue
Honolulu HI 96816

Phone: 808-735-4700
Fax: 808-739-8328
E-mail: dcoleman@chaminade.edu
URL: www.chaminade.edu

TYPE OF INSTITUTION: Private, Catholic
EXECUTIVE OFFICER: Sue Wesselkamper, President
CHAIRPERSON: David L. Coleman
UNDERGRADUATE ENROLLMENT: 7
GRADUATE ENROLLMENT: 37

Champlain College

Burlington VT 05401

Chapman University

Dept of Religion, Orange CA 92666

College of Charleston

Dept of Philosophy and Religious Studies
Charleston SC 29424-0001

Phone: 843-953-5687
Fax: 843-953-6388
E-mail: mcdanielj@cofc.edu
URL: www.cofc.edu

TYPE OF INSTITUTION: Public
CHAIRPERSON: Hugh Wilder, Chair
COORDINATOR: June McDaniel, Director
UNDERGRADUATE ENROLLMENT: 10,000

GRADUATE ENROLLMENT: 1,993

DEGREES OFFERED: BA in Religious Studies

UNDERGRADUATE MAJORS: 37

DEGREES CONFERRED: 14

DESCRIPTION OF UNDERGRADUATE PROGRAM: Undergraduate courses include survey and advanced work in the major religious traditions of the world, both Eastern and Western, as well as in selected aspects of religious thought. Various perspectives and methods are brought to bear on the materials—historical, anthropological, philosophical, textual, and psychological. The study of religion within the department is broad in subject matter and interdisciplinary in approach. The program for undergraduate majors entails 30 semester hours of work.

FACULTY:

Bjerken, Zeff, MA, University of Michigan (1993), 1999, Assistant Professor—Buddhism, 843-953-5687, Fax: 843-953-6388, E-mail: bjerkenz@cofc.edu

Cormack, Margaret, PhD, Yale University (1983), 1995, Assistant Professor—Christianity, Scandinavian religion and mythology, world religions, Islam, 843-953-8033, Fax: 843-953-6388, E-mail: cormackm@cofc.edu

Huddlestun, John, PhD, University of Michigan (1996), 1996, Assistant Professor—Bible and ancient Near East, Egyptology, Judaica, 843-953-4996, Fax: 843-953-6388, E-mail: huddlestunj@cofc.edu

Irwin, Lee, PhD, Indiana University (1989), 1991, Associate Professor—Native American religions, Eastern religions, Western esotericism and comparative spirituality, 843-953-8034, Fax: 843-953-6388, E-mail: irwinl@cofc.edu

McDaniel, June, PhD, University of Chicago (1986), 1988, Associate Professor—mysticism and religious experience, women and religion, world religions, 843-953-5956, Fax: 843-953-6388, E-mail: mcdanielj@cofc.edu

The University of Charleston
2300 MacCorkle Ave SE, Charleston WV 25304

Charleston Southern University
PO Box 10087, Charleston SC 29411

Chatham College
Pittsburgh PA 15232

Chestnut Hill College
Philadelphia PA 19118

University of Chicago

Divinity School
1025 E 58th Street
Chicago IL 60637

Phone: 312-702-8217
Fax: 312-702-6048
E-mail: raroseng@midway.uchicago.edu

TYPE OF INSTITUTION: Private, Non-Denominational

EXECUTIVE OFFICER: W. Clark Gilpin, Dean

GRADUATE ENROLLMENT: 300

GRADUATE PROGRAM

Member of the Council on Graduate Studies in Religion

Graduate Degrees Offered: MA; PhD

Degrees Conferred: 32 MA; 25 PhD

Graduate Students in Residence: 90 MA; 200 PhD

Not in Residence: 0 MA; 30 PhD

Average No. Of New Students Enrolled: 40 MA; 30 PhD

Women Students: 45 MA; 90 PhD

Minority Students: 6 MA; 9 PhD

Foreign Students: 2 MA; 10 PhD

Minimum GRE Score Requisite to Admission: No

Minimum GPA Score Requisite to Admission: No

Foreign Language Proficiency Evaluated: Yes

Financial Aid to First Year Students: 90% MA; 95% PhD

Financial Aid to Other Students: 90% MA; 95% PhD

Attrition Among Students: 2% MA; 5% PhD

Graduates Placed: 100% MA (many go on to this PhD program); 100% PhD (significant majority in academic jobs; some in related careers (academic administration, ministry, foundation and endowment work, research and think tanks etc.)

DESCRIPTION OF GRADUATE PROGRAM AND RESEARCH FACILITIES: The Divinity School curriculum serves four degree programs: 1) the AM in Religious Studies, a one-year program for the student who wishes to pursue the study of religion at the graduate level and does not intend to pursue doctoral study; 2) the AM in Divinity, a two-year foundational program for PhD study; 3) the MDiv, a three-year degree program for the professional ministry; and 4) the PhD, which students pursue with a concentration in one of nine areas of study (Biblical Studies, Ethics, History of Christianity, History of Judaism, History of Religions, Philosophy of Religion, Psychology and Sociology of Religion, Religion and Literature, Theology). Students frequently work closely with other departments and programs at the University, e.g. the Oriental Institute, the Department of Anthropology, and the Committee on Social Thought. In addition, Divinity School students enjoy access to excellent research facilities. The University's Joseph Regenstein Library holds 6,000,000 volumes, some 84,000 serials titles, including 43,000 regular continuations and more than 12,000 periodical and journal titles, and a number of special collections. Library resources in the University bearing upon religion are conservatively estimated at over 600,000 volumes. Students also have privileges at the Jesuit/Krauss/McCormick Library located at the Lutheran School of Theology in Hyde Park, and to the holdings of other theological schools in the greater Chicago area, the Center for Research Libraries, and such private collections as the Newberry Library.

ACADEMIC PLAN, ADMISSIONS REQUIREMENTS, FINANCIAL AID: All applicants submit 1) an essay on intellectual development and academic and professional objectives, 2) four letters of reference, 3) transcripts, and 4) GRE general scores. PhD applicants must include a second essay describing their proposed area of doctoral study. Financial aid, in the form of scholarships, fellowships, and loans, is based on academic promise and need. All applicants for financial aid must submit a Free Application for Federal Student Aid (FAFSA).

FACULTY:

Betz, Hans Dieter, ThD, Mainz (1957), 1978, Professor—New Testament

Boden, Alison, MDiv, Union (1991), 1995, Dean of Rockefeller Memorial Chapel and Lecturer—ministry

Brekus, Catherine A., PhD, Yale (1993), 1993, Assistant Professor—history of Christianity

Browning, Don S., PhD, Chicago (1964), 1965, Professor—ethics and the social sciences

Carr, Anne E., PhD, Chicago (1971), 1975, Professor—theology

Collins, Adela Yarbro, PhD, Harvard (1975), 1991, Professor—New Testament

Collins, John J., PhD, Harvard (1972), 1991, Professor—Hebrew Bible, history of Judaism

Culp, Kristine, PhD, Chicago (1987), 1991, Dean of Disciples Divinity House and Senior Lecturer—theology

Davidson, Arnold, PhD, Harvard (1981), 1996, Professor—philosophy of religion

Doniger, Wendy, PhD, Harvard (1968), DPhil, Oxford (1973), 1978, Professor—history of religions

Elshtain, Jean Bethke, PhD, Brandeis (1973), 1994, Professor—ethics

Fishbane, Michael, PhD, Brandeis (1971), 1990, Professor—Hebrew Bible, history of Judaism,

Frymer-Kensky, Tikva, PhD, Yale (1977), 1994, Professor—Hebrew Bible, history of Judaism

Gamwell, Franklin I., PhD, Chicago (1973), 1979, Professor—ethics, theology

Gilpin, W. Clark, PhD, Chicago (1974), 1984, Dean and Professor—history of Christianity, theology

Griffiths, Paul J., PhD, Wisconsin (1983), 1990, Associate Professor—philosophy of religion

Hopkins, Dwight N., PhD, Union (1988), 1996, Associate Professor—theology

Johnson, Willis, PhD, California (1997), 1997, John Nuveen Instructor—history of Judaism

Kapstein, Matthew, PhD, Brown (1987), 1998, Professor—philosophy of religion

Kraemer, Joel, PhD, Yale (1967), 1994, Professor—history of Judaism

Krupnick, Mark L., PhD, Brandeis (1968), 1990, Professor—religion and literature

Lincoln, Bruce, PhD, Chicago (1976), 1992, Professor—history of religions

Mahmood, Suba, PhD, Stanford (1998), 1999, Assistant Professor—history of religions

Marion, Jean-Luc, Agrégation de philosophie, Doctorat d'Etat, 1994, Visiting Professor—philosophy of religion

McGinn, Bernard, PhD, Brandeis (1970), 1969, Professor—history of Christianity, theology

Meltzer, Francoise, PhD, (1975), 1997—religion and literature

Mendes-Flohr, Paul, PhD, Brandeis (1972), 1999, Professor—modern Jewish thought

Mitchell, Margaret, PhD, Chicago (1989), 1998, Associate Professor—New Testament

Murrin, Michael J., PhD, Yale (1965), 1963, Professor—religion and literature

Paulsell, Stephanie, PhD, Chicago (1993), 1997—Director of Ministry Studies and Senior Lecturer—ministry, religion and literature

Pick, Lucy, PhD, Toronto (1995), 1997—John Nuveen Instructor—history of Christianity

Reynolds, Frank E., PhD, Chicago (1971), 1967, Professor—history of religions

Riesebrodt, Martin, PhD, Heidelberg (1973), 1990, Associate Professor—sociology of religion

Rosengarten, Richard, PhD, Chicago (1994), 1991, Dean of Students and Senior Lecturer—religion and literature

Schreiner, Susan E., PhD, Duke (1983), 1987, Associate Professor—history of Christianity, theology

Schweiker, William, PhD, Chicago (1985), 1989, Associate Professor—theology, ethics

Tanner, Kathryn, PhD, Yale (1985), 1995, Associate Professor—theology

Tracy, David, STD, Gregorian (1969), 1967, Professor—theology

Yu, Anthony C., PhD, Chicago (1969), 1968, Professor—religion and literature

Chicago Baptist Institute

5120 S King Drive #1, Chicago IL 60615

Chicago Theological Seminary

5757 South University Ave
Chicago IL 60637

Phone: 773-752-5757
Fax: 773-752-0905
E-mail: vmorris@ch90sem.edu
URL: www.ch90sem.edu

TYPE OF INSTITUTION: Private, related to United Church of Christ
EXECUTIVE OFFICER: Susan Thistlethwaite, President
CHAIRPERSON: Theodore Jennings
UNDERGRADUATE ENROLLMENT: 59

Chowan College

Jones Drive
Murfreesboro NC 27855

Phone: 252-398-6500
Fax: 252-398-6455
E-mail: dgowler@chowan.edu
URL: www.chowan.edu/acadp/
religion/dept.htm

TYPE OF INSTITUTION: Private, Baptist
EXECUTIVE OFFICER: Stanley Lott, President
CHAIRPERSON: David B. Gowler
UNDERGRADUATE ENROLLMENT: 12

Christ College Irvine

1530 Concordia, Irvine CA 92715

Christ the King Seminary

PO Box 607
711 Knox Rd
East Aurora NY 14052

Phone: 716-652-8900
Fax: 716-652-8903
E-mail: cksacad@pcom.net

TYPE OF INSTITUTION: Private
EXECUTIVE OFFICER: Richard Siepka, President-Rector
GRADUATE ENROLLMENT: 100

Christ the Saviour Seminary

225 Chandler Ave
Johnstown PA 15906

Phone: 814-539-0116
Fax: 814-536-4699

TYPE OF INSTITUTION: Private, Eastern Orthodox
EXECUTIVE OFFICER: Metropoutan Nicholas Smisko, Rector
UNDERGRADUATE ENROLLMENT: 7

Christendom College

134 Christendom Drive
Front Royal VA 22630

Phone: 540-636-2900, ext 274
Fax: 540-636-1655
E-mail: theo@christendom.edu

TYPE OF INSTITUTION: Private
EXECUTIVE OFFICER: Timothy T. O'Donnell, President
CHAIRPERSON: Robert A. Skeris
UNDERGRADUATE ENROLLMENT: 235
GRADUATE ENROLLMENT: 125

Christian Brothers University

Program in Religion, Memphis TN 38104-5581

Christian Education Centers

PO Drawer B, Gainesville GA 30501

Christian Heritage College

2100 Greenfield Dr, El Cajon CA 92019

Christian International

Rt 2 Box 3800, PO Box 9000, Santa Rosa Beach FL 32459

Christian Life College

9023 W Lane
Stockton CA 95210

Phone: 209-476-7840
E-mail: info@clc.edu
URL: www.clc.edu

TYPE OF INSTITUTION: Private, United Pentecostal Church
EXECUTIVE OFFICER: Dan Segraves, Executive Vice President
UNDERGRADUATE ENROLLMENT: 198

Christian Life College

400 E Gregory St, Mt Prospect IL 60056

Christian Outreach School of Ministry

8945 Old Lemay Ferry Rd, Hillsboro MO 63050

Institute for Christian Studies

1909 University Ave
Austin TX 78705

Phone: 512-476-2772
Fax: 512-476-3919
E-mail: burgess@mail.ics.edu
URL: www.ics.edu

TYPE OF INSTITUTION: Private, Church of Christ
EXECUTIVE OFFICER: David R. Worley, President
CHAIRPERSON: R. Mark Shipp
UNDERGRADUATE ENROLLMENT: 80

Christian Theological Seminary

1000 West 42nd Street, Indianapolis IN 46208

Christian Union Bible College

1090 N Washington St
PO Box 27
Greenfield OH 45123-0027

Phone: 937-981-2897
Fax: 937-981-2897
E-mail: cubc@bright.net

TYPE OF INSTITUTION: Private, Christian Union
EXECUTIVE OFFICER: Gerry Doolittle, Academic Dean

Christopher Newport University

One University Place
Newport News VA 23606-2998

Phone: 757-594-7110
E-mail: @cnu.edu
URL: www.cnu.edu/academics/phil

TYPE OF INSTITUTION: Public
EXECUTIVE OFFICER: Paul Trinle, President
CHAIRPERSON: George Teschner
UNDERGRADUATE ENROLLMENT: 10

Rabbinical College of Ch'san Sofer

1876 50th St, Brooklyn NY 11204

Church Divinity School of the Pacific

2451 Ridge Road
Berkeley CA 94709-1217

Phone: 510-204-0700
Fax: 510-644-0712
E-mail: info@csdp.edu
URL: cdsp.edu

TYPE OF INSTITUTION: Private, Episcopal
EXECUTIVE OFFICER: Donn F. Morgan, President and Dean
GRADUATE ENROLLMENT: 114

Church of God School of Theology

900 Walker St
PO Box 3330
Cleveland TN 37320

Phone: 423-478-1131
Fax: 423-478-7711

TYPE OF INSTITUTION: Private, Church of God
EXECUTIVE OFFICER: Cecil B. Knight, President
GRADUATE ENROLLMENT: 275

University of Cincinnati

Dept of Judaic Studies
Cincinnati OH 45221

Phone: 513-556-2297
Fax: 513-556-0142

TYPE OF INSTITUTION: Public
EXECUTIVE OFFICER: Joseph A. Steger, President
CHAIRPERSON: R. M. Selya (Acting Head)
UNDERGRADUATE ENROLLMENT: 15

Cincinnati Bible College and Seminary

2700 Glenway Ave
Cincinnati OH 45204

Phone: 513-244-8100
Fax: 513-244-8434
E-mail: jnorth@cincybible.edu
URL: www.cincybible.edu/home.html.

TYPE OF INSTITUTION: Private, Christian Church/Church of Christ
EXECUTIVE OFFICER: David Grubbs, President
CHAIRPERSON: James B. North
UNDERGRADUATE ENROLLMENT: 619
GRADUATE ENROLLMENT: 249

Cincinnati Christian College

3800 Reading Rd, Cincinnati OH 45229

Circleville Bible College

1476 Lancaster Pike
PO Box 458
Circleville OH 43113

Phone: 614-474-8896
Fax: 614-477-7755
E-mail: cbc@biblecollege.edu

TYPE OF INSTITUTION: Private, Churches of Christ in Christian Union
EXECUTIVE OFFICER: Bruce Moyer, Academic Dean
CHAIRPERSON: David Case
UNDERGRADUATE ENROLLMENT: 192

The Citadel

Charleston SC 29409

Citadel Baptist College and Seminary

8230 Ehrhardt Ave, Sacramento CA 95823

City University of New York, Brooklyn College

Bedford Ave and Avenue H, Brooklyn NY 11210

Claremont Graduate University

Religion Department
831 North Dartmouth Ave
Claremont CA 91711-6160

Phone: 909-621-8085
Fax: 909-621-8390
E-mail: religion@cgu.edu
URL: www.cgu.edu

TYPE OF INSTITUTION: Private, AA/EOE
EXECUTIVE OFFICER: Steadman Upham, President
CHAIRPERSON: Lori Anne Ferrell
ADMINISTRATOR: Patrick Rogers Horn
GRADUATE ENROLLMENT: 2,265

We are a graduate program. There are undergraduate programs in religion at Pomona, Claremont McKenna, and Scripps Colleges, and joint BA/MA programs with Scripps and Claremont McKenna Colleges, with UC Riverside, and with CSU Fullerton.

GRADUATE PROGRAM

Member of the Council on Graduate Studies in Religion

Graduate Advisor: First year students are assigned an academic advisor in their area of specialization.

Graduate Degrees Offered: MA; MA in Women's Studies in Religion; PhD

Degrees Conferred: 12 MA; 15 PhD

Graduate Students in Residene: 13 MA; 74 PhD

Not in Residence: 15 MA; 110 PhD

Average No. of New Students Enrolled: 7 MA; 27 PhD

Women Students: 24 MA; 65 PhD

Minority Students: 0 MA; 28 PhD

Foreign Students: 3 MA; 35 PhD

Minimum GRE Score Requisite to Admission: No

Minimum GPA Score Requisite to Admission: No

Foreign Language Proficiency Evaluated: Proficiency is demonstrated by translation examination.

Financial Aid to First Year Students: 13% MA; 81% PhD

Financial Aid to Other Students: 5%; 25% PhD

Attrition Among Students: 24% MA; 9% PhD

Graduates Placed: 70% MA; 70% PhD

DESCRIPTION OF GRADUATE PROGRAM: CGU offers programs in religion with the cooperation and faculty participation of Claremont School of Theology and the undergraduate Claremont Colleges. CGU offers the MA in general religious studies, and the MA and PhD in Philosophy of Religion and Theology; Theology, Ethics and Culture; Hebrew Bible; New Testament; Women's Studies in Religion; and History of Christianity. The General and specialized MA require 30 units of course work (36 units for Women's Studies in Religion), French or German, qualifying examinations, and a thesis or critique. The PhD requires 72 units (up to 24 of which may be transferred from previous graduate course work), validation of competence in three areas outside the specialization, interdisciplinary courses, French and German (with additional language requirements in the biblical studies fields), qualifying examinations, and the dissertation. Affiliated institutions and resources include the Center for Process Studies, the Institute for Antiquity and Christianity, and the Ancient Biblical Manuscript Center.

ACADEMIC PLAN, ADMISSION REQUIREMENTS, AND FINANCIAL AID: Claremont Graduate University operates on the semester system (fall and spring). A BA degree is required for admission to the MA program. Admission to the PhD program requires a BA, and, if the program with two years of course work is envisaged, either an MA or MDiv or their equivalent. All applicants must submit GRE scores (or TOEFL if applicable), academic letters of recommendation, personal statement, and transcripts. Financial aid is available in the form of fellowships, assistantships, and work-study opportunities.

FACULTY:

Baker-Fletcher, Garth, ThD, Harvard Divinity School (1991), 1993, Associate Professor—theological and philosophical ethics, theology and culture

Baker-Fletcher, Karen, PhD, Harvard University (1991), 1993, Associate Professor—theology and culture, womanist theology

Coogan, W. Jack, ThD, Claremont School of Theology (1967), 1964, Professor—religion and the arts, theology and culture

Davis, Stephen T., PhD, Claremont Graduate University (1970), 1977, Professor—philosophy of religion

Dornish, Margaret H., PhD, Claremont Graduate University (1969), 1971, Professor—history of religions, Buddhism

Erickson, Stephen A., PhD, Yale University (1964), 1966, Professor—philosophy

Ferrell, Lori Anne, PhD, Yale University (1991), 1991, Associate Professor—history of Christianity, English reformation

Gilbert, Gary, PhD, Columbia University (1992), 1998, Assistant Professor—second temple and Rabbinic Judaism

Griffin, David R., PhD, Claremont Graduate University (1968), 1973, Professor—philosophy of religion, theology, process thought

Henry, Granville C., PhD, Claremont Graduate University (1965), Professor—philosophy of religion

Humes, Cynthia A., PhD, University of Iowa (1990), 1990, Associate Professor—history of religions, Hinduism

Irish, Jerry A., PhD, Yale University (1967), 1986, Professor—philosophy of religion and theology

Jackson, Howard M., PhD, Claremont Graduate University (1983), 1986, Adjunct Professor (part-time)—classics, Hellenistic Greek

Kassam, Zayn, PhD, McGill University (1995), 1995, Assistant Professor—history of religions, Islam

Kim, Chan-Hie, PhD, Vanderbilt University (1970), 1987, Professor—New Testament

Kim, Stephen S., PhD, Drew University (1988), 1987, Associate Professor—historical theology and history of religions

Kucheman, Clark, PhD, University of Chicago (1965), 1967, Professor—ethics

MacDonald, Dennis R., PhD, Harvard University (1978), 1998, Professor—New Testament

Min, Anselm K., PhD, Fordham University (1974), PhD, Vanderbilt University (1989), 1992, Professor—philosophy of religion, theology, liberation theology

Moore, Mary Elizabeth, PhD, Claremont School of Theology (1981), 1979, Professor—feminist theology, psychology of religion, theology

Parker, Joseph D., PhD, Harvard University (1989), 1991, Associate Professor—history of religions, Asian religions

Phillips, D. Z., MA, University of Wales (1958), Blitt, Oxon (1961), 1992, Professor—philosophy of religion, ethics, epistemology

Rhoades, Dan D., PhD, Yale University (1963), 1968, Professor—ethics, religion and society

Riley, Gregory J., PhD, Harvard University (1990), 1992, Associate Professor—New Testament, Greco-Roman religions

Robinson, James M., ThD, Princeton Theological Seminary (1955), 1960, Professor—New Testament, sayings Gospel Q

Rogers, Frank, Jr., PhD, Princeton Theological Seminary (1991), 1989, Associate Professor—theology, spirituality

Roth, John K., PhD, Yale University (1966), 1966, Professor—philosophy of religion

Schneider, Tammi J., PhD, University of Pennsylvania (1991), 1993, Assistant Professor—Hebrew Bible, Ancient Near East

Shaw, Teresa M., PhD, Duke University (1992), 1992, Adjunct Assistant Professor (part-time)—history of Christianity

Smith, Richard M., MFA, The University of Iowa (1968), 1984, Visiting Lecturer (part-time)—Coptic

Sontag, Frederick, PhD, Yale University (1952), 1960 Professor—philosophy

Suchocki, Marjorie H., PhD, Claremont Graduate University (1974), 1990, Professor—theology, process and feminist theology

Sweeney, Marvin A., PhD, Claremont Graduate University (1983), 1994, Professor—Hebrew Bible, theology, biblical criticism

Taves, Ann, PhD, University of Chicago (1983), 1983, Professor—history of Christianity, American religion

Torjesen, Karen Jo, PhD, Claremont Graduate University (1982), 1987, Professor—history of Christianity, women's studies and religion

De Troyer, Kristin, STB, Catholic University (Louvain) (1987), 1998, Assistant Professor—Hebrew Bible

Verheyden, Jack, PhD, Harvard University (1968), 1965, Professor—philosophy of religion, theology, 19th-century thought

Whedbee, J. William, PhD, Yale University (1968), 1968, Professor—Hebrew Bible

Wicker, Kathleen O., PhD, Loyola University Chicago (1966), 1971, Professor—New Testament

Winace, Eleutherius, OSB, PhD, University of Louvain, Lecturer (part-time)—philosophy of religion, theology

---

Claremont School of Theology

1325 N College Ave   Phone: 909-626-3521
Claremont CA 91711-3199   Fax: 909-626-7062
                                          E-mail: msuchocki@cst.edu
                                                  URL: www.cst.edu

TYPE OF INSTITUTION: Denominational: Methodist
EXECUTIVE OFFICER: Bob Edgar, President
GRADUATE ENROLLMENT: 400

Clark University

1 Downing Street, Worcester MA 01610

Clark Atlanta University

Dept of Religion/Philosophy, Atlanta GA 30314

Clarke College

Dubuque IA 52001

Clear Creek Baptist Bible College

300 Clear Creek Rd   Phone: 606-337-3196
Pineville KY 40977   Fax: 606-337-2372

TYPE OF INSTITUTION: Private, Baptist
EXECUTIVE OFFICER: Bill Whittaker, President
UNDERGRADUATE ENROLLMENT: 125

Clearwater Christian College

3400 Gulf-to-bay Blvd, Clearwater FL 33519

Clemson University

Philosophy and Religion Dept
101 Hardin Hall, Box 341508
Clemson SC 29634-1508

Phone: 864-656-2584
Fax: 864-656-2858
E-mail: makerw@clemson.edu
URL: hubcap.clemson.edu/aah/phil/

TYPE OF INSTITUTION: Public, land-grant university
EXECUTIVE OFFICER: C. W. Curris, President
CHAIRPERSON: William A. Maker
UNDERGRADUATE ENROLLMENT: 12,000
GRADUATE ENROLLMENT: 6,000

Cleveland College of Jewish Studies

26500 Shaker Blvd
Beachwood OH 44122

Phone: 216-464-4050
Fax: 216-464-5827
URL: www.ccjs.edu

TYPE OF INSTITUTION: Private, Jewish
EXECUTIVE OFFICER: David S. Ariel, President
UNDERGRADUATE ENROLLMENT: 18
GRADUATE ENROLLMENT: 65

Cleveland State University

Dept of Religious Studies, Cleveland OH 44115

Coe College

Cedar Rapids IA 52402

Coker College

Hartsville SC 29550

Colby College

4640 Mayflower Hill
Waterville ME 04901-8846

Phone: 207-872-3416
Fax: 207-872-3802
E-mail: religion@colby.edu

TYPE OF INSTITUTION: Private
EXECUTIVE OFFICER: Edward H. Yeterian, Academic Vice President, Dean of Faculty

CHAIRPERSON: Debra Campbell
UNDERGRADUATE ENROLLMENT: 1,750

Colby-Sawyer College

New London NH 03257

Colegio Universitario Bautista

PO Box 403, Bayamon PR 00960

Colegio Biblico Pentecostal De Puerto

Box 901, Saint Just PR 00750

Colgate University

Department of Philosophy and Religion
13 Oak Dr
Hamilton NY 13346-1398

Phone: 315-824-7681
Fax: 315-824-7998
E-mail: emyers@center.colgate.edu
URL: www2.colgate.edu

TYPE OF INSTITUTION: Private
EXECUTIVE OFFICER: Neil R. Grabois, President
CHAIRPERSON: Marilyn Thie
UNDERGRADUATE ENROLLMENT: 2,753
GRADUATE ENROLLMENT: 3

Colgate Rochester Divinity School, Bexley Hall, Crozier Theological Seminary

1100 S Goodman St, Rochester NY 14620

Colorado College

14 East Cache La Poudre
Colorado Springs CO 80903

Phone: 719-389-6636
Fax: 719-389-6179
E-mail: rwolfe@coloradocollege.edu
URL: coloradocollege.edu

TYPE OF INSTITUTION: Private
EXECUTIVE OFFICER: Kathryn Mohrman, President
CHAIRPERSON: Maxwell F. Taylor
UNDERGRADUATE ENROLLMENT: 1,900
DEGREES OFFERED: BA
UNDERGRADUATE MAJORS: 15

DEGREES CONFERRED: 15

DESCRIPTION OF UNDERGRADUATE PROGRAM: The Department offers a significant number of courses in three trans-cultural traditions—Buddhism, Christianity, and Islam. ("Trans-cultural" here refers to a religious tradition that has moved with notable success from its original cultural base to others, maintaining its identity even as it has adjusted and adapted to various new cultural settings.) We also offer courses in ethnic- or culture-specific traditions (Confucianism, Hinduism, Judaism, Taoism,) courses on religions in particular geographic areas (China, Japan, the United States), and courses that emphasize thematic and methodological issues in religious studies.

FACULTY:

Gardiner, David. L., PhD, Stanford University (1995), 1998, Assistant Professor—East Asian religions, 719-389-6195, E-mail: dgardiner@coloradocollege.edu

Kassam, Tazim R., PhD, McGill University (1992), 1997, Associate Professor—South Asian religions, 719-389-6616, E-mail: tkassam@coloradocollege.edu

Pickle, Joseph W., PhD, University of Chicago (1969), 1964, Professor—history of Christian thought, theology, religion and science, 719-389-6615, E-mail: jpickle@coloradocollege.edu

Taylor, Maxwell F., PhD. Emory University (1970), 1992, Adjunct Associate Professor—religion and American culture, 719-389-6844, E-mail: mtaylor@coloradocollege.edu

Williams, Sam K., PhD, Harvard University (1972), 1971, Professor—biblical studies, 719-389-6617, E-mail: swilliams@coloradocollege.edu

---

University of Colorado at Boulder

Department of Religious Studies
CB 292
Boulder CO 80309-0292

Phone: 303-492-8041
Fax: 303-735-2050
E-mail: rlst@colorado.edu
URL: www.colorado.edu/religiousstudies

TYPE OF INSTITUTION: Public

EXECUTIVE OFFICER: Peter D. Spear, Dean

CHAIRPERSON: Frederick M. Denny

UNDERGRADUATE ENROLLMENT: 21,000

GRADUATE ENROLLMENT: 5,000

DEGREES OFFERED: BA, MA

UNDERGRADUATE MAJORS: 49

DEGREES CONFERRED: 14

DESCRIPTION OF UNDERGRADUATE PROGRAM: The study of religion in the University setting provides students with a broad knowledge of human culture, a specific knowledge of types of religious experience and expression, a background in many religions of the world, and an understanding of the interrelationship between religion and other areas of human thought. The curriculum leading to the BA degree draws from both the humanities and social sciences to provide a descriptive and analytical approach to religious traditions and phenomena. Asian, Western, and traditional cultures, including Native American, are analyzed in historical perspective. Students explore many forms of religious expression, including myth, symbol, ritual, theology, ethics, scriptures, and social institutions. There is also an emphasis on the interrelations between religion and other aspects of human experience, such as politics, science, literature, and the arts.

GRADUATE PROGRAM

Graduate Advisor: Ira Chernus

Graduate Degrees Offered: MA

Degrees Conferred: 9 MA

Graduate Students in Residence: 41 MA

Not in Residence: 0 MA

Average No. of New Students Enrolled: 15 MA

Women Students: 21 MA

Minority Students: 6 MA

Foreign Students: 3 MA

Minimum GRE Score Requisite to Admission: No

Minimum GPA Score Requisite to Admission: Yes; 2.75 on 4.0 scale

Foreign Language Proficiency Evaluated: No

Financial Aid to First Year Students: 80% MA

Financial Aid to Other Students: 46% MA

Attrition Among Students: 10% MA

Graduates Placed: 35% MA

DESCRIPTION OF GRADUATE PROGRAM AND RESEARCH FACILITIES: The Department of Religious Studies pursues a critical and comparative study of religions in their cultural and historical settings. This study aims to illuminate the dynamics of religion as a dimension of human culture and to develop theories and methods that advance our understanding of this phenomenon. The faculty offers courses in most of the world's religions: Hinduism, Buddhism, religions of China and Japan, Native American and other traditional religions, Judaism, Christianity, and Islam. In addition, many religions are studied in interaction in their U.S. setting. Faculty expertise encompasses most of the current methodological options, including sociological and anthropological approaches, ritual and performance theories, critical theory, feminist theory, and comparative study of religions. Interdisciplinary study is encouraged through work in anthropology, sociology, East Asian languages and literatures, comparative literature, classics, women studies, theatre and dance, and fine arts.

ACADEMIC PLAN, ADMISSION REQUIREMENTS, FINANCIAL AID: The MA in Religious Studies prepares students to study for the PhD, as well as providing a terminal degree for those who wish. Because of the small size of the Department, students work closely with individual faculty members. To fulfill the requirements for the MA, students must 1) complete 24 hours of course work, including 3 core seminars, 2) take courses in at least 3 traditions or culture areas, 3) gain familiarity with several different approaches to the study of religion, 4) acquire competence (4th semester) in a language other than English and use it in one's course of study, and 5) complete and be exmained on a thesis. Most students complete the degree within 3 years. Admission is determined by examining the record of each applicant, including GREs. Twelve hours undergraduate background in religious studies are required, including Western and Asian religions. Financial aid is available in the form of Teaching and Research Assistantships, Fellowships, and loans.

FACULTY:

Biernacki, Loriliai, PhD, University of Pennsylvania (1999), 1999, Assistant Professor—Hinduism, 303-735-4730. E-mail: loriliai.biernacki@colorado.edu

Chernus, Ira, PhD, Temple University (1975), 1976, Professor—Judaism, peace studies, 303-492-6169, E-mail: ira.chernus@colorado.edu

Churchill, Mary, PhD, University of California, Santa Barbara (1997), 1995, Assistant Professor of women studies—women and religion, Native American religions, women's literature, 303-492-4531, E-mail: mary.churchill@colorado.edu

Deloria, Vine, Jr., MTS, Lutheran School of Theology (1963); JD, University of Colorado (1970), 1990, Professor of History—Native American religions, 303-492-5814, E-mail: vine.deloria@colorado.edu

Denny, Frederick M., PhD, University of Chicago (1974), 1978, Professor—Islamic studies, theory and method, ritual studies, 303-492-6358, E-mail: frederick.denny@colorado.edu

Dodson, Jualynne, PhD, University of California, Berkeley (1984), 1992, Associate Professor of Ethnic Studies—sociology of religion, African-American religions, 303-492-6468, E-mail: jualynne.dodson@colorado.edu

Gill, Sam D., PhD, University of Chicago (1974), 1983, Professor—religions of traditional peoples, religion and play, religion and dance, 303-492-7319, E-mail: sam.gill@colorado.edu

Hoover, Stewart, PhD, University of Pennsylvania (1985), 1991, Professor of Journalism—religion and mass communication, 303-492-4833, E-mail: hoover@colorado.edu

Horton, Sarah, MPhil, Yale (1998), 1999, Instructor—Chinese and Japanese religions, 303-492-7649, E-mail: sarah.horton@colorado.edu

Kleeman, Terry, PhD, University of California, Berkeley (1988), 1998, Assistant Professor—Chinese religious studies, Chinese and Japanese religions, ecstatic religion, ritual, 303-492-6984, E-mail: terry.kleeman@colorado.edu

Lester, Robert C., PhD, Yale University (1963), 1970, Professor Emeritus—Hinduism, Indian Buddhism, E-mail: robert.lester@colorado.edu

Miller, Eddie L., PhD, University of Southern California (1966); Dr Theol, University of Basel (1981), 1976, Professor of Philosophy—New Testament, Christian studies, 303-492-8414, E-mail: eddie.miller@colorado.edu

Pesantubbee, Michelene, PhD, University of California, Santa Barbara (1994), 1994, Assistant Professor—American Indian religious traditions, revitalization movements, religions in America, 303-492-7095, E-mail: michelene.pesantubbee@colorado.edu

Ray, Reginald A., PhD, University of Chicago (1973), 1986, Senior Instructor—Tibetan Buddhism, E-mail: reginald.ray@colorado.edu

Ross-Bryant, Lynn, PhD, University of Chicago (1973), 1987, Associate Professor—religions and American culture, women and religion, Christian studies, 303-492-1634, E-mail: lynn.ross-bryant@colorado.edu

Taylor, Rodney L., PhD, Columbia University (1974), 1978, Professor—Chinese and Japanese religions, theory and method, 303-492-7408, E-mail: rodney.taylor@colorado.edu

Colorado State University
Dept of Philosophy, Fort Collins CO 80523

Colorado Christian University
180 S Garrison St, Lakewood CO 80226

Columbia College
1001 Rogers, Columbia MO 65216

Columbia College

1301 Columbia College Dr
Columbia SC 29203

Phone: 803-786-3749
Fax: 803-786-3798
E-mail: rcrews@colacoll.edu
URL: www.colacoll.edu/academic/
religion/index.html

TYPE OF INSTITUTION: Private, United Methodist
EXECUTIVE OFFICER: Phyllis Bonanno, President
CHAIRPERSON: Rowan D. Crews
UNDERGRADUATE ENROLLMENT: 1,200

Columbia University

Department of Religion, Kent Hall/RM 617
Mail Code 3949
1140 Amsterdam Ave
New York NY 10027

Phone: 212-854-3218
E-mail: abl4@columbia.edu
URL: www.columbia.edu/cu/religion/

TYPE OF INSTITUTION: Private
CHAIRPERSON: David Halivui
UNDERGRADUATE ENROLLMENT: 6,000
GRADUATE ENROLLMENT: 10,000
DEGREES OFFERED: BA
UNDERGRADUATE MAJORS: 44
DEGREES CONFERRED: 20
DESCRIPTION OF UNDERGRADUATE PROGRAM: The undergraduate program in religion seeks to provide a student with a broad background in the major approaches to the academic study of religion, including the literary-critical, historical, philosophical and social-scientific approaches. The student is given the opportunity to apply these methods to a wide ranging spectrum of religious data from the major Western and Asian traditions, both ancient and modern.

GRADUATE PROGRAM

Member of the Council on Graduate Studies in Religion

Graduate Advisor: Ryuichi Abe

Graduate Degrees Offered: MA; PhD

Degrees Conferred: 3 MA; 4 PhD

Graduate Students in Residence: 5 MA; 39 PhD

Not in Residence: 0 MA; 11 PhD

Average No. of New Students Enrolled: 3 MA; 6 PhD

Women Students: 2 MA; 22 PhD

Minority Students: 0 MA; 2 PhD

Foreign Students: 2 MA; 1 PhD

Minimum GRE Score Requisite to Admission: No

Minimum GPA Score Requisite to Admission: No

Financial Aid to First Year Students: 0% MA; 100% PhD

Financial Aid to Other Students: 0% MA; 80% PhD

Attrition Among Students: 0% MA; 5% PhD

Graduates Placed: 90% PhD

DESCRIPTION OF GRADUATE PROGRAM AND RESEARCH FACILITIES: The graduate program in religion is a cooperative program between the Departments of Religion at Columbia University and Barnard College and Union theological Seminary. It is designed for the study of religion in its various forms within different societies and cultures. A distinctive feature of the program is the opportunity for students not only to gain advanced training in specific fields of religious studies, but also to acquire a basic knowledge of the world's major religious traditions and of the principal methods and theories employed in the study of religion.

FACULTY:

Abe, Ryuichi, PhD, Columbia University (1991), 1990, Kao Associate Professor of Japanese Religions—Chinese and Japanese religions

Alexakis, Alexander, DPhil, Oxford University (1992), 1994, Assistant Professor—Byzantine studies

Awn, Peter J., PhD, Harvard University (1978), 1978, Professor—Islam

Bagger, Matthew C., PhD, Columbia University (1994), 1998, Assistant Professor—philosophy of religion

Balmer, Randall, (Barnard College) PhD, Princeton University (1985), 1985, Ann Whitney Olin Professor of American Religious History—History of religion in America

Bender, Courtney J., PhD, Princeton University (1997), 1999, Assistant Professor—sociology of religion

Castelli, Elizabeth, (Barnard College) PhD, Claremont Graduate School (1987), 1995, Assistant Professor—Early Christianity

Deutsch, Celia, (Barnard College) PhD St Michael's College, University of Toronto, (1985), 1985, Adjunct Associate Professsor—Early Christianity

Halivni, David Weiss, DHL, Jewish Theological Seminary (1958), 1986, Lucius N. Littauer Professor of Classical Jewish Civilization—Judaism

Hawley, John S., (Barnard College) PhD, Harvard University (1977), 1986, Professor—religions of India and Southeast Asia

Kent, Bonnie, PhD, Columbia University (1984), 1999, Associate Professor—philosophy of religion

Lindt, Gillian, PhD, Columbia University (1965), 1973, Professor—Sociology of religion

McGuckin, John A., (Union Theological Seminary) PhD, Durham University (1980), 1999, Adjunct Professor—early Christianity

Proudfoot, Wayne L., PhD, Harvard University (1972), 1972, Professor—philosophy of religion

Segal, Alan, (Barnard College) PhD, Yale University (1975), 1980, Professor—Judaism

Shapiro, Susan, PhD, University of Chicago (1983), 1993, Assistant Professor—Judaism

Somerville, Robert, PhD, Yale University (1968), 1976, Professor—history of Christianity

Thurman, Robert, PhD, Harvard University (1972), 1988, Jey Tsong Khapa Professor of Indo-Tibetan Studies—Buddhism

Tubb, Gary, PhD, Harvard University (1979), 1995, Senior Lecturer—religions of India and Southeast Asia

Weisenfeld, Judith, (Barnard College) PhD, Princeton University (1992), 1991, Assistant Professor—history of religion in America

Wimbush, Vincent, (Union Theological Seminary) PhD, Harvard University (1983), 1991, Adjunct Professor—New Testament

Yavari, Neguin, PhD, Columbia University (1982), 1999, Assistant Professor—Islam

Columbia Bible College

7435 Monticello Road
PO Box 3122
Columbia SC 29230-3122

Phone: 800-777-2227
Fax: 803-786-4209
E-mail: yesciu@ciu.edu

TYPE OF INSTITUTION: Private, Multi-Denominational
EXECUTIVE OFFICER: Johnny V. Miller, President
UNDERGRADUATE ENROLLMENT: 550

Columbia Biblical Seminary and Graduate School of Missions

7435 Monticello Rd
PO Box 3122
Columbia SC 29230-3122

Phone: 800-777-2227
Fax: 803-786-4209
E-mail: yescbs@ciu.edu

TYPE OF INSTITUTION: Private, Multi-Denominational
EXECUTIVE OFFICER: Johnny V. Miller, President
GRADUATE ENROLLMENT: 450

Columbia Christian College

9101 E Burnside, Portland OR 97216-1515

Columbia International University

7435 Monticello Road
PO Box 3122
Columbia SC 29230-3122

Phone: 800-777-2227
Fax: 803-786-4209
URL: www.ciu.edu

TYPE OF INSTITUTION: Private
EXECUTIVE OFFICER: Johnny V. Miller, President
UNDERGRADUATE ENROLLMENT: 528
GRADUATE ENROLLMENT: 345

Columbia Theological Seminary

PO Box 520
Decatur GA 30031-0520

Phone: 404-378-8821
Fax: 404-377-9696

TYPE OF INSTITUTION: Denominational: Presbyterian Church (USA)
EXECUTIVE OFFICER: Douglas W. Oldenburg, President
GRADUATE ENROLLMENT: 108

Columbia Union College

7600 Flower Ave, Takoma Park MD 20012

Conception Seminary College

PO Box 502
Conception MO 64433

Phone: 660-944-2218
Fax: 660-944-2829

TYPE OF INSTITUTION: Denominational: Roman Catholic
EXECUTIVE OFFICER: Benedict Neenan, President-Rector
COORDINATOR: James Polich
UNDERGRADUATE ENROLLMENT: 85

Concordia College

4090 Geddes Rd, Ann Arbor MI 48105

Concordia College/Moorhead

Religion Dept, Moorhead MN 56562

Concordia College

800 N Columbia Ave, Seward NE 68434

Concordia College

171 White Plains Rd
Bronxville NY 10708

Phone: 914-337-9300
Fax: 914-395-4500
E-mail: mdr@concordia-NY.edu

TYPE OF INSTITUTION: Private, Lutheran Church-Missouri Synod
EXECUTIVE OFFICER: David Jacobson, Academic Dean
CHAIRPERSON: Merlin D. Rehm
UNDERGRADUATE ENROLLMENT: 600

Concordia University

7400 Augusta Street
River Forest IL 60305-1499

Phone: 708-771-8300
Fax: 708-209-3176
E-mail: crfjastranr@crf.cuis.edu
URL: www.curf.edu

TYPE OF INSTITUTION: Denominational: Lutheran Church-Missouri Synod
EXECUTIVE OFFICER: George Heider, President
CHAIRPERSON: Nathan Jastram, Theology Department
COORDINATOR: Nathan Jastram, Master of Arts in Religion Program
UNDERGRADUATE ENROLLMENT: 1,300
GRADUATE ENROLLMENT: 600

Concordia University/St Paul

275 N Syndicate
St Paul MN 55104

Phone: 651-641-8278
Fax: 651-659-0207

TYPE OF INSTITUTION: Private, Lutheran-Missouri Synod
EXECUTIVE OFFICER: Robert Holst, President
CHAIRPERSON: David A. Lumpp
UNDERGRADUATE ENROLLMENT: 1,300-1,325
DEGREES OFFERED: BA
UNDERGRADUATE MAJORS: 25-33
DEGREES CONFERRED: 8-10
DESCRIPTION OF UNDERGRADUATE PROGRAM: The department of religion and theology
  both unfolds the Christian message from the perspective of Lutheran theology and explores
  the diversity of human religious experience. It supports the university's professional church
  work programs (pre-seminary, director of Christian education, director of Christian out-
  reach, and church teacher). It offers majors in theology and in outreach, along with several
  minors (among them confessional Lutheranism and theological languages).
FACULTY:

Carter, Richard E., ThD, Luther-Northwestern Theological Seminary, St Paul (1991), 1991, Associate Professor and coordinator of pre-seminary program—world religions, religion and
  culture, outreach, doctrine, 612-641-8271, E-mail: Carter@luther.csp.edu
DeWerff, Robert E., EdD, University of St Thomas, St Paul (1994), 1994, Associate Professor
  and Dean of Graduate and Continuing Studies, 612-641-8277, E-mail:
  deweff@luther.csp.edu
Ernst, Roger, MDiv, Concordia Seminary, St Louis (1973), 1994, Adjunct Professor and coordinator of Director of Christian Outreach program, 612-641-8246
Holst, Robert A., PhD, Princeton Theological Seminary (1970), 1991, President and Professor—New Testament, 612-641-8211, E-mail: holst@luther.csp.edu
Jastram, Daniel N., PhD, University of Wisconsin, Madison (1989), 1989, Assistant Professor—classical languages and New Testament, 612-641-8836, E-mail:
  jastram@luther.csp.edu
Lumpp, David A., ThD, Concordia Seminary, St Louis (1988), 1990, Professor and department
  chair—Christian doctrine and history, 612-641-8217, E-mail: lumpp@luther.csp.edu
Mueller, Paul, DMiss, Concordia Theological Seminary, Ft Wayne (1995), 1993, Assistant Pro-
  fessor and Director of the Oswald Hoffman School of Christian Outreach—cross cultural out-
  reach, 612-641-8830, E-mail: pmueller@luther.csp.edu
Schuler, Mark T., ThD, Concordia Seminary, St Louis (1991), 1994, Assistant Professor—New
  Testament and Greek, 612-641-8736, E-mail: schuler@luther.csp.edu
Stohlmann, Stephen C., PhD, Brandeis University, Waltham (1971), 1976, Professor—Old Tes-
  tament Hebrew, 612-641-8824, E-mail: stohlmann@luther.csp.edu
Trapp, Thomas H., ThD, University of Heidelberg (1973), 1982, Professor—Hebrew and Old
  Testament, 612-641-8837, E-mail: ttrapp@luther.csp.edu

Concordia University, Portland

2811 NE Holman
Portland OR 97211-6099

Phone: 503-288-9371
Fax: 503-280-8531
E-mail: bschmi@cu-portland.edu
URL: www.cu-portland.edu

TYPE OF INSTITUTION: Private, Lutheran Church-Missouri Synod
EXECUTIVE OFFICER: Charles Schlimpert, President
CHAIRPERSON: Robert Schmidt, Dean, School of Theological Studies
UNDERGRADUATE ENROLLMENT: 950
GRADUATE ENROLLMENT: 75

Concordia University at Austin

3400 I35-N
Austin TX 78705

Phone: 512-452-7661
Fax: 512-459-8517
E-mail: zersen@concordia.edu
URL: www.concordia.edu

TYPE OF INSTITUTION: Denominational: Lutheran Church-Missouri Synod
EXECUTIVE OFFICER: David Zersen, President
COORDINATOR: Paul Puffe, Director of Pre-Seminary Program
UNDERGRADUATE ENROLLMENT: 800
GRADUATE ENROLLMENT: 10

Concordia University Wisconsin

12800 N Lake Shore Dr
Mequon WI 53097-2041

Phone: 414-243-5700
Fax: 414-243-4351
E-mail: lbecher@bach.cuw.edu
URL: www.cuw.edu

TYPE OF INSTITUTION: Denominational: Lutheran Church-Missouri Synod
EXECUTIVE OFFICERS: Patrick Ferry, President; David Eggebrecht, Academic Dean
CHAIRPERSON: Timothy Maschke
COORDINATOR: David Borst, Independent Masters' Degree programs
UNDERGRADUATE ENROLLMENT: 4,000
GRADUATE ENROLLMENT: 250

Concordia University

2060 Mackay
Montreal PQ H3G 1M8 Canada

Phone: 514-848-2065
Fax: 514-848-4541
E-mail: religion@vax2.concordia.ca
URL: 132.205.57.9/religion/reli.html

TYPE OF INSTITUTION: Public
CHAIRPERSON: Leslie Orr

UNDERGRADUATE ENROLLMENT: 2,000

GRADUATE ENROLLMENT: 86

DEGREES OFFERED: BA in Religion and Judaic Studies, BA honors, major, minor

UNDERGRADUATE MAJORS: 150

DEGREES CONFERRED: 28

DESCRIPTION OF UNDERGRADUATE PROGRAM: The Department offers a variety of courses in the areas of world religions, ethical issues, and religion and culture. There are introductory courses in Understanding Religion, World Religions, and the History of Judaism. There are also courses which focus on particular religious traditions (Judaism, Christianity, Islam, Hinduism, and Buddhism) and on particular topics such as Women and Religion, Contemporary Ethical Issues, Religion and Literature, and Death and Dying.

GRADUATE PROGRAM

Member of the Council on Graduate Studies in Religion

Graduate Advisors: Michel Despland, MA; Michael Oppenheim, MA; Frederick Bird, PhD

Graduate Degrees Offered: MA; PhD

Degrees Conferred: 2 MA; 1 PhD

Graduate Students in Residence: 46 MA; 33 PhD; 3 Other

Average No. of New Students Enrolled: 8 MA; 3 PhD

Women Students: 36 MA; 21 PhD; 2 Other

Minimum GRE Score Requisite to Admission: No

Minimum GPA Score Requisite to Admission: Yes; B

Foreign Language Proficiency Evaluated: Yes; GSFLT Score: German; French; Hebrew for MA Judaic

DESCRIPTION OF GRADUATE PROGRAM AND RESEARCH FACILITIES: The MA program in History and Philosophy of Religion offers courses in World Religions, Religious and Philosophical Thought, Religion and Society, Women and Religion, and Judaic Studies. The MA program in Judaic Studies offers courses in Judaism in Late Antiquity, Medieval Judaism, and Modern Judaism. The two fields of concentration for the PhD program are Comparative Ethics and Judaic Studies. A joint PhD program with the University of Quebec in Montreal, focuses on the additional fields of Religion in Quebec and Religion and Theory. All courses are offered in the evening to permit the attendance of both full-time and part-time students.

ACADEMIC PLAN, ADMISSION REQUIREMENTS, FINANCIAL AID: The two Masters Programs have both a thesis and a non-thesis option. The PhD program requires a minimum of two years of full-time graduate study beyond the Masters's degree. For admission to the MA program in History and Philosophy of Religion: an honors degree in Religious or Judaic Studies, or its equivalent. Qualified applicants requiring prerequisite courses may be required to take up to 3 such courses in addition to their regular graduate program. Applicants with deficiencies in their undergraduate preparation may be required to take a qualifying year. For admission to the MA program in Judaic Studies: an honors degree in Judaic Studies or its equivalent. Candidates must demonstrate proficiency in the reading of Hebrew by taking an examination at the time of admission. Applicants otherwise qualified but who lack adequate preparation in particular areas may be required to take up to 3 full courses in addition to their regular graduate program or to undertake a qualifying year. There are Canada and Quebec Government Fellowships, Concordia University Fellowships, Research and Teaching Assistantships available to students in the Masters and PhD Programs.

FACULTY:

Bird, Frederick B., PhD, Graduate Theological Union (1973), 1971, Professor—sociology of religion, 514-848-2070

Clarke, Lynda, PhD, McGill University (1995), 1998, Assistant Professor—Islam/Shiism, 514-848-2073, E-mail: lclarke@akor.concordia.ca

Despland, Michel, ThD, Harvard University (1966), 1965, Professor—philosophy of religion, ethics, 514-848-2076

Hale, Rosemary, PhD, Harvard University (1992), 1992, Associate Professor—Christianity, 514-848-2069, E-mail: hale@vax2.concordia.ca

Joseph, Norma, PhD, Concordia University (1995), 1973, Associate Professor—women and religion, 514-848-2078, E-mail: nojo@vax2.concordia.ca

Lightstone, Jack N., PhD, Brown University (1977), 1976, Professor—Judaism in late antiquity, 514-848-4891, E-mail: lightst@vax2.concordia.ca

Oppenheim, Michael D., PhD, University of California, Santa Barbara (1976), 1974, Associate Professor—modern Jewish philosophy, 514-848-2067, E-mail: oppm@vax2.concordia.ca

Orr, Leslie, PhD, McGill University (1993), 1991, Associate Professor—religions of India, 514-848-2066, E-mail: orr@vax2.concordia.ca

Ravvin, Norman, PhD, University of Toronto (1994), Assistant Professor—Judaic studies, 514-848-2068, E-mail: ravvinbutler@sprint.ca

Robinson, Ira, PhD, Harvard University (1980), 1979, Professor—medieval Judaism, 514-848-2074, E-mail: robinso@vax2.concordia.ca

Rukmani, T. S., PhD, Delhi University (1958), DLitt, Delhi University (1991), 1995, Professor—Hindu Studies, 514-848-4085

Concordia Lutheran Seminary

7040 Ada Boulevard
Edmonton, Alberta T5B 4E3
Canada

Phone: 780-474-1468
Fax: 780-479-3067
E-mail: clsadmin@connect.ab.ca
URL: www.connect.ab.ca/~clslip

TYPE OF INSTITUTION: Private, Lutheran Church-Canada
EXECUTIVE OFFICER: L. Dean Hempelmann, President
GRADUATE ENROLLMENT: 30

Concordia Lutheran Theological Seminary

470 Glenridge Avenue
St Catharines, Ontario L2T 4C3
Canada

Phone: 905-688-2362
Fax: 905-688-9744

TYPE OF INSTITUTION: Private, Lutheran Church - Canada
EXECUTIVE OFFICER: Jonathan Grothe, President
GRADUATE ENROLLMENT: 30

Concordia Seminary

801 DeMun Avenue
St Louis MO 63105

Phone: 314-505-7000
Fax: 314-505-7001
E-mail: csl.edu
URL: csl.edu

TYPE OF INSTITUTION: Private, Lutheran Church-Missouri Synod

EXECUTIVE OFFICER: John F. Johnson, President
UNDERGRADUATE ENROLLMENT: 387
GRADUATE ENROLLMENT: 68

Concordia Theological Seminary

6600 N Clinton Street
Fort Wayne IN 46825

Phone: 219-452-2100
Fax: 219-452-2121
E-mail: klemsz@ctsfw.edu
URL: www.ctsfw.edu

TYPE OF INSTITUTION: Private, Lutheran Church-Missouri Synod
EXECUTIVE OFFICER: Dean O. Wenthe, President

Connecticut College

270 Mohegan Ave
New London CT 06320-4196

Phone: 860-439-2800
Fax: 860-439-5340
E-mail: ggre@conncoll.edu

TYPE OF INSTITUTION: Private
EXECUTIVE OFFICER: Claire L. Gaudiani, President
CHAIRPERSON: Garrett Green
UNDERGRADUATE ENROLLMENT: 1,600

University of Connecticut

405 Babbidge Rd
Storrs CT 06269

Phone: 860-486-2271
Fax: 860-486-4582
E-mail: dashef@uconnvm.uconn.edu
URL: www.ucc.uconn.edu/~dashef

TYPE OF INSTITUTION: Public
EXECUTIVE OFFICER: Phillip Austin, President
COORDINATORS: Arnold Dashefsky, Department of Sociology; Jocelyn Linnekin, Department of Anthropology
We are in the process of forming a faculty committee for the academic study of religion within the College of Liberal Arts and Sciences.

Conrad Grebel College

University of Waterloo
Waterloo, Ontario N2L 3G6 Canada

Phone: 519-885-0220
Fax: 519-885-0014
E-mail: grebel@uwaterloo.ca
URL: grebel.uwaterloo.ca/index.html

TYPE OF INSTITUTION: Mennonite
EXECUTIVE OFFICER: John E. Toews, President
ACADEMIC DEAN OF THE COLLEGE: Conrad G. Brunk

GRADUATE ENROLLMENT: 34

GRADUATE PROGRAM

Graduate Advisor: A. James Reimer

Graduate Degrees Offered: MTS

Degrees Conferred: 30

DESCRIPTION OF GRADUATE PROGRAM AND RESEARCH FACILITIES: The Master of Theological Studies is a two-year interdisciplinary program designed for full-time or part-time students preparing for ministry, further graduate work or personal growth. Its uniqueness lies in its consortium approach whereby up to 50% of the courses can be taken from a variety of participating institutions from other denominations. It focuses on the study of Christianity and the mission of the Christian church in the world from an Anabaptist-Mennonite perspective in cooperation with other denominational schools. Students can choose to study within one or three options: Biblical-Theological, Historical-Cultural, or Ministry.

FACULTY:

Balmer, Brice H., DMin, University of St Michael's College, Toronto School of Theology, Adjunct Professor—practical theology, spirituality and social justice

Brunk, Conrad G., PhD, Northwestern University, Academic Dean of Conrad Grebel College and Professor of Philosophy and PACS—social ethics and applied professional ethics, peace and conflict studies, 519-885-0220, ext 233

Ewert, Lowell, JD, Washburn University College of Law, LLM, International Law, Washington College of Law, The American University, Adjunct Professor—conflict resolution, human rights, civil society and peace-building, 519-885-0220, ext 380

Froese Tiessen, Hildi, PhD, University of Alberta, Associate Professor of English and PACS—literature, peace and conflict studies, 519-885-0220, ext 252

Harder, Gary, DMin, St Stephen's College, Adjunct Professor—pastoral theology

Hull, Kenneth, PhD, Princeton University, Associate Professor of Music—519-885-0220, ext 244

Martin, Laurence J., DMin, Pittsburgh Theological Seminary, Adjunct Professor—ministry courses

Miller, John W., ThD, University of Basel, Adjunct Professor—biblical studies

Neufeld Harder, Lydia, ThD, Toronto School of Theology, Adjunct Professor—systematic and pastoral theology

Packull, Werner O., PhD, Queen's University, Professor of History—519-885-0220, ext 241

Peachey, Dean E., PhD, University of Waterloo, Adjunct Professor—peace and conflict studies

Reimer, A. James, PhD, University of St Michael's College, Academic Advisor of Graduate Studies and Professor of Religious Studies—theology, 519-885-0220, ext 234

Snyder, C. Arnold, PhD, McMaster University, Professor of History and PACS—church history, 519-885-0220, ext 260

Yoder Neufeld, Thomas R., ThD, Harvard University, Associate Professor of Religious Studies and PACS—biblical studies, peace and conflict studies, 519-885-0220, ext 261

Seminary Consortium for Urban Pastoral Education

200 N Michigan Ave Suite 502
Chicago IL 60601-5909

Phone: 312-726-1200
Fax: 312-726-0425
E-mail: scupe200@aol.com

TYPE OF INSTITUTION: Private

EXECUTIVE OFFICER: David Frenchak, President
COORDINATOR: William Wylie-Kellermann
GRADUATE ENROLLMENT: 12

Converse College

580 E Main   **Phone: 803-596-9100**
Spartanburg SC 29302-0006   **Fax: 803-596-9158**
E-mail: hauckr@stc2.spt.tec.sc.us

TYPE OF INSTITUTION: Private, Non-Denominational
EXECUTIVE OFFICERS: Sandra Thomas, President; Thomas McDaniel, Provost
CHAIRPERSON: Robert J. Hauck
UNDERGRADUATE ENROLLMENT: 1,000
DEGREES OFFERED: BA
UNDERGRADUATE MAJORS: 15
DEGREES CONFERRED: 6
DESCRIPTION OF UNDERGRADUATE PROGRAM: The Department treats the study of religion as one of the humanistic disciplines in the liberal arts. We offer courses in philosophy, world religions, the western religions traditions, ethical analysis, archaeology and biblical studies (including the biblical languages), as well as supplying faculty to the College's core curriculum in history and culture. A major in religion consists of 30 hours of course work; a minor consists of 18 hours.
FACULTY:

McCane, Byron R., PhD, Duke University (1992), 1995, Associate Professor and Chair—biblical studies and archaeology, 864-596-9106, Fax: 864-596-9526, E-mail: byron.mccane@converse.edu

Norman, Corrie E., ThD, Harvard (1994), 1999, Assistant Professor—history of Christianity, 864-596-9100, Fax: 864-596-9526, E-mail: corrie.norman@converse.edu

---

Cornell College

600 First St W   **Phone: 319-895-4000 ext 4237**
Mt Vernon IA 52314   **Fax: 319-895-4492**
E-mail: dweddle@cornell-iowa.edu
URL: www.cornell-iowa.edu

TYPE OF INSTITUTION: Private, United Methodist
EXECUTIVE OFFICER: Leslie H. Garner, Jr., President of the College
CHAIRPERSON: David L. Weddle
UNDERGRADUATE ENROLLMENT: 1,050
DEGREES OFFERED: BA, BSS
UNDERGRADUATE MAJORS: 18
DEGREES CONFERRED: 10
DESCRIPTION OF UNDERGRADUATE PROGRAM: Religious ideas, values, and practices are fundamental elements in human culture. Our mission is to teach students how to understand major world religious traditions in their historical contexts and to appreciate their creative role in the contemporary world. We focus on the Jewish and Christian traditions as founda-

tions of Western culture, offering courses in the Bible and in modern theology and ethics. We also offer courses in comparative mysticism, Islam, religions of ancient Mexico, and religious sects. Our survey of world religions is part of programs in international relations and international business. We also offer internships in the practice of religion for our majors.

FACULTY:

Gillespie, Emory, MDiv, San Francisco Theological Seminary (1987), 1994, Instructor (part-time)—religion and literature, 319-895-4000, Fax: 319-895-4492

Vernoff, Charles E., PhD, University of California at Santa Barbara (1979), 1978, Professor—Hebrew Bible, Jewish studies, comparative religion, 319-895-4209, Fax: 319-895-4492, E-mail: cvernoff@cornell-iowa.edu

Weddle, David L., PhD, Harvard University (1973), 1973, Professor—theology, New Testament, medical ethics, religious sects, Islam, 319-895-4237, Fax: 319-895-4492, E-mail: dweddle@cornell-iowa.edu

Cornell University

259 Goldwyn Smith Hall
Ithaca NY 14853-3201

Phone: 607-255-8545
Fax: 607-255-1454
E-mail: jml16@cornell.edu

TYPE OF INSTITUTION: Private, Non-Denominational
CHAIRPERSON: Jane-Marie Law
UNDERGRADUATE ENROLLMENT: 20

Cornerstone Baptist Bible College

3615 Vickers Dr, Colorado Springs CO 80918

Covenant College

14049 Scenic Highway
Lookout Mountain TN 37350

Phone: 706-820-1560
Fax: 706-820-2165
URL: www.covenant.edu

TYPE OF INSTITUTION: Private, Presbyterian Church of America
EXECUTIVE OFFICER: Frank Brock, President
UNDERGRADUATE ENROLLMENT: 750
GRADUATE ENROLLMENT: 60

Covenant Theological Seminary

12330 Conway Rd
St Louis MO 63141

Phone: 314-434-4044
Fax: 314-434-4819
URL: covenantseminary.edu

TYPE OF INSTITUTION: Private, Presbyterian Church in America
EXECUTIVE OFFICER: Bryan Chapell, President
GRADUATE ENROLLMENT: 734

Creighton University

Theology Dept
2500 California Plaza
Omaha NE 68178-0302

Phone: 402-280-2501
Fax: 402-280-2502
E-mail: hausersj@creighton.edu
URL: puffin.creighton.edu/theo/index.html

TYPE OF INSTITUTION: Private, Roman Catholic (Jesuit)
EXECUTIVE OFFICER: Michael G. Morrison, SJ, President
CHAIRPERSON: Richard J. Hauser, SJ

Crichton College

6655 Winchester Rd
PO Box 757830
Memphis TN 38175-7830

Phone: 901-367-9800
Fax: 901-367-3866
E-mail: info@crichton.edu
URL: www.crichton.edu

TYPE OF INSTITUTION: Private, Non-Denominational
EXECUTIVE OFFICER: Ronald R. Schmidt, President
CHAIRPERSON: James Thorne
UNDERGRADUATE ENROLLMENT: 800

Criswell College

4010 Gaston Ave, Dallas TX 75246

Crown College

6425 County Rd #30, St Bonifacius MN 55375

Culver-Stockton College

#1 S College Hill
Canton MO 63435

Phone: 217-231-6000
Fax: 217-231-6611
E-mail: @culver.edu
URL: www.culver.edu

TYPE OF INSTITUTION: Private, Christian Church (Disciples of Christ)
EXECUTIVE OFFICER: Edwin Strong, President
CHAIRPERSON: Edward H. Sawyer
UNDERGRADUATE ENROLLMENT: 900

Cumberland College

7989 College Station Dr
Williamsburg KY 40769

Phone: 606-539-4227
Fax: 606-539-4490
E-mail: bdunston@cc.cumber.edu
URL: www.cumber.edu

TYPE OF INSTITUTION: Private
EXECUTIVE OFFICER: James Taylor, President
CHAIRPERSON: Robert C. Dunston
UNDERGRADUATE ENROLLMENT: 1500
GRADUATE ENROLLMENT: 100 (Master of Education)

Cummins Memorial Theological Seminary

705 S Main St, Summerville SC 29483

C. W. Post College

Greenvale NY 11548

Daemen College

4380 Main Street, Amherst NY 14226

Dakota Wesleyan University

1200 West University Avenue
Mitchell SD 57301

Phone: 605-995-2600
URL: www.dwu.edu

TYPE OF INSTITUTION: Private, United Methodist
EXECUTIVE OFFICER: Dr. John Ewing, Jr., President

Dalhousie University

6209 University Avenue
Halifax, Nova Scotia B3H 3J5
Canada

Phone: 902-494-3579
Fax: 902-494-1997
E-mail: ravi.ravindra@dal.ca
URL: www.dal.ca

TYPE OF INSTITUTION: Public, Non-Denominational
EXECUTIVE OFFICER: Tom Traves, President
CHAIRPERSON: Ravi Ravindra
COORDINATOR: Tom Faulkner
UNDERGRADUATE ENROLLMENT: 8,000
GRADUATE ENROLLMENT: 2,000
DEGREES OFFERED: Major and advanced major
UNDERGRADUATE MAJORS: 8
DEGREES CONFERRED: 4
DESCRIPTION OF UNDERGRADUATE PROGRAM: Created in 1973, the department offers
    courses designed to introduce undergraduate students from many fields to the insights of
    the great religions and to the academic study of religion. Name changed to the Department
    of Comparative Religion in 1985.
FACULTY:

Faulkner, Charles Thompson, PhD, University of Chicago (1975), 1975, Professor—religious
    history of Canada, 902-494-3579, Fax: 902-494-1977, E-mail: tom@is.dal.ca
Ravindra, Ravi, PhD, University of Toronto (1965), 1975, Professor and Chair—science and
    spirituality, Indian religions, comparative spirituality, 902-494-3578, Fax: 902-479-1070, E-
    mail: ravi.ravindra@dal.ca

University of Dallas

1845 E Northgate Dr
Irving TX 75062-4736

Phone: 972-721-5219
Fax: 972-721-4007
E-mail: lowery@acad.udallas.edu

TYPE OF INSTITUTION: Private, Roman Catholic
EXECUTIVE OFFICER: Glen Thurow, Provost
CHAIRPERSON: David Balás

COORDINATOR: Mark Lowery, Undergraduate Coordinator
UNDERGRADUATE ENROLLMENT: 60
GRADUATE ENROLLMENT: 30

Dallas Baptist College

Dallas TX 75211

Dallas Christian College

2700 Christian Pkwy
Dallas TX 75234

Phone: 972-241-3371
Fax: 972-241-8021
E-mail: dcc@popi.net
URL: www.popi.net/dcc

TYPE OF INSTITUTION: Private, Christian Church—Independent
EXECUTIVE OFFICER: John L. Derry, President
UNDERGRADUATE ENROLLMENT: 277

Dallas Theological Seminary

3909 Swiss Avenue
Dallas TX 75204

Phone: 800-992-0998
Fax: 214-841-3664
E-mail: admissions@dts.edu
URL: www.dts.edu

TYPE OF INSTITUTION: Private, Non-Denominational
EXECUTIVE OFFICER: Charles R. Swindoll, President
GRADUATE ENROLLMENT: 1,602

Damen College

Buffalo NY 14226

Dana College

Blair NE 68008

Darkei No'am Rabbinical College

2822 Avenue J, Brooklyn NY 11220

Dartmouth College

Dept of Religion
6036 Thornton
Hanover NH 03755-3592

Phone: 603-646-2386
Fax: 603-646-1699

TYPE OF INSTITUTION: Private
CHAIRPERSON: Nancy Frankenberry
UNDERGRADUATE ENROLLMENT: 4,000

Davidson College

Dept of Religion
PO Box 1719
Davidson NC 28036

Phone: 704-892-2259
Fax: 704-892-2005
E-mail: kaplank@davidson.edu
URL: www.davidson.edu/academic/
religion/religion.html

TYPE OF INSTITUTION: Private, Presbyterian Church (USA)
EXECUTIVE OFFICER: Robert F. Vagt, President
CHAIRPERSON: Karl A. Plank
UNDERGRADUATE ENROLLMENT: 1,600
DEGREES OFFERED: AB Major
UNDERGRADUATE MAJORS: 31
DEGREES CONFERRED: 13

DESCRIPTION OF UNDERGRADUATE PROGRAM: Inseparable from the fabric of the liberal arts, the Religion Department seeks to cultivate a humane literacy, responsive to the mixture of mystery and meaning in human life. Critical, cross-cultural, and interdisciplinary perspectives inform a spectrum of courses that study: systems of belief and patterns of religious behavior; the history of religious traditions; the function of religion in society; forms of religious expression and theological reflection.

FACULTY:

Csikszentmihalyi, Mark Alexander, PhD, Stanford (1994), 1994, Assistant Professor—East Asian religions, 704-892-2260, E-mail: macsikszentm@davidson.edu

Foley, William Trent, PhD, Chicago (1984), 1984, Professor—ancient and medieval Christianity, 704-892-2263, E-mail: trfoley@davidson.edu

Kuykendall, John Wells, PhD, Princeton (1975), 1984, Professor—American religion, 704-892-2262, E-mail: jokuykendall@davidson.edu

Mahony, William K., PhD, Chicago (1982), 1982, Professor—history of religions, Asian religions, 704-892-2258, E-mail: bimahony@davidson.edu

Plank, Karl A., PhD, Vanderbilt (1983), 1982, James W. Cannon Professor—biblical studies, Jewish studies, 704-892-2259, E-mail: kaplank@davidson.edu

Poland, Lynn M., PhD, Chicago (1981), 1991, Associate Professor—theories of religion, religion and literature, 704-892-2261, E-mail: lypoland@davidson.edu

---

Davis and Elkins College
Elkins WV 26241

University of Dayton

Dept of Religious Studies
300 College Park
Dayton OH 45469-1530

Phone: 937-229-4321
Fax: 937-229-4330
E-mail: relstudy@checkov.hm.udayton.edu

TYPE OF INSTITUTION: Private, Catholic
EXECUTIVE OFFICER: Raymond L. Fitz, SM, President
CHAIRPERSON: Terrence W. Tilley
UNDERGRADUATE ENROLLMENT: 6,600
GRADUATE ENROLLMENT: 3,450

Defiance College

701 N Clinton, Defiance OH 43512

University of Delaware

Newark DE 19711

Denison University

Dept of Religion
Granville OH 43023

Phone: 740-587-6589
Fax: 740-587-6417
E-mail: woodyard@cc.denison.edu

TYPE OF INSTITUTION: Private
EXECUTIVE OFFICER: David Anderson, Provost
CHAIRPERSON: David O. Woodyard
UNDERGRADUATE ENROLLMENT: 2,000
DEGREES OFFERED: BA, BS
UNDERGRADUATE MAJORS: 58
DEGREES CONFERRED: 19
DESCRIPTION OF UNDERGRADUATE PROGRAM: The Denison Religion Department is an essential part of humanistic studies in a liberal arts curricular. The goals of the department are to familiarize the student with the nature of religion, to give him or her an understanding of both Western and non-Western religious tradition, to help the student develop critical and analytical skills for examining the various religious systems offered in a pluralistic society, and to examine his or her own religious perceptions.

FACULTY:

Cort, John E., PhD, Harvard (1989), Associate Professor—non-Western Studies, 740-587-6254, E-mail: cort@cc.denison.edu

Jackson, John L., PhD, The Ohio State University (1989), Associate Professor—Black religion, 740-587-6560, E-mail: jackson@cc.denison.edu

Novak, Joan M., PhD, University of Iowa (1979), Associate Professor—ethics, 740-587-6205, E-mail: novak@cc.denison.edu

Van Broekhoven, Harold, PhD, Boston University Graduate School (1988), Associate Professor—biblical studies, 740-587-6303, E-mail: vanbroek@cc.denison.edu

Woodyard, David O., DMin, Vanderbilt Divinity School (1960), Professor—theological, 740-587-6589, E-mail: woodyard@cc.denison.edu

University of Denver

2150 S Race St
Pioneer Hall South, Room 301
Denver CO 80208-2740

Phone: 303-871-2740
Fax: 303-871-2750
E-mail: rlgs@du.edu
URL: www.du.edu

TYPE OF INSTITUTION: Private, Non-Denominational
CHAIRPERSON: Frederick E. Greenspahn
UNDERGRADUATE ENROLLMENT: 2,800
GRADUATE ENROLLMENT: 3,000

Denver Seminary

PO Box 10000, Denver CO 80210

DePaul University

Religious Studies Dept
2320 N Kenmore Ave
Chicago IL 60614

Phone: 773-325-7385
Fax: 773-325-4439
E-mail:@ffurmancondor.depaul.edu
URL: condor.depaul.edu/~religion

TYPE OF INSTITUTION: Private, Roman Catholic
EXECUTIVE OFFICER: John P. Minogue, President
CHAIRPERSON: Frida Kerner Furman
UNDERGRADUATE ENROLLMENT: 11,186
GRADUATE ENROLLMENT: 7,379
DEGREES OFFERED: BA
UNDERGRADUATE MAJORS: 41
DEGREES CONFERRED: 8
DESCRIPTION OF UNDERGRADUATE PROGRAM: The department offers courses with a comparative, thematic, or ethical focus, as well as courses in specific traditions. It is committed to DePaul's Catholic, Vincentian heritage, offering many courses exploring the theological, ethical, and social elements of Christianity past and present. Of equal importance to the department is its commitment to a wide range of courses investigating various world religious traditions, great and small, as well as the international, urban character of Chicago itself. The *major* has two concentrations. The Standard Concentration exposes all students to a variety of religious traditions, elements and issues. Additional work within the concentration allows the student to continue exploring a broad range of topics or to concentrate in one area. The second concentration, Cultural Studies in Religion, explores the relationship between religions and cultures. Specialization in a particular area (Asia, the Americas, Europe and the Middle East, or Africa and the African Diaspora) is complemented by work in a variety of cross-cultural issues such as religious expressions in literature and the arts, in socio-political realities, ethics, and ritual.

FACULTY:

Camenisch, Paul F., PhD, Princeton University (1971), 1968, Professor—religious ethics, business, medical and professional ethics, 773-325-1270, E-mail: pcamenis@wppost.depaul.edu

Carlson, Jeffrey, PhD, University of Chicago (1988), 1989, Associate Professor and Associate Dean, College of Liberal Arts and Sciences—Christian theology, religious pluralism, modern thought, 773-325-7733, E-mail: jcarlson@condor.depaul.edu

Cedzich, U. Angelika, PhD, Julius-Maximilians-Universität, Germany (1987), 1994, Assistant Professor—religions of China and Japan, 773-325-1291, E-mail: adzich@aol.com

Dyson, Michael Eric, PhD, Princeton University, 1999, Ida B. Wells-Barnett University Professor—ethics and politics, religion and culture, African-American studies

Furman, Frida Kerner, PhD, University of Southern California (1980), 1986, Professor and Department Chair—social ethics, feminist studies in religion, 773-325-7386, E-mail: ffurman@condor.depaul.edu

Furman, Roy S., MAHL Rabbinic Ordination, Hebrew Union College (1971), 1993, PhD, (cand.), Chicago Theological Seminary, Teaching Associate—Judaic studies, comparative religion, 773-325-1186, E-mail: rfurman@wppost.depaul.edu

Gitomer, David L., PhD, Columbia University (1987), 1993, Associate Professor and Director, Master of Arts in Liberal Studies Program—religions and literatures of pre-modern India, 773-325-1282, E-mail: dgitomer@condor.depaul.edu

Halstead, James, OSA, PhD, STD, University of Louvain, Belgium (1986), 1988, Associate Professor and Director, Catholic Studies Program—ethics, Catholic studies, 773-325-1275, E-mail: jhalstea@wppost.depaul.edu

Harrill, J. Albert, PhD, University of Chicago (1993), 1996, Assistant Professor—New Testament, early Christian literature, Roman social history, 773-325-1283, E-mail: jharrill@condor.depaul.edu

Hinga, Teresia M., PhD, University of Lancaster, U.K. (1990), 1994, Associate Professor—African religions, Christian theology, women's studies, 773-325-1281, E-mail: thinga@wppost.depaul.edu

Leahy, John T., STD, MEd, Marianum, Rome, (1964), 1969, Associate Professor—ethics, 773-325-7453, E-mail: jleahy@wppost.depaul.edu

McCloud, Aminah Beverly, PhD, Temple University (1993), 1990, Associate Professor—Islamic studies, 773-325-1290, E-mail: amccloud@condor.depaul.edu

Read, Kay A., PhD, University of Chicago (1991), 1987, Associate Professor—history of religion, Mesoamerica, comparative ethics, 773-325-1280, E-mail: kread@wppost.depaul.edu

Steinberg, Naomi A., PhD, Columbia University (1984), 1987, Associate Professor—Hebrew Bible, women across cultures, 773-325-1288, E-mail: nsteinbe@wppost.depaul.edu

Stewart, Elizabeth-Anne, PhD, University of Malta (1999), 1976, Teaching Associate—Christian spirituality, psychology and religion, religion and literature, 773-325-4460, E-mail: estewart@wppost.depaul.edu

Strain, Charles R., PhD, University of Chicago (1976), 1976, Professor and Associate Vice President for Academic Affairs—American religious history, liberation theology, Zen Buddhism, 773-325-7199, E-mail: cstrain@wppost.depaul.edu

Tomasiewicz, Edward J., CM, DMin, Andover Newton Theological School (1990), 1996, Assistant Professor—psychology, religion, symbolism, 773-325-1271, E-mail: etomasie@wppost.depaul.edu

Turner, Richard Brent, PhD, Princeton University (1986), 1999, Associate Professor—history of religion in America, African-American religious history, African religions, 773-325-4275, E-mail: rturner@wppost.depaul.edu

DePauw University

Dept of Religious Studies
212 Harrison Hall
Greencastle IN 46135

Phone: 317-658-4038
Fax: 317-658-4177
E-mail: pwatt@depauw.edu

TYPE OF INSTITUTION: Private, Methodist
EXECUTIVE OFFICER: Robert Bottoms, President
CHAIRPERSON: Paul B. Watt
UNDERGRADUATE ENROLLMENT: 2,100

Derech Ayson Rabbinical Seminary

802 Hicksville Rd, Far Rockaway NY 11691

Detroit Baptist Theological Seminary

4801 Allen Rd, Allen Park MI 48101

University of Detroit Mercy

4001 W McNichols Rd
Detroit MI 48219-0900

Phone: 313-993-1287
Fax: 313-993-6397
URL: www.udmercy.edu

TYPE OF INSTITUTION: Private, Roman Catholic
EXECUTIVE OFFICER: Maureen A. Fay, OP, President
CHAIRPERSON: Gloria H. Albrecht
UNDERGRADUATE ENROLLMENT: 4,000
GRADUATE ENROLLMENT: 2,000

Dickinson College

Department of Religion
Carlisle PA 17013

Phone: 717-245-1494
Fax: 717-245-1942
E-mail: donaldsm@dickinson.edu

TYPE OF INSTITUTION: Private
CHAIRPERSON: Mara E. Donaldson
UNDERGRADUATE ENROLLMENT: 1,790
DEGREES OFFERED: AB
UNDERGRADUATE MAJORS: 42
DEGREES CONFERRED: 12

DESCRIPTION OF UNDERGRADUATE PROGRAM: Focus on both the form and content of major traditions in Buddhism, Judaism, Hinduism, Islam, Christianity; and Native America; and on the interactions of those traditions with other dimensions of the cultures in which they live, especially aesthetic and social-ethical dimensions. Faculty participation in interdisciplinary programs—e.g. Environmental Studies, Humanities, Policy Studies, Freshman Seminars.

FACULTY:

Cozort, Daniel, PhD, University of Virginia (1989), 1988, Associate Professor—South Asia, Tibetan Buddhism, 717-245-1385, Fax: 717-245-1942, E-mail: cozort@dickinson.edu

Donaldson, Mara E., PhD, Emory University (1984), 1990, Associate Professor—religion and literature, feminist theology, religion and culture, 717-245-1228, Fax: 717-245-1942, E-mail: donaldsm@dickinson.edu

Lieber, Andrea B., PhD, Columbia University (1998), 1998, Assistant Professor and Director of Judaic Studies—ancient Judaism, Jewish mysticism, 717-245-1482, Fax: 717-245-1942, E-mail: lieber@dickinson.edu

Pulcini, Theodore, PhD, University of Pittsburgh (1994), 1995, Assistant Professor—Bible, Islam, Eastern Orthodoxy, 717-245-1208, Fax: 717-245-1942, E-mail: pulcini@dickinson.edu

Divine Word College

Epworth IA 52045

Doane College

Crete NE 68333

Dominican College

50 Acacia Ave
San Rafael CA 94901

Phone: 415-485-3279
Fax: 415-485-3205
E-mail: novak@dominican.edu
URL: www.dominican.edu

TYPE OF INSTITUTION: Private, Catholic
EXECUTIVE OFFICER: Denise Lucy, Vice President of Academic Affairs
CHAIRPERSON: Philip Novak
UNDERGRADUATE ENROLLMENT: 1,030
GRADUATE ENROLLMENT: 440

Dominican College

470 Western Hwy
Orangeburg NY 10962

Phone: 914-359-7800
Fax: 914-359-2313
URL: www.dc.edu

TYPE OF INSTITUTION: Private
EXECUTIVE OFFICER: Sr. Mary Eileen O'Brien, President
COORDINATOR: John B. Lounibos
UNDERGRADUATE ENROLLMENT: 1,700
GRADUATE ENROLLMENT: 150

Collège Dominicain, Institut de Pastorale

2715 chemin Cote Sainte-Catherine, Montreal, Quebec H3T 1B6 Canada

Collège Dominicain de Philosophie et de Théologie

96 Empress Ave
Ottawa, Ontario K1R 7G3 Canada

Phone: 613-233-5696
Fax: 613-233-6064

TYPE OF INSTITUTION: Denominational: Roman Catholic
EXECUTIVE OFFICER: Michel Gourgues, President
CHAIRPERSON: Yvon-D Gélinas, Dean of the Faculty of Theology
UNDERGRADUATE ENROLLMENT: 40
GRADUATE ENROLLMENT: 25

Dominican House of Studies

487 Michigan Ave NE
Washington DC 20017

Phone: 202-529-5300
Fax: 202-636-4460
E-mail: jtort728@aol.com

TYPE OF INSTITUTION: Private, Roman Catholic
EXECUTIVE OFFICER: Thomas McCreesh, OP, President
GRADUATE ENROLLMENT: 67

Dominican School of Philosophy and Theology

2401 Ridge Road
Berkeley CA 94709

Phone: 510-849-2030
Fax: 510-849-1372

TYPE OF INSTITUTION: Denominational: Roman Catholic
EXECUTIVE OFFICERS: Gregory Rocca, OP, President; Edward Krasevac, OP, Dean
CHAIRPERSONS: Hilary Martin, OP, Philosophy; Michael Dodds, OP, Theology
UNDERGRADUATE ENROLLMENT: 7
GRADUATE ENROLLMENT: 79

Dominican Study Center of Bayamon

Apartado Postal 1968, Bayamon PR 00960-1968

Dordt College

Sioux Center IA 51250

Drake University

Des Moines IA 50311

Drew University

Undergraduate Religion Dept, Madison NJ 07940

Drew University

The Graduate School
Madison NJ 07940-4000

Phone: 201-408-3285
Fax: 201-408-3040

TYPE OF INSTITUTION: Denominational: Methodist
EXECUTIVE OFFICER: James H. Pain, Dean
CHAIRPERSON: William D. Stroker, Undergraduate Dept.
UNDERGRADUATE ENROLLMENT: 1,475
GRADUATE ENROLLMENT: 402

Drew University Theological School

Madison Ave, Madison NJ 07940

University of Dubuque

2000 University Ave
Dubuque IA 52001

Phone: 319-589-3669
E-mail: rebertz@dbq.edu
URL: www.dbq.edu

TYPE OF INSTITUTION: Private, Presbyterian Church (USA)
EXECUTIVE OFFICER: Jeffrey Bullock, President
CHAIRPERSON: Roger Ebertz
UNDERGRADUATE ENROLLMENT: 20
GRADUATE ENROLLMENT: 180

University of Dubuque Theological Seminary

2000 University Ave, Dubuque IA 52001

Duke University

Dept of Religion
PO Box 90964
Durham NC 27708-0964

Phone: 919-660-3510
Fax: 919-660-3530
E-mail: bbl@acpub.duke.edu
URL: www.duke.edu/religion/

TYPE OF INSTITUTION: Private
EXECUTIVE OFFICER: Nannerl O. Keohane, President
CHAIRPERSON: Bruce Lawrence
UNDERGRADUATE DIRECTOR: Kalman Bland
GRADUATE DIRECTOR: David Steinmetz

UNDERGRADUATE ENROLLMENT: 6,000

GRADUATE ENROLLMENT: 4,500

DEGREES OFFERED: BA

UNDERGRADUATE MAJORS: 128

DEGREES CONFERRED: 62

DESCRIPTION OF UNDERGRADUATE PROGRAM: Study in the Department of Religion arises from the recognition that religion, although it takes many forms, is a constitutive element of human existence individually and collectively. The curriculum pursues the study of religion through the examination of the particulars of specific religious traditions; and through theoretical studies of an analytic, comparative, and constructive nature.

GRADUATE PROGRAM

Member of the Council on Graduate Studies in Religion

Graduate Advisor: David Steinmetz

Graduate Degrees Offered: MA; PhD

Degrees Conferred: 1 MA; 11 PhD

Graduate Students in Residence: 56 PhD

Not in Residence: 22 PhD

Average No. of New Students Enrolled: 10-12 PhD

Women Students: 30 PhD

Minority Students: 8 PhD

Foreign Students: 1 PhD

Minimum GRE Score Requisite to Admission: No

Minimum GPA Score Requisite to Admission: No

Foreign Language Proficiency Evaluated: No

Financial Aid to First Year Students: 100% PhD

Financial Aid to Other Students: 68% PhD

Attrition Among Students: 3% PhD

Graduates Placed: 64% PhD

DESCRIPTION OF GRADUATE PROGRAM AND RESEARCH FACILITIES: The Department of Religion is a free-standing University Program which is staffed by faculty from both the Divinity School and the Department of Religion. Currently, 34 scholars hold appointments in its graduate faculty. Areas of study include Hebrew Bible/Semitics; New Testament and Christian Origins; History of Christianity; Theology and Ethics; Judaica; Islamic Studies and History of Religions; Religion, Culture, and Critical Theory. Work with other departments/programs at Duke is encouraged, as well as with faculty at UNC-Chapel Hill. The Divinity Library contains over 300,000 volumes and 598 journals; Perkins Library and Lilly Library contain over 3,420,000 volumes. Academic plan, admission requirements, financial aid: Students spend 2-3 years in coursework; prepare for and take preliminary examinations; and prepare a dissertation. Length of time to degree is about 5-6 years. The Graduate Program in Religion receives about 200 applications a year. Full funding (tuition, fees, and stipends of $11,500) are given to about ten entering students a year. Students successful in winning these fellowships customarily have earned A/A- undergraduate averages, have strong letters of recommendation, previous training in some of the languages they will need, and combined verbal/quantitative GRE scores of about 1500. Some limited funding is available through preceptorships in the Divinity School, research assistantships, and teaching assistantships in the Department of Religion, but none of these is sufficient to support a student.

FACULTY OF THE DEPARTMENT OF RELIGION:

Bland, Kalman P., PhD, Brandeis (1971), 1973, Professor—Judaic studies, 919-660-3518, E-mail: kpb@acpub.duke.edu

Clark, Elizabeth A., PhD, Columbia (1965), 1982, John Carlisle Kilgo Professor—history of Christianity, 919-660-3505, E-mail: lizclark@acpub.duke.edu

Cornell, Vincent J., PhD, University of California, Los Angeles (1989), 1991, Associate Professor—Islamic studies, North African and American, 919-660-3502, E-mail: vmansur@acpub.duke.edu

Hart, William D., PhD, Princeton (1993), 1994 Assistant Professor—religion and culture, African-American religion, 919-660-3509, E-mail: wdhart@acpub.duke.edu

Hillerbrand, Hans J., PhD, University of Erlangen, Germany (1957), 1988, Professor—history of Christianity, 919-660-3511, E-mail: hjh@acpub.duke.edu

Joyce, Kathleen M., PhD, Princeton (1995), 1995, Andrew W. Mellon Assistant Professor—American religious history, 919-660-3513, E-mail: kmjoyce@acpub.duke.edu

Kort, Wesley A., PhD, University of Chicago (1965), 1965, Professor—religion and culture, religion and literature, 919-660-3519, E-mail: wkort@acpub.duke.edu

Lawrence, Bruce B., PhD, Yale (1972), 1971, Professor—history of religion, religions of India, 919-660-3506, E-mail: bbl@acpub.duke.edu

Meyers, Carol L., PhD, Brandeis (1975), 1979, Professor—Hebrew Bible, archaeology, 919-660-3514, E-mail: carol@acpub.duke.edu

Meyers, Eric M., PhD, Harvard (1969), 1969, Professor—Judaic studies, Hebrew Bible and archaeology, 919-660-3517, E-mail: emc@acpub.duke.edu

Nickerson, Peter, PhD, University of California-Berkeley (1995), 1995, Assistant Professor—Chinese religions, 919-660-3522, E-mail: nickersn@acpub.duke.edu

Peters, Melvin K. H., PhD, Toronto (1975), 1983, Associate Professor—Hebrew Bible, Septuagint studies, Intertestamental period, 919-660-3508, E-mail: melopete@acpub.duke.edu

Sanders, Ed P., ThD, Union Theological Seminary, NY (1966), 1989, Arts and Sciences Professor—New Testament and Christian origins, 919-660-3503, E-mail: epsan@acpub.duke.edu

FACULTY WITH COURTESY APPOINTMENTS IN RELIGION:

Aers, David, PhD, University of York, England (1971), 1995 Adjunct Professor—medieval religion, 919-684-5065, Fax: 919-684-4871

Beckwith, Sarah, PhD, King's College, University of London, 1995, Associate Professor—medieval religion, 919-684-2640, E-mail: ott@acpub.duke.edu

Gilbert, Paula E., PhD, Duke (1984), 1994 Adjunct Assistant Professor—historical studies, American religious thought, 919-684-5383, Fax: 919-681-8235, E-mail: pgilbert@mail.duke.edu

FACULTY OF THE GRADUATE PROGRAM IN RELIGION:

Bland, Clark, Cornell, Hart, Hillerbrand, Joyce, Kort, Lawrence, C. Meyers, E. Meyers, Nickerson, Peters, Sanders, (for details, see Department of Religion listing)

Ayres, Lewis, DPhil, Merton College, Oxford University, UK (1994), 1999, Assistant Professor of Christian Theology, 919-660-3540

Battle, Michael, PhD, Duke University (1995), 1999, Assistant Professor of Spirituality and Black Church Studies, 919-660-3499, E-mail: mbattle@duke.edu

Berger, Teresa, DrTheol, Ruprecht Karl Universitat (1984), 1985, Associate Professor—ecumenical theology, 919-660-3464, E-mail: tberger@mail.duke.edu

Carroll, Jackson W., PhD, Princeton Theological Seminary (1970), 1993, Ruth W. and A. Morris Williams Professor—religion and society, 919-660-3423, E-mail: jack@mail.duke.edu

Crenshaw, James L., PhD, Vanderbilt University (1964), 1987, Robert L. Flowers Professor—Old Testament, 919-660-3413, E-mail: jicren@mail.duke.edu

Hall, Amy Laura, ABD, Yale University, 1999, Assistant Professor of Christian Ethics, 919-660-3403, E-mail: divalh@duke.edu

Hauerwas, Stanley M., PhD, Yale University (1968), 1984, Gilbert T. Rowe Professor—theological ethics, 919-660-3420

Hays, Richard B., PhD, Emory (1981), 1991, Professor—New Testament, 919-660-3411, E-mail: rhays@mail.duke.edu

Heitzenrater, Richard B., PhD, Duke University (1972), 1993, Professor—church history and Wesley studies, 919-660-3403, E-mail: rheitz@mail.duke.edu

Huetter, Reinhard, Dr. theol.habil., University of Erlangen (1995), 1999, Associate Professor of Christian Theology, 919-660-3463, E-mail: rhuetter@duke.edu

Jennings, Willie J., PhD, Duke University (1993), 1994, Assistant Professor—theology and Black Church studies, 919-660-3431, E-mail: jennings@mail.duke.edu

Jones, L. Gregory, PhD, Duke University (1988), 1997, Dean of the Divinity School and Professor—theology, 919-660-3434, E-mail: lgjones@mail.duke.edu

Keefe, Susan A., PhD, University of Toronto (1981), 1988, Associate Professor—church history, 919-660-3469

LaRocca-Pitts, Elizabeth, PhD, Harvard University (1994), 1996, Assistant Professor—Old Testament studies, 919-660-3467, E-mail: laroccap@mail.duke.edu

Lischer, Richard A., PhD, King's College, University of London (1972), 1989, James T. & Alice Mead Cleland Professor of Preaching, 919-660-3421, E-mail: rlischer@acpub.duke.edu

McClintock Fulkerson, Mary, PhD, Vanderbilt University (1986), 1983, Associate Professor—theology, 919-660-3458, E-mail: mfulk@mail.duke.edu

Richey, Russell E., PhD, Princeton (1970), 1986, Professor—church history, 919-660-3408, E-mail: rrichey@mail.duke.edu

Smith, D. Moody, PhD, Yale University (1961), 1965, George Washington Ivey Professor—New Testament, 919-660-3466, E-mail: dmsmith@mail.duke.edu

Steinmetz, David C., ThD, Harvard (1967), 1971, Director of Graduate Studies and Amos Ragan Kearns Professor of the history of Christianity, 919-660-3438, E-mail: steinmtz@mail.duke.edu

Turner, William C., Jr., PhD, Duke University (1984), 1982, Associate Professor—theology and Black church studies, 919-660-3419

Wacker, Grant, PhD, Harvard (1979), 1992, Associate Professor—history of religion in American, 919-660-3462, E-mail: gwacker@mail.duke.edu

Wainwright, Geoffrey, ThD, University of Geneva (1983), 1983, Robert Earl Cushman Professor—Christian theology, 919-660-3460, E-mail: gwain@mail.duke.edu

---

Duke University Divinity School

107 New Divinity
2 Chapel Drive
Box 90968
Durham NC 27708

Phone: 919-660-3400 or 660-3436
Fax: 919-660-3473 or 660-3535
E-mail: divinity-info@duke.edu
URL: www.divinity.duke.edu

TYPE OF INSTITUTION: Private, United Methodist

EXECUTIVE OFFICER: Dean L. Gregory Jones, Dean and Professor of Theology

GRADUATE ENROLLMENT: 484

Duquesne University

615 Fisher Hall   **Phone: 412-396-6530**
Pittsburgh PA 15282   **Fax: 412-396-4904**

TYPE OF INSTITUTION: Denominational: Roman Catholic

CHAIRPERSON: Sean P. Kealy, CSSp

UNDERGRADUATE ENROLLMENT: 4,700

GRADUATE ENROLLMENT: 4,300

DEGREES OFFERED: BA, MA, MAPM, MARE, PhD

UNDERGRADUATE MAJORS: 12

DEGREES CONFERRED: 4

DESCRIPTION OF UNDERGRADUATE PROGRAM: Duquesne's Department of Theology affirms that the academic study of religious experience is essential to complete education. The Department fulfills its role in theological studies by the pursuit of the following aims: 1) it emphasizes Catholic theology, in dialogue with other Christian traditions, non-Christian traditions, and Judaism, as the key element in Duquesne's commitment to Catholic education on the university level; 2) it acknowledges the fact of the universal search for religious meaning and experience, and seeks not only to offer the possibility of a study of the varying approaches to religious witnesses in history, but also to place Catholic theology in communion with that quest; 3) it aspires to a fruitful encounter with other university disciplines, since the Department is convinced that theology's concerns are related to all vital human issues. Accordingly, the Department has organized its courses into three divisions: Biblical Studies, Christian Studies, and Selected Religious Studies.

GRADUATE PROGRAM

Graduate Degrees Offered: MA; PhD; MAPM, MARE

Degrees Conferred: 18 MA; 2 PhD; 1 MAPM; 1 MARE

Graduate Students in Residence: 15 MA; 60 PhD/ThD

Not in Residence: 26 MA; 30 PhD/ThD; 20 MAPM; 23 MARE

Average No. of New Students Enrolled: 13 MA; 10 PhD/ThD

Women Students: 28 MA; 27 PhD/ThD

Minority Students: 1 MA; 4 PhD/ThD

Foreign Students: 7 MA; 11 PhD/ThD

Minimum GRE Score Requisite to Admission: No

Minimum GPA Score Requisite to Admission: Yes; 3.5 on 4.0 scale

Foreign Language Proficiency Evaluated: No

Financial Aid to First Year Students: 75% MA; 85% PhD

Financial Aid to Other Students: 60% MA; 75% PhD

Attrition Among Students: 10% MA; 7% PhD

Graduates Placed: 75% MA; 96% PHD

DESCRIPTION OF GRADUATE PROGRAM: The Master of Arts in Theology: The purpose of the Master of Arts in Theology is to acquaint the student with broad areas of theology enabling them to both experience and research the Catholic tradition and provide a professional competence that will be of service to others. It also offers a basis for continual theological studies on a doctoral level. Master of Arts in Pastoral Ministry: The purpose of the Master's Program in Pastoral Ministry is to provide persons who want to be involved in the ministry of their church with a solid knowledge of theology as well as with a contemporary and professional understanding of the ministry in which they intend to work. The student can choose to specialize in Health Care Ministry. Other specialties may be added when their need is proven. PhD in Roman Catholic Systematic Theology: The PhD program offers a perspective and identity which has, as its origin and focus, the Roman Catholic faith-tradition. It specializes in systematic theology, encompassing doctrinal and moral theology. It pursues what the Church since Vatican II has urged, the development of contemporary systematic theology that incorporates the best of the human and physical sciences. The Master of Arts in Religious Education prepares students to serve as parish directors of religious education or in other catechetical ministries, and is offered in cooperation with the Diocese of Pittsburgh.

ACADEMIC PLAN, ADMISSION REQUIREMENTS, FINANCIAL AID: Duquesne University operates on the semester system with summer programs of three or six weeks. Preparation for graduate study should preferably be an undergraduate major in theology or religious studies or philosophy. Ample opportunities for supplementing incomplete undergraduate preparation in religious studies are available. Documents required: transcripts; three letters of recommendation (preferably from former professors in theology). Financial aid in the form of tuition remission is available. Religious and ordained clergy receive a 50% tuition reduction on the MA level. Sections of the annual Graduate School Catalogue give details on current "Fees and Charges."

FACULTY:

Baird, Marie, PhD, Duquesne University (1992), 1995, Assistant Professor—spiritual theology, world religions, 412-396-6029

Cahill, Michael, PhD, Institut Catholique, Paris (1985), 1989, Professor—biblical studies, 412-396-5473, E-mail: cahill@cc.duq.edu

Clifford, Anne M., CSJ, PhD, The Catholic University of America (1988), 1988, Assistant Professor—systematic theology, creation theology, religion and science, 412-396-5148, E-mail: clifford@duq3.cc.duq.edu

Grey, Michael, CSSp, PhD, Duquesne University (1997), Assistant Professor—moral theology, 412-396-4087, E-mail: grey@duq2.cc.duq.edu

Hanigan, James P., PhD, Duke University (1983), 1979, Professor—moral theology, social and sexual ethics, 412-396-6524, E-mail: hanigan@duq2.cc.duq.edu

Kealy, Sean P., CSSp, LSS, Biblical Institute, Rome (1968), 1995, Professor—biblical studies, 412-396-5619

Kelly, David F., PhD, University of Saint Michael's College (1978), 1981, Director of Health Care Ethics Program and Professor—medical ethics, 412-396-6532, E-mail: kellyd@duq3.cc.duq.edu

Mackler, Aaron, PhD, Georgetown University (1992), 1994, Assistant Professor—medical ethics and Judaic studies, 412-396-5985, E-mail: mackler@duq3.cc.duq.edu

McIntyre, Moni, IHM, PhD, St Michael's College, Toronto (1990), 1990, Assistant Professor—moral theology and ecological ethics, 412-396-5618, E-mail: mcintyre@duq3.cc.duq.edu

O'Brien, Maureen R., PhD, Boston College (1990), Assistant Professor—pastoral ministry, 412-396-6528

Schaub, Marilyn M., PhD, University of Fribourg, Switzerland (1957), 1969, Professor—Old Testament, 412-396-6526, E-mail: schaub@duq3.cc.duq.edu

Slusser, Michael, DPhil, Oxford University (1975), 1987, Associate Professor—patristic theology and systematic theology, 412-396-5716, E-mail: slusser@duq3.cc.duq.edu

Thompson, William M., PhD, St Michael's College, Toronto (1973), 1985, Professor—systematic theology, christology, philosophical theology, 412-396-6523, E-mail: thompsonw@duq3.cc.duq.edu

Worgul, George S., Jr., STD, PhD, Louvain (1974), 1978, Professor—systematic theology, sacraments, ecclesiology, 412-396-6525, E-mail: worgul@duq2.cc.duq.edu

D'Youville College

Buffalo NY 14201

Earlham College

Richmond IN 47374

Earlham School of Religion

228 College Ave
Richmond IN 47374-4095

Phone: 800-432-1377
765-983-1423
Fax: 765-983-1688
E-mail: marshja@earlham.edu
URL: www.earlham.edu/~esr

TYPE OF INSTITUTION: Private, Religious Society of Friends

EXECUTIVE OFFICER: Jay W. Marshall, Dean

GRADUATE ENROLLMENT: 64

GRADUATE PROGRAM

Graduate Degrees Offered: MA

Average No. of New Students Enrolled: 12 MA; 52 Other

Women Students: 5 MA; 33 Other

Minority Students: 1 MA; 0 Other

Foreign Students: 1 MA; 0 Other

Minimum GRE Score Requisite to Admission: No

Minimum GPA Score Requisite to Admission: No

Foreign Language Proficiency Evaluated: Yes: TOEFL 550

DESCRIPTION OF GRADUATE PROGRAM AND RESEARCH FACILITIES: The School is located in Richmond, Indiana, on the campus of Earlham College, which was founded by Friends in 1847. Earlham is situated on the southwest side of this Midwestern city of 35,000. The School of Religion was opened on an experimental basis by Earlham College in 1960. After a two-year period during which only the MA in religion was offered, the Board of Trustees authorized the expansion of the program to include a three-year Bachelor of Divinity degree, now called the Master of Ministry or Master of Divinity degree.

The Earlham School of Religion is accredited by the Association of Theological Schools in the United States and Canada (ATS) and by the North Central Association of Colleges and Schools through affiliation with Earlham College. The School greatly benefits from the numerous cultural activities on the Earlham College campus. These include frequent concerts, plays, and films; outstanding lecturers from all parts of the world; and a full program of intramural and varsity athletics. The purpose of the Earlham School of Religion (ESR) is to be a seeking, caring seminary community after the manner of Friends grounded in the Christian tradition. Its main function is to prepare servant leaders for ministry.

ESR has a vision of holistic education—education of whole persons in their cognitive, emotional, and spiritual relationships and the development of gifts and skills in ministry. At ESR, faculty and students worship together daily and understand that the religious experience of God is a foundation of their study together and a personal arena for developing theological clarity, emotional maturity, and spiritual depth.

ESR's two-degree program (the Master of Divinity/Ministry and the Master of Arts in religion) has dual features—it provides basic courses necessary for a variety of ministries, and it equips students in specific areas of ministry that address the needs of the local meeting or church, such as pastoral, counseling, spirituality, writing for the Religious market, Christian education, and the work of meeting secretaries in Friends' settings. For those pursuing the

MA degree, ESR can offer specialized work in Biblical studies, theological studies, Quaker studies, and peace and justice studies. The MA program is primarily intended for students wishing to pursue secondary-level teaching, work in certain areas of peace and justice, or continue toward a doctoral program in religious studies.

The School is a place where students can undertake a theological education from a Quaker perspective as well as benefit from the diversity of denominations and faith found in the classroom and community. It is intended that Quaker values permeate the life of the School, though not at the expense of a certain degree of academic objectivity. Beyond providing a general Quaker influence, ESR serves as a place where people can engage in serious religious study and research in the history and thought of Quakerism. The library collections of Earlham College contain more than 35,200 volumes, some 1,400 periodicals, and 15 foreign and domestic newspapers that have regular subscriptions. The newly remodeled Kelson Religion Section of Lilly Library comprises a collection of approximately 38,000 volumes on religion belonging to Earlham School of Religion and the Religion Department of Earlham College. There are approximately 130 subscriptions to periodicals relating to theological studies. Extensive reference works are available. The Quaker collection, totaling more than 10,000 volumes, serves the particular interest of Friends.

ACADEMIC PLANS, ADMISSION REQUIREMENTS, FINANCIAL AID: Any student who has a Bachelor of Arts or Bachelor of Science degree or its equivalent from an accredited institution and whose personal and vocational objectives are compatible with the goals of ESR may apply for admission. Applications should be submitted by July 31 for the fall term or one month prior to the term for which the student plans to enroll. A nonrefundable application fee of $35 is required. Along with the application, the student should provide a college or university transcript of academic work and the names and addresses of three references, including at least one who knows the applicant's academic work. It is assumed that persons applying for admission will have been interviewed before being admitted. When possible, the student should arrange for the interview to be held on the ESR campus. Such a visit is the best way for the student to learn about the community at ESR and for the School to become aware of the applicant's interests and goals. Factors considered in granting aid include a student's need, leadership potential, and academic ability. Aid is available through grants, loans, and employment. Grants are generally limited to some portion of tuition, and employment opportunities are made available through the federally funded College Work-Study Program. In this program, many students work for nonprofit agencies. Loans are made through the federal Stafford Student Loan Program, the Perkins Loan Program, denominational loan programs, family or patron loans, and the ESR loan program.

FACULTY:

Baisley, Phil, MDiv, Earlham School of Religion, 1993, Assistant Professor—pastoral studies

Bowen, Nancy, PhD, Princeton Theological Seminary, 1994, Associate Professor—Old Testament

Miller, Ann, MMin, Earlham School of Religion, 1987, Associate Professor—Christian spirituality

Miller, John, PhD, Emory, 1972, Professor—theology

Punshon, John, MA, Oxford (England), 1959, Geraldine C. Leatherock Professor—Quaker studies

Ratliff, J. Bill, PhD, Southern Baptist Theological Seminary, 1970, Professor—applied theology

Valentine, Lonnie, PhD, Emory, 1989, Associate Professor—peace and justice studies

PART-TIME FACULTY:

Davis, Richard, PhD, Yale University, 1971, Professor—Christian ethics

Garman, Mary, PhD, Northwestern University, 1989, Associate Professor—religion

ADJUNCT FACULTY:

Bill, Brent, MDiv, Earlham School of Religion, Adjunct Instructor—writing

---

East Carolina University

Greenville NC 27858

Phone: 252-328-4310
Fax: 252-328-6301
E-mail: mercerc@mail.ecu.edu
URL: www.ecu.edu/religious/

TYPE OF INSTITUTION: Public
EXECUTIVE OFFICER: Richard R. Eakin, Chancellor
CHAIRPERSON: Calvin Mercer
DEGREES OFFERED: BA, BS
UNDERGRADUATE MAJORS: 15
DEGREES CONFERRED: 2
DESCRIPTION OF UNDERGRADUATE PROGRAM: Religion is studied in a nonsectarian, interdisciplinary fashion, providing an understanding of religion as a historical and cultural phenomenon. Programs neither exclude nor promote any religious tradition or viewpoint. Courses are taught by professors from a variety of backgrounds, bringing diverse scholarly interests to the subject. While degrees in religious studies are offered only at the undergraduate level, there are a number of master level programs through which a student's interest in religion can be satisfied. East Carolina University is a public comprehensive institution committed to rich and distinctive undergraduate and graduate education, exemplary teaching, research and scholarship, public service, and human and intellectual diversity. Although enrollment is nearly 18,000 students, the student to faculty ratio is only sixteen to one. The university is conveniently located one hour from the coast and the Triangle cities of Raleigh, Durham, and Chapel Hill. For more information, see www.ecu.edu/religious/
FACULTY:
Courses taught by professors from several academic disciplines.

East Coast Bible College

6900 Wilkinson Blvd, Charlotte NC 28214

East Texas Baptist University

1209 North Grove
Marshall TX 75670

Phone: 903-935-7963
Fax: 903-927-4448
E-mail: rel@etbu.edu

TYPE OF INSTITUTION: Private, Baptist
EXECUTIVE OFFICER: Bob Riley, President
CHAIRPERSON: Donald R. Potts
UNDERGRADUATE ENROLLMENT: 1,300
GRADUATE ENROLLMENT: 100

East Texas State University

Commerce TX 75428

Eastern College

Dept of Christian Studies and Ministries
1300 Eagle Road
St Davids PA 19087

Phone: 615-929-4425
Fax: 615-929-4348
URL: www.eastern.edu

TYPE OF INSTITUTION: Private, American Baptist
EXECUTIVE OFFICER: David R. Black, President
CHAIRPERSON: Dwight N. Peterson
UNDERGRADUATE ENROLLMENT: 42

Eastern Baptist Theological Seminary

6 Lancaster Avenue, Wynnewood PA 19096

Eastern Kentucky University

Dept of Philosophy and Religion
Case Annex 268
Richmond KY 40475-3140

Phone: 606-622-1400
Fax: 606-622-1020
E-mail: phimille@acs.eku.edu

TYPE OF INSTITUTION: Public
EXECUTIVE OFFICER: Dan Robinette, Dean of Arts and Humanities
CHAIRPERSON: Robert Miller
UNDERGRADUATE ENROLLMENT: 15,500
GRADUATE ENROLLMENT: 2,000

Eastern Mennonite Seminary

1200 Park Road
Harrisonburg VA 22802

Phone: 540-432-4260
Fax: 540-432-4444
E-mail: info@emu.edu

TYPE OF INSTITUTION: Denominational: Mennonite
EXECUTIVE OFFICER: Sara Wenger Shenk, Interim Seminary Dean
GRADUATE ENROLLMENT: 89

Eastern Michigan University

Ypsilanti MI 48197

E

Eastern Montana College
1500 N 27th St, Billings MT 59101

Eastern Nazarene College
23 E Elm Ave, Wollaston MA 02170

Eastern New Mexico University
Dept of Religion, Portales NM 88130

Eckerd College
4200 54th Ave S, St Petersburg FL 33711-4744

Eden Theological Seminary

475 East Lockwood Ave
Webster Groves MO 63119

Phone: 314-961-3627
Fax: 314-961-9063

TYPE OF INSTITUTION: UCC
EXECUTIVE OFFICER: David M. Greenhaw, President
GRADUATE ENROLLMENT: 201
GRADUATE PROGRAM
Member of the Council on Graduate Studies in Religion
Graduate Degrees Offered: MTS
Degrees Conferred: 3 MTS
Graduate Students in Residence: 5
Not in Residence: 8
Average No. of New Students Enrolled: 4
Women Students: 10
Minority Students: 1
Foreign Students: 4
Minimum GRE Score Requisite to Admission: No.
Minimum GPA Score Requisite to Admission: Yes, 2.7 on a scale of 4.0
Foreign Language Proficiency Evaluated: Yes.
Financial Aid to First Year Students: 14%
Financial Aid to Other Students: 0
Attrition Among Students: .07%
Graduates Placed: 100%
DESCRIPTION OF GRADUATE PROGRAM AND RESEARCH FACILITIES: The Master of Theological Studies degree program (MTS) focuses upon the biblical, historical and theological foundations of Christian faith and the theoretical dimensions of the practice of ministry. Students will be engaged in classroom study and directed research, but no experiential compo-

nent in the practice of ministry is included in this degree program. The MTS is intended for the academic study of theology and is to be distinguished from a professional degree which leads to ordination. The MTS degree program is designed for students who possess an undergraduate degree: 1) who wish to develop a basic competence in theological studies; 2) who wish to specialize in some area of ministry but not the broad range of skills and understanding needed for ordination; 3) from other countries for whom an MTS degree may be more desirable than a professional degree. A MTS degree requires a total of fifty-four (54) credit hours. Students will usually need two years to complete the degree program. This degree program consists of the following elements: required courses (21 credit hours), major area of concentration (24 hours), minor area of concentration (12 hours), a thesis, and comprehensive evaluations (oral and written).

ACADEMIC PLAN, ADMISSION REQUIREMENTS, FINANCIAL AID: The information upon which MTS admissions decisions will be based includes: 1) The applicant's undergraduate and any graduate academic records (official transcripts are required). 2) Letters of reference and information gathered through conversation with those personal references furnished by the applicant. 3) The applicant's statement of vocational intent (which also serves as a writing sample). 4) When requested by the Masters Committee, a pre-admission interview to be conducted by the Committee or its appointees.

FACULTY:

Arther, Donald E., DMin., Eden Theological Seminary (1975), 1990, part-time—theology

Bracke, John M., PhD, Union Theological Seminary in Virginia (1983), 1984, Professor—biblical studies, 314-961-3627, Fax: 314-961-9063, E-mail: jbracke@eden.edu

Greenhaw, David M., PhD, Drew University (1987), 1997, President, Professor—preaching and worship, 314-961-3627, Fax: 314-961-918-9212, E-mail: dgreenhaw@eden.edu

Kaplansky, Howard G., MAHL, Hebrew Union College (1971),1988, part-time—Judaism

Krause, Deborah, PhD, Emory University (1996), 1992, Assistant Professor—New Testament, 314-961-3627, Fax: 314-961-9063, E-mail: dkrause@eden.edu

McCann, J. Clinton, Jr., PhD, Duke University (1985), 1987, Professor—biblical studies, 314-961-3627, Fax: 314-961-9063, E-mail: jmccann@eden.edu

McMichael, Steven J., STD, Gregorian University (1992), 1998, part-time—church history

Oglesby, Enoch H., PhD, Boston University School of Theology (1973), 1978, Professor—theology, history, 314-961-3627, Fax: 314-961-9063, E-mail: eoglesby@eden.edu

Patterson, Stephen J., PhD, Claremont Graduate School (1988), 1988, Associate Professor—New Testament, 314-961-3627, Fax: 314-961-9063, E-mail: spatterson@eden.edu

Riggs, John W., PhD, University of Notre Dame (1986), 1990, Assistant Professor—historical studies, systematic theology, 314-961-3627, Fax: 314-961-9063, E-mail: jriggs@,eden.edu

Robinson, Marcia C., MA, Emory University (1991), 1996, Assistant Professor—church history, 314-961-3627, Fax: 314-961-9063, E-mail: mrobinson@eden.edu

Schroer, A. Hale, DMin, Eden Theological Seminary (1974), 1974, Professor—pastoral theology: 314-961-3627, Fax: 314-961-9063, E-mail: hschroer@eden.edu

Stavenger, Marilyn L., DMin, San Francisco Theological Seminary (1992), 1988, Professor—field education, practice of ministry, 314-961-3627, Fax: 314-961-9063, E-mail: mstavenger@eden.edu

Tye, Karen B., EdD, Presbyterian School of Christian Education (1987), 1991, Associate Professor—Christian education, 314-961-3627, Fax: 314-961-9063, E-mail: ktye@eden.edu

Way, Peggy B., PhD, Princeton Theological Seminary (1979), 1990, Professor—pastoral studies, 314-961-3627, Fax: 314-961-9063, E-mail: pway@eden.edu

Edgewood College

855 Woodrow Street
Madison WI 53711

Phone: 608-663-2824
Fax: 608-663-3291
E-mail: bmiller@edgewood.edu
www.edgewood.edu

TYPE OF INSTITUTION: Private, Roman Catholic

EXECUTIVE OFFICER: James Ebben, President

CHAIRPERSON: Barbara B. Miller

UNDERGRADUATE ENROLLMENT: 1,500

GRADUATE ENROLLMENT: 500

DEGREES OFFERED: BA or BS in Religious Studies, MA in Religious Studies

UNDERGRADUATE MAJORS: 15

DEGREES CONFERRED: 3

DESCRIPTION OF UNDERGRADUATE PROGRAM: The Department offers strong programs for 1) personal enrichment; 2) directors of religious education; 3) other ministries, such as youth ministry, liturgy, ministry to the sick; 4) those who wish to teach in public or independent schools. Of special interest is the program for secondary teachers certifiable by the Department of Public Instruction of the State of Wisconsin; 5) seminary related programs. Undergraduate goals and courses adapted to student plan with sound program of research, preprofessional and professional programs including scriptures, theologies, and religion in the human community.

GRADUATE PROGRAM

Member of the Council on Graduate Studies in Religion

Graduate Degrees Offered: MA

Degrees Conferred: 2 MA

Minimum GPA Score Requisite to Admission: Yes; 2.75 on a 4.0 scale

Foreign Language Proficiency Evaluated: Yes

DESCRIPTION OF GRADUATE PROGRAM AND RESEARCH FACILITIES: Master of Arts in Religious Studies, designed for persons who want to develop their personal values, faith, and/or professional ministries. Curriculum includes world religions, scriptures, theologies, religion in the human community. Students adapt research and field experiences to individual goals. Thirty-six credits required.

FACULTY:

Dornisch, L., PhD, Marquette (1973), Professor—hermeneutics, worship, theology

Leonard, J. K., PhD, Notre Dame University (1988)—liturgy, theology, spirituality

Miller, B., PhD, University of Michigan, Ann Arbor (1994)—biblical studies, early Christian history and women's studies

Edinboro University of Pennsylvania

Philosophy Department, Edinboro PA 16444

Edward Waters College

1658 Kings Rd, Jacksonville FL 32209

Elizabethtown College

1 Alpha Drive
Elizabethtown PA 17022-2298

Phone: 717-361-1000
Fax: 717-361-1390
E-mail: bucherca@etown.edu
URL: www.etown.edu

TYPE OF INSTITUTION: Private, Church of the Brethren
EXECUTIVE OFFICER: Theodore E. Long, President
CHAIRPERSON: Christina Bucher
UNDERGRADUATE ENROLLMENT: 1,500
DEGREES OFFERED: BA
UNDERGRADUATE MAJORS: 5
DEGREES CONFERRED: 0
DESCRIPTION OF UNDERGRADUATE PROGRAM: The Religious Studies Department at Elizabethtown College offers courses in biblical studies, the history of Christianity, ethics and peace studies, and comparative religion. It offers a major and a minor in religious studies and an interdisciplinary minor in peace and conflict studies. Students may take courses at the college's Young Center for the Study of Anabaptist and Pietist Groups. They may also undertake internships in religion as part of their programs.
RELIGIOUS STUDIES DEPARTMENT FACULTY:
Bucher, Christina, PhD, Claremont Graduate University (1988), 1988, Associate Professor—biblical studies, 717-361-1182, Fax: 717-361-1390, E-mail: bucherca@etown.edu
Clemens, Eugene P., PhD, University of Pennsylvania (1970), 1965, Professor—social ethics, 717-361-1251, Fax: 717-361-1390, E-mail: clemenep@etown.edu
Eller, David B., PhD, Professor—church history, Anabaptist and Pietist studies, 717-361-1467, Fax: 717-361-1443, E-mail: ellerdb@etown.edu

Elmhurst College

Dept of Theology and Religion
190 Prospect
Elmhurst IL 60126

Phone: 630-617-3557
Fax: 630-617-3631
URL: www.elmhurst.edu

TYPE OF INSTITUTION: Private, United Church of Christ
EXECUTIVE OFFICER: Brian Cureton, President
CHAIRPERSON: Ronald Goetz

Elon College

Box 2209
Elon College NC 27244

Phone: 336-584-2242
E-mail: wilson@elon.edu
URL: elon.edu

TYPE OF INSTITUTION: Private, United Church of Christ
EXECUTIVE OFFICER: Fred Young, President
CHAIRPERSON: J. Christian Wilson
UNDERGRADUATE ENROLLMENT: 365
GRADUATE ENROLLMENT: 385

Emmanuel College

School of Christian Ministries
PO Box 129
Franklin Springs GA 30639
Phone: 706-245-7226
URL: emmanuel-college.edu

TYPE OF INSTITUTION: Private, International Pentecostal Holiness
EXECUTIVE OFFICER: David Hopkins, President
CHAIRPERSON: Darrel Cox
UNDERGRADUATE ENROLLMENT: 120

Emmanuel College

400 The Fenway
Boston MA 02115
Phone: 617-735-9882
Fax: 617-735-9877
E-mail: wetheri@emmanuel.edu
URL: emmanuel.edu

TYPE OF INSTITUTION: Private, Roman Catholic
EXECUTIVE OFFICER: Janet Eisner, President
CHAIRPERSON: Ann K. Wetherilt (Undergrad)
UNDERGRADUATE ENROLLMENT: 1,500

Emmanuel College

75 Queen's Park Crescent
Toronto, Ontario M5S 1K7
Canada
Phone: 416-585-4539
Fax: 416-585-4516
E-mail: ec.office@utoronto.ca
URL: vicu.utoronto.ca/emmanuel/index.htm

TYPE OF INSTITUTION: Private, United Church of Canada
EXECUTIVE OFFICER: Roger C. Hutchinson, Principal
GRADUATE ENROLLMENT: 65
GRADUATE PROGRAM
Member of the Council on Graduate Studies in Religion
Graduate Advisor: Phyllis D. Airhart
Graduate Degrees Offered: MA; PhD; ThD; ThM, DMin
Degrees Conferred: 1 MA; 1 PhD; 1 ThD; 3 DMin; 1 ThM
Not in Residence: 27 ThD; 14 DMin; 10 PhD; 7 ThM; 0 MA; 2 SpSt
Average No. of New Students Enrolled: 4 ThD; 2 DMin; 5 ThM; 1 Sp., 2 PhD, 1 MA
Minority Students: 7 ThD; 3 DMin; 2 PhD; 2 ThM; 2 MA; 2 Sp.
Foreign Students: 4 ThD; 2 PhD; 2 ThM; 1 MA
Minimum GRE Score Requisite to Admission: No
Minimum GPA Score Requisite to Admission: No
Foreign Language Proficiency Evaluated: Yes
Financial Aid to First Year Students: 80% MA; 100% PhD/ThD; 50% Other
Financial Aid to Other Students: 30% MA; 59% PhD/ThD; 10% Other

DESCRIPTION OF GRADUATE PROGRAM AND RESEARCH FACILITIES: The ThM, ThD, and DMin degree programs of Emmanuel College are administered by the Advanced Degree Council of the Toronto School of Theology which, in turn, is part of the University of Toronto. Excellent faculty and library resources are available through the close cooperation between TST and the U of Toronto. The MA and PhD programs are administered by the Toronto School of Theology, but the degrees are awarded by the University of St Michael's College.

ACADEMIC PLAN, ADMISSION REQUIREMENTS, FINANCIAL AID: The minimum requirement for admission to the ThM degree program is a second class MDiv degree. For admission to the doctoral programs a first class MDiv is the minimum requirement. The advanced degrees (ThM, ThD) are awarded conjointly by the Senate of Victoria University and the University of Toronto through the Toronto School of Theology. Applications for all degree programs are to be sent to the Toronto School of Theology, 47 Queen's Park Crescent, Toronto, Ontario M5S 2C3. For information on the college's financial aid program write to Emmanuel College, Director for Advanced Degree Studies, 75 Queen's Park Crescent, Toronto, Ontario M5S 1K7, Canada.

FACULTY:

Airhart, Phyllis D., PhD, Chicago, Associate Professor—church history

Barthel, Alan, ThD, Trinity College, MM, Butler, Associate Professor—church music

Demson, David E., DPhil, Oxford, Professor—systematic theology

Hutchinson, Roger C., ThD, Victoria, Professor—church and society

Johnson, Abigail J., DMin, Victoria, Director—field education

Kervin, William S., ThD, Victoria, Assistant Professor—public worship

Legge, Marilyn J., PhD, Union, Associate Professor—Christian ethic

Ng, G. A. Wenh-In, PhD, Columbia, Associate Professor—Christian education

Redcliffe, Gary L., PhD, McGill, Associate Professor—pastoral theology

Sheppard, Gerald T., PhD, Yale, Professor—Old Testament literature and exegesis

Vaage, Leif E., PhD, Claremont, Associate Professor—New Testament

Wells, Harold G., PhD, McGill, Professor—systematic theology

Wilson, Paul Scott, PhD, London, Professor—homiletics

Emmanuel School of Religion

One Walker Dr
Johnson City TN 37601

Phone: 423-926-1186
Fax: 423-926-6198
URL: www.esr.edu

TYPE OF INSTITUTION: Private
EXECUTIVE OFFICERS: C. Robert Wetzel, President
GRADUATE ENROLLMENT: 200

Emmaus Bible College

2570 Ashbury Rd, Dubuque IA 52001

Emory University

Department of Religion
S214 Callaway Center
Atlanta GA 30322

Phone: 404-727-7596 (Undergrad)
404-727-6333 (Grad Div of Religion)
Fax: 404-727-7597
E-mail: rells@emory.edu (Undergrad)
sthom11@emory.edu (Grad)
URL: www.emory.edu/UDR/handbook/
handbook.html (Undergrad)
www.emory.edu/GDR/ (Grad)

TYPE OF INSTITUTION: Private, United Methodist

EXECUTIVE OFFICER: Rebecca Chopp, Provost

CHAIRPERSON: Laurie L. Patton, Dept of Religion

DIRECTOR: Steven M. Tipton, Graduate Division of Religion

UNDERGRADUATE ENROLLMENT: 6,316

GRADUATE ENROLLMENT: 3,394

DEGREES OFFERED: BA

UNDERGRADUATE MAJORS: 84

DEGREES CONFERRED: 30

DESCRIPTION OF UNDERGRADUATE PROGRAM: Within the Emory University liberal arts tradition, faculty and students in the Department of Religion engage in inquiry into religion in its diverse expressions in different times and places in history. The curriculum offers a broad, cross-cultural, and interdisciplinary program with courses in Christian, Jewish, Hindu, Buddhist, Muslim, and Native American religious traditions. In addition, thematic courses take up common human issues and explore them from the perspectives of diverse religious traditions. Such courses address themes of death and dying, gender, theology, religious performance, ethics, religion and violence, legal and political analysis, historical and social scientific analysis, theological and philosophical interpretation, religion and literature, art, and film, the comparative study of sacred texts, and the psychological dimensions of religion. The four major goals of the Department are 1) enable students to develop expertise in interpreting the plurality of religions in their historical settings and critically appreciate the influence religions exert in shaping experience and society, 2) assist students who desire to prepare for graduate and professional study in religion and related fields, 3) help students learn to write well about the religious, social, historical, artistic, and intellectual accomplishments of cultures, and 4) engage students in understanding themselves as moral agents in the world and help them appreciate the moral and spiritual dimensions of the interpretive activity they pursue in the study of religion.

GRADUATE PROGRAM

Member of the Council on Graduate Studies in Religion

Graduate Advisor: Steven M. Tipton

Graduate Degrees Offered: PhD

Degrees Conferred: 14 PhD

Graduate Students in Residence: 98 PhD

Not in Residence: 34 PhD

Average No. of New Students Enrolled: 18 PhD

Women Students: 68 PhD

Minority Students: 14 PhD

Foreign Students: 17 PhD

Minimum GRE Score Requisite to Admission: No

Minimum GPA Score Requisite to Admission: No

Foreign Language Proficiency Evaluated: Yes

Financial Aid to First Year Students: 100% PhD

Financial Aid to Other Students: 100% PhD

Attrition Among Students: 2% PhD

Graduates Placed: 98% PhD

DESCRIPTION OF GRADUATE PROGRAM AND RESEARCH FACILITIES: The Graduate Division of Religion prepares students for teaching and scholarship in seven programs of study: Ethics and Society; Hebrew Bible; Historical Studies in Theology and Religion; New Testament; Person, Community, and Religious Practices; Theological Studies; and West and South Asian Religions. Interdisciplinary work is fostered in several ways: within each program; through special concentrations such as Religion and American Culture; and through cooperation with other programs in the university including especially Jewish Studies, Law and Religion, Near Eastern languages and literature, history, philosophy, English, sociology, and anthropology. Preparation for general teaching in the area of religion is achieved through the required seminar, "Mapping the Landscape of Religion and Theology"; and the seminar "Teaching Religion," part of the extensive teacher training program. Library facilities include the Pitts Theology Library, one of the largest theological collections in the nation, plus the university library and associated Georgia libraries.

ACADEMIC PLAN, ADMISSION REQUIREMENTS, FINANCIAL AID: The PhD program requires two years (48 semester hours) of course work in residence, at least five of which must be seminars. Beyond the required divisional seminar, the program permits flexibility in the ordering of courses and requires courses and examinations outside one's field of specialization. The third year is given to doctoral examinations and the preparation of a dissertation prospectus. The program may be completed in four years. Most students take four to six years. Applicants are expected to have a Master's degree (MDiv, MTS, MA or equivalent) with work in their proposed field of study as well as broad knowledge in areas such as biblical studies, theology, history of religions, philosophy, social and psychological studies. Students must demonstrate research competence in two modern languages, German and typically either French or Spanish, through written examination, the first taken at the beginning of the first year, the second prior to preliminary examinations. All applicants, including international students, must submit scores from the GRE, taken within the last five years. Financial aid includes full tuition grants plus a substantial living stipend ($11,400 in 1999-2000), renewable for four years. Competive university awards at a higher level are also available.

DEPARTMENT OF RELIGION FACULTY:

Berger, Michael S., PhD, Columbia University (1992), 1994, Assistant Professor—philosophy of religion, rabbinic Judaism

Bianchi, Eugene C., PhD, Columbia University, Union Theological Seminary (1966), Professor—spirituality of aging, religious humanism and naturalism, narrative theology

Blumenthal, David R., PhD, Columbia University (1972), 1976, Jay and Leslie Cohen Professor—Judaic studies, constructive Jewish theology, medieval Jewish philosophy and mysticism

Buss, Martin J., PhD, Yale University (1958), 1959, Professor—Hebrew Bible, interpretation, comparative law

Courtright, Paul B., PhD, Princeton University (1975), 1989, Professor—history of religions, South Asian religions

DeConcini, Barbara, PhD, Emory University (1980), 1991, Professor—arts, literature and religion

Farley, Wendy Lee, PhD, Vanderbilt University (1988), 1988, Associate Professor—Christian theology and ethics

Flueckiger, Joyce B., PhD, University of Wisconsin (1984), 1992, Associate Professor—performance and folklore, women and religion in South Asia

Jordan, Mark D., PhD, University of Texas-Austin (1977), 1999, Professor—history of Christian thought, religion, and sexuality

Laderman, Gary, PhD, University of California, Santa Barbara (1994), 1994, Assistant Professor—American religious history and culture

Lipstadt, Deborah E., PhD, Brandeis University (1976), 1992, Professor—modern Judaism, Holocaust studies

Martin, Richard C., PhD, New York University, (1975), 1996, Professor—Islam, Near Eastern religious traditions, history of religions

Patterson, Barbara, PhD, Emory University (1994), 1995, Assistant Professor—theology and feminist theory

Patton, Laurie L., PhD, University of Chicago (1991), 1996, Associate Professor—Hinduism, Asian religions, comparative religion, religion and literature

Reinders, Eric, PhD, University of California, Santa Barbara (1997), 1998, Assistant Professor—Buddhism, East Asian religious traditions

Robbins, Vernon K., PhD, University of Chicago Divinity School (1969), 1984, Professor—New Testament, Hellenistic rhetoric, biography and religion, comparative methods, social analysis and literature

Smith, Theophus H., PhD, Graduate Theological Union (1987), 1987, Associate Professor—Black spirituality, Christian theology

DIVISION OF RELIGION FACULTY:

An-Na'im, Abdullahi, PhD, University of Edinburgh, 1976, Professor—Islamic Law and human rights

Berger, Michael, PhD, Columbia University, 1992, Assistant Professor—Jewish ethics

Bianchi, Eugene C., PhD, Columbia University, 1966, Professor—religion and life story

Blumenthal, David R., PhD, Columbia University, 1966, Cohen Professor—Judaic studies, constructive Jewish thought; problem of evil, ethics, and obedience

Bondi, Roberta C., DPhil, Oxford University, 1973, Professor—Eastern patristics

Bounds, Elizabeth, PhD, Union Theological Seminary (1994), Associate Professor—Christian social ethics, feminist ethics, applied ethics, social theory and public policy

Buss, Martin J., PhD, Yale University, 1958, Professor—Hebrew Bible

Chopp, Rebecca, PhD, University of Chicago, 1983 (on leave as University Provost), Professor—systematic and feminist theology, American pragmatism

Courtright, Paul B., PhD, Princeton, 1974, Professor—Hinduism, religion, and colonial culture

Eiesland, Nancy L., PhD, Emory University, 1995, Assistant Professor—sociology of religion

Erskine, Noel L., PhD, Union Theological Seminary, 1978, Associate Professor—Black theology, theologies of liberation

Farley, Wendy Lee, PhD, Vanderbilt University, 1988, Associate Professor—philosophical and systematic theology, comparative theology

Flueckiger, Joyce Burkhalter, PhD, University of Wisconsin, 1984, Associate Professor—popular religion in South Asia, religion and performance

Flynn, William T., PhD, Duke University, 1992, Assistant Professor—medieval liturgy

Foster, Charles R., EdD, Columbia University, 1971, Professor—religious education

Fowler, James W., PhD, Harvard University, 1971, Professor—faith development.

Gunnemann, Jon P., PhD, Yale University, 1975, Professor—Christian social ethics and social theory

Hayes, John H., PhD, Princeton Theological Seminary, 1964, Professor—Israelite history

Holifield, E. Brooks, PhD, Yale University, 1970, Candler Professor of American Church History

Holladay, Carl R., PhD, University of Cambridge, 1975, Professor—Hellenistic Judaism

Hunter, Rodney J., PhD, Princeton Theological Seminary, 1974, Professor—pastoral theology

Jackson, Timothy P., PhD, Yale University, 1984, Assistant Professor—Christian ethics

Johnson, Luke T., PhD, Yale University, 1976, Robert W. Woodruff Professor of New Testament and Christian Origins

Jordan, Mark D., PhD, University of Texas-Austin (1977), 1999, Professor—history of Christian thought, religion, and sexuality

Laderman, Gary M., PhD, University of California at Santa Barbara, 1994, Assistant Professor—American religious history and culture

Lipstadt, Deborah, PhD, Brandeis University, 1976, Associate Professor—modern Jewish studies, the Holocaust, women in Judaism

Lowe, Walter J., PhD, Yale University, 1972, Professor—God and being, trinity, problem of evil, postmodern critiques of religion

Mallard, William, PhD, Duke University, 1956, Professor—Augustine, Western patristics

Martin, Richard, PhD, New York University, 1975, Professor—Arabic and Islamic studies, history of religions, Islamic theology, religion and social conflict

Newby, Gordon, PhD, Brandeis University, 1966, Professor—Early Islam, Muslim-non-Muslim relations

Newsom, Carol A., PhD, Harvard University, 1982, Professor—Ancient Israelite religion, Dead Sea Scrolls

O'Day, Gail R., PhD, Emory University, 1983, Almar H. Shatford Associate Professor of Biblical Preaching

Pacini, David S., PhD, Harvard University, 1979, Associate Professor—modern European religious thought

Patton, Laurie L., PhD, University of Chicago, 1991, Associate Professor—religion in ancient India, Vedic studies, history of religions

Reynolds, P. Lyndon, PhD, University of Toronto, 1986 Assistant Professor—medieval theology, scholasticism

Robbins, Vernon K., PhD, University of Chicago, 1969, Professor—religions of Hellenistic Mediterranean, comparative study of sacred texts

Saliers, Don E., PhD, Yale University, 1967, Professor—liturgical theology, religious affections

Smith, Theophus H., PhD, Graduate Theological Union, 1987, Associate Professor—philosophy of religion, African-American religious studies, religion and violence

Snarey, John, EdD, Harvard University, 1982, Professor—psychology of social-moral development

Strom, Jonathan, PhD, University of Chicago Divinity School (1996), Assistant Professor—church history

Tipton, Steven M., PhD, Harvard University, 1979, Professor—sociology of religion

Walls, Neal H., PhD, Johns Hopkins University, 1991, Assistant Professor—Israelite and Canaanite religion, ancient near eastern myth, semitic philology

Wilson, Walter T., PhD, University of Chicago (1990), Assistant Professor—New Testament and early Christian literature

Emory and Henry College

Dept of Religion
Emory VA 24327-0947

Phone: 540-944-6784
Fax: 540-944-6934
E-mail: jtreiff@ehc.edu
URL: ehc.edu

TYPE OF INSTITUTION: Private, United Methodist
EXECUTIVE OFFICER: Thomas R. Morris, President
CHAIRPERSON: Joseph T. Reiff
UNDERGRADUATE ENROLLMENT: 850

Emporia State University

1200 Commerical St, Emporia KS 66801

Episcopal Divinity School

99 Brattle St
Cambridge MA 02138-3494

Phone: 617-868-3450
Fax: 617-864-5385
E-mail: aframe@episdivschool.org
URL: www.episdivschool.org

TYPE OF INSTITUTION: Private, Episcopal
EXECUTIVE OFFICER: William Rankin, President and Dean
GRADUATE ENROLLMENT: 24

Episcopal School of Theology

1325 N College Ave, Claremont CA 91711

Episcopal Theological Seminary of the Southwest

PO Box 2247
Austin TX 78768

Phone: 512-472-4133
Fax: 512-472-3098
E-mail: dmcdonald@etss.edu
URL: www.etss.edu

TYPE OF INSTITUTION: Private, Episcopal
EXECUTIVE OFFICER: Durstan McDonald, Dean
GRADUATE ENROLLMENT: 118

Erindale College

University of Toronto, Mississauga, Ontario L5L 1C6 Canada

Erskine College

2 Washington St
Due West SC 29639

Phone: 864-379-2131
Fax: 864-379-2167
URL: www.erskine.edu

TYPE OF INSTITUTION: Private, Associate Reformed Presbyterian Church
EXECUTIVE OFFICER: John L. Carson, President
CHAIRPERSON: William B. Evans

Erskine Theological Seminary

PO Box 207, Due West SC 29639

Eugene Bible College

2155 Bailey Hill Rd, Eugene OR 97405

Eureka College

300 E College Ave
Eureka IL 61530

Phone: 309-467-6331
Fax: 309-467-6386
E-mail: jmccoy@eureka.edu
URL: www.eureka.edu

TYPE OF INSTITUTION: Private, Christian Church (Disciples of Christ)
EXECUTIVE OFFICER: George A. Hearne, President
CHAIRPERSON: Jerry D. McCoy
UNDERGRADUATE ENROLLMENT: 500

Evangel University

1111 N Glenstone Avenue
Springfield MO 65802

Phone: 417-865-2815
Fax: 417-865-9599
E-mail: palmerm@evangel.edu
URL: www.evangel.edu

TYPE OF INSTITUTION: Private, Assembly of God
EXECUTIVE OFFICER: Robert Spence, President
CHAIRPERSON: Michael D. Palmer
UNDERGRADUATE ENROLLMENT: 1,650

Evangelical Bible Seminary

400 Jackson Ave, Lake Worth FL 33463

Evangelical School of Theology

Myerstown PA 17067

Evangelical Theological Seminary

PO Box 559, Dixon MO 65419

University of Evansville

1800 Lincoln Ave
Evansville IN 47714

Phone: 812-479-2259
Fax: 812-479-2320
E-mail: rp7@evansville.edu
URL: cedar.evansville.edu/philweb/

TYPE OF INSTITUTION: Private, United Methodist-related

EXECUTIVE OFFICERS: James S. Vinson, President; Lawrence Colter, Dean, College of Arts and Sciences

CHAIRPERSON: R. Wayne Perkins, Dept of Philosophy and Religion

UNDERGRADUATE ENROLLMENT: 3,300

E

Fairfield University

Dept of Religious Studies	Phone: 203-254-4000 ext 2492
North Benson Road	Fax: 203-254-4074
Fairfield CT 06430-7524	URL: www.fairfield.edu

TYPE OF INSTITUTION: Private, Roman Catholic/Jesuit

EXECUTIVE OFFICER: Aloysius P. Kelley, SJ, President

CHAIRPERSON: Paul Lakeland

UNDERGRADUATE ENROLLMENT: 3,300

GRADUATE ENROLLMENT: 340

DEGREES OFFERED: BA (Religious Studies)

UNDERGRADUATE MAJORS: 30

DEGREES CONFERRED: 3

DESCRIPTION OF UNDERGRADUATE PROGRAM: Religious Studies within a liberal arts setting; strong commitment to Christian theology, especially in the context of the Roman Catholic tradition. Judaic Studies, Asian religions, and religions, and religion and culture are avenues of study in the curriculum. Faculty are involved in interdisciplinary programs throughout the university.

FACULTY:

Benney, Alfred F., PhD, Hartford Seminary Foundation (1975), 1967, Professor—nontraditional American religions, systematics, 203-254-4000, ext 2398, E-mail: benney@fair1.fairfield.edu

Dallavalle, Nancy A., PhD, University of Notre Dame (1993), 1993, Assistant Professor—systematics, feminist theology, 203-254-4000, ext 2364, E-mail: ndallavalle@fair1.fairfield.edu

Davidson, Ronald M., PhD, University of California, Berkeley (1985), 1990, Associate Professor—Buddhism, Asian religions, tribal religions, 203-254-4000, ext 2489, E-mail: rdavidson@fair1.fairfield.edu

Dreyer, Elizabeth A., PhD, Marquette University (1983), 1999, Associate Professor—historical theology, feminist spirituality, 203-254-4000, ext 3127, E-mail: eadreyer@fair1.fairfield.edu

Humphrey, Hugh M., PhD, Fordham University (1977), 1968, Professor—Jewish wisdom literature, New Testament studies, 203-254-4000, ext 2493, E-mail: humphrey@fair1.fairfield.edu

Lakeland, Paul F., PhD, Vanderbilt University (1981), 1981, Professor—liberation theology, systematics, religion and literature, 203-254-4000, ext 2492, E-mail: pflakeland@fair1.fairfield.edu

Lang, Martin A., PhD, Catholic University (1964), 1979, Professor—Old Testament studies, religion and psychology, 203-254-4000, ext 2420, E-mail: malang@fair1.fairfield.edu

Schmidt, David P., PhD, University of Chicago (1987), 1993, Associate Professor—social ethics, theology and public policy, 203-254-4000, ext 2837, E-mail: dschmidt@fair1.fairfield.edu

Thiel, John E., PhD, McMaster University (1978), 1977, Professor—systematics, history of Christian religious thought, 203-254-4000, ext 2130, E-mail: jethiel@fair1.fairfield.edu

Umansky, Ellen M., PhD, Columbia University (1981), 1994, Professor—Judaism, women and religion, 203-254-4000, ext 2065, E-mail: eumansky@fair1.fairfield.edu

Fairleigh Dickinson University

Teaneck NJ 07666

Faith Baptist Bible College and Seminary

1900 Northwest 4th St
Ankeny IA 50021

Phone: 515-964-0601
Fax: 515-964-1638
E-mail: fbbcenroll@aol.com

TYPE OF INSTITUTION: Private, GARBC
EXECUTIVE OFFICER: James Collogan, Executive Vice President
UNDERGRADUATE ENROLLMENT: 349
GRADUATE ENROLLMENT: 53

Faith Bible College

1207 Hamilton Brg Rd, Milton FL 32570

Faith Evangical Lutheran Seminary

3504 N Pearl St
Tacoma WA 98407

Phone: 253-752-2020
Fax: 253-759-1790
E-mail: fsinfo@faithseminary.edu
URL: www.faithseminary.edu

TYPE OF INSTITUTION: Denominational: Lutheran (Conservative Lutheran Association)
EXECUTIVE OFFICERS: R. H. Redal, President; Michael J. Adams, Dean and Executive Vice
    President
GRADUATE ENROLLMENT: 150

Faith Theological Seminary

1001 70th Avenue, Philadelphia PA 19126-2104

Faulkner University

V P Black School of Biblical Studies
5345 Atlanta Hwy
Montgomery AL 36109-3378

Phone: 334-386-7154
Fax: 334-386-7577
URL: www.faulkner.edu

TYPE OF INSTITUTION: Private, Church of Christ
EXECUTIVE OFFICER: Billy D. Hilyer, President
CHAIRPERSON: Cecil May Jr., Dean

Felician College

South Main Street
Lodi NJ 07644

Phone: 201-559-6000, ext 2
Fax: 201-472-8936
E-mail: henchyd@inet.felician.edu
URL: www.felician.edu

TYPE OF INSTITUTION: Private, Roman Catholic
EXECUTIVE OFFICER: Sr. Theresa Mary Martin, President
CHAIRPERSON: Mara Kelly-Zukowski (Undergraduate); Dolores Henchy (Graduate)
UNDERGRADUATE ENROLLMENT: 62
GRADUATE ENROLLMENT: 13

Ferrum College

Ferrum VA 24088

The University of Findlay

1000 N Main Street
Findlay OH 45840-3695

Phone: 419-424-4563
Fax: 419-424-4822
E-mail: wallen@lucy.findlay.edu

TYPE OF INSTITUTION: Private, Churches of God, General Conference
EXECUTIVE OFFICER: Kenneth Zirkle, President
COORDINATOR: Rae Wallen
UNDERGRADUATE ENROLLMENT: 15

Fisk University

Nashville TN 37203

Flagler College

PO Box 1027, St Augustine FL 32085

University of Florida

125 Dauer Hall
PO Box 117410
Gainesville FL 32611-7410

Phone: 352-392-1625
Fax: 352-392-7395

TYPE OF INSTITUTION: Public
EXECUTIVE OFFICER: Willard W. Harrison, Dean College of Liberal Arts and Sciences
CHAIRPERSON: Shaya Isenberg
COORDINATOR: Dennis Owen (Undergraduate)
UNDERGRADUATE ENROLLMENT: 50
GRADUATE ENROLLMENT: 15

Florida A and M University

Tallahassee FL 32307

Florida Baptist Theological College

PO Box 1306 , Graceville FL 32440-3306

Florida Beacon College

7100 142nd Ave N
Largo FL 33771

Phone: 727-531-4498
Fax: 727-397-6282
E-mail: beacon@flanet.com

TYPE OF INSTITUTION: Private, Non-Denominational
EXECUTIVE OFFICER: Dwight D. Martin, President
UNDERGRADUATE ENROLLMENT: 30
GRADUATE ENROLLMENT: 4

Florida Bible College

9300 Pembroke Rd, Miramar FL 33025-1640

Florida Christian College Inc

1011 Osceola Blvd, Kissimmee FL 34744

Florida Christian Bible College

747 S Federal Hwy, Deerfield Beach FL 33441

Florida International University

Dept of Religious Studies, DM302
University Park
Miami FL 33199

Phone: 305-348-2186
Fax: 305-348-1879
E-mail: religion@fiu.edu
URL: www.fiu.edu/~religion

TYPE OF INSTITUTION: Public
EXECUTIVE OFFICER: Modesto A. Maidique, President
CHAIRPERSON: Nathan Katz, Dept of Religious Studies
COORDINATORS: Steven Heine (Undergraduate); Lesley A. Northup (Graduate)
UNDERGRADUATE ENROLLMENT: 24,229
GRADUATE ENROLLMENT: 6,354
DEGREES OFFERED: BA; BA Honors; BA Minor; MA
UNDERGRADUATE MAJORS: 23

DEGREES CONFERRED: 8

DESCRIPTION OF UNDERGRADUATE PROGRAM: The Department of Religious Studies was established in 1995 and inaugurated an MA in 1996. Instruction is offered in all of the major religions of the world and in a number of thematic areas. The department is closely linked with a number of interdisciplinary programs, including: African-New World studies, Asian studies, Environmental studies, Judaic studies, Latin American and Caribbean studies, and Women's studies. Florida International University is a member of the Florida State University System. Established in 1972, FIU is one of the fastest-growing, most diverse and dynamic universities in the nation. The Religious Studies major serves as a basis for students who wish to pursue the study of religion or theology as a career, for students preparing for a career in counseling, education, business, law or medicine, or for students who wish to undertake a dual major in a related field of study. The major is designed to allow students to focus either on comparative topics, using a critical approach to understanding religious phenomena and their relation to society in a broad cultural context, or on the theory and practice of a specific religious tradition in its historical setting. The major requires 33 credits distributed in the following sequence: Foundation courses, 6 credits; Focus courses, 24 credits, and Capstone courses, 3 credits. Foundation courses are selected to provide students with an introduction to multicultural approaches and interdisciplinary methodologies in the study of religion, providing a foundation for more specialized studies. Focus courses include 18 or more credits in Religious Studies and up to 6 credits in related area. Through these courses the student develops an area of concentration. Capstone courses are senior or capstone seminars in advanced studies in religion.

GRADUATE PROGRAM

Graduate Advisor: Lesley A. Northup

Graduate Degrees Offered: MA

Degrees Conferred: 3 MA

Graduate Students in Residence: 25 MA

Not in Residence: 2

Average No. of New Students Enrolled: 12

Women Students: 8

Minority Students: 4

Foreign Students: 3

Minimum GRE Score Requisite to Admission: Yes; 1000

Minimum GPA Score Requisite to Admission: Yes; 3.0 on a 1-4 scale

Foreign Language Proficiency Evaluated: Departmental examinations are used; TOEFL for non-native speakers of English.

Financial Aid to First Year Students: On average, 3 TAs per year

Financial Aid to Other Students: 20%.

DESCRIPTION OF GRADUATE PROGRAM AND RESEARCH FACILITIES: The MA is a 36-hour program: 6 hours of core seminars ("Seminar on Sacred Texts," offered each fall, and "Modern Analysis of Religion," offered each spring), 12 hours of "track" courses, 12 hours of electives, and 6 hours of thesis work. Graduation requirements include a 3.0 GPA and successful oral defense of the thesis before a faculty committee. Individual theses may involve language requirements. Research facilities on the main campus, which houses the graduate program, include a two million volume library collection, with 25,000 volumes in the general area of religion, and 50,000 volumes in the Mishkin Collection in Judaic Studies, as well as 60 journals in religion, and another 20 which include religious studies research.

ACADEMIC PLAN, ADMISSION REQUIREMENTS, FINANCIAL AID: FIU's MA in Religious Studies is designed to give students maximum flexibility in pursuing their research interests, while providing a firm foundation in both the general academic study of religion and the student's track or area of specialization. Possible tracks include: Judaism, Christianity, Asian religions, Ethics, Biblical studies, Women and religion, Religion and culture, and Philosophy of religion. Each "track" is comprised of four related courses and independent study projects. Admission requirements include a 3.0 undergraduate GPA and/or a minimum score of 1000 on the GRE, and two academic letters of recommendation. A writing sample is required. Non-native speakers of English must submit a minimum TOEFL score of 550. Applicants without a degree in religious studies may be required to complete undergraduate courses as prerequisites for graduate study. FIU offers two graduate assistantships of $8,000 plus tuition each to graduate students in religious studies. Students with financial need are eligible for other forms of financial aid as well

FACULTY:

Gudorf, Christine E., PhD, Columbia University/Union Theological Seminary (1979), 1993, Professor—Christian ethics, liberation theology, feminism, 305-348-2729, E-mail: gudorf@fiu.edu

Heine, Steven, PhD, Temple University (1980), 1997, Professor and Undergraduate Program Director—religions of Japan, Zen Buddhism, religion and the social sciences, 305-348-2354, E-mail: heines@fiu.edu

Huchingson, James E., PhD, Emory University (1977), 1973, Associate Professor—contemporary religious thought, religion and science, environmental ethics, 305-348-3348, E-mail: huchings@fiu.edu

Katz, Nathan, PhD, Temple University (1978), 1994, Professor and Chair—South Asian religions, Indian Judaism, history of religions, 305-348-3909, E-mail: katzn@fiu.edu

Larson, Erik, PhD, New York University (1995), 1995, Assistant Professor—New Testament, Christian origins, Ancient Judaism, Dead Sea Scrolls, 305-348-3518, E-mail: larsone@fiu.edu

Northup, Lesley, PhD, Catholic University (1991), 1993, Associate Professor and Graduate Program Director—ritual studies, women and religion, religion in America, 305-348-2956, E-mail: northupl@fiu.edu

Olupona, Jacob, PhD, Boston University (1983), 1999, Visiting Eminent Scholar—African religions, 305-348-6728, E-mail: oluponaj@fiu.edu

Rey, Terry, PhD, Temple University (1996), 1997, Assistant Professor—Caribbean religions, African religions, 305-348-1860, E-mail: reyt@fiu.edu

Stier, Oren B., PhD, University of California, Santa Barbara (1996), 1998, Assistant Professor—Judaic studies, religion and culture, 305-348-6729

Florida Memorial College
Miami FL 33054

Florida Southern College

111 Lake Hollingsworth Dr   Phone: 941-680-4180
Lakeland FL 33801-5698   Fax: 941-680-4357

TYPE OF INSTITUTION: Private
EXECUTIVE OFFICER: Thomas L. Reuschling, President
CHAIRPERSON: Frank Johnson
UNDERGRADUATE ENROLLMENT: 1,600

Florida State University

Dept of Religion
MO5 Dodd Hall
Tallahassee FL 32306-1520

Phone: 850-644-1020
Fax: 850-644-7225
E-mail: pjl2094@garnet.acns.fsu.edu
URL: www.fsu.edu/~religion

TYPE OF INSTITUTION: Public, Non-Denominational

EXECUTIVE OFFICER: Talbot D'Alemberte, President

CHAIRPERSON: John Kelsay

COORDINATORS: David Levenson (Undergraduate); Shannon Burkes (Graduate)

UNDERGRADUATE ENROLLMENT: 23,875

GRADUATE ENROLLMENT: 5,685

DEGREES OFFERED: Major or Minor in Religion

UNDERGRADUATE MAJORS: 57

DEGREES CONFERRED: 22

DESCRIPTION OF UNDERGRADUATE PROGRAM: Since its founding in 1965, the religion department of The Florida State University has been a leader among America's public universities in the study of religious life of humanity. From 1972 until 1978 the department served as the national headquarters of the American Academy of Religion, the principal professional organization for America's teachers of religious studies. It continues to be one of America's largest and most highly respected departments for the academic study of religion. The religion department offers instruction in the religious traditions of the world and the religious dimension of human life. Religious life, whatever else it may be, is a part of human life. Therefore, the religion department is located in the humanities area of the College of Arts and Sciences and uses methods appropriate to other humanities disciplines.

GRADUATE PROGRAM

Member of the Council on Graduate Studies in Religion

Graduate Advisor: Shannon Burkes

Graduate Degrees Offered: MA; PhD

Degrees Conferred: 9 MA; 0 PhD

Graduate Students in Residence: 22 MA; 9 PhD

Not in Residence: 3 PhD

Average No. of New Students Enrolled: 11 MA; 2 PhD

Women Students: 11 MA; 3 PhD

Minority Students: 3 MA; 1 PhD

Foreign Students: 0 MA; 1 PhD

Minimum GRE Score Requisite to Admission: Yes; 1000

Minimum GPA Score Requisite to Admission: Yes; 3.0 on 4.0 scale

Foreign Language Proficiency Evaluated: No

Financial Aid to First Year Students: 90% MA; 100% PhD

Financial Aid to Other Students: 90% MA; 60% PhD

Graduates Placed: 100% MA

DESCRIPTION OF GRADUATE PROGRAM AND RESEARCH FACILITIES: The Department of Religion at The Florida State University offers the MA and PhD in the study of religion. In addition, department faculty participate in the doctoral program in humanities. The MA and PhD in the study of religion combine broad exposure to the field with the development of a particular area of expertise. MA students concentrate in one of four areas: religions of western antiquity; religions of Asia; religion in Europe and the Americas; or religion, ethics, and philosophy. PhD programs focus in two areas: Religions of Western Antiquity and Religion, Ethics, and Philosophy. The doctoral program in humanities (with a religion concentration) is intended for students wishing to combine the study of religion with an interdisciplinary approach to the humanities.

ACADEMIC PLAN, ADMISSION REQUIREMENTS, FINANCIAL AID: The minimum criterion for admission to the MA program is a "B" average on all undergraduate work or a score of 1000 on the quantitative and verbal sections of the Graduate Record Examinations. Students entering the program are normally expected to have as background the equivalent of at least an undergraduate minor in the study of religion. For the PhD, applicants should have an MA in religion or its equivalent, and outstanding CPA and GRE scores. The Department of Religion offers a number of assistantships with annual stipends and waivers of a portion of tuition. Outstanding applicants may be nominated for University Fellowships. The application deadline is March 15, but later applications may be considered in certain cases.

FACULTY:

Aubin, Melissa, PhD, Duke University (1998), 1998, Assistant Professor—early Judaism and early Christianity, 850-644-0688, E-mail: maubin@mailer.fsu.edu

Bartholomeusz, Tessa J., PhD, University of Virginia (1991), 1993, Associate Professor—history of religion, Buddhist studies, 850-644-0214, E-mail: tbarthol@mailer.fsu.edu

Burkes, Shannon, PhD, University of Chicago (1997), 1997, Assistant Professor—Hebrew Bible, 850-644-0205, E-mail: slburkes@mailer.fsu.edu

Erndl, Kathleen M., PhD, University of Wisconsin (1987), 1993, Associate Professor—South Asian language and literature, religions of South Asia, 850-644-0207, E-mail: kerndl@mailer.fsu.edu

Kalbian, Aline, PhD, University of Virginia (1996), 1998, Assistant Professor—ethics, contemporary Roman Catholic thought, 850-644-9878, E-mail: akalbian@mail.fsu.edu

Kangas, David, PhD, Yale University (1999), 1999, Assistant Professor—philosophy of religion, modern religious thought, ethics, 850-644-0210

Kelsay, John, PhD, University of Virginia (1985), 1987, Chair and Professor—ethics, Islam, 850-644-0209, E-mail: jkelsay@garnet.acns.fsu.edu

Levenson, David B., PhD, Harvard University (1980), 1976, Associate Professor—New Testament and Christian origins, 850-644-0212, E-mail: dlevenso@garnet.acns.fsu.edu

Neelis, Jason, ABD, University of Washington, 1999, Visiting Instructor—religions of South Asia, Sanskrit, 850-644-9879

Sandon, Leo, Jr., PhD, Boston University (1971), 1969, Professor—religious thought in America, 850-644-0201, E-mail: lsandon@garnet.acns.fsu.edu

Watson, H. Justin, PhD, Florida State University (1996), 1997, Visiting Lecturer—religious thought in America, 850-644-9232, E-mail: jwtson@mailer.fsu.edu

Florida Technological University

Orlando FL 32816

Fontbonne College

6800 Wydoun Blvd, St Louis MO 63105

Fordham University

Dept of Theology, 101 Collins Hall
441 E Fordham Rd
Bronx NY 10458
Phone: 718-817-3240

TYPE OF INSTITUTION: Private
EXECUTIVE OFFICER: Robert F. Himmelberg, Dean Graduate School of Arts and Sciences
CHAIRPERSON: Mary C. Callaway
UNDERGRADUATE ENROLLMENT: 9,500
GRADUATE ENROLLMENT: 5,000

Fordham University

College at Lincoln Center, New York NY 10023

Franciscan School of Theology

1712 Euclid Avenue, Berkeley CA 94709

Franciscan University of Steubenville

Theology Department
1235 University Blvd
Steubenville OH 43952-1763
Phone: 740-283-6530
Fax: 740-283-6401
E-mail: theology@franuniv.edu
URL: not yet available

TYPE OF INSTITUTION: Private, Catholic
EXECUTIVE OFFICER: Michael Scanlan, TOR, President
CHAIRPERSON: Stephen F. Miletic
UNDERGRADUATE ENROLLMENT: 350
GRADUATE ENROLLMENT: 112

Francis Marion University

PO Box 100547
Florence SC 29501-0547
Phone: 843-661-1654
E-mail: rhall@fmarion.edu

TYPE OF INSTITUTION: Public
EXECUTIVE OFFICER: Lee A. Vickers, President
COORDINATOR: Ronald L. Hall
UNDERGRADUATE ENROLLMENT: 4,000
GRADUATE ENROLLMENT: 1,000

Franklin College of Indiana

501 E Monroe St, Franklin IN 46131

Franklin and Marshall College

PO Box 3003
Lancaster PA 17604

Phone: 717-291-3917

CHAIRPERSON: Joel Martin

Fredericksburg Bible Institute

PO Box 507, Fredericksburg VA 22404

Freed-Hardeman College

Henderson TN 38340

Fresno Pacific University

1717 S Chestnut Ave
Fresno CA 93702

Phone: 209-453-2000, ext 2063
E-mail: wfriesen@fresno.edu

TYPE OF INSTITUTION: Private, Mennonite Brethren
EXECUTIVE OFFICER: Allen Carden, President
CHAIRPERSON: Will Friesen
COORDINATOR: Devon Wiens & Edmund Janzen
UNDERGRADUATE ENROLLMENT: 800
GRADUATE ENROLLMENT: 850

Free Will Baptist Bible College

3606 West End Ave
Nashville TN 37205

Phone: 615-383-1340
Fax: 615-269-6028
E-mail: bert@fwbbc.edu
URL: www.fwbbc.edu

TYPE OF INSTITUTION: Private, Free Will Baptist
EXECUTIVE OFFICER: C. Thomas Malone, President
CHAIRPERSON: Ralph Hampton, Dept of Biblical & Ministry Studies
UNDERGRADUATE ENROLLMENT: 370

Friends University

Dept of Religion and Philosophy
2100 W University St
Wichita KS 67213

Phone: 316-295-5876
Fax: 316-262-5027
E-mail: brightl@friends.edu
URL: www.friends.edu

TYPE OF INSTITUTION: Private
EXECUTIVE OFFICER: Biff Green, President
CHAIRPERSON: Kim Spangler

COORDINATOR: Leroy Brightup
UNDERGRADUATE ENROLLMENT: 2,500
GRADUATE ENROLLMENT: 500
DEGREES OFFERED: BA in Religion and Philosophy
UNDERGRADUATE MAJORS: 25
DEGREES CONFERRED: 8
DESCRIPTION OF UNDERGRADUATE PROGRAM: Friends University is a private Christian liberal arts university founded by Quakers in 1898. A wide variety of courses and faculty expertise provide a solid foundation for many types of professional and volunteer Christian service, as well as for additional education at the graduate level. Majors in the BA degree program may pursue general preparation, or may emphasize youth ministry. A less extensive Christian Studies major is also available, as well as a religion and philosophy minor and a 2-year Associate degree. Both faculty and students represent a variety of denominations.
GRADUATE PROGRAM
Member of the Council on Graduate Studies in Religion
Graduate Advisor: Leroy Brightup
Graduate Degrees Offered: MA
Degrees Conferred: 6 MA
Graduate Students in Residence: 30 MA
Not in Residence: 0 MA
Women Students: 12 MA
Minority Students: 4 MA
Foreign Students: 0 MA
Minimum GRE Score Requisite to Admission: No.
Minimum GPA Score Requisite to Admission: Yes, 2.75 on a scale of 4.00.
Foreign Language Proficiency Evaluated: No.
Financial Aid to First Year Students: 80% MA
Financial Aid to Other Students: 80% MA
Attrition Among Students: 15% MA
DESCRIPTION OF GRADUATE PROGRAM AND RESEARCH FACILITIES: The Master of Arts in Christian Ministry is a non-traditional 36-hour program designed for both clergy and layworkers. Courses are 8 weeks long with students enrolled for only one course at a time. Designed to facilitate the working adult, classes meet for 4 hours one night per week, plus two Saturday mornings per course. Besides a 21-hour core curriculum which provides a common foundation, students also select one area for specialized individual preparation (e.g., biblical studies, family ministry). Fifteen hours of the program focus on the chosen area through individualized studies and practical application. The 36-hour program can be completed in two calendar years while maintaining full-time employment. The program is supported by a library of over 10,000 volumes in Religion, plus numerous periodicals, journals, and indices, and complete on-line services.
ACADEMIC PLAN, ADMISSION REQUIREMENTS, FINANCIAL AID: Semester system. Core courses are offered during fall and spring semesters, with enrollments in individual emphases during the summer. Students may be admitted at the beginning of any 8-week course. Admission requires an undergraduate degree with a 2.75 or higher GPA, coursework or proficiency in both Old and New Testament, two satisfactory letters of recommendation, and a satisfactory interview with the Admissions Committee. The Federal Financial Aid program is available to most students.

FACULTY:

Brightup, Leroy, ThD, Iliff School of Theology (1970), 1964, Professor—Old Testament, practical theology, 316-295-5876, Fax 316-262-5027, E-mail: brightl@friends.edu

Hedrick, Terry, MA, Friends University (1995), 1994, Lecturer, part-time—biblical studies, ethics, 316-295-5831, Fax 316-262-5027, E-mail: hedrickt@friends.edu

Hinshaw, Verlin O., PhD, Vanderbilt (1964), 1958, Professor—New Testament, Greek, 316-295-5517, Fax 316-262-5027, E-mail: hinshaw@friends.edu

Kettler, Christian, PhD, Fuller Theological Seminary (1987), 1987, Professor—theology, philosophy, 316-295-5562, Fax 316-262-5027, E-mail: kettler@friends.edu

McCrary, Larry, PhD, Southwestern Baptist Theological Seminary (1985), 1998, Lecturer, part-time—New Testament, Greek, ethics, 316-295-5871, Fax 316-262-5027, E-mail: larrym@friends.edu

Muller, Kathleen, MA, Friends University (1992), 1999, Lecturer, part-time—spiritual formation, 316-295-5871, Fax 316-262-5027

Smith, James Bryan, DMin, Fuller Theological Seminary (1998), 1990, Assistant Professor—spiritual formation, practical theology, 316-295-5840, Fax 316-262-5027, E-mail: smithj@friends.edu

---

Fuller Theological Seminary

4636 E University, Ste 175   **Phone: 602-517-1414**
Phoenix AZ 85034   **Fax: 602-517-1492**
     E-mail: fsw@fuller.edu

TYPE OF INSTITUTION: Private, Multi-Denominational
EXECUTIVE OFFICER: Tom Parker, Area Director
GRADUATE ENROLLMENT: 120

Fuller Theological Seminary

135 North Oakland Ave, Pasadena CA 91182

Fuller Theological Seminary

101 Nickerson, Ste 330   **Phone: 206-284-9000**
Seattle WA 98109   **Fax: 206-284-4735**
     E-mail: seattle@vax.fuller.edu

TYPE OF INSTITUTION: Private
EXECUTIVE OFFICER: Richard J. Erickson, Director
GRADUATE ENROLLMENT: 300 (headcount); 75 FTE

Furman University

3300 Poinsett Highway   **Phone: 864-294-2162**
Greenville SC 29613-0474   **Fax: 864-294-2041**
     E-mail: john.shelley@furman.edu
     URL: www.furman.edu

TYPE OF INSTITUTION: Private
EXECUTIVE OFFICER: David E. Shi, President
CHAIRPERSON: John C. Shelley
UNDERGRADUATE ENROLLMENT: 2,500
FACULTY:

Blackwell, Albert L., PhD, Harvard University (1971), 1971, Professor—Christian theology, Christian thought, 864-294-3293, E-mail: albert.blackwell@furman.edu

Britt, Sam I., PhD, University of Virginia (1992), 1992, Assistant Professor—history of religion, African religions, 864-294-3518, E-mail: sam.britt@furman.edu

Greene, Victor A., Jr., DMin, Southern Baptist Theological Seminary (1983), Assistant Professor—psychology of religion, 864-294-2138, E-mail: victor.greene@furman.edu

Matthews, Shelly A., ThD, Harvard Divinity School (1997), 1998, Assistant Professor—New Testament, Christian origins, 864-294-3741, E-mail: shelly.matthews@furman.edu

McKnight, Edgar V., PhD, Southern Baptist Theological Seminary (1960), 1962, William R. Kenan, Jr. Professor—New Testament, hermeneutics, 864-294-3297, E-mail: edgar.mcknight@furman.edu

Pitts, James M., DMin, Southern Baptist Theological Seminary, 1982, Associate Professor—pastoral theology (part-time), 864-294-2138, E-mail: jim.pitts@furman.edu

Rogers, Jeffrey S., PhD, Princeton Theological Seminary (1992), 1988, Dana Associate Professor—Old Testament, Ancient Near East 864-294-3089, E-mail: jeff.rogers@furman.edu

Rutledge, David W., PhD, Rice University (1979), 1980, Professor—religion and literature, religion and science, 864-294-3296, E-mail: david.rutledge@furman.edu

Shelley, John C., PhD, Vanderbilt University (1977), 1980, Professor—Christian theology, Christian ethics, 864-294-3292, E-mail: john.shelley@furman.edu

Stulting, Claude N., PhD, University of Virginia (1993), 1996, Assistant Professor—religion and literature, history of religion, 864-294-2189, E-mail: claude.stulting@furman.edu

Teipen, Alfons H., PhD, Temple University (1997), 1997, Assistant Professor—Islam, history of religion, 864-294-2162, E-mail: alfons.teipen@furman.edu

Turner, Helen Lee, PhD, University of Virginia (1990), 1983, Associate Professor—Christian traditions, American religion, 864-294-3295, E-mail: helen.turner@furman.edu

Gallaudet University

Philosophy and Religion Department
8th and Florida Ave
Washington DC 20002

Phone: 202-651-5160

TYPE OF INSTITUTION: Private
EXECUTIVE OFFICER: I. K. Jordan, President
CHAIRPERSON: Gary F. Seifert
COORDINATOR: Jane D. Hurst

Gannon College

Erie PA 16501

Gardner-Webb College

PO Box 997, Boiling Spring NC 28017

Garrett-Evangelical Theological Seminary

2121 Sheridan Rd
Evanston IL 60201

Phone: 847-866-3900
Fax: 847-866-3957
E-mail: seminary@nwu.edu

TYPE OF INSTITUTION: Private, Non-Denominational
EXECUTIVE OFFICERS: Neal F. Fisher, President; Jack L. Seymour, Academic Dean
COORDINATOR: James N. Poling
GRADUATE ENROLLMENT: 41
GRADUATE PROGRAM
Graduate Advisor: James N. Poling
Graduate Degrees Offered: PhD
Degrees Conferred: 1 PhD
Graduate Students in Residence: 13 PhD
Not in Residence: 28 PhD
Average No. of New Students Enrolled: 6 PhD
Women Students: 18 PhD
Minority Students: 15 PhD
Foreign Students: 5 PhD
Minimum GRE Score Requisite to Admission: No
Minimum GPA Score Requisite to Admission: No
Foreign Language Proficiency Evaluated: Yes
Financial Aid to First Year Students: 100% PhD
DESCRIPTION OF GRADUATE PROGRAM AND RESEARCH FACILITIES: The
Garrett-Evangelical PhD Program prepares persons for teaching and research in theological
seminaries and departments of religion in colleges and universities, and for leadership in the
church. The program draws widely upon faculty resources of Northwestern University, other

approved universities, and the Association of Chicago Theological Schools (ACTS). Students may concentrate in one of five program areas: 1) Bible and Culture; 2) Contemporary Theology and Culture; 3) Liturgical Studies; 4) Religious Education and Congregational Studies; and 5) Pastoral Theology, Personality and Culture. Faculty research includes specialization in such topics as cross-cultural hermeneutics; textual criticism; the relationship between the Hebrew Scriptures and the New Testament; the letters of Paul; apocalyptic literature; Methodist studies; religion and American cultural studies, especially women and minorities; religion and personality; religion and anthropology; religious ethics and social issues; religious education; liberation theologies, especially feminist, Womanist, African American, and Third World; theological interpretations of the church and God. Students enter with a master's degree in religious or theological studies and pursue a program of study guided by a member of the faculty. Eighteen courses, exclusive of prerequisites and research tools, constitute the minimum course requirement. Students participate in four core couses: Biblical and Theological Hermeneutics, Religion and Culture, and teaching and research seminars. Students are required to successfully complete three general evaluations—First-Year Evaluation, Qualifying Examinations, and Dissertation Defense—as well as fulfill at least four quarters of residence.

ACADEMIC PLAN, ADMISSION REQUIREMENTS, FINANCIAL AID: Minimum of 2 years of course work, two research tools, seminar in teaching, dissertation. Admission on the basis of research-oriented master's degree in religious or theological studies, recent GRE scores, letters of reference, sample research paper; pre-application interview with director (847-866-3982) to identify available resources and suitability strongly recommended. Application forms: Admissions Office. Part-time study (if approved). Entry only in the fall. Deadline for applications: January 20. Up to 8 fellowships awarded annually on the basis of merit.

FACULTY:

Bird, Phyllis A., ThD, Harvard (1972), Professor—Hebrew scriptures

Caldwell, Alva R., DMin, Mundelein Seminary (St Mary of the Lake) (1993), Associate Professor—ministries

Chatfield, Donald A., PhD, Edinburgh (1964), Professor—preaching

Crain, Margaret Ann, EdD, Vanderbilt (1992), Assistant Professor—Christian education

Duck, Ruth C., ThD, Boston University (1989), Associate Professor—worship

Duncan, Julie A., PhD, Harvard (1989), Assistant Professor—Hebrew scriptures

Fisher, Neal F., PhD, Boston University (1966), Professor—theology and society

Hansen, Adolf M., PhD, Garrett-Northwestern (1968), Associate Professor—New Testament interpretation

Hogue, David A., PhD, Garrett-Northwestern (1985), Associate Professor—pastoral theology and counseling

Kalantzis, George, PhD, Garrett-Northwestern (1998), Assistant Professor—history of Christianity

Long, D. Stephen, PhD, Duke (1991), Assistant Professor—systematic theology

Meadows, Philip R., PhD, Cambridge (1997), Assistant Professor—historical theology and Wesley studies

Murphy, Larry G., PhD, Graduate Theological Union (1973), Professor—history of Christianity

Phillips, L. Edward, PhD, Notre Dame (1992), Associate Professor—historical theology

Poling, James N., PhD, Claremont (1980), Professor—pastoral care, counseling, and theology

Rector, Lallene J., PhD, Boston University (1986), Associate Professor—psychology of religion and psychotherapy

Ruether, Rosemary R., PhD, Claremont (1965), Professor—applied theology

Scott, Martha L., PhD, Garrett-Northwestern (1984), Assistant Professor—church administration

Seymour, Jack L., PhD, George Peabody (Vanderbilt) (1982), Professor—religious education

Thomas, Linda E., PhD, American (1993), Associate Professor—theology and anthropology

Troxell, Barbara B., MDiv, Union (1959), Associate Professor—practical theology

Vaux, Kenneth, DTh, Hamburg (1968), Professor—theological ethics

Vena, Osvaldo D., ThD, Instituto Superior Evangelico de Estudios Teologicos (1989), Assistant Professor—early Christian literature

Vogel, Dwight W., PhD, Garrett/Northwestern (1968), Professor—theology and ministry

Vogel, Linda J., PhD, University of Iowa (1981), Professor—Christian education

Yeo, Khiok-Khng, PhD, Garrett/Northwestern University (1992), Associate Professor—New Testament interpretation

Young, Henry J., PhD, Hartford Seminary (1974), Professor—systematic theology

---

General Theological Seminary

175 Ninth Ave **Phone: 212-243-5150**
New York NY 10011 **Fax: 212-727-3907**
E-mail: academicaffairs@gts.edu
URL: www.gts.edu

TYPE OF INSTITUTION: Private, Episcopal

EXECUTIVE OFFICER: Ward Ewing, Dean and President

COORDINATOR: Robert Bruce Mullin

GRADUATE ENROLLMENT: 22

GRADUATE PROGRAM

Member of the Council on Graduate Studies in Religion

Graduate Advisor: Robert Bruce Mullin

Graduate Degrees Offered: ThD; STM

Degrees Conferred: 1 ThD; 7 Other: STM

Graduate Students in Residence: 13 ThD; 4 Other

Not in Residence: 5 ThD; 5 Other

Average No. of New Students Enrolled: 3 ThD; 8 Other

Women Students: 6 ThD; 2 Other

Minority Students: 2 ThD; 2 Other

Foreign Students: 2 ThD

Minimum GRE Score Requisite to Admission: No

Minimum GPA Score Requisite to Admission: No

Foreign Language Proficiency Evaluated: No

Financial Aid to First Year Students: 100% ThD; 100% Other

Financial Aid to Other Students: 100% ThD; 100% Other

Graduates Placed: 100% ThD; 100% Other

FACULTY:

Breidenthal, Thomas E., DPhil, Oxon (1991), 1992, Professor—Christian ethics and moral theology, 212-243-5150, Fax: 212-242-4451, E-mail: breidenthal@gts.edu

Corney, Richard W., ThD, Union Theological Seminary (1970), 1960, Professor—Old Testament, 212-243-5150, Fax: 212-242-4451, E-mail: corney@gts.edu

DeChamplain, Mitties M., PhD, University of Southern California (1987), 1998, Professor—homiletics, 212-243-5150, Fax: 212-242-4451, E-mail: dechamplain@gts.edu

Doubleday, William A., MDiv, Episcopal Divinity School (1976), 1986, Professor—pastoral theology, 212-243-5150, Fax: 212-242-4451, E-mail: doubleday@gts.edu

Ewing, Ward B., MDiv, (1967), 1998, Professor—pastoral theology, 212-243-5150, Fax: 212-242-4451, E-mail: ewing@gts.edu

Good, Deirdre J., ThD, Harvard Divinity School (1983), 1986, Professor—New Testament, 212-243-5150, Fax: 212-242-4451, E-mail: good@gts.edu

Green, David, MLS, University of California at Berkeley (1968), 1982, Professor and Director of the Library, 212-243-5150, Fax: 212-242-4451, E-mail: green@gts.edu

Hurd, David J., MusD, Berkeley Divinity School at Yale (1987), 1976, Professor—church music, 212-243-5150, Fax: 212-242-4451, E-mail: hurd@gts.edu

Koenig, Elisabeth, PhD, Columbia University-Union Theological Seminary (1983), 1986, Professor—ascetical theology, 212-243-5150, Fax: 212-242-4451, E-mail: ekoenig@gts.edu

Koenig, John T., ThD, Union Theological Seminary (1971), 1978, Professor—New Testament, 212-243-5150, Fax: 212-242-4451, E-mail: jkoenig@gts.edu

Mullin, R. Bruce, PhD, Yale (1983), 1998, Professor—church history, 212-243-5150, Fax: 212-242-4451, E-mail: mullin@gts.edu

Newman, Judith H., PhD, Harvard (1996), 1998, Assistant Professor—Old Testament, 212-243-5150, Fax: 212-242-4451, E-mail: newman@gts.edu

Richardson, Mark W., PhD, Graduate Theological Union (1991), 1999, Associate Professor—systematic theology, 212-243-5150, Fax: 212-242-4451, E-mail: richardson@gts.edu

Stewart-Sykes, Alistair, PhD, University of Birmingham (1992), 1998, Assistant Professor—liturgics, 212-243-5150, Fax: 212-242-4451, E-mail: sykes@gts.edu

Wright, J. Robert, DPhil, Oxon (1967), 1968, Professor—church history, 212-243-5150, Fax: 212-242-4451, E-mail: wright@gts.edu

---

Geneva College

College Ave, Beaver Falls PA 15010

George Fox College

Division of Religious Studies, Newberg OR 97132

George Mason University

Dept of Philosophy and Religious Studies   Phone: 703-993-1290
B465 Robinson Hall
4400 University Drive
Fairfax VA 22030-4444
TYPE OF INSTITUTION: Public

CHAIRPERSON: David A. Kaufmann

UNDERGRADUATE ENROLLMENT: 23,000

DEGREES OFFERED: BA in Philosophy and BA in Philosophy with Religious Studies Track, MAIS/LS Independent Studies/Liberal Studies

UNDERGRADUATE MAJORS: 46

DEGREES CONFERRED: 17

DESCRIPTION OF UNDERGRADUATE PROGRAM: The Department of Philosophy and Religious Studies offers a religious track concentration option for philosophy majors which focuses on the historical, philosophical, and comparative study of religion. The department offers a minor in Philosophy. The Department houses the degree of Master of Arts in Interdisciplinary/Liberal Studies and teaches the core courses for that degree. George Mason University is a state supporteded university in Northern Virginia offering undergraduate and graduate degrees in the humanities, sciences and social sciencesl It has a School of Nursiiing, a Sfhool of Information Technology, and School of Business, and a Law School.

FACULTY:

Bergoffen, Debra B., PhD, Georgetown University (1974), 1971, Professor—existentialism, phenomenology, history of philosophy

Burns, John Barclay, PhD, University of St Andrews, Scotland (1971), 1986, Associate Professor—Old Testament, Ancient Near Eastern religion, religion and literature

Cherubin, Rose M., PhD, City University of New York (1996), 1995, Assistant Professor—ancient philosophy, metaphysics

DeNys, Martin J., PhD, Loyola University (1974), 1981, Associate Professor—Marx, Hegel, ontology, philosophy, theology, political science

Fletcher, James J., PhD, Indiana University (1973), 1972, Associate Professor—aesthetics

Froman, Wayne J., PhD, Fordham University (1975), 1985, Associate Professor—continental philosophy, aesthetics

Holman, Emmett L., PhD, University of Maryland (1973), 1972, Associate Professor—philosophy of science, philosophy of mind, epistemology

Kinnaman, Theodore, PhD, University of Wisconsin at Madison (1996), 1996, Assistant Professor—modern philosophy, especially Kant and Berkeley, ethics, social and political philosophy

Lavine, Thelma Z., PhD, Harvard University (1940), 1985, Professor—philosophy of the social sciences, American philosophy, literary, theory, political philosophy

McDermott, Michael, PhL, Loyola University (1959), 1967, Associate Professor—logic, classical and modern, philosophy of language, medieval philosophy, information technology and cognitive science

McFarlane, William H., PhD, University of Virginia (1957), 1968, Professor Emeritus—metaphysics, logic

Nguyen, Cuong Tu, PhD, Harvard University (1990), Associate Professor—South Asian religions, Hinduism, Buddhism

Paden, Roger K., PhD, (1981), 1989, Assistant Professor—ethics, social and political philosphy

Ro, Young-chan, PhD, University of California at Santa Barbara (1982), 1981, Associate Professor—East Asian religions, comparative religion, Confucianism, cross-cultural studies

Rothbard, Daniel, PhD, Washington University (1978), 1979, Associate Professor—philosophy of science, medical ethics

Shiner, Whitney T., PhD, Yale University (1992), Assistant Professor—New Testament, early Christian thought

Skousgaard, Shannon M., PhD, University of Georgia (1981), 1981, Associate Professor—ethics, environmental philosophy, philosophy of law

Wehrle, Walter, PhD, Florida State University (1988), 1988, Assistant Professor—ancient philosophy

Yance, Norman A., PhD, George Washington University (1973), 1968, Associate Professor Emeritus—wolrd religion, biblical studies

---

George Washington University

2106 G Street NW	Phone: 202-994-6325
Washington DC 20052	Fax: 202-994-9379
	E-mail: duff@gwu.edu
	URL: www.gwu.edu/~religion/

TYPE OF INSTITUTION: Private

CHAIRPERSON: Paul B. Duff

UNDERGRADUATE ENROLLMENT: 6,000

GRADUATE ENROLLMENT: 12,000

DEGREES OFFERED: BA

UNDERGRADUATE MAJORS: 30

DEGREES CONFERRED: 9

DESCRIPTION OF UNDERGRADUATE PROGRAM: The curriculum represents the judgment that critical analysis and synthesis of the data of religious traditions are central in the study of the human experience. Tools from many disciplines are involved in presenting the world's religions, their history, literature, and intellectual and community structures. Special emphases in the program include biblical studies; history of Christianity, Judaism, Islam, and the religions of India; theological movements, mysticism, women and religion; ethics and sociology of religion; and American religion. Students may also participate in the interdisciplinary program of Judaic Studies or in independently formed cross-disciplinary programs.

DESCRIPTION OF THE GRADUATE PROGRAM AND RESEARCH FACILITIES: Although the Religion Department has no formal graduate program in religion, students may study religion at the graduate level through several other programs. 1) The George Washington University Religion Department participates in a Consortium MA in Hinduism and Islam with other universities in the District of Columbia. 2) The History Department offers a PhD in American Religious History to which the Religion Department contributes. 3) There is a PhD offered in the Human Sciences, an interdisciplinary program, in which one can specialize in religion. The Metropolitan Washington, DC area is unusually rich in library resources including, but by no means restricted to, the Library of Congress. There are substantial living communities from all of the world religions as well. The Consortium of Universities offers a wealth of additional supporting scholars as do local museum staffs.

ACADEMIC PLAN, ADMISSION REQUIREMENTS, FINANCIAL AID: Admission requirements and plans of study vary with each program. In general a strong academic record with substantial work in religion are the basis for a successful application. Prior work in relevant languages is viewed favorably.

FACULTY:

Duff, Paul Brooks, Chicago (1988), 1991, Associate Professor—Bible, 202-994-6363, E-mail: duff@gwu.edu

Eisen, Robert, PhD, Brandeis (1990), 1990, Associate Professor—Judaic studies, medieval philosophy, 202-994-6327, E-mail: eisen@gwu.edu

Hiltebeitel, Alfred John, PhD, Chicago (1973), 1968, Professor—history of religion (Hinduism), 202-994-1674, E-mail: beitel@gwu.edu

Nasr, Seyyed Hossein, PhD, Harvard (1958), 1984, University Professor—Islamic studies, history of science, 202-994-5704

Urubshurow, Victoria, PhD, Chicago (1984), 1998, Assistant Professor—East Asian religion, 202-994-1675, E-mail: vku@gwu.edu

Wallace, Dewey D., Jr., PhD, Princeton (1965), 1963, Professor—history of Christianity, religion in America, 202-994-6326, E-mail: dwallace@gwu.edu

Yeide, Harry E., Jr., PhD, Harvard (1966), 1963, Professor—ethics, sociology of religion, 202-994-3967, E-mail: yeide@gwu.edu

Georgetown College

400 East College Street
Georgetown KY 40324

Phone: 502-863-8000
Fax: 502-868-8888
E-mail: @gtc.georgetown.ky.us

TYPE OF INSTITUTION: Denominational: Baptist
EXECUTIVE OFFICER: William H. Crouch, Jr,
CHAIRPERSON: Paul L. Redditt
UNDERGRADUATE ENROLLMENT: 1,300
GRADUATE ENROLLMENT: 300

Georgetown University

Theology Dept
120 New North
Washington DC 20057-0998

Phone: 202-687-5846
Fax: 202-687-8000
URL: www.georgetown.edu/departments
/theology

TYPE OF INSTITUTION: Private, Catholic
EXECUTIVE OFFICER: Leo J. O'Donovan, President
CHAIRPERSON: Anthony J. Tambasco
UNDERGRADUATE ENROLLMENT: 6,338
GRADUATE ENROLLMENT: 6,291
DEGREES OFFERED: BA with major in Christian Theology, Biblical Studies, Christian Ethics, World Religions, and Religion and Culture.
UNDERGRADUATE MAJORS: 86
DEGREES CONFERRED: 27
DESCRIPTION OF UNDERGRADUATE PROGRAM: All undergraduates take two Theology courses; freshmen take either Problem of God or Introduction to Biblical Literature; sophomores choose from over 20 elective offerings. Major program in Christian Theology (Bible, history of Christian thought, systematic theology), Biblical Studies, Christian Ethics, World Religions, or Religion and Culture (student organizes a program around a particular problem in which religious thought or values are of predominant interest).
FACULTY:
Abramowitz, A. Nathan, MHL, Jewish Theological Seminary (1955), 1967, Professorial Lecturer (part-time)—Judaic studies, 202-687-4513, E-mail: abramoan@gunet.georgetown.edu

Bunnell, Adam E., PhD, University of Minnesota (1985), 1998, Adjunct Assistant Professor (part-time)—European religious history, 202-687-1395, E-mail: bunnella@gunet.georgetown.edu

Cho, Francisca, PhD, University of Chicago (1992), 1992, Associate Professor—Buddhism, Chinese religions, 202-687-6110, E-mail: chof@gunet.georgetown.edu

Donohue, James A., PhD, Graduate Theological Union (1984), 1986, Associate Professor—theological ethics, social ethics, 202-687-2912, E-mail: donohuej@gunet.georgetown.edu

Epperly, Bruce G., PhD, Claremont Graduate School (1980), 1983, Adjunct Assistant Professor (part-time)—Protestant theology, 202-687-5846

Esposito, John L., PhD, Temple University (1974), 1993, Professor—religion and international affairs, Islamic studies, 202-687-8375, E-mail: espositj@gusun.georgetown.edu

Faruqi, Maysam Al, PhD, Temple University (1988), 1990, Visiting Assistant Professor (part-time)—Islamic thought and practice, 202-687-5846, E-mail: faruqim@gunet.georgetown.edu

Fields, Stephen M., PhD, Yale University (1993), 1993, Assistant Professor—philosophy of religion, systematic and spiritual theology, 202-687-5822, E-mail: fieldss@gunet.georgetown.edu

Gillis, Chester, PhD, University of Chicago (1986), 1988, Associate Professor—inter-religious dialogue, philosophy of religion, 202-687-4514, E-mail: gillisc@gunet.georgetown.edu

Glucklich, Ariel, PhD, Harvard University (1984), Assistant Professor—Hinduism, 202-687-4513, E-mail: glucklia@gunet.georgetown.edu

Haught, John F., PhD, Catholic University of America (1970), 1969, Professor—systematic theology, 202-687-6119, E-mail: haughtjf@gunet.georgetown.edu

Hayes, Diana L., STD, Catholic University of Louvain (1988), 1988, Associate Professor—liberation theology, Black theology, political theology, 202-687-4515, E-mail: hayesd@gunet.georgetown.edu

Hentz, Otto, PhD, University of Chicago (1977), 1973, Associate Professor—contemporary Christology, systematic theology, 202-687-5851, E-mail: hentzo@gunet.georgetown.edu

King, Thomas M., PhD, University of Strassbourg (1968), 1968, Professor—philosophy of religion, 202-687-6101, E-mail: kingt@gunet.georgetown.edu

Lamm, Julia A., PhD, University of Chicago (1991), 1989, Associate Professor—historical theology, systematic theology, 202-687-6261, E-mail: lammj@gunet.georgetown.edu

Linafelt, Tod A., PhD, Emory University (1997), 1996, Assistant Professor—biblical studies, 202-687-6238, E-mail: linafelt@gunet.georgetown.edu

McFadden, William C., STD, Gregorian University (1963), 1963, Associate Professor—theology and sexuality, religion and literature, 202-687-6230, E-mail: mcfaddew@gunet.georgetown.edu

McKeown, Elizabeth, PhD, University of Chicago (1972), 1972, Professor—history of Christianity, American religious history, 202-687-4516, E-mail: mckeowne@gunet.georgetown.edu

Miller, Vincent J., PhD, University of Notre Dame (1997), Assistant Professor—systematic theology, 202-687-6118, E-mail: millerv@gunet.georgetown.edu

Mitchell, Alan C., PhD, Yale University (1986), 1985, Associate Professor—biblical studies, New Testament and Christian origins, 202-687-5756, E-mail: mitchea2@gusun.georgetown.edu

Murphy, Joseph M., PhD, Temple (1981), 1983, Associate Professor—African and African-American religions, 202-687-7138, E-mail: murphyj@gunet.georgetown.edu

O'Donovan, Leo J., DrTheo, University of Munster (1971), 1989, Professor—systematic theology

Pilch, John J., PhD, Marquette University (1972), 1993, Adjunct Assistant Professor (part-time)—biblical studies, 202-687-5846, E-mail: pilchjj@gusun.georgetown.edu

Reynolds, Terrence P., PhD, Brown University (1983), 1991, Associate Professor—contemporary theology, Christian ethics, philosophy of religion, 202-687-4610, E-mail: reynoldt@gunet.georgetown.edu

Ruf, Frederick J., PhD, Harvard University (1988), 1988, Associate Professor—modern religious thought, religion and literature, 202-687-6233, E-mail: ruff@gunet.georgetown.edu

Sanders, Theresa M., PhD, Syracuse University (1991), 1991, Assistant Professor—systematic theology, 202-687-6106, E-mail: sanderst@gunet.georgetown.edu

Sloyan, Gerard S., PhD, Catholic University of America (1948), 1997, Distinguished Professorial Lecturer (part-time)—New Testament, 202-687-5846

Soltes, Ori Z., PhD (cand.), Johns Hopkins University, 1997, Professorial Lecturer (part-time)—Judaic studies, 202-687-5846, E-mail: orisoltes@aol.com

Steck, Christopher, PhD (cand.), Yale University, 1999, Instructor—Christian ethics, 202-687-5846

Sweek, Joel, PhD, University of Chicago (1996), 1996, Assistant Professor—history of ancient civilizations, biblical studies, 202-687-6236, E-mail: sweekj@gusun.georgetown.edu

Tambasco, Anthony J., PhD, Union Theological Seminary, New York (1980), 1979, Professor—biblical studies, Christian ethics, 202-687-6234, E-mail: tambasca@gunet.georgetown.edu

Walsh, James P. M., PhD, Harvard University (1978), 1973, Associate Professor—biblical studies, 202-687-6235, E-mail: walshj@gunet.georgetown.edu

Weaver, Darlene F., PhD, University of Chicago (1998), 1998, Visiting Assistant Professor—Christian ethics, 202-687-4551, E-mail: weaverd@gusun.georgetown.edu

White, Harold S., MHL, Jewish Theological Seminary (1959), 1968, Professorial Lecturer (part-time)—Old Testament, intertestamental period, twentieth-century Jewish religious and secular thought, 202-687-3480, E-mail: whitehs@gunet.georgetown.edu

Winters, Francis X., PhD, Fordham University (1973), 1972, Professor—ethics and international relations, faith and ethics, 202-687-5916, E-mail: wintersf@gunet.georgetown.edu

Yeager, Diane, PhD, Duke University (1981), 1976, Associate Professor—theology and literature, philosophical theology, ethics, 202-687-6232, E-mail: yeagerd@gunet.georgetown.edu

---

Georgia College

231 W Hancock St, Milledgeville GA 31061

University of Georgia

Peabody Hall-1625
Athens GA 30602

Phone: 706-542-5356
Fax: 706-542-6724
URL: www.uga.edu/~religion/

TYPE OF INSTITUTION: Public

EXECUTIVE OFFICER: Michael Adams, President

CHAIRPERSON: Sandy D. Martin

COORDINATORS: Russell Kirkland (Undergraduate); Thomas B. Slater (Graduate)

UNDERGRADUATE ENROLLMENT: 24,000

GRADUATE ENROLLMENT: 7,000

DEGREES OFFERED: AB

UNDERGRADUATE MAJORS: 69

DEGREES CONFERRED: 16

DESCRIPTION OF UNDERGRADUATE PROGRAM: An Undergraduate Degree in Religion Requirements: 21 semester hours numbered 3000 or above taken in religion (RELI) courses. One three-hour course is required to be taken from each of the following three categories (=9 hours); Category I (Judaism, Christianity, Islam), Category II (Religions of India, China, Japan), and Category III (Religious and Philosophical Thought). The remaining 12 hours maybe selected from any upper division course offered by the department.

GRADUATE PROGRAM

Graduate Advisor: David S. Williams

Graduate Degrees Offered: MA

Degrees Conferred: 6 MA

Graduate Students in Residence: 16 MA

Average No. of New Students Enrolled: 4 MA

Women Students: 6 MA

Minority Students: 0 MA

Minimum GRE Score Requisite to Admission: No

Minimum GPA Score Requisite to Admission: No

Foreign Language Proficiency Evaluated: Yes

Financial Aid to First Year Students: 100% MA

Financial Aid to Other Students: 80% MA

Attrition Among Students: 5% MA

Graduates Placed: 100% MA

DESCRIPTION OF GRADUATE PROGRAM AND RESEARCH FACILITIES: MA Graduate Degree in Religion: The Master of Arts in Religious Studies is designed for persons interested in teaching in secondary schools and junior or community colleges, in preparing for further advanced religious studies leading to the PhD or equivalent, and in entering a seminary or theological school and other professional schools. In addition to these specialized purposes, the program is designed for those interested in continuing education for its own sake in the broad area of Humanities.

ACADEMIC PLAN, ADMISSION REQUIREMENTS, FINANCIAL AID: The graduate program is designed to give the student a thorough training in the field of Religion with a specialization in some area of concentration. Areas of concentration include: Biblical Studies, Christian Studies, Jewish Studies, Islamic Studies, Indian and East Asian Religious Studies and American Religion. Prerequisites for acceptance are normally a balanced undergraduate major in Religion or its equivalent and acceptable scores on the GRE Aptitude tests. Reading knowledge of one pertinent foreign language is required. Financial aid is available in the form of Departmental and University Assistantships. Some out-of-state tuition waivers are available through the Graduate School.

FACULTY:

Godlas, Alan, PhD, Berkeley (1991), 1991, Associate Professor—Islam, Quranic studies, Sufism, Arabic, E-mail: godlas@arches.uga.edu

Honerkamp, Kenneth L., PhD, University Aix-en-Provence, France (1999), 1999, Assistant Professor—Arabic and Islam, E-mail: hnrkmp@arches.uga.edu

Kirkland, J. Russell, PhD, Indiana University (1986), 1994, Associate Professor—Chinese religions, Taoism, Asian religions, E-mail: kirkland@arches.uga.edu

Lewis, Theodore J., PhD, Harvard University (1986), 1987, Associate Professor—Hebrew Bible (Old Testament), Semitic languages, Ancient Near Eastern, E-mail: lewis@arches.uga.edu

Martin, Sandy D., PhD, Columbia University (1981), 1988, Professor and Head—history of Christianity, American and Afro-American religious history, E-mail: martin@arches.uga.edu

Power, William L., PhD, Emory Univerisity (1965), 1967, Professor—historical theology, systematic theology, philosophy of religion, E-mail: power@arches.uga.edu

Ratnayaka, Shanta, PhD, Northwestern University (1973), 1974, Professor—Buddhism, Indian philosophy, Asian religions, E-mail: shanta@arches.uga.edu

Slater, Thomas B., PhD, King's College-London (1997), 1996, Associate Professor—New Testament and African-American religion, E-mail: tslater@arches.uga.edu

Williams, David S., PhD, Hebrew Union College (1987), 1989, Associate Professor—Hellenistic, Rabbinic and Modern Judaism, Hebrew, E-mail: dwilliam@arches.uga.edu

ASSOCIATED FACULTY:

Friedman, Jean E., PhD, Lehigh—history of religon in America

Klein, Jared, PhD, Yale—anthropology and linguistics

Rubin, Nancy F., PhD, Columbia—religion and classical culture

---

Georgia Southwestern College

Americus GA 31709

Georgia State University

Religious Studies Area
Dept of Philosophy
PO Box 4089
Atlanta GA 30302-4089

Phone: 404-651-2277
Fax: 404-651-1563
URL: www.gsu.edu/~wwwphl/religion.html

TYPE OF INSTITUTION: Public

COORDINATOR: Timothy M. Renick

UNDERGRADUATE ENROLLMENT: 18,000

GRADUATE ENROLLMENT: 7,000

DEGREES OFFERED: BA in Religious Studies, MA

UNDERGRADUATE MAJORS: 50

DEGREES CONFERRED: 15

DESCRIPTION OF UNDERGRADUATE PROGRAM: The study of religion at Georgia State University is a nonsectarian and interdisciplinary pursuit, grounded in the traditions of the liberal arts. Students can choose from among twenty-five upper-level courses in religious studies offered by the Department of Philosophy. Majors also can apply toward their BA in Religious Studies a series of courses from other departments in the College of Arts and Sciences, including history, sociology, music and anthropology. For course descriptions, sample syllabi, and faculty resumes, visit our web page.

GRADUATE PROGRAM

Graduate Advisor: Timothy M. Renick

Graduate Degrees Offered: MA

Degrees Conferred: 5 MA

Graduate Students in Residence: 15 MA
Average No. of New Students Enrolled: 6 MA
Women Students: 6 MA
Minority Students: 5 MA
Foreign Students: 2 MA

DESCRIPTION OF GRADUATE PROGRAM AND RESEARCH FACILITIES: The Department of Philosophy offers a range of courses at the graduate level taught by faculty members specifically trained in Religious studies. It also offers the opportunity for graduate students to take appropriate offerings from other units and programs within the university. Students work toward the completion of a MA thesis within their area of specialization. For descriptions and sample syllabi of graduate courses, as well as faculty resumes, visit our web page.

ACADEMIC PLAN, ADMISSION REQUIREMENTS, FINANCIAL AID: A prospective student seeking admissions to full graduate status must be a graduate of an accredited college or university and possess the baccalaureate degree. The GRE is required for admission. Requests for admissions materials and financial aid information should be directed to: Office of Graduate Studies, College of Arts and Sciences, Georgia State University, Atlanta, GA 30303-3099.

FACULTY:

Herman, Jonathan R., PhD, Harvard University (1992), 1996, Assistant Professor—Taoism, Confucianism, Buddhism, comparative study of mysticism, method and study of religion, 404-651-2277, Fax: 404-651-1563, E-mail: phljrh@panther.gsu.edu

McClymond, Kathryn, PhD, University of California at Santa Barbara (1999), 1999, Assistant Professor—Judaism, Hinduism, ritual studies, religion and literature, women and religion

Renick, Timothy M., PhD, Princeton University (1986), 1986, Associate Professor—religious ethics, contemporary religioius thought, just-war tradition, Augustine and Aquinas, 404-651-2277, Fax: 404-651-1563, E-mail: phltmr@panther.gsu.edu

Woodhouse, Mark, PhD, University of Miami (1970), 1974, Associate Professor—Eastern religions and philosophy, metaphysics, paranormal domains of religious experience, 404-651-2277, Fax: 404-651-1563

Georgian Court College
900 Lakewood Ave, Lakewood NJ 08701-2697

Gettysburg College
Dept of Religion, Box 408, Gettysburg PA 17325

Glassboro State College
Glassboro NJ 08028

Goddard College
Plainfield VT 05667

God's Bible School and College

1810 Young St
Cincinnati OH 45210

Phone: 513-721-7944
Fax: 513-721-3971
E-mail: fwiwg@gbs.edu

TYPE OF INSTITUTION: Private, Independent
EXECUTIVE OFFICER: Michael Avery, President
UNDERGRADUATE ENROLLMENT: 220

Golden Gate Baptist Theological Seminary

Strawberry Point
201 Seminary Dr
Mill Valley CA 94941

Phone: 415-380-1300
Fax: 415-380-1302
E-mail: admissions@ggbts.edu
URL: www.ggbts.edu

TYPE OF INSTITUTION: Private, Southern Baptist
EXECUTIVE OFFICER: William O. Crews, President
GRADUATE ENROLLMENT: 715

Golden State School of Theology

2870 Adeline St Apt 103, Berkeley CA 94703-2245

Gonzaga University

Spokane WA 99258

Phone: 509-323-6782
Fax: 509-323-5718
E-mail: large@gonzaga.edu
URL: www.gonzaga.edu

TYPE OF INSTITUTION: Private, Roman Catholic
CHAIRPERSON: Ron Large
COORDINATORS: John Downey (Undergraduate); Leonard Doohan (Graduate)
UNDERGRADUATE ENROLLMENT: 2,812
GRADUATE ENROLLMENT: 1,050
DEGREES OFFERED: BA
UNDERGRADUATE MAJORS: 31
DEGREES CONFERRED: 10
DESCRIPTION OF UNDERGRADUATE PROGRAM: As part of a humanistic, Catholic, and Jesuit educational tradition, Gonzaga University seeks the full development of the human person and preparation for leadership in service. An atmosphere of community on campus and interactive learning in the classroom characterize the collaboration of students and faculty in seeking academic excellence. The undergraduate major requires courses in Hebrew Scriptures, New Testament, systematic theology, ecclesiology, morality, five electives, and a senior symposium with synthetic research paper.
GRADUATE PROGRAM
Graduate Advisor: Leonard Doohan

Graduate Degrees Offered: MA Religious Studies, Spirituality, Pastoral Ministry; Master of Divinity

Degrees Conferred: 6 MA

Graduate Students in Residence: 47 MA

Average No. of New Students Enrolled: 20 MA

Women Students: 30 MA

Minority Students: 3 MA

Foreign Students: 3 MA

Minimum GRE Score Requisite to Admission: Yes; 50%

Minimum GPA Score Requisite to Admission: Yes; 3.0 on 4.0 scale

Foreign Language Proficiency Evaluated: No.

Financial Aid to First Year Students: 70% MA

DESCRIPTION OF GRADUATE PROGRAM AND RESEARCH FACILITIES: The Religious Studies Department seeks the integration of academic competency and personal development. Programs are personalized and operate in a supportive community atmosphere marked by high faculty availability. Required core courses provide a solid foundation and a variety of available electives enables students to develop programs according to their needs and interests. Foley Center, a $20 million state-of-the-art library, opened Fall 1992 and provides sophisticated online computer access to libraries across the U.S.

ACADEMIC PLAN, ADMISSION REQUIREMENTS, FINANCIAL AID: Admission requirements: BA from accredited college or university with major in religious studies or introductory courses in Hebrew scriptures, New Testament, systematic theology, applied theology; MAT or GRE, 2 recommendations, statement of purpose. A limited amount of financial aid is available, based on need.

FACULTY:

Cook, Michael, ThD, Graduate Theological Union (1974), 1989, Professor—Christology, systematic theology, 509-323-6782

Dallen, James, STD, Catholic University (1976), 1982, Professor—liturgy and sacraments, 509-328-6787, E-mail: dallen@gonzaga.edu

Doohan, Helen, PhD, Gonzaga University (1983), 1976, Professor—biblical theology, Christian leadership, 509-328-6788, E-mail: hdoohan@gonzaga.edu

Doohan, Leonard, STD, Teresianum, Rome (1971), 1975, Professor—biblical theology, Christian spirituality, 509-328-3546, E-mail: ldoohan@gonzaga.edu

Downey, John K., PhD, Marquette University (1983), 1982, Associate Professor—systematic and fundamental theology, method, 509-328-6780, E-mail: downey@gonzaga.edu

Egan, Robert, PhD, Graduate Theological Union, Berkeley (1994), 1984, Assistant Professor—Christian spirituality, systematic theology, 509-328-3625

Garvin, Mary, DMin, Andover Newton Theological School (1990), 1991, Assistant Professor—pastoral theology, 509-328-6798, E-mail: mgarvin@gonzaga.edu

Hartin, Patrick J., DTh, University of South Africa (1981, 1988), 1995, Associate Professor—New Testament, 509-328-6789, E-mail: hartin@gonzaga.edu

Kuder, Stephen, PhD, Graduate Theological Union (1975), 1977, Professor—religion and literature, liturgy, 509-328-6702, E-mail: kuder@gonzaga.edu

Kugler, Robert A., PhD, University of Notre Dame (1994), 1993, Associate Professor—Hebrew scriptures, 509-328-6777, E-mail: kugler@gonzaga.edu

Large, W. Ronald, PhD, Graduate Theological Union (1985), 1988, Associate Professor—social ethics, peace studies, 509-328-6767, E-mail: large@gonzaga.edu

McCormick, Patrick, STD, Gregorian University (1984), 1994, Associate Professor—moral theology, Christian ethics, 509-328-6715, E-mail: mccormick@gonzaga.edu

Milos, Joy, PhD, Catholic University (1987), 1988, Associate Professor—Christian spirituality, women's studies, 509-328-6714, E-mail: milos@gonzaga.edu

Mossi, John P., DMin, Catholic University of America (1985), 1991, Associate Professor—pastoral theology, pastoral counseling, 509-328-6779, E-mail: mossi@gonzaga.edu

Schearing, Linda, PhD, Emory University (1992), 1993, Associate Professor—Hebrew scriptures, 509-328-6797, E-mail: schearing@gonzaga.edu

Siejk, Catherine L., PhD, Boston College (1991), 1991, Associate Professor—religious education, 509-328-6776, E-mail: swlcp@aol.com

Skok, Charles D., STD, University of St Thomas Aquinas, Rome (1962), 1980, Professor Emeritus—Christian ethics, ecclesiology, ministry, 509-328-6799, E-mail: skok@gonzaga.edu

Tyrrell, Bernard J., PhD, Fordham University (1972), 1972, Professor Emeritus—systematic theology, Christian spirituality, Christotherapy, 509-328-6036, E-mail: btyrrell@gonzaga.edu

Gordon College
255 Grapevine Rd, Wenham MA 01984

Gordon-Conwell Theological Seminary
130 Essex St, South Hamilton MA 01982

Goshen College

1700 S Main Street
Goshen IN 46526

Phone: 219-535-7000
Fax: 219-535-7293
E-mail: joannab@goshen.edu
URL: www.goshen.edu/bibrelphil/

TYPE OF INSTITUTION: Private, Mennonite
EXECUTIVE OFFICER: Shirley Showalter, President
CHAIRPERSON: Jo-Ann A. Brant
UNDERGRADUATE ENROLLMENT: 900

Goucher College
Dulaney Valley Rd, Towson MD 21204

Grace College

200 Seminary Dr
Winona Lake IN 46590

Phone: 219-372-5100
Fax: 219-372-5265
E-mail: forbeswm@grace.edu
URL: www.grace.edu

TYPE OF INSTITUTION: Private, Fellowship of Grace Brethren Churches
EXECUTIVE OFFICER: Ron Monahan, President
CHAIRPERSON: Skip Forbes
UNDERGRADUATE ENROLLMENT: 700
GRADUATE ENROLLMENT: 100

Grace University

1311 South 9th Street
Omaha NE 68108

Phone: 402-449-2800
Fax: 402-341-9587
E-mail: gupres@graceu.edu
URL: www.graceu.edu

TYPE OF INSTITUTION: Private, Non-Denominational
EXECUTIVE OFFICER: James P. Eckman
UNDERGRADUATE ENROLLMENT: 450
GRADUATE ENROLLMENT: 100

Grace Bible College

1011 Aldon St SW
Box 910
Grand Rapids MI 49509

Phone: 616-538-2330
Fax: 616-538-0599
URL: www.gbcol.edu

TYPE OF INSTITUTION: Private, Grace Gospel Fellowship
EXECUTIVE OFFICER: E. Bruce Kemper, President
UNDERGRADUATE ENROLLMENT: 150

Grace Theological Seminary

Winona Lake IN 46590

Graceland College

700 E College Ave
Lamoni IA 50140

Phone: 515-784-5184
Fax: 515-784-5410
E-mail: bobmesle@graceland.edu
URL: www2.graceland.edu/index.html

TYPE OF INSTITUTION: Private, RLDS
EXECUTIVE OFFICER: David Clinefelter, President
COORDINATOR: C. Robert Mesle
UNDERGRADUATE ENROLLMENT: 1,100

Graduate Theological Union

2400 Ridge Rd	Phone: 510-649-2460
Berkeley CA 94709	Fax: 510-649-1730 (Admissions and Registrar)
	510-649-1417 (Dean and President)
	E-mail: gtuadm@gtu.edu
	URL: www.gtu.edu

TYPE OF INSTITUTION: Non-Denominational

EXECUTIVE OFFICER: Margaret R. Miles, Dean

GRADUATE ENROLLMENT: 366

GRADUATE PROGRAM

Member of the Council on Graduate Studies in Religion

Graduate Degrees Offered: MA; PhD; ThD

Degrees Conferred: 33 MA; 20 PhD; 0 ThD

Graduate Students in Residence: 115 MA; 228 PhD/ThD

Not in Residence: 3 MA; 20 PhD/ThD

Average No. of New Students Enrolled: 55 MA; 40 PhD/ThD

Women Students: 57 MA; 123 PhD/ThD

Minority Students: 16 MA; 34 PhD/ThD

Foreign Students: 15 MA; 37 PhD/ThD

Minimum GRE Score Requisite to Admission: Yes; 600 verbal

Minimum GPA Score Requisite to Admission: No

Foreign Language Proficiency Evaluated: Yes, by translation examination or by transcript

Financial Aid to First Year Students: 85% MA; 85% PhD/ThD

Financial Aid to Other Students: 80% MA; 75% PhD/ThD

Attrition Among Students: 8% MA; 5% PhD/ThD

Graduates Placed: 62% PhD/ThD

DESCRIPTION OF GRADUATE PROGRAM AND RESEARCH FACILITIES: A theological consortium of nine seminaries and eleven centers representing a range of thought and practice. Doctoral degrees are offered in eleven areas of study including a cross-disciplinary program. PhD programs in Near Eastern Religions and in Jewish Studies are offered jointly with the University of California, Berkeley. PhD programs focus on theological studies in the context of university disciplines, hence some coursework is taken through the University of California, Berkeley. ThD programs focus on specifically formulated courses of study in the context of the entire theological spectrum. Doctoral students assume major responsibility for the shaping and direction of their own research. Two years of residency are required. The MA is offered jointly with member schools of the consortium. Two years of residency are required, including 14 semester courses plus 2 courses in thesis work. The program provides a broad experience in theological studies. For additional information, contact the Director of Admissions, Kathleen Kook.

ACADEMIC PLAN, ADMISSION REQUIREMENTS, FINANCIAL AID: The GTU operates on a two-semester system: fall and spring, with a January intersession for special research projects. A BA/BS is required for admission to all programs. An MA in Theology or Religious Studies or MDiv or equivalent is required for admission to the doctoral programs. All previous transcripts, three letters of recommendation, statement of purpose, and GRE (general) are required for admission. Full tuition for each of the first two years of the doctoral programs is $14,100 (1999-2000). After the first two years, doctoral students pay a continuing fee of $4,000 per year. MA tuition is $8,500 (1999-2000), with a reduction to one-half that amount after the two years of residence. Most doctoral candidates in residence receive financial assistance through direct grants applied to tuition and through research/teaching grants, loan funds, and work/study.

AREA CONVENERS FOR 1999-2000:

Adams, Doug, ThD, Graduate Theological Union (1974), 1976, Professor—Christianity and the arts, Area 7A: Religion and the Arts, 510-848-0528

Berling, Judith A., PhD, Columbia University (1976), 1987, Professor—Chinese and Comparative Religions, Interdisciplinary Studies, 510-649-2460

Clader, Linda L., PhD, Harvard University (1973), 1991, Associate Professor—homiletics, Area 7H: Homiletics, 510-204-0700

Liebert, Elizabeth, PhD, Vanderbilt University (1986), 1987, SFTS Director of the Program in Christian Spirituality and Professor—spiritual life, Area 8S, 415-258-6500

Ludwig, Eugene M., OFM Cap, ThD, Graduate Theological Union (1983), 1974, Professor—history and patristic theology, Area 2: Historical Studies, 510-849-2030

O'Neill, William R., SJ, PhD, Yale University (1988), 1988, Associate Professor—social ethics, Area 4: Religion and Society, 510-841-8804

Payne, Richard K., PhD, Graduate Theological Union (1985), 1986, Associate Professor—Japanese Buddhism and IBS Dean, Area 8HR: Cultural and Historical Study of Religions, 650-938-7192

Pence, Gary, PhD, Princeton (1981), 1976, Associate Professor—pastoral theology, Area 5: Religion and Psychology, 510-524-5264

Russell, Robert J., PhD, University of California, Santa Cruz (1978), 1981, Professor in Residence—theology and science, Area 3: Systematic and Philosophical Theology, Philosophy of Religion, 510-848-8152

Tolbert, Mary Ann, PhD, University of Chicago (1977), 1994, George H. Atkinson Professor—biblical studies, Area 1: Old and New Testament Studies, 510-848-0582

FACULTY:

Adams, Doug, ThD, Graduate Theological Union (1974), 1976, Professor—Christianity and the arts, Area 7, 510-848-0528

Aune, Michael B., PhD, University of Notre Dame (1981), 1978, Professor—worship, Area 7, 510-524-5264

Berling, Judith A., PhD, Columbia University (1976), 1987, Professor—Chinese and comparative religions, Area 8HR and Interdisciplinary Studies, 510-649-2400

Biale, David, PhD, University of California, Los Angeles (1977), 1986, Director of Center for Jewish Studies and Koret Professor—Jewish history, Area 8HR, 510-649-2400

Bretzke, James, STD, Pontifical Gregorian University, Rome (1989), 1993, Assistant Professor—fundamental Christian ethics, Area 4, 510-841-8804

Brown, Sandra Read, PhD, Princeton Theological Seminary (1980), 1991, Director of SFTS Lloyd Center Pastoral Counseling Services and Associate Professor—pastoral theology, Area 5, 415-258-6500

Buckles, Luke, STD, Pontifical University of St Thomas Aquinas, Rome (1985), 1985, Director of Theological Field Education and Associate Professor—theology, Areas 3 and 8S, 510-849-2030

Buckley, Thomas E., PhD, University of California, Santa Barbara (1973), 1996, Professor—American religious history, Area 2, 510-841-8804

Caloca-Rivas, Rigoberto, PhD, Universidad Iberoamericana, Mexico City (1999), 1991, Executive Director of The Multi-cultural Institute and Instructor—multi-cultural theology, social anthropology, Area 4, 510-848-5232

Chaney, Marvin L., PhD, Harvard University (1976), 1969, Nathaniel Gray Professor—Hebrew Exegesis, Old Testament, Area 1, 415-258-6500

Childers, Jana, PhD, Graduate Theological Union (1992), 1985, Associate Professor—homiletics, speech communications, Area 7, 415-258-6500

Chinnici, Joseph P., DPhilOxon, Oxford University (1976), 1976, Professor—church history, Area 2, 510-848-5232

Chinnici, Rosemary, PhD, Graduate Theological Union (1980), 1980, Professor—pastoral theology, Area 5, 510-845-6232

Choy, Birstan Bock-Yong, DMin, San Francisco Theological Seminary (1995), 1992, Assistant Professor—ministry, 415-258-6500

Chuck, James, ThD, Pacific School of Religion (1962), 1991, Professor—theology, church ministry, Area 3 and Ministry Studies, 510-841-1905

Cieslak, William M., PhD, Graduate Theological Union (1979), 1979, FST President and Professor—liturgical theology, Areas 3 and 7, 510-848-5232

Clader, Linda Lee, PhD, Harvard University (1973), 1991, Associate Professor—homiletics, Area 7, 510-204-0700

Compier, Don H., PhD, Emory University (1992), 1992, Associate Professor—systematic theology, Area 3 and Interdisciplinary Studies, 510-204-0700

Coote, Robert B., PhD, Harvard University (1972), 1975, Professor—Old Testament, Area 1, 510-258-6500

Countryman, L. William, PhD, University of Chicago (1977), 1983, Professor—New Testament, Area 8S and Interdisciplinary Studies, 510-204-0700

Cummings, George C. L., PhD, Union Theological Seminary (1990), 1987, Pearl Rawlings Hamilton Professor—systematic theology, Area 3, 510-841-1905

Davis, Walter T., Jr., PhD, Boston University (1974), 1981, Professor—sociology of religion, Area 4, 415-528-6500

Delbridge, Lynette, MPhil, Union Theological Seminary, New York (1994), 1998, Assistant Professor—New Testament, Area 7, 510-841-1905

Dodds, Michael J., STD, University of Fribourg, Switzerland (1986), 1985, Professor—philosophy, systematic theology, Area 3, 510-883-2085

Donahue, John R., PhD, University of Chicago (1972), 1992, Professor—New Testament, Area 1, 510-549-5016

Donovan, Mary Ann, PhD, University of St Michael's College, Toronto (1977), 1977, Professor—historical theology, spirituality, Areas 2 and 8S, 510-549-5016

Driskill, Joseph D., PhD, Graduate Theological Union (1996), 1993, Assistant Dean of Disciples Seminary Foundation and Assistant Professor—spirituality, Area 8S, 510-848-0528

Endres, John C., PhD, Vanderbilt University (1982), 1982, Associate Professor—sacred scripture (Old Testament), Areas 1 and 8S, 510-549-5016

Ernest, Stephen T., PhD, Fordham University (1973), 1996, Professor—history of philosophy, Area 3, 510-883-2085

Ernst, Eldon G., PhD, Yale University (1968), 1967, Professor—American church history, Area 2, 510-841-1905

Falkenberg, Reindert, PhD, University of Amsterdam (1985), 1999, Luce/Bertelsen Chair—western art history and religion, Area 7A, 510-841-8804

Farajaje-Jones, Elias, ThD, University of Bern (1986), 1996, Professor—cultural studies, Area 8HR, 510-845-6232

Fischer, Clare B., PhD, Graduate Theological Union (1979), 1981, Aurelia Henry Reinhardt Professor—religion and culture, Areas 4 and 8HR, 510-845-6232

Flesher, Leann Snow, PhD, Drew University (1997), 1994, Assistant Professor—Old Testament, Area 1, 510-841-1905

Forsey, Alicia, PhD, Union Institute (1995), 1988, Dean, 510-845-6232

Garcia-Rivera, Alejandro, ThD, Lutheran School of Theology at Chicago, (1994) 1993, Assistant Professor—systematic theology, Area 3, 510-549-5016

Gelpi, Donald L., PhD, Fordham University (1970), 1973, Professor—historical and systematic theology, Area 3, 510-549-5016

Gold, Victor R., PhD, Johns Hopkins University (1951), 1962, Professor—biblical theology, Area 1, 510-524-5264

Green, Barbara, PhD, University of California, Berkeley and Graduate Theological Union (1980), 1992, Professor—biblical studies, Areas 1 and 8S, 510-849-2030

Griener, George E., ThD, Eberhard-Karl Universität, Tübingen, (1989), 1989, JSTB Senior Vice President/Academic Dean and Assistant Professor—systematic theology, Area 3, 510-841-8804

Guinan, Michael D., PhD, Catholic University of America (1972), 1972, Professor—Old Testament and Semitic languages, Areas 1 and 8S, 510-848-5232

Gula, Richard M., PhD, University of St Michael's College (1979), 1996, Professor—moral theology, Area 4, 510-848-5232

Hall, Nancy E., DMin, San Francisco Theological Seminary (1995), 1989, Director and Assistant Professor—field education, Area 7, 510-841-1905

Hens-Pizza, Gina, PhD, Union Theological Seminary (1992), 1992, Associate Professor—biblical studies, 510-549-5016

Holder, Arthur G., PhD, Duke University (1987), 1986, Dean of Academic Affairs and Professor—Christian spirituality, Area 8S, 510-204-0700

Kalin, Everett R., ThD, Harvard Divinity School (1967), 1983, Professor—New Testament, Area 1, 510-524-5264

Kater, John L., Jr., PhD, McGill University (1973), 1990, CDSP Professor—ministry development, 510-204-0700

Kirk-Duggan, Cheryl A., PhD, Baylor University (1992), 1997, Director of the Center for Women and Religion and Assistant Professor—theology, womanist studies, Areas 3 and 4, 510-649-2490

Klentos, John, PhD, University of Notre Dame (1996), 1999, Assistant Professor—Orthodox studes, Area 7L, 510-649-2450

Krasevac, Edward L., PhD, Graduate Theological Union (1986), 1985, Dean and Associate Professor—theology, Areas 3 and 4, 510-883-2085

Kuan, Kah-Jin (Jeffrey), PhD, Emory University (1994), 1991, Associate Professor—Old Testament, Area 1, 510-848-0528

Lasselle-Klein, Robert, PhD, Graduate Theological Union (1995), 1995, JSTB Director of Field Education and Assistant Professor—field education and systematic theology, Area 3, 510-549-5016

Lebacqz, Karen, PhD, Harvard University (1974), 1972, Robert Gordon Sproul Professor—theological ethics, Area 4, 510-848-0528

Lee, Warren W., DMin, San Francisco Theological Seminary (1974), 1981, Professor—ministry in the Asian American context, 415-258-6500

Liebert, Elizabeth, PhD, Vanderbilt University (1986), 1987, SFTS Director of the Program in Christian Spirituality and Professor—spiritual life, Areas 5 and 8S, 415-258-6500

Ludwig, Eugene M., ThD, Graduate Theological Union (1983), 1974, Professor—history and patristic theology, Area 2, 510-883-2085

Lull, Timothy F., PhD, Yale University (1977), 1989, PLTS President and Professor—systematic theology, Area 3, 510-524-5264

Lumas, Eva Marie, DMin, Howard University School of Divinity (1994), 1994, Assistant Professor—religious education and culture, 510-848-5232

Lyman, Rebecca J., DPhil, University of Oxford (1983), 1983, Samuel M. Garrett Professor—church history, Area 2, 510-204-0700

Martin, John Hilary, PhD, University of California, Los Angeles, (1978), 1965, Professor—history and history of religions, Areas 2 and 8HR, 510-883-2085

Matsuoka, Fumitaka, PhD, Union Theological Seminary, Richmond (1978), 1993, PSR Dean and Vice President for Academic Affairs and Professor—theology, Area 3, 510-848-0528

Matt, Daniel C., PhD, Brandeis University (1977), 1979, Professor—Jewish spirituality, Area 8HR, 510-649-2400

McCullough, Donald, PhD, University of Edinburgh (1980), 1994, SFTS President and Professor—theology and preaching, Area 3, 415-258-6500

McGann, Mary E., PhD, Graduate Theological Union (1996), 1996, Assistant Professor—liturgy and music, Area 7, 510-828-5232

McKinney, William, PhD, Pennsylvania State University (1979), 1996, PSR President and Professor—American Religion, Area 4, 510-848-0528

Mendiola, Michael M., PhD, Graduate Theology Union (1991), 1991, Assistant Professor—Christian ethics, Area 4, 510-848-0528

Menten, Jane Maynard, MDiv, Church Divinity School of the Pacific (1992), 1996, Director of Field Education, 510-204-0700

Miles, Margaret R., PhD, Graduate Theological Union (1977), 1996, GTU Dean and Vice President for Academic Affairs and Dillenberger Professor of Historical Theology, Areas 2 and 7, 510-649-2400

Moeser, Marion, PhD, University of Notre Dame (1998), 1998, Assistant Professor—New Testament, Area 1, 510-848-5232

Moon, Cyris Hee-Suk, PhD, Emory University (1971), 1990, Professor—Old Testament, Area 1, 415-258-6500

Morgan, Donn F., PhD, Claremont Graduate School (1974), 1972, CDSP Dean and President and Professor—Old Testament, Area 1, 510-204-0700

Morris, Michael T., PhD, University of California, Berkeley (1986), 1979, Professor—religion and the arts, Area 7, 510-883-2085

Mudge, Lewis S., PhD, Princeton University (1961), 1987, Robert Leighton Stuart Professor—systematic theology, Area 3, 415-258-6500

Nakasone, Ronald Y., PhD, University of Wisconsin (1980), 1987, Professor—Buddhist, studies, Area 8HR, 510-848-0528

Nasu, Eisho, PhD, Graduate Theological Union (1996), 1997, Assistant Professor—Shin Buddhism, Area 8HR, 650-938-7192

Nieman, Frank B., PhD, Marquette University (1972), 1970, SAT Dean and President, 510-652-1651

Noel, James A., PhD, Graduate Theological Union (1998), 1987, Assistant Professor—racial-ethnic and urban ministries, Area 2, 415-258-6500

Ocker, Christopher, PhD, Princeton Theological Seminary (1991), 1991, Associate Professor—church history, Area 2, 415-258-6500

O'Neill, William R., PhD, Yale University (1988), 1988, Associate Professor—social ethics, Area 4, 510-549-5016

Osborne, Kenan B., DrTheol, Ludwig-Maximilians-Universität, Munich (1967), 1968, Professor—systematic theology, Area 3, 510-848-5232

Park, Eung Chun, PhD, University of Chicago (1991), 1996, Assistant Professor—New Testament, Area 1, 415-258-6500

Parker, Rebecca, DMin, School of Theology at Claremont (1979), 1990, SKSM President and Professor—theology, Area 3, 510-845-6232

Payne, Richard K., PhD, Graduate Theological Union (1985), 1986, IBS Dean and Associate Professor—Japanese Buddhism, Area 8HR, 650-938-7192

Pence, Gary, PHD, Princeton University (1981), 1976, Associate Professor—pastoral theology, Area 5, 510-524-5264

Peters, Ted, PhD, University of Chicago (1973), 1978, Professor—systematic theology, Area 3, 510-524-5264

Porter, Andrew, PhD, University of California, Davis (Applied Science) (1976); PhD, Graduate Theological Union (1991), 1998, Assistant Professor—systematic and philosophical theology, Area 3, 510-848-8152

Rambo, Lewis R., PhD, University of Chicago (1975), 1978, Tully Professor—psychology and religion, Areas 5 and 8HR, 415-258-6500

Rhodes, Lynn, ThD, Boston University School of Theology (1983), 1983, Associate Professor—ministry and field education, 510-848-0528

Robb, Carol, PhD, Boston University (1978), 1985, Margaret Dollar Professor—Christian social ethics, Area 4, 415-258-6500

Rocca, Gregory P., PhD, Catholic University of America (1989), 1989, Associate Professor—philosophy and theology, Area 3, 510-883-2085

Rogers, Jack, ThD, Free University of Amsterdam (1967), 1990, Vice President for Southern California Theological Programs and Professor—theology, Area 3, 415-258-6500

Rogers, Thomas G., PhD, Graduate Theological Union (1995), 1990, Associate Professor—homiletics, Area 7, 510-524-5264

Russell, Keith A., DMin, New York Theological Seminary (1976), 1997, ABSW President and Professor—pastoral theology, Area 7H, 510-841-1905

Russell, Robert J., PhD, University of California, Santa Cruz (1978), 1981, Director of the Center for Theology and the Natural Sciences and Professor—theology and science, Areas 3 and 8S, 510-649-2400

Sanks, T. Howland, PhD, University of Chicago (1971), 1980, Professor—historical/systematic theology, Area 3, 510-549-5016

Schenk, Richard, DrTheol, Ludwig-Maximilians-Universität, Munich (1986), 1991, Professor—philosophy and theology, Area 3, 510-883-2085

Schneiders, Sandra M., STD, Pontifical Gregorian University, Rome (1975), 1976, Professor—New Testament studies, Christian spirituality, Areas 1 and 8S, 510-549-5016

Seidman, Naomi, PhD, University of California, Berkeley (1993), 1995, Associate Professor]7Jewish culture, Area 8HR, 510-649-2400

Short, William J., STD, Pontifical Gregorian University, Rome, (1983), 1983, FST Dean and Professor—Christian spirituality, Areas 2 and 8S, 510-848-5232

Silva-Netto, Benoni R., PhD, Northwestern University (1985); DMin, Christian Theological Seminary (1975), 1985, Professor—pastoral care and Methodist studies, Area 5, 510-848-0528

Smith, Archie, Jr., PhD, Brandeis University (1973), 1975, James and Clarice Foster Professor—pastoral psychology and counseling, Areas 4 and 5, 510-848-0528

Smith, J. Alfred, Sr., DMin, Golden Gate Baptist Theological Seminary (1975), 1975, Professor—preaching and church ministries, Area 7, 510-841-1905

Smith, Robert H., ThD, Concordia Theological Seminary, St Louis (1962), 1983, Professor—New Testament, Area 1, 510-524-5264

Song, Choan-Seng, PhD, Union Theological Seminary (1965), 1985, Professor—theology and Asian cultures, Area 3, 510-848-0528

Stagaman, David, DrenTh, Institute Catholique de Paris (1975), 1972, Associate Professor—systematic theology, Area 3, 510-549-5016

Stortz, Martha Ellen, PhD, University of Chicago Divinity School (1984), 1981, Associate Professor—historical theology and ethics, Area 4, 510-524-5264

Strohl, Jane E., PhD, University of Chicago (1989), 1996, Associate Professor—Reformation history and theology, Area 2, 510-524-5264

Tatum, Gregory T., PhD, Duke University (1997), 1996, Assistant Professor—New Testament, Area 1, 510-883-2085

Tolbert, Mary Ann, PhD, University of Chicago (1977), 1994, George H. Atkinson Professor—biblical studies, Area 1, 510-848-0528

Turner, Mary Donovan, PhD, Emory University (1991), 1991, Associate Professor—preaching, Area 7, 510-848-0528

Walker, Randi, PhD, Claremont Graduate School (1983), 1992, Assistant Professor—church history, Area 2, 510-848-0528

Weil, Louis, STD, Institute Catholique de Paris (1972), 1988, Professor—liturgics, Area 7, 510-204-0700

Welch, Claude, PhD, Yale University (1950), 1971, GTU Dean Emeritus and Professor—historical theology, Areas 2 and 3, 510-649-2400

West, Thomas, PhD, California Institute of Integral Studies (1994), 1995, Director of Field Education and Assistant Professor—pastoral theology, Area 5, 510-848-5232

White, Ronald C., PhD, Princeton University (1972), 1997, SFTS Dean and Vice President for Academic Affairs and Professor—church history, Area 2, 415-258-6500

Wickeri, Philip, PhD, Princeton Theological Seminary (1988), 1998, Flora Lamson Hewlett Professor—evangelism and mission, Areas 2 and 3, 415-258-6500

Wire, Antoinette C., PhD, Claremont Graduate School (1974), 1973, Professor—New Testament, Area 1, 415-258-6500

Yee, Edmond, PhD, University of California, Berkeley (1977), 1978, Professor—multi-cultural studies, Area 8HR, 510-524-5264

Graham Bible College

PO Box 1630, Bristol VA 24203

Grand Canyon University

3300 W Camelback Rd
Phoenix AZ 85017

Phone: 602-589-2464
Fax: 602-589-2693
E-mail: cgaines@enet.net

TYPE OF INSTITUTION: Private, Southern Baptist
EXECUTIVE OFFICER: Chuck Gaines, Dean, College of Christian Studies
UNDERGRADUATE ENROLLMENT: 70

Grand Rapids Baptist Seminary

1001 E Beltline NE
Grand Rapids, MI 49525

Phone: 616-222-1422
Fax: 616-222-1414
E-mail: semadm@cornerstone.edu
URL: www.cornerstone.edu/grbs

TYPE OF INSTITUTION: Private, Baptist
EXECUTIVE OFFICER: Robert W. Nienhuis, President
GRADUATE ENROLLMENT: 218

Grand View College

1200 Grandview Ave
Des Moines IA 50316

Phone: 515-263-2903
Fax: 515-263-6095

TYPE OF INSTITUTION: Private, ELCA Lutheran
EXECUTIVE OFFICER: Ronald Taylor, Academic Dean and Provost
CHAIRPERSON: Kenneth Diable
UNDERGRADUATE ENROLLMENT: 1,450

Gratz College

Old York and Melrose Rds, Melrose Park PA 19126

University of Great Falls

1301 20th Street S
Great Falls MT 59405

Phone: 406-791-5357
Fax: 406-791-5394
E-mail: jtaylor@ugf.edu
URL: home.att.net/~taylor.jon

TYPE OF INSTITUTION: Private, Catholic
EXECUTIVE OFFICER: Frederick Gilliard, President
CHAIRPERSON: Jon Taylor
UNDERGRADUATE ENROLLMENT: 1,250
GRADUATE ENROLLMENT: 200

Great Lakes Christian College

6211 W Willow Hwy	Phone: 517-321-0242
Lansing MI 48917	Fax: 517-321-5902
	E-mail:[department]@glcc.edu
	URL: glcc.edu

TYPE OF INSTITUTION: Private, Christian Church/Chuches of Christ
EXECUTIVE OFFICER: James R. Estep, Academic Dean
UNDERGRADUATE ENROLLMENT: 160

Greensboro College

815 W Market St	Phone: 336-272-7102
Greensboro NC 27420	Fax: 336-271-6634
	URL: www.gborocollege.edu

TYPE OF INSTITUTION: Private, United Methodist
EXECUTIVE OFFICER: Craven E. Williams, President
COORDINATORS: W. Barnes Tatum, Philip A. Rolnick, Rhonda Burnette-Bletsch
UNDERGRADUATE ENROLLMENT: 1,050

Greenville College

Greenville IL 62246

Grinnell College

PO Box 805	Phone: 515-269-3157
Grinnell IA 50112-0806	Fax: 515-269-4414
	E-mail: gilday@grinnell.edu
	URL: www.grinnell.edu/religiousstudies/

TYPE OF INSTITUTION: Private
EXECUTIVE OFFICER: James E. Swartz, Dean of the College
CHAIRPERSON: Edmund T. Gilday
UNDERGRADUATE ENROLLMENT: 1,314
DEGREES OFFERED: BA
UNDERGRADUATE MAJORS: 30
DEGREES CONFERRED: 10
DESCRIPTION OF UNDERGRADUATE PROGRAM: As teachers of religious studies, we seek to cultivate in students an awareness and knowledge of the various ways human beings have practiced, represented, and reflected on their religious lives. We want our students to gain a critical appreciation and an interdisciplinary understanding of humanity's religious traditions from both historical and contemporary points of view.
FACULTY:
Gilday, Edmund, PhD, University of Chicago (1987), 1995, Associate Professor—Chinese and Japanese religious traditions, 515-269-4227, Fax: 515-269-4414, E-mail: gilday@grinnell.edu

Kasimow, Harold, PhD, Temple, (1976), 1972, Professor—Judaism, Islam, Buddhism, 515-269-3180, Fax: 515-269-4414, E-mail: kasimow@grinnell.edu

Rietz, Henry W. L., MDiv, Princeton Theological Seminary (1992), 1998, Instructor—biblical studies, early Judaism, 515-269-4558, Fax: 515-269-4414, E-mail: rietz@grinnell.edu

Roberts, Tyler T., ThD, Harvard University, Divinity School (1993), 1997, Assistant Professor—Christian tradition, 515-269-4472, Fax: 515-269-4414, E-mail: robertst@grinnell.edu

Skerrett, K. Roberts, PhD, Harvard (1993), 1997, Assistant Professor—Christian tradition, 515-269-3138, Fax: 515-269-4414, E-mail: skerrett@grinnell.edu

Thorson-Smith, Sylvia, MA, Wichita State University (1980), 1988, Lecturer—women and religion, 515-269-4872, Fax: 515-269-4414, E-mail: thorsons@grinnell.edu

Grove City College

100 Campus Dr   Phone: 412-458-2000
Grove City PA 16127-2104

TYPE OF INSTITUTION: Private, Presbyterian USA
EXECUTIVE OFFICER: John Moore, President
CHAIRPERSON: Dale R. Bowne
UNDERGRADUATE ENROLLMENT: 83

Gruss Girls Seminary

1 Adams Ln, Spring Valley NY 10977

University of Guelph

Guelph, Ontario N1G 2W1 Canada

Guilford College

Greensboro NC 27410

Gulf Coast Seminary

4101 W 21st St, Panama City FL 32405

Gustavus Adolphus College

800 W College Ave   Phone: 507-933-7317
St Peter MN 56082   Fax: 507-933-7041

TYPE OF INSTITUTION: Private, Lutheran (ELCA)
EXECUTIVE OFFICERS: Axel Steuer, President; Elizabeth Baer, Dean
CHAIRPERSON: Garret Paul
UNDERGRADUATE ENROLLMENT: 2,200
DEGREES OFFERED: BA

UNDERGRADUATE MAJORS: 20

DESCRIPTION OF UNDERGRADUATE PROGRAM: The program of the department of Religion is designed to meet the needs of all students for a better understanding of religion as a basic aspect of human experience, of the Christian heritage and its contemporary expressions, and of the methods appropriate to the study of religion. Study involves the use of perspectives and methods from several fields including the arts and foreign languages, social sciences and literature, history and philosophy, offering a unique opportunity for the type of integrated study that is desirable in a liberal arts education.

FACULTY:

Cha, John, PhD, Northwestern (1992.), 1997, Assistant Professor—history of religion, 507-933-7485, Fax: 507-933-7041, E-mail: jcha@gac.edu

Clark, Jack, PhD, Yale University (1962), 1962, Professor—Bible, New Testament

Hawkins, Faith Kirkham, ABD, Emory University, 1998, Instructor in Religion—New Testament, 507-933-6295, E-mail: fhawkins@gac.edu

Jodock, Darrell, PhD, Yale University (1969), 1999, Bernhardson Chair in Lutheran Studies—religious studies, 507-933-7474, Fax: 507-933-7041

Trelstad, Marit, ABD, Claremont Graduate School, 1998, Visiting Instructor, 507-933-7474, Fax: 507-933-7041

Paul, Garrett, PhD, University of Chicago (1980), 1983, Professor and Chair—theology, ethics, 507-933-7041, Fax: 507-933-7041, E-mail: gpaulc&gac.edu

Solberg, Mary, PhD, Union Seminary (New York) (1995), 1996, Visiting Assistant Professor (1997-99)—theology, ethics, 507-933-7470, Fax: 507-933-7041, E-mail: msolberg@gac.edu

Vaughn, Andrew, PhD, Princeton University (1996), 1997, Assistant Professor—Bible, Old Testament, 507-933-7475, Fax: 507-933-7041, E-mail: avaughn@gac.edu

Verman, Mark, PhD, Harvard University (1984), 1996, Visiting Associate Professor (1997-98)—Bible, Judaism, 507-933-7472, Fax: 507-933-7041, E-mail: mverman@gac.edu

G

Hadar Hatorah Rabbinical Seminary

824 Eastern Pkwy, Brooklyn NY 11213

Hamilton College

Dept of Religion, Clinton NY 13323

Hamline University

1536 Hewitt Ave
St Paul MN 55104

Phone: 651-523-2800
URL: www.hamline.edu

TYPE OF INSTITUTION: Private, United Methodist
EXECUTIVE OFFICER: Larry Osnes
CHAIRPERSON: Timothy Polk
UNDERGRADUATE ENROLLMENT: 1,600
DEGREES OFFERED: BA
UNDERGRADUATE MAJORS: 30
DEGREES CONFERRED: 9

DESCRIPTION OF UNDERGRADUATE PROGRAM: The Hamline University Religion Department is made up of scholar-practitioners—Christian, Jewish, and Buddhist—each of whom embraces the school's mission as a United Methodist-related institution "dedicated to preparing compassionate citizens of the world." Seeking to model the reciprocal relation between the academic study of a particular religion and its practice, in our diversity we also aim to honor the Methodist emphasis on ecumenical openness to other faiths. We interpret the church affiliation as a charter of hospitality by which Hamline invites students of different backgrounds to develop a critical understanding of their own stance and to explore other faiths with respect for their intrinsic worth. The Department offers a major with concentrations in biblical studies, theological/historical studies, Jewish studies, social justice/ethics, and nonwestern religions. All courses stress the connections between religious studies and other academic diciplines in the humanities, arts, and social sciences.

FACULTY:

Berkson, Mark A., PhD, Stanford University (1999), 1999, Assistant Professor—Asian religions, philosophy of religion, 651-523-2918, E-mail: mberkson@gw.hamline.edu

Mason, Theresa M., PhD, University of Oregon (1995), 1996, Assistant Professor and Chaplain—religion and the arts, 651-523-2315, E-mail: tmason@gw.hamline.edu

Polk, Timothy H., PhD, Yale University (1982), 1982, Professor and Dept Chair—biblical studies, 651-523-2232, E-mail: tpolk@gw.hamline.edu

Schwartz, Earl, BA, University of Minnesota (1975), 1993, Instructor (part-time)—Jewish studies, E-mail: eschwartz@gw.hamline.edu

Thompson, Deanna A., PhD, Vanderbilt University (1997), 1996, Assistant Professor—theology and ethics, 651-523-2313, E-mail: dthompson@gw.hamline.edu

Hampden-Sydney College

Dept of Religion, Hampden-Sydney VA 23943

Hampton Institute

Hampton VA 23368

Hannibal-LaGrange College

2800 Palmyra Rd
Hannibal MO 63401

Phone: 573-221-3675
Fax: 573-221-6594
E-mail: mbergen@hlg.edu

TYPE OF INSTITUTION: Private, Southern Baptist
EXECUTIVE OFFICER: Woodrow Burt, President
CHAIRPERSON: Martha Bergen
UNDERGRADUATE ENROLLMENT: 1,000

Hanover College

Dept of Theology, Hanover IN 47243

Hardin-Simmons University

Abilene TX 79601

Harding University

College of Bible and Religion
Box 2280 Searcy AR 72149-0001

Phone: 501-279-4448
Fax: 501-279-4042

TYPE OF INSTITUTION: Private, Churches of Christ
EXECUTIVE OFFICERS: David B. Burks, President; Thomas C. Alexander, Dean of College of
Bible and Religion
UNDERGRADUATE ENROLLMENT: 3,500
GRADUATE ENROLLMENT: 350

Harding University Graduate School of Religion

1000 Cherry Rd
Memphis TN 38117

Phone: 800-680-0809
901-761-1356
Fax: 901-761-1358
E-mail: smcleod@hugsr.edu
URL: www.hugsr.edu

TYPE OF INSTITUTION: Private, Church of Christ affiliation
EXECUTIVE OFFICER: Bill Flatt, Dean/CEO
GRADUATE ENROLLMENT: 225

University of Hartford
West Hartford CT 06117

Hartford Seminary

77 Sherman St
Hartford CT 06105

Phone: 860-509-9500
Fax: 860-509-9509
E-mail: hartsem@hartsem.edu

TYPE OF INSTITUTION: Private, Non-Denominational
EXECUTIVE OFFICER: Barbara Brown Zikmund, President
GRADUATE ENROLLMENT: 128

Hartwick College

Dept of Phil and Religious Studies
Oneonta NY 13820

Phone: 607-431-4933
Fax: 607-431-4351
E-mail: heriong@hartwick.edu

TYPE OF INSTITUTION: Private, Non-Denominational
EXECUTIVE OFFICER: Richard A. Detweiler, President
CHAIRPERSON: Gary Herion
UNDERGRADUATE ENROLLMENT: 1,450
DEGREES OFFERED: BA in Religious Studies, BA Philosophy and Religious Studies
UNDERGRADUATE MAJORS: 25
DEGREES CONFERRED: 10
DESCRIPTION OF UNDERGRADUATE PROGRAM: Although housed in the same department, the Religious Studies curriculum functions independent of the Philosophy curriculum. A range of introductory survey, intermediate, and advanced seminar courses cover three broad areas: the biblical tradition; the Eastern religions; and contemporary theology. In part to complement major college initiatives in global pluralism, the College has recently created a new full-time position in Asian religions. The College also supports numerous courses abroad during its month-long January Term, and several such courses have been offered and supported by Religious Studies (Archaeology and the Bible, Semester in India).
FACULTY:
Capper, Dave, ABD, University of Chicago, 1997, Adjunct Instructor—Islam, religion and culture
Herion, Gary A., PhD, University of Michigan (1982), 1991, Associate Professor—biblical studies
Huntington, C. W., PhD, University of Michigan (1986), 1995, Assistant Professor—Asian religions

Harvard University

Committee on the Study of Religion
Barker Center, 12 Quincy St
Cambridge MA 02138

Phone: 617-495-5781
Fax: 617-496-5798
E-mail: csrel@fas.harvard.edu
URL: www.fas.harvard.edu/~csrel

TYPE OF INSTITUTION: Private, Non-Denominational

EXECUTIVE OFFICER: Neil Rudenstine, President

CHAIRPERSON: David D. Hall

UNDERGRADUATE ENROLLMENT: 6,500

GRADUATE ENROLLMENT: 3,000

DEGREES OFFERED: AB

UNDERGRADUATE MAJORS: 65

DEGREES CONFERRED: 7

DESCRIPTION OF UNDERGRADUATE PROGRAM: The undergraduate concentration in the Comparative Study of Religion provides students with a basic understanding of one or two of the major religious traditions of the world through study of the sacred books, ritual and artistic symbolism, philosophy and theology, and social history. It also includes a critical overview of the literature on theory and methodology in the study of religion. An honors only concentration, the Comparative Study of Religion offers a tutorial program during the sophomore, junior and senior years. Reading knowledge of a foreign language, general examinations, and a thesis are required.

GRADUATE PROGRAM

Member of the Council on Graduate Studies in Religion

Graduate Advisors: Peter Machinist, Director of PhD Studies; Francois Bovon, Director of ThD Studies

Graduate Degrees Offered: MA; PhD; ThD

Degrees Conferred: 6 MA; 8 PhD; 3 ThD

Graduate Students in Residence: 134 PhD/ThD

Not in Residence: 16 PhD/ThD

Average No. of New Students Enrolled: 14 PhD/ThD

Women Students: 72 PhD/ThD

Minority Students: 12 PhD/ThD

Foreign Students: 22 PhD/ThD

Minimum GRE Score Requisite to Admission: No

Minimum GPA Score Requisite to Admission: No

Foreign Language Proficiency Evaluated: No

Financial Aid to First Year Students: 100% PhD/ThD

Financial Aid to Other Students: 95% PhD/ThD

Attrition Among Students: 3% PhD/ThD

Graduates Placed: 75% PhD/ThD

DESCRIPTION OF GRADUATE PROGRAMS AND RESEARCH FACILITIES: The Committee on the Study of Religion administers both the PhD, granted by the Faculty of Arts and Sciences, and the ThD, granted by the Faculty of Divinity. The principal research facilities are the libraries of the university and resources such as the Center for the Study of World Religions. The PhD degree combines mastery, at an advanced level, of some specialization in religious studies, with an emphasis on understanding it within the context of a particular religious or cultural whole of which it is a part, and within the context of human religiousness at large. The ThD program emphasizes the study of the institutions, languages, and religious literatures that have shaped the Jewish, Christian, and Western humanistic traditions in their histories and in their encounters with other cultures and religions in past and present. This study is conducted with special attention to the concerns of the Christian theological tradition.

ACADEMIC PLAN, ADMISSION REQUIREMENTS, FINANCIAL AID: Harvard University operates on the two-term system. Applicants to the PhD program must have earned at least the BA degree; a masters is preferred. Applicants to the ThD must have earned an MDiv degree or equivalent. All doctoral candidates are expected to demonstrate a reading competence in French and German by the end of their first year. For more information on options for study, program requirements, admission and financial aid, write to: Program Administrator, Committee on the Study of Religion, Barker Center, 12 Quincy Street, Cambridge MA 02138.

FACULTY OF THE COMMITTEE ON THE STUDY OF RELIGION:

Anderson, Gary A., Professor of Hebrew Bible (Divinity School)

Asani, Ali S., Professor of the Practice of Indo-Muslim Language and Culture

Bovon, François, Frothingham Professor of the History of Religion (Divinity School), Director of ThD Studies

Coakley, Sarah, Edward Mallinckrodt, Jr., Professor of Divinity (Divinity School)

Cox, Harvey G., Victor S. Thomas Professor of Divinity (Divinity School)

Eck, Diana L., Professor of Comparative Religion and of Indian Studies

Fiorenza, Francis, Charles Chauncey Stillman Professor of Roman Catholic Theological Studies (Divinity School)

Gomes, Peter J., Plummer Professor of Christian Morals (Divinity School)

Graham, William A., Professor of the History of Religion and Islamic Studies

Hackett, Jo Ann, Professor of the Practice of Biblical Hebrew and Northwest Semitic Epigraphy

Hall, David D., Director of PhD Studies and Professor of American Religious History on the Bartlett and Emerson Funds (Divinity School) (Chair)

Hallisey, Charles, John L. Loeb Associate Professor of the Humanities

Kloppenberg, James, Professor of History (on leave spring term)

Lamberth, David, Assistant Professor of Theology (Divinity School)

Lamothe, Kimerer, Lecturer on the Study of Religion and Head Tutor

Little, David, Professor of Religion, Ethnicity, and International Conflict (Divinity School)

Machinist, Peter, Hancock Professor of Hebrew and Other Oriental Languages, and member of the faculty of Divinity, Director of PhD Studies

Patton, Kimberley, Assistant Professor in the Comparative and Historical Study of Religion (Divinity School)

Putnam, Hilary, Cogan University Professor

Tu, Wei-Ming, Professor of Chinese History and Philosophy

Van der Kuijp, Leonard, Professor of Tibetan and Himalayan Studies

Williams, Preston, Houghton Professor of Theology and Contemporary Change (Divinity School)

OTHER FACULTY OFFERING INSTRUCTION IN THE STUDY OF RELIGION:

Alexiou, Margaret, George Sefaris Professor of Modern Greek Thought (on leave spring term)

Atkinson, Clarissa W., Senior Lecturer on the History of Christianity (Divinity School)

Bryant, Edwin, Lecturer on South Asian Religions

Callahan, Allen D., Assistant Professor of New Testament (Divinity School) (on leave fall term)

Carman, John B., Parkman Professor of Divinity and Professor of Comparative Religion (Divinity School)

Dyck, Arthur J., Mary B. Saltonstall Professor of Population Ethics (Public Health and Divinity School)

Hanson, Paul D., Florence Corliss Lamont Professor of Divinity (Divinity School)

Hardacre, Helen, Reischauer Institute Professor of Japanese Religions and Society

Harris, Jay M., Harry Austryn Wolfson Professor of Jewish Studies

Harris, Joseph C., Professor of English and Folklore

Hehir, J. Bryan, Professor of the Practice in Religion and Society (Divinity School)

Henrichs, Albert, Eliot Professor of Greek Literature

Higginbotham, Evelyn Brooks, Professor of Afro-American Studies (FAS) and Professor of African American Religious History (Divinity School) (on leave spring term)

Hutchison, William, Charles Warren Professor of the History of Religion in America (Divinity School) (on leave 99-00)

King, Karen, Professor of New Testament Studies and the History of Ancient Christianity (Divinity School)

Koester, Helmut, John H. Morison Professor of New Testament Studies and Winn Professor of Ecclesiastical History (Divinity School) (Emeritus)

Kugel, James L., Harry Starr Professor of Classical and Modern Jewish and Hebrew Literature and Professor of Comparative Literature

Levenson, Jon D., Albert A. List Professor of Jewish Studies (Divinity School) (on leave 99-00)

McAfee, Eugene, Lecturer on the Study of Religion

Mitten, David G., James C. Loeb Professor of Classical Art and Archaeology

Niebuhr, Richard R., Hollis Professor of Divinity (Divinity School)

Potter, Ralph, Professor of Social Ethics (Divinity School)

Queen, Christopher S., Lecturer in the Study of Religion

Schüssler Fiorenza, Elisabeth, Krister Stendahl Professor of Divinity (Divinity School) (on leave spring term)

Sullivan, Lawrence E., Professor of the History of Religions (Divinity School) (on leave 99-00)

Tambiah, Stanley J., Professor of Anthropology (on leave 99-00)

Thiemann, Ronald F., John Lord O'Brian Professor of Theology (Divinity School) (on leave 99-00)

West, Cornel, Professor of Afro-American Studies (FAS) and Professor of the Philosophy of Religion (Divinity School)

Winter, Irene J., William Dorr Boardman Professor of Fine Arts (on leave 99-00)

Harvard Divinity School

45 Francis Ave
Cambridge MA 02138

Phone: 617-495-5796
Fax: 617-495-9489
E-mail: admissions@hds.harvard.edu
URL: www.hds.harvard.edu

TYPE OF INSTITUTION: Private
EXECUTIVE OFFICER: J. Bryan Hehir, Chair of the Executive Committee
GRADUATE ENROLLMENT: 513

GRADUATE PROGRAM

Graduate Degrees Offered: ThD; ThM

Degrees Conferred: 116 MTS; 3 ThD; 7 ThM

Graduate Students in Residence: 265 MTS; 47 ThD; 13 ThM

Not in Residence: 0 MTS; 9 ThD; 0 ThM

Average No. of New Students Enrolled: 99 MTS; 5 ThD; 9 ThM

Women Students: 142 MTS; 33 ThD; 3 ThM

Minority Students: 61 MTS; 6 ThD; 2 ThM

Foreign Students: 19 MTS; 6 ThD; 6 ThM

Minimum GRE Score Requisite to Admission: Yes, ThD only.

Minimum GPA Score Requisite to Admission: No

Foreign Language Proficiency Evaluated: Requirement fulfilled by HDS language exam or by an honor grade in an intermediate course.

Financial Aid to First Year Students: 97% MTS; 100% ThD; 0% Other

Financial Aid to Other Students: 82% MTS; 78%ThD; 0% other

Attrition Among Students: 2% MTS; 0% ThD; 8% Other

DESCRIPTION OF GRADUATE PROGRAMS AND RESEARCH FACILITIES: Degree programs offered are the MDiv, MTS, ThM, and ThD. Also offered are a Summer Language Program and a Program in Religion and Secondary Education. Library facilities available to students include the 500,000 volume Andover-Harvard Theological Library at HDS, the other libraries of Harvard University, and the libraries of the Boston Theological Institute, of which HDS is a member. Non-degree programs include Merrill Fellows and Urban Fellows (post-graduate training for those engaged in ministry), Visiting Scholars, Special Students, Resident Graduates, and ministers in the vicinity. The Women's Studies in Religion Program supports five senior scholar-teachers each year. Affiliated institutions include the Center for the Study of World Religions and the Center for the Study of Values in Public Life. HDS faculty also participate in the Faculty of Arts and Sciences programs leading to the PhD in the Study of Religion and the PhD in Near Eastern Languages and Civilizations.

ACADEMIC PLAN, ADMISSION REQUIREMENTS, FINANCIAL AID: The academic year consist of two semesters (fall and spring), the normal course load being four half courses (16 credit hours). Applicants for admission to the ThM and ThD programs should have a bachelor's degree and the MDiv or its equivalent. Applicants for the MTS program should have a bachelor's degree. Applicants must submit letters of recommendation, a letter of intent, and academic transcripts as part of the application. The ThM requires eight half courses to be taken in one year of full-time or up to two years of part-time study. The MTS requires sixteen half courses to be taken in two years of full-time or up to three years of part-time study. The ThD requirements include a minimum of two years full-time study in residence, General Examinations within three years, and completion of the thesis and final examination within seven years. Financial aid is available to degree candidates (excluding ThM candidates) in the form of grants and loans. About 90% of degree candidates receive financial aid.

FACULTY:

Ahmed, Leila, Professor of Women's Studies in Religion

Aitken, Ellen Bradshaw, Visiting Assistant Professor of New Testament

Anderson, Gary Alan, Professor of Hebrew Bible

Atkinson, Clarissa Webster, Associate Dean for Academic Affairs and Senior Lecturer on the History of Christianity

Bovon, François, Frothingham Professor of the History of Religion

Braude, Ann D., Director of the Women's Studies in Religion Program and Senior Lecturer in American Religious History

Callahan, Allen Dwight, Associate Professor of New Testament and Horace DeY. Lentz Lecturer

Carman, John Braisted, Parkman Professor of Divinity and Professor of Comparative Religion

Coakley, Sarah Anne, Edward Mallinckrodt, Jr., Professor of Divinity

Constas, Nicholas P., Assistant Professor of Theology

Cox, Harvey Gallagher, Jr., Victor S. Thomas Professor of Divinity

Dyck, Arthur James, Mary B. Saltonstall Professor of Population Ethics in the School of Public Health and Member of the Faculty of Divinity

Eck, Diana L., Professor of Comparative Religion and Indian Studies in the Department of Sanskrit and Indian Studies, Faculty of Arts and Sciences, and Member of the Faculty of Divinity

Fiorenza, Francis Schüssler, Charles Chauncey Stillman Professor of Roman Catholic Theological Studies

Giles, Cheryl A., Professor of the Practice in Pastoral Care and Counseling

Gomes, Peter John, Plummer Professor of Christian Morals and Pusey Minister in the Memorial Church

Hall, David D., Professor of American Religious History on the Bartlett and Emerson Funds

Hanson, Paul David, Florence Corliss Lamont Professor of Divinity and Professor of Old Testament in Harvard Divinity School and the Department of Near Eastern Languages and Civilizations

Hehir, J. Bryan, Professor of the Practice in Religion and Society and Faculty Associate, Harvard Center for International Affairs

Highbaugh, Claudia Ann, Chaplain, Associate Director of Ministerial Studies, and Member of the Faculty of Divinity

Hutchison, William Robert, Charles Warren Professor of the History of Religion in America

Kienzle, Beverly Mayne, Professor of the Practice of Latin and Romance Languages

King, Karen Leigh, Professor of New Testament Studies and the History of Ancient Christianity

Kugel, James L., Starr Professor of Hebrew Literature in the Faculty of Arts and Sciences and Member of the Faculty of Divinity

Lamberth, David Clements, Assistant Professor of Theology

Levenson, Jon D., Albert A. List Professor of Jewish Studies

Little, David, T. J. Dermot Dumphy Professor of the Practice in Religion, Ethnicity, and International Conflict

Machinist, Peter B., Hancock Professor of Hebrew and Other Oriental Languages in the Faculty of Arts and Sciences and Member of the Faculty of Divinity

Patton, Kimberley C., Assistant Professor in the Comparative and Historical Study of Religion

Potter, Ralph Benajah, Jr., Professor of Social Ethics

Richardson, Nancy D., Associate Dean for Ministry and Director, Program in Religion and Secondard Education

Rose, Dudley Corwin, Director of Field Education and Member of the Faculty of Divinity

Schüssler Fiorenza, Elisabeth, Krister Stendahl Professor of Divinity

Sullivan, Lawrence, Professor of the History of Religions and Director of the Center for the Study of World Religions

Theimann, Ronald F., John Lord O'Brian Professor of Divinity and Dean of the Divinity School

West, Cornel, Professor of Afro-American Studies in the Faculty of Arts and Sciences and Professor of the Philosophy of Religion in the Divinity School

Williams, Preston Noah, Houghton Professor of Theology and Contemporary Change

AREA CHAIRS:

Bovon, François, Scripture and Interpretation

Carman, John B., Religions of the World

Fiorenza, Francis Schüssler, Christianity and Culture

Hastings College

800 Turner Avenue
Hastings NE 68901

Phone: 402-463-2402
Fax: 402-461-7490
E-mail: admissions@hastings.edu
URL: www.hastings.edu/academic/philrelig/P&R.htm

TYPE OF INSTITUTION: Private, Presbyterian Church (USA)

EXECUTIVE OFFICER: Richard E. Hoover, President

CHAIRPERSON: David Lovekin

UNDERGRADUATE ENROLLMENT: 1,030

GRADUATE ENROLLMENT: 29

Haverford College

Dept of Religion
Haverford PA 19041

Phone: 610-896-1031
Fax: 610-896-1224
E-mail: abarone@haverford.edu
URL: www.haverford.edu/

TYPE OF INSTITUTION: Private, Related to Society of Friends

EXECUTIVE OFFICER: Thomas Tritton, President

CHAIRPERSON: David Dawson

UNDERGRADUATE ENROLLMENT: 1,147

DEGREES OFFERED: BA

UNDERGRADUATE MAJORS: 19 (juniors and seniors)

DEGREES CONFERRED: 10

DESCRIPTION OF UNDERGRADUATE PROGRAM: The department's goal is to enable students to become critically-informed, independent, and creative interpreters of some of the religious movements that have decisively shaped human experience. In their coursework, students develop skills in the critical analysis of the texts, images, beliefs, and performances of religions. Like other liberal arts majors, the religion major is meant to prepare students for a broad array of vocational possibilities. Religion majors typically find careers in law, public service (including both religious and secular organizations), medicine, business, ministry, and education. Religion majors have also pursued advanced graduate degrees in Anthropology, History, Political Science, Biology, Near Eastern Studies, and Religious Studies. The department cooperates with various programs at Bryn Mawr College, Swarthmore College, and the University of Pennsylvania to broaden the scope of its offerings. The Gest Program in the Cross-Cultural Study of Religion provides additional resources for the study of a variety of religious traditions. Majors undertake a program of 10 courses culminating in a senior thesis.

FACULTY:

Dawson, John David, PhD, Yale University (1988), 1987, Professor—modern religious thought, Christian theology and literary theory, religion and public life

Hucks, Tracey, PhD, Harvard University (1997), 1999, Assistant Professor—American religious history, African American religious history, West African religious traditions, women and religion in America

Koltun-Fromm, Kenneth, PhD, Stanford University (1997), 1997, Assistant Professor—modern Jewish thought, Medieval Jewish thought, Jews and Judaism in America

Koltun-Fromm, Naomi, PhD, Stanford University (1993), 1997, Assistant Professor—Hebrew Bible, Judaism in the Greco-Roman world, Midrash and Rabbinics (on leave fall semester 1997)

McGuire, Anne, PhD, Yale University (1983), 1982, Associate Professor—New Testament, gnosticism, Graeco-Roman religions, women in early Christianity (on leave fall 1999)

Sells, Michael, PhD, The University of Chicago (1982), 1984, Professor—Islamic studies, comparative religion, religions of the East, comparative mysticism, Qur'an, Middle East literature (on leave spring 2000)

University of Hawaii at Hilo
Hilo HI 96720

University of Hawaii at Manoa

Sakamaki Hall A311　　　　　　　　　　　　　　Phone: 808-956-8299
2530 Dole St　　　　　　　　　　　　　　　　　　Fax: 808-956-9894
Honolulu HI 96822　　　　　　　　　　　E-mail: gtanabe@hawaii.edu
　　　　　　　　　　　　　　　　　　　　URL: www2.hawaii.edu/rel

TYPE OF INSTITUTION: Public

EXECUTIVE OFFICER: Kenneth P. Mortimer, President and Chancellor

CHAIRPERSON: George J. Tanabe, Jr.

UNDERGRADUATE ENROLLMENT: 16,825

GRADUATE ENROLLMENT: 4,094

DEGREES OFFERED: BA, MA

UNDERGRADUATE MAJORS: 15

DESCRIPTION OF UNDERGRADUATE PROGRAM: Undergraduate education in Religion includes survey courses in Western, Asian and Pacific religions. Students must complete 27 credit hours at the 200 level and above, including at least 9 credit hours in 300- and 400-level courses. For a minor in religion, students must complete 15 credit hours at the 300 level and above.

GRADUATE PROGRAM

Member of the Council on Graduate Studies in Religion

Graduate Degrees Offered: MA

Minimum GPA Score Requisite to Admission: Yes, 3.00 on a 4.00 scale

Foreign Language Proficiency Evaluated: Yes, TOEFL, 600 and above

DESCRIPTION OF GRADUATE PROGRAM AND RESEARCH FACILITIES: Out of a commitment to both scholarship and pedagogy, the Department has developed two graduate program plans leading to the MA degree: a thesis-based MA program (Plan A, 30 credits) in which students conduct advanced research in the religious traditions of a selected geographical area in Asia or Polynesia; and a non-thesis track (Plan B, 30 credits). Plans A and B are both two-year programs. Students may apply for the Certificate of Study program (15 credits). Application requirements are the same as for the MA degree program. This is a two-semester program for students who want to pursue graduate study in Religion but do not necessarily need or want a Master's degree. Applicants must hold a bachelor's degree from an accredited US college/university or its equivalent from a recognized foreign institution of higher learning. Applicants will be considered for the Fall Semester only.

ACADEMIC PLAN, ADMISSION REQUIREMENTS, FINANCIAL AID: Applicants must submit the following documents to the UH Graduate Division by March 1: 1) Graduate Admission Application, 2) One official transcript from each post-secondary institution attended, 3) Official TOEFL score report (foreign applicants only), 4) Verification of financial status (foreign applicants only); to the Department of Religion: 1) Three original letters of recommendation from referees familiar with the applicant's academic work, 2) A sample of written work, 3) One official transcript from each post-secondary institution attended, 4) Official Graduate Record Examination (GRE) scores are recommended but not required.

FACULTY:

Baroni, Helen J., PhD, Columbia University (1993), 1993, Assistant Professor—Japanese religions

Chappell, David W., PhD, Yale (1976), 1971, Professor—Buddhism, Chinese religions

Charlot, John P., PhD, University of Munich (1968), 1991, Professor—Hawaiian/Polynesian religions

Crawford, S. Cromwell, ThD, Pacific School of Religion (1965), 1965, Professor—Indian religions, Asian and Christian ethics

Lamb, Ramdas, PhD, University of California, Santa Barbara (1991), 1991, Associate Professor—methodology of religion, South Asian religions

Siegel, Lee A., PhD, Oxford (1975), 1976, Professor—Buddhism, Indian religions

Tanabe, George J., Jr., PhD, Columbia (1983), 1978, Professor—Japanese religions

---

Hebrew College

43 Hawes St
Brookline MA 02446

Phone: 617-278-4948
Fax: 617-264-9264
E-mail: admissions@hebrewcollege.edu
URL: www.hebrewcollege.edu

TYPE OF INSTITUTION: Private, Jewish
EXECUTIVE OFFICER: David Gordrs, President
UNDERGRADUATE ENROLLMENT: 51
GRADUATE ENROLLMENT: 199

Hebrew Theological College

7135 N Carpenter Rd, Skokie IL 60077

Hebrew Union College

Jewish Institute for Religion
3077 University Ave
Los Angeles CA 90007
TYPE OF INSTITUTION: Private, Jewish
EXECUTIVE OFFICER: Lewis M. Barth, Dean

Phone: 213-749-3424
Fax: 213-747-6128

Hebrew Union College-Jewish Institute

One W 4th Ave, New York NY 10012

Hebrew Union College-Jewish Institute of Religion

School of Graduate Studies
3101 Clifton Ave
Cincinnati OH 45220-4588

Phone: 513-221-1875
Fax: 513-221-0321
E-mail: gradschool@cn.huc.edu
URL: www.huc.edu

TYPE OF INSTITUTION: Private, Jewish
EXECUTIVE OFFICER: Adam Kamesar, Director
GRADUATE ENROLLMENT: 69
GRADUATE PROGRAM
Member of the Council on Graduate Studies in Religion
Graduate Advisor: A faculty member designated by student
Graduate Degrees Offered: MA; PhD; DHL
Degrees Conferred: 2 MA; 4 PhD; 6 MPhil
Graduate Students in Residence: 1 MA; 50 PhD
Not in Residence: 15 PhD; 1 DHL
Average No. of New Students Enrolled: 1 MA; 7 PhD
Women Students: 18 PhD
Minority Students: 5 PhD
Foreign Students: 6 PhD
Minimum GRE Score Requisite to Admission: No; 600+ verbal
Minimum GPA Score Requisite to Admission: No; normally A/A-
Foreign Language Proficiency Evaluated: No
Financial Aid to First Year Students: 60% PhD
Financial Aid to Other Students: 65% PhD
Attrition Among Students: 0 PhD
Graduates Placed: 100% PhD
DESCRIPTION OF GRADUATE PROGRAM AND RESEARCH FACILITIES: The College offers
MA and PhD programs in the following areas: Bible and ancient Near East; history of biblical
interpretation; Jewish studies in the Greco-Roman period; Rabbinics; medieval Jewish history and literature; philosophy and Jewish religious thought; and modern Jewish history and
literature. The program in Jewish studies in the Greco-Roman period is jointly sponsored by
the College and the Department of Classics, University of Cincinnati. Students have the use
of Klau Library, which contains about 400,000 volumes in Judaica, Hebraica, and ancient

Near Eastern studies, as well as one of the world's greatest collections of Hebrew incunabula and rare books. Students may also avail themselves of the facilities of the Nelson Glueck School of Biblical Archaeology in Jerusalem, Israel; the American Jewish Archives; and the University of Cincinnati.

ACADEMIC PLAN, ADMISSION REQUIREMENTS, FINANCIAL AID: MA (terminal): 45 credit hours of graduate work, or 36 hours plus a thesis, with an academic record of B or better. At least 12 credit hours must be taken in the student's area of specialization, and the program also includes an intensive 12 credit hour Hebrew course (all or part of which may be waived for students with demonstrated competence). All specific details of the program are determined in close consultation with a Faculty Advisor. PhD: At least two years of residency are required. The normal program includes completion of 72 credit hours of graduate course work (credits may be awarded for prior work), three 5-hour written candidacy examinations, and completion of a doctoral dissertation. Students who complete their candidacy examinations are eligible to receive the MPhil degree. The details of individual programs are determined successively in consultation with a faculty advisor, a three-person examining committee, and two faculty members who serve as dissertation supervisors. An accredited Bachelor's degree (or equivalent) is a minimum requirement for admission, although many entering students already hold advanced degrees. A basic knowledge of Hebrew is another prerequisite. New students take a proficiency examination during the orientation period prior to registration. On the basis of their performance, they may be required to take a pre-residency intensive Hebrew course that has been designed especially for graduate students. Students may take courses for graduate credit concurrently with the Hebrew course, but they are not officially admitted into residency until they successfully complete the Hebrew requirement. In addition to studying Hebrew, students are normally required to demonstrate reading knowledge of French and German, by tests administered by the relevant departments at the University of Cincinnati. Virtually all students receive financial aid, which is awarded solely on the basis of merit. A unique aspect of the School of Graduate Studies is its Interfaith Fellows Program, which provides fellowship support to Christian students who pursue their graduate work at the College. The College has long been renowned for fostering the spirit of free and open academic inquiry in a context of interfaith cooperation and understanding.

FACULTY:

Aaron, David, PhD, Brandeis University (1991), 1998, Professor—Bible

Cohen, Jonathan, PhD, University of Liverpool (1999), 1998, Assistant Professor—Talmud and Halachic literature

Cook, Michael J., PhD, Hebrew Union College (1975), 1973, Sol and Arlene Bronstein Professor—Judaeo-Christian studies

Ehrlich, Kenneth E., MAHL, Hebrew Union College (1974), 1987, Dean and Director of Rabbinic School

Einbinder, Susan, PhD, Columbia University (1991), 1993, Associate Professor—Hebrew literature

Fox, Nili, PhD, University of Pennsylvania (1997), 1998, Assistant Professor—Bible

Goldman, Edward A., PhD, Hebrew Union College (1974), 1969, Professor—Rabbinics

Goldman, Karla A., PhD, Harvard University (1994), 1991, Associate Professor—American Jewish history

Gottschalk, Alfred, PhD, University of Southern California (1965), 1971, Chancellor and Professor—Bible and Jewish thought

Greengus, Samuel, PhD, University of Chicago (1963), 1963, Julian Morgenstern Professor—Bible and Near Eastern literature

Jerusalmi, Isaac, PhD, Sorbonne, France (1962), 1963, Professor—Bible and Semitic languages

Joseph, Samuel K., PhD, Clayton University (1979), 1979, Professor—Jewish religious education

Kamesar, Adam, DPhil, University of Oxford (1987), 1987, Professor—Judaeo-Hellenistic literature

Katz, Robert L., DHL, Hebrew Union College (1952), 1960, Joseph and Helen Regenstein Professor Emeritus—religion, ethics and human relations

Kaufman, Stephen A., PhD, Yale University (1970), 1976, Professor—Bible and cognate literature

Kogan, Barry S., PhD, University of Toronto (1977), 1976, Gustave and Mamie Efroymson Professor—philosophy and Jewish religious thought

McCoy, Lowell G., MA, Ohio State University (1949), 1954, Professor Emeritus—speech

Meyer, Michael A., PhD, Hebrew Union College (1964), 1967, Professor—Jewish history

Mihaly, Eugene, PhD, Hebrew Union College (1949), 1951, Deutsch Professor Emeritus—Jewish jurisprudence and social justice, rabbinic literature and homiletics

Paper, Herbert H., PhD, University of Chicago (1951), 1977, Professor Emeritus—linguistics and Near Eastern language

Reines, Alvin J., PhD, Harvard University (1958), 1958, Professor—Jewish philosophy

Rivkin, Ellis, PhD, Johns Hopkins University (1946), 1949, Adolph S. Ochs Professor Emeritus—Jewish history

Sarason, Richard S., PhD, Brown University (1977), 1979, Professor—rabbinic literature and thought

Spicehandler, Ezra, PhD, Hebrew Union College (1952), 1950, Distinguished Service Professor Emeritus—Hebrew literature

Tsevat, Matitiahu, PhD, Hebrew Union College (1953), 1961, Professor Emeritus—Bible

Wacholder, Ben Zion, PhD, University of California, Los Angeles (1960), 1963, Solomon B. Freehof Professor Emeritus—Jewish law and practice, Talmud and rabbinics

Washofsky, Mark, PhD, Hebrew Union College (1987), 1985, Associate Professor—rabbinics

Weisberg, David B., PhD, Yale University (1965), 1967, Professor—Bible and Semitic languages

Zafren, Herbert C., AMLS, University of Michigan (1950), 1950, Professor Emeritus—Jewish bibliography

Zimmerman, Sheldon, MHL, Hebrew Union College (1970), 1996, President

---

Heidelberg College

Tiffin OH 44883

Phone: 419-448-2051
Fax: 419-448-2124
E-mail: rel-phi@heidelberg.edu

TYPE OF INSTITUTION: Private, United Church of Christ

Hellenic College/Holy Cross

50 Goddard Ave
Brookline MA 02445

Phone: 617-731-3500
Fax: 617-850-1460
E-mail: admissions@hchc.edu
URL: www.hchc.edu

TYPE OF INSTITUTION: Private, Greek Orthodox
EXECUTIVE OFFICER: Bishop Methodios, President
UNDERGRADUATE ENROLLMENT: 53
GRADUATE ENROLLMENT: 110

Hendrix College

Dept of Religion
1600 Washington Ave
Conway AR 72032

Phone: 501-450-1284
Fax: 501-450-1213
URL: www.hendrix.edu

TYPE OF INSTITUTION: Private, United Methodist
EXECUTIVE OFFICER: Ann Die, President
CHAIRPERSON: Jane Harris
UNDERGRADUATE ENROLLMENT: 1,080
DEGREES OFFERED: BA
UNDERGRADUATE MAJORS: 25-30
DEGREES CONFERRED: 12
DESCRIPTION OF UNDERGRADUATE PROGRAM: The Department of Religion at Hendrix
College, a seletive liberal arts college affiliated with the United Methodist Church, offers both
a major and a minor in religion. Majors must complete courses from at least four of six areas:
world religions, biblical studies, history of Christianity, American religion, theology and phi-
losophy of religion, and religion and culture. Graduates who recently majored in religion
have entered a variety of professions; including ministry, education, social work, law, medicine, and businss. While the 1,100 undergraduates need not take a religion course to meet
graduation requirements, hundreds of students find the study of religion a significant part of
their liberal arts education.
FACULTY:
Farthing, John, PhD, Duke University (1978), 1978, Professor—history of Christianity, history
of the Reformation, Roman Catholicism, Eastern Orthodoxy, African-American religion,
501-450-1394, Fax: 501-450-1213, E-mail: farthing@mercury.hendrix.,edu
Flannery-Dailey, Frances, MA, University of Iowa (1994), 1999, Instructor—biblical studies,
Ancient Near Eastern religions, Hebrew Bible, Judaism, 501-450-1284, Fax: 501-450-1213,
E-mail: dailey@mercury.hendrix.edu
Harris, Jane, PhD, University of North Carolina-Chapel Hill (1994), 1990, Associate Profes-
sor—history of American religion, women and religion, religion and culture, 501-450-1392,
Fax: 501-450-1213, E-mail: harris@mercury.hendrix.edu
McDaniel, Jay, PhD, Claremont Graduate School (1978), 1979, Professor—world religions,
contemporary theology and philosophy of religion, spirituality and sustainability, Buddhism,
501-450-1366, Fax: 501-450-1213, E-mail: mcdaniel@mercury.hendrix.edu

Heritage College

6000 W Colonial Dr, Orlando FL 32808

Heritage Bible College

PO Box 1628
Dunn NC 28334

Phone: 910-892-3178
Fax: 910-892-1809
E-mail: hbchead@intrstar.net

TYPE OF INSTITUTION: Private, Pentecostal Free Will Baptist
EXECUTIVE OFFICER: William L. Ellis, President
UNDERGRADUATE ENROLLMENT: 70

High Point University

University Station
High Point NC 27262

Phone: 336-841-4599
URL: www.highpoint.edu

TYPE OF INSTITUTION: Private, United Methodist
EXECUTIVE OFFICER: Jacob C. Martinson, President
CHAIRPERSON: Hal Warlick
UNDERGRADUATE ENROLLMENT: 2,958
GRADUATE ENROLLMENT: 189

Hillsdale College

Hillsdale MI 49242

Phone: 517-437-7341
E-mail: tom.burke@ac.hillsdale.edu
URL: www.hillsdale.edu

TYPE OF INSTITUTION: Private
EXECUTIVE OFFICER: George Rocle, President
CHAIRPERSONS: Thomas J. Burke, Jr.; Michael Bauman, Director of Christian Studies
UNDERGRADUATE ENROLLMENT: 1,200

Hillsdale Free Will Baptist College

PO Box 7208
Moore OK 73153-1208

Phone: 405-794-6661
Fax: 405-794-6663

TYPE OF INSTITUTION: Private, Free Will Baptist
EXECUTIVE OFFICER: Timothy Eaton, Vice President for Academic Affairs
CHAIRPERSON: Mike Garner
UNDERGRADUATE ENROLLMENT: 150

Hiram College

Dept of Religious Studies
Hiram OH 44234

Phone: 330-569-5148
Fax: 330-569-5130
E-mail: slingerlandh@hiram.edu
URL: www.hiram.edu

TYPE OF INSTITUTION: Private, Christian Church

EXECUTIVE OFFICER: G. Benjamin Oliver, President

CHAIRPERSON: Dixon Slingerland

UNDERGRADUATE ENROLLMENT: 1,050

DEGREES OFFERED: BA in Religious Studies

UNDERGRADUATE MAJORS: 12

DEGREES CONFERRED: 3

DESCRIPTION OF UNDERGRADUATE PROGRAM: The academic study of religion at Hiram College occurs in a setting free from sectarian point of view. The program offers a wide variety of courses for general students as well as majors and minors, supports a student organization, the Religion Symposium, and provides opportunity for study abroad.

FACULTY:

Moody, Jonathan F., PhD, Claremont Graduate School (1978), 1991, Associate Professor and Chaplain—introduction to religion, religion and culture, social ethics, contemporary religious movements, 330-569-5147, Fax: 330-569-5130, E-mail: moodyjf@hiram.edu

Skora, Kerry M., PhD, expected 1999, University of Virginia, 1999, Instructor—history of religions, Asian religions, 330-569-5149, Fax: 330-569-5130, E-mail: skorakm@hiram.edu

Slingerland, Dixon, PhD, Union Theological Seminary (1973), 1979, Professor—Hebrew Scriptures, New Testament, Apocrypha and Pseudepigrapha, Jewish studies, Greco-Roman religions, Holocaust, 330-569-5148, Fax: 330-569-5130, E-mail: slingerlandh@hiram.edu

Williams, Robert R., PhD, Union Theological Seminary (1971), 1976, Professor of Philosophy—philosophy of religion, 330-569-5146, Fax: 330-569-5130, E-mail: williamrr@hiram.edu

Hobart and William Smith Colleges

Dept of Religious Studies
Geneva NY 14456

Phone: 315-781-3368
Fax: 315-781-3348
E-mail: bloss@hws.edu
URL: www.hws.edu

TYPE OF INSTITUTION: Private

EXECUTIVE OFFICER: Richard Hersh, President

CHAIRPERSON: Lowell W. Bloss

Hobe Sound Bible College

PO Box 1065
11298 SE Gomez Ave
Hobe Sound FL 33475

Phone: 561-546-5534
Fax: 561-545-1422
E-mail: drcwc@aol.com
URL: www.hsbc.edu

TYPE OF INSTITUTION: Non-Denominational

EXECUTIVE OFFICER: Clifford W. Churchill, Academic Dean
UNDERGRADUATE ENROLLMENT: 113

Hofstra University

Program in Religion
Heger Hall
Hempstead NY 11550

Phone: 516-463-5612
Fax: 516-463-2201
URL: www.hofstra.edu

TYPE OF INSTITUTION: Private, Non-Denominational
EXECUTIVE OFFICER: James Short, President
CHAIRPERSON: Warren Frisina
UNDERGRADUATE ENROLLMENT: 6,000
GRADUATE ENROLLMENT: 5,000

Hollins College

Roanoke VA 24020

Holmes College of the Bible

115 Briggs Ave, Greenville SC 29601

Holy Apostles College and Seminary

33 Prospect Hill Road
Cromwell CT 06416

Phone: 860-632-3000
Fax: 860-632-3075
E-mail: rector@holy-apostles.org
URL: www.holy-apostles.org

TYPE OF INSTITUTION: Private, Roman Catholic
EXECUTIVE OFFICER: Douglas L. Mosey, Rector
CHAIRPERSON: Maurice W. Sheehan, Academic Dean
UNDERGRADUATE ENROLLMENT: 17
GRADUATE ENROLLMENT: 36

College of the Holy Cross

1 College Street
PO Box 42A
Worcester MA 01610-2395

Phone: 508-793-3404
Fax: 508-793-3708
URL: sterling.holycross/depart-
ments/religiousstudies

TYPE OF INSTITUTION: Private, Roman Catholic
EXECUTIVE OFFICER: Frank Vellaccio, Acting President
CHAIRPERSON: Mary Ann Hinsdale, IHM
UNDERGRADUATE ENROLLMENT: 2,700
DEGREES OFFERED: BA

UNDERGRADUATE MAJORS: 19

DEGREES CONFERRED: 13

DESCRIPTION OF UNDERGRADUATE PROGRAM: The Department of Religious Studies has a twofold function—that of servicing the general student body in a liberal arts college and that of preparing students who wish to concentrate in the area of religious studies for their future work. Believing that religion is a fundamental dimension of the human experience that deserves to be studied for that reason alone and also that students are in the process of coming to terms with their own traditions and personal identities, the department has designed courses for the student body at large that will enable them to achieve both these purposes. Since Holy Cross is a Jesuit college and the majority of the students come from Roman Catholic tradition, the department believes it is necessary to provide them with an opportunity to know and understand this tradition as well as to situate it in the larger context of other religious traditions and in the broader cultural context in which they live.

FACULTY:

Avery-Peck, Alan J., PhD, Brown University (1981), 1993, Kraft-Hiatt Professor—Judaic studies, 508-793-3411, Fax: 508-793-3708, E-mail: aavery@holycross.edu

Bashir, Shazad, PhD, Yale University (1997), 1996, Assistant Professor—Islamic studies, 508-793-2762, Fax: 508-793-3708, E-mail: sbashir@holycross.edu

Hinsdale, Mary Ann, IHM, PhD, Chair, University of St Michael's College (1984), 1987, Associate Professor—systematic theology, 508-793-3405, Fax: 508-793-3708, E-mail: mhinsdal@holycross.edu

Hobgood, Mary E., PhD, Temple University (1988), 1994, Assistant Professor—social ethics, 508-793-3435, Fax: 508-793-3708, E-mail: mhobgood@holycross.edu

Laffey, Alice L., SSD, Pontifical Biblical Institute (1981), 1981, Associate Professor—Old Testament, 508-793-3359, Fax: 508-793-3708, E-mail: alaffey@holycross.edu

Lewis, Todd T., PhD, Columbia University (1984), 1990, Associate Professor—history of religions (Buddhism and Hinduism), 508-793-3436, Fax: 508-793-3708, E-mail: tlewis@holycross.edu

Linnane, Brian F., SJ, PhD, Yale University (1994), 1994, Assistant Professor—foundational and medical ethics, 508-793-3446, Fax: 508-793-3708, E-mail: blinnane@holycross.edu

Murphy, Frederick J., PhD, Harvard University (1984), 1983, Professor—New Testament, intertestamental literature, 508-793-3467, Fax: 508-793-3708, E-mail: fmurphy@holycross.edu

Nickoloff, James B., PhD, Graduate Theological Union (1988), 1989, Associate Professor—systematic theology, 508-793-3466, Fax: 508-793-3708, E-mail: jnickolo@holycross.edu

Pierce, Joanne M., PhD, University of Notre Dame (1988), 1992, Associate Professor—historical theology, liturgical studies, 508-793-3452, Fax: 508-793-3708, E-mail: jpierce@holycross.edu

Reiser, William E., SJ, PhD, Vanderbilt University (1977), 1978, Associate Professor—systematic theology, 508-793-3413, E-mail: wreiser@holycross.edu

Schmalz, Mathew, PhD, University of Chicago (1999), 1998, Assistant Professor—Catholicism in Asia, 508-793-2762, Fax: 508-793-3708, E-mail: mschmalz@holycross.edu

Stein, Valerie, ThD (cand.), Harvard University, Visiting Assistant Professor—Old Testament, 508-793-3661, Fax: 508-793-3708, E-mail: vstein@holycross.edu

Stewart, Dianne, PhD, Union Theological Seminary in NYC (1997), 1998, Assistant Professor—systematic theology, 508-793-3412, Fax: 508-793-3708, E-mail: dstewart@holycross.edu

Holy Family College

Humanities Dept, Philadelphia PA 19114-2094

Holy Family College

Manitowoc WI 54220

Holy Names College

Religious Studies Program, Oakland CA 94619

Holy Trinity Orthodox Seminary

PO Box 36
Jordanville NY 13361

Phone: 315-858-0945
Fax: 315-858-0945
E-mail: seminary@telenet.net

TYPE OF INSTITUTION: Private, Russian Orthodox
EXECUTIVE OFFICER: Archbishop Laurus, Rector
COORDINATOR: Luke Murianka
UNDERGRADUATE ENROLLMENT: 50

Hood College

401 Rosemont Ave
Frederick MD 21701-8575

Phone: 301-696-3435
Fax: 301-696-3531
E-mail: hein@hood.edu
URL: www.hood.edu/academic/religion

TYPE OF INSTITUTION: Private
EXECUTIVE OFFICER: Shirley D. Peterson, President
CHAIRPERSON: David Hein
UNDERGRADUATE ENROLLMENT: 10

Hood Theological Seminary

800 W Thomas St
Salisbury NC 28144

Phone: 704-797-1113
Fax: 704-797-1897
E-mail: hoodsem@salisbury.net

TYPE OF INSTITUTION: Denominational: AME-Zion Church
EXECUTIVE OFFICER: Albert J. D. Aymer, Dean and Vice President
GRADUATE ENROLLMENT: 105

Hope College

126 E 10th St
PO Box 9000
Holland MI 49423

Phone: 616-395-7750
Fax: 616-395-7396
E-mail: verhey@hope.edu
URL: www.hope.edu/academic/
religion

TYPE OF INSTITUTION: Private, Reformed Church in America

EXECUTIVE OFFICER: James Bultman, President

CHAIRPERSON: Allen Verhey

UNDERGRADUATE ENROLLMENT: 2,800

DEGREES OFFERED: BA

UNDERGRADUATE MAJORS: 60

DEGREES CONFERRED: 20

FACULTY:

Bandstra, Barry L., PhD, Yale University (1982), 1983, Professor—biblical studies, Old Testament, 616-395-7752, E-mail: bandstra@hope.edu

Bouma-Prediger, Steven, PhD, University of Chicago (1992), 1994, Associate Professor—theology, 616-395-7757, E-mail: boumapred@hope.edu

DeLaTorre, Miguel, PhD, Temple University (1999), 1999, Assistant Professor—contextual theology, 616-395-7756, E-mail: delatorre@hope.edu

Hoogerwerf, Steven, PhD, Duke University (1992), 1992, Adjunct Professor—ethics, 616-395-7436, E-mail: hoogerwerf@hope.edu

Japinga, Lynn, PhD, Union Theological Seminary (1992), 1992, Associate Professor—church history, feminist theology, 616-395-7753, E-mail: japingal@hope.edu

Munoa, Phillip, PhD, University of Michigan (1993), 1993, Associate Professor—biblical studies, New Testament, 616-395-7755, E-mail: munoa@hope.edu

Powers, Janet Everts, PhD, Duke University (1985), 1985, Associate Professor—biblical studies, New Testament, 616-395-7754, E-mail: powers@hope.edu

Tyler, J. Jeffrey, PhD, University of Arizona (1995), 1995, Assistant Professor—church history, 616-395-7436, E-mail: tyler@hope.edu

Verhey, Allen, PhD, Yale University (1975), 1975, Professor—ethics, 616-395-7751, E-mail: verhey@hope.edu

Wilson, Boyd, PhD, University of Iowa (1982), 1982, Professor—world religions, 616-395-7749, E-mail: wilson@hope.edu

Hope International University

2500 E Nutwood Ave
Fullerton CA 92831

Phone: 714-879-3901
Fax: 714-879-1041
URL: www.hiu.edu

TYPE OF INSTITUTION: Denominational: Christian Churches/Churches of Christ

EXECUTIVE OFFICERS: LeRoy Lawson, PhD, President and Graduate Dean

UNDERGRADUATE ENROLLMENT: 971

GRADUATE ENROLLMENT: 155

Houghton College

1 Willard Ave
Houghton NY 14744

Phone: 716-567-9451
Fax: 716-567-9570
E-mail: hkingdon@houghton.edu
URL: www.houghton.edu

TYPE OF INSTITUTION: Private, Wesleyan

EXECUTIVE OFFICER: Ronald J. Oakerson, Dean

CHAIRPERSON: Harold E. Kingdon

UNDERGRADUATE ENROLLMENT: 1,200

DEGREES OFFERED: BA/BS

UNDERGRADUATE MAJORS: 110

DEGREES CONFERRED: 25

DESCRIPTION OF UNDERGRADUATE PROGRAM: Religious studies are an integral part of the liberal arts curriculum at Houghton. All students are required to take 13 hours of religion courses. Majors are offered in Bible, Religion, Philosophy, and Christian Education. A ministerial curriculum is available as well as several preseminary curricula which combine the liberal arts and religious studies. In addition to the main campus (rural) a suburban campus (West Seneca) and an inner-city one (Buffalo) provide excellent opportunities for research and practica.

FACULTY:

Eckley, Richard K., PhD, Duquesne University (1998), 1990, Assistant Professor of Christian Ministries—practical theology, 716-674-6363, Fax: 716-567-9570, E-mail: reckley@houghton.edu

Fisher, Carlton D., PhD, University of Notre Dame (1984), 1985, Professor of Philosophy—philosophy, 716-567-9315, Fax: 716-567-9572, E-mail: cfisher@houghton.edu

Kingdon, Harold E., DMin, Bethel Theological Seminary (1978), 1967, Professor of Christian Ministries—biblical studies and educational ministries, 716-567-9458, Fax: 716-567-9570, E-mail: hkingdon@houghton.edu

O'Byrne, William L., PhD, New York University (1978), 1983, Professor of Christian Education—educational ministries, 716-567-9459, Fax: 716-567-9570, E-mail: wobyrne@houghton.edu

O'Roarke, Shannon K., PhD, University of Connecticut (1997), 1997, Assistant Professor of Philosophy—philosophy, 716-567-9467, Fax: 716-567-9570, E-mail: soroarke@houghton,edu

Paige, Terence P., PhD, University of Sheffield, England (1994), 1994, Associate Professor of New Testament—New Testament, 716-567-9455, Fax: 716-567-9570, E-mail: tpaige@houghton.edu

Schultz, Carl, PhD, Brandeis University (1973), 1965, Professor of Old Testament—Hebrew language and Hebrew Bible, 716-567-9452, Fax: 716-567-9570, E-mail: cschultz@houghton.edu

Shea, Paul W., DMiss, Trinity Evangelical Divinity (1995), 1994, Assistant Professor of Religion (part-time)—missions, 716-567-9634, Fax: 716-567-9570, E-mail: pshea@houghton.edu

Stewart, W. Christopher, PhD, University of Notre Dame (1992), 1993, Associate Professor of Philosophy—philosophy, 716-567-9637, Fax: 716-567-9570, E-mail: cstewart@houghton.edu

Tyson, John R., PhD, Drew University (1983), 1979, Professor of Theology—systematic and biblical theology, 716-567-9457, Fax: 716-567-9570, E-mail: jtyson@houghton.edu

Walters, J. Michael, DMin, Trinity Evangelical Divinity School (1991), Professor of Christian Ministries, 716-567-9453, Fax: 716-567-9570, E-mail: mwalters@houghton.edu

ADJUNCT FACULTY:

Bence, Philip A., PhD, St Mary's College, University of St Andrews, Scotland (1989), 1999, Adjunct Associate Professor of Religion

Carter, Jeff E., MS, Canisus College (1978), 1995, Adjunct Assistant Professor of Religion

Dixon, John Ross, MA, King Seminary Graduate School of Theology (1992), 1955, Adjunct Associate Professor of Religion

Linton, John, PhD, University of Wisconsin (1973), 1987, Adjunct Professor at the Oregon Extension

Tice, Robert C., ThM, Fuller Theological Seminary (1986), 1987, Adjunct Assistant Professor of Christian Education

---

University of Houston
Houston TX 77058

Houston Baptist University

7502 Fondren
Houston TX 77074

Phone: 281-649-3000
Fax: 281-649-3012
URL: www.hbc.edu

TYPE OF INSTITUTION: Private, Baptist-Southern
EXECUTIVE OFFICER: James S. Taylor, Dean of Humanities and Philosophy
CHAIRPERSON: Joe Blair
UNDERGRADUATE ENROLLMENT: 130
GRADUATE ENROLLMENT: 8

Houston Graduate School of Theology
1311 Holman Ste 200, Houston TX 77004

Howard University
Washington DC 20059

Howard University School of Divinity
1400 Shepherd St NE, Washington DC 20017

Howard Payne College
Brownwood TX 76801

Humboldt State University

Dept of Religious Studies
Arcata CA 95521-8299

Phone: 707-826-4126
Fax: 707-826-4122

TYPE OF INSTITUTION: Public
EXECUTIVE OFFICER: Ronald R. Young, Dean
CHAIRPERSON: William Herbrechtsmeier
UNDERGRADUATE ENROLLMENT: 6,257
GRADUATE ENROLLMENT: 773

Hunter College

695 Park Avenue
New York NY 10021

Phone: 212-772-4989
Fax: 212-879-4571

TYPE OF INSTITUTION: Public, Non-Denominational
CHAIRPERSON: Barbara C. Sproul
UNDERGRADUATE ENROLLMENT: 15,000
DEGREES OFFERED: BA
UNDERGRADUATE MAJORS: 45
DEGREES CONFERRED: 10
DESCRIPTION OF UNDERGRADUATE PROGRAM: The Program in Religion at Hunter College is the oldest, largest, and most comprehensive program of religious studies in the City University of New York. It offers over sixty-five courses, including several courses in aspects of each of the major world religions (Judaism, Christianity, Islam, Hinduism, and Buddhism) as well as in the traditional religions of Africa, Oceania, and the Americas; courses in various methodological approaches to the study of religions; and courses in specific issues (such as faith and disbelief, religious experience, ethics, the meaning of love and sex, and the meaning of death) that are fundamental to all religions.

FACULTY:

Cohen, Michael, MA, Columbia University (1994), 1998, Adjunct Lecturer—Hinduism and Eastern religions

Forman, Robert K. C., PhD, Columbia University (1988), 1990, Associate Professor—mysticism, Eastern religions

LeVine, Mark, PhD, New York University (1997), 1998, Adjunct Professor—Islam

Long, Ron, PhD, Columbia University (1985), 1978, Acting Assistant Professor—contemporary theology

Nordstrom, Lou, PhD, Columbia (1963), 1990, Adjunct Assistant Professor (part-time)—Buddhism, problem of evil

Raver, Wendy, PhD, New York University (1998), 1998, Adjunct Professor—Ancient Near Eastern

Schwebel, Lisa, PhD, Fordham University (1997), 1992, Assistant Professor—psychology and religion, religion and social justice

Sproul, Barbara C., PhD, Columbia University (1972), 1971, Associate Professor—tribal religions, ethics

Tirana, Gail, MA, Union Theological Seminary (1982), 1987, Adjunct Lecturer (part-time)—women and religion, politics and religion, biblical religions

Huntingdon College

Montgomery AL 36106

Huntington College

2303 College Ave	Phone: 219-356-6000
Huntington IN 46750	E-mail: cbergdall@huntington.edu
	URL: www.huntington.edu

TYPE OF INSTITUTION: Private, United Brethren in Christ
EXECUTIVE OFFICER: Ronald Webb, Dean
CHAIRPERSON: Chaney R. Bergdall
UNDERGRADUATE ENROLLMENT: 900
GRADUATE ENROLLMENT: 50

Huron College

Huron SD 57350

Huron College

Faculty of Theology	Phone: 519-438-7224
1349 Western Rd	Fax: 519-438-3938
London ON N6H 1H3 Canada	E-mail: srice@julian.uwo.ca

TYPE OF INSTITUTION: Public, Multi-Denominational: primarily Anglican
EXECUTIVE OFFICER: David Bevan, Principal
CHAIRPERSON: Bradley McLean, Dean of Theology
UNDERGRADUATE ENROLLMENT: 925
GRADUATE ENROLLMENT: 70

Huston-Tillotson College

900 Chicon Street	Phone: 512-505-3000
Austin TX 78702-2795	Fax: 512-505-3190

CHAIRPERSON: Walter Redmond

H

Idaho State University

Pocatello ID 83209

Iliff School of Theology

2201 S University Blvd
Denver CO 80210-4798

Phone: 303-744-1287
Fax: 303-777-0164
E-mail: admissions@iliff.edu
URL: www.iliff.edu

TYPE OF INSTITUTION: Denominational: United Methodist Church

EXECUTIVE OFFICER: Delwin Brown, Vice President and Dean of Academic Affairs

GRADUATE ENROLLMENT: 128

GRADUATE PROGRAM

Member of the Council on Graduate Studies in Religion

Graduate Degrees Offered: MA; PhD

Degrees Conferred: 2 MA; 5 PhD; 11 Other

Graduate Students in Residence: 22 MA; 32 PhD; 33 Other

Not in Residence: 51 PhD

Average No. of New Students Enrolled: 9 MA; 13 PhD; 14 Other

Women Students: 13 MA; 32 PhD; 26 Other

Minority Students: 3 MA; 10 PhD; 4 Other

Foreign Students: 1 MA; 10 PhD; 2 Other

Minimum GRE Score Requisite to Admission: Yes; 600-verbal, quant, analytical (PhD only)

Minimum GPA Score Requisite to Admission: Yes; 3.0 on 4.0 scale

Foreign Language Proficiency Evaluated: Yes; GSFLT Score: 500 German; 500 French; 500 Other

Financial Aid to First Year Students: 95% MA; 100% PhD; 95% Other

Financial Aid to Other Students: 80% MA; 95% PhD; 80% Other

Attrition Among Students: 7% MA; 5% PhD; 7% Other

DESCRIPTION OF GRADUATE PROGRAMS AND RESEARCH FACILITIES: MA requires 80 quarter credit hours of study (24 quarter hours in a field of concentration). The MA degree is designed for persons preparing for doctoral work. The curriculum requires a concentration of study in one area, with 12 quarter hours outside the concentration, proficiency by examination in one foreign language and a research thesis. The Joint PhD degree, offered by the University of Denver and the Iliff School of Theology, is available in four areas: Religion and Social Change; Biblical Interpretation; Religion and Psychological Studies; and Theology, Philosophy and Cultural Theory. Requirements: 90 quarter credit hours, two foreign languages plus research tools, comprehensive exams, and dissertation. Resources include two libraries, two faculties, and the Denver metropolitan environment.

ACADEMIC PLAN, ADMISSION REQUIREMENTS, FINANCIAL AID: A baccalaureate degree from an accredited college is required for the MA degree, with GPA, personal references, and a statement of purpose also considered. MA requires a writing sample. The Joint PhD requires a broad and relevant MA or MDiv or equivalent, at least a B average, recommendations for doctoral work, and the aptitude portion of the GRE. Iliff School of Theology has a strong program of Student Financial Aid for master's level students. Every effort is made to assist students to meet financial needs through grants, scholarships, student assistantships, fellowships, loans and employment in accordance with the Association of Theological Schools and Federal guidelines.

FACULTY:

All Iliff faculty may be reached at Telephone: 303-744-1287, Fax: 303-777-0164

For faculty members co-responsible with the Iliff faculty for courses in the PhD program, see the entry for the University of Denver.

Alumkal, Antony W., PhD, Princeton University (expected 1999), 1999, Assistant Professor—sociology of religion, E-mail: aalumkal@iliff.edu

Antonio, Edward P., PhD, University of Cambridge (1991), 1997, Visiting Assistant Professor—theology and social theory, E-mail: eantonio@iliff.edu

Brown, Delwin, PhD, Claremont Graduate School (1965), 1983, Vice President and Dean of Academic Affairs, Harvey H. Potthoff Professor—Christian theology, E-mail: dbrown@iliff.edu

Cabezón, José I., PhD, University of Wisconsin (1987), 1989, Associate Professor—philosophy and religion, E-mail: jcabezon@iliff.edu

Davaney, Sheila G., ThD, Harvard University (1980), 1980, Professor—theology, E-mail: sdavaney@iliff.edu

Dean, William D., PhD, University of Chicago, The Divinity School (1967), 1996, Professor—constructive theology, E-mail: wdean@iliff.edu

Eisenbaum, Pamela M., PhD, University of Colombia (1994), 1994, Assistant Professor—biblical studies and Christian origins, E-mail: peisenbaum@iliff.edu

George, Mark K., PhD, Princeton Theological Seminary (1995), 1996, Visiting Assistant Professor—Old Testament, E-mail: mgeorge@iliff.edu

Graham, Larry K., PhD, Princeton Theological Seminary (1978), 1978, Professor—pastoral theology and care, E-mail: lgraham@iliff.edu

Harding, Vincent, PhD, University of Chicago (1965), 1981, Professor—religion and social transformation, E-mail: vharding@iliff.edu

Kim, Eunjoo Mary, PhD, Princeton Theological Seminary (1996), 1998, Assistant Professor—homiletics, E-mail: ekim@iliff.edu

Mahan, Jeffrey, PhD, Northwestern University (1986), 1995, Director of Ministry Studies and Associate Professor—ministry, media and culture, E-mail: jmahan@iliff.edu

Marshall, Joretta L., PhD, Vanderbilt University (1990), 1993, Associate Dean of Academic Affairs and Associate Professor—pastoral care and counseling, E-mail: jmarshall@iliff.edu

Messer, Donald E., PhD, Boston University Graduate School (1969), 1981, President and Henry White Warren Professor—practical theology

Myers, Sara J., PhD, Emory University (1990), 1985, Librarian and Associate Professor—theological bibliography, E-mail: smyers@iliff.edu

Parel, Kamala E., PhD, University of Cambridge (1995), 1997, Assistant Professor—history of Christianity, E-mail: kparel@iliff.edu

Petersen, David L., PhD, Yale University (1972), 1983, Professor—Old Testament, E-mail: dpetersen@iliff.edu

Richards, Kent H., PhD, Claremont Graduate School (1969), 1972, Professor—Old Testament, E-mail: krich03@emory.edu

Schmidt, Jean Miller, PhD, University of Chicago (1969), 1975, Professor—modern church history, E-mail: jschmidt@iliff.edu

Smith, Yolanda Y., PhD, Claremont School of Theology (1998), 1998, Visiting Assistant Professor—Christian religious education, E-mail: ysmith@iliff.edu

Tinker, George E., PhD, Duke University (1968), 1985, Professor—cross-cultural ministries, E-mail: gtinker@iliff.edu

Troeger, Thomas H., MDiv, Colgate Rochester Divinity School (1970), 1991, Ralphe E. and Norma E. Peck Professor—preaching and communications, E-mail: ttroeger@iliff.edu

Valantasis, Richard, ThD, Harvard University (1988), 1999, Professor—New Testament and Christian origins, E-mail: rvalantasis@iliff.edu

Ward, Richard F., PhD, Northwestern University (1997), 1998, Director of the Doctor of Ministry Program in Preaching and Pastoral Leadership and Associate Professor—preaching and performance studies, E-mail: rward@iliff.edu

Wilbanks, Dana W., PhD, Duke University (1968), 1968, Professor—Christian ethics, E-mail: dwilbanks@iliff.edu

Illinois College

Jacksonville IL 62650

University of Illinois, Urbana-Champaign

Program for the Study of Religion
3014 Foreign Lang Bldg
707 S Mathews
Urbana IL 61801

Phone: 217-333-0473
Fax: 217-244-0190
E-mail: patgxl.cso.uiuc.edu

TYPE OF INSTITUTION: Public
EXECUTIVE OFFICER: Peter N. Gregory
UNDERGRADUATE ENROLLMENT: 26,000
GRADUATE ENROLLMENT: 10,000

Illinois Missionary Baptist Institute

209 Vohland St
Washington IL 61571-1933

Phone: 309-745-9229
Fax: 309-745-8927
E-mail: dhillard@imbi.edu
URL: www.imbi.edu

TYPE OF INSTITUTION: Private, Baptist
EXECUTIVE OFFICER: Daniel Hillard, Dean
UNDERGRADUATE ENROLLMENT: 20

Illinois Wesleyan University

Dept of Religion
PO Box 2900
Bloomington IL 61702

Phone: 309-556-3331
Fax: 309-556-3719

TYPE OF INSTITUTION: Private, Non-Denominational
EXECUTIVE OFFICER: Janet M. McNew, Provost and Dean of the Faculty
CHAIRPERSON: Brian A. Hatcher
UNDERGRADUATE ENROLLMENT: 1,850

DEGREES OFFERED: BA

UNDERGRADUATE MAJORS: 12

DEGREES CONFERRED: 2

DESCRIPTION OF UNDERGRADUATE PROGRAM: The comparative study of religion is an integral part of liberal arts education at Illinois Wesleyan. The Religion Department approaches religion as a complex historical phenomenon and emphasizes critical and constructive thinking about the theoretical, practical, and existential questions that religious communities address. Department curriculum includes the religious traditions of Asia, the Middle East, Africa, the Americas, and Europe, and department faculty are also active in interdisciplinary programs.

FACULTY:

DeConick, April D., PhD, University of Michigan (1994), 1997, Assistant Professor—religion, Christian origins, Second Temple Judaism, Gnosticism and mysticism, E-mail: adeconic@titan.iwu.edu

Fryer, David R., PhD, Brown University (1999), 1999, Assistant Professor—religion, religion and culture, contemporary religious thought, ethics, liberation thought

Hatcher, Brian A., PhD, Harvard University (1992), 1992, Associate Professor—religion and humanities, history of religion, South Asian religions, Hinduism, Buddhism, E-mail: bhatcher@titan.iwu.edu

Myscofski, Carole A., PhD, University of Chicago (1981), 1991, Associate Professor—religion, history of religions, women and religion, E-mail: myscofsk@titan.iwu.edu

---

Immaculata College

Theology Dept, Immaculata PA 19345

Seminary of the Immaculate Conception

440 West Neck Road　　　　　　　　　　**Phone: 516-423-0483**
Huntington NY 11743　　　　　　　　　　**Fax: 516-423-2346**

TYPE OF INSTITUTION: Denominational: Roman Catholic

EXECUTIVE OFFICER: Vincent F. Fullam, Rector

GRADUATE ENROLLMENT: 126

Immaculate Conception Seminary School of Theology

Seton Hall University　　　　　　　　　**Phone: 973-761-9575**
400 South Orange Ave　　　　　　　　　　**Fax: 973-761-9577**
South Orange NJ 07079　　　　　**E-mail: theology@shu.edu**
　　　　　　　　　　URL: www.shu.edu/academic/theology/
　　　　　　　　　　　　　　　　　　　index.html

TYPE OF INSTITUTION: Private, Roman Catholic

EXECUTIVE OFFICER: John W. Flesey, Rector-Dean

GRADUATE ENROLLMENT: 116.16

Immanuel Baptist Theological Seminary

PO Box 2667, Peachtree City GA 30269

Immanuel Lutheran College

501 Grover Rd
Eau Claire WI 54701

Phone: 715-836-6621
Fax: 715-836-6634
E-mail: ilcpresident@yahoo.com

TYPE OF INSTITUTION: Private, Lutheran
EXECUTIVE OFFICER: John K. Pfeiffer, President
UNDERGRADUATE ENROLLMENT: 40
GRADUATE ENROLLMENT: 7

Incarnate Word College

4301 Broadway
San Antonio TX 78209

Phone: 210-829-3887
Fax: 210-829-3880
E-mail: eryan@universe.uiwtx.edu

TYPE OF INSTITUTION: Private, Catholic
EXECUTIVE OFFICER: Louis J. Agnese, Jr., President
CHAIRPERSON: M. L. Mueller
UNDERGRADUATE ENROLLMENT: 2,500
GRADUATE ENROLLMENT: 500

Independent Baptist College

3940 Blue Ridge, Dallas TX 75233

Indiana University

Dept of Religious Studies
Sycamore Hall 230
Bloomington IN 47405

Phone: 812-855-3531
Fax: 812-855-4687
E-mail: religion@indiana.edu
URL: www.indiana.edu/~relstud/

TYPE OF INSTITUTION: Public
EXECUTIVE OFFICER: Russell Hanson, Acting Dean, College of Arts and Sciences
CHAIRPERSON: Robert A. Orsi
UNDERGRADUATE ENROLLMENT: 26,792
GRADUATE ENROLLMENT: 6,432
DEGREES OFFERED: AA, BA, MA, PhD in Religious Studies
UNDERGRADUATE MAJORS: 85
DEGREES CONFERRED: Approximately 25 annually
DESCRIPTION OF UNDERGRADUATE PROGRAM: The Undergraduate program offers students an opportunity to explore the religious traditions of the world, as well as to study ex-

pressions of religious life and thought that may not fall within traditional patterns. Presenting a variety of approaches to religious studies, the program provides both a major and minor and serves the academic interests of undergraduate and graduate non-majors who want courses in religious studies or advanced courses coordinated with their special interests. Interdisciplinary work is encouraged.

GRADUATE PROGRAM

Member of the Council on Graduate Studies in Religion

Graduate Advisor: Richard Miller

Graduate Degrees Offered: MA; PhD

Degrees Conferred: 3 MA; 2 PhD

Graduate Students in Residence: 15 MA; 12 PhD

Not in Residence: 10 PhD

Average No. of New Students Enrolled: 12 MA; 3 PhD

Women Students: 6 MA; 12 PhD

Minority Students: 1 MA; 3 PhD

Foreign Students: 1 MA; 2 PhD

Minimum GRE Score Requisite to Admission: Yes; 600 verbal

Minimum GPA Score Requisite to Admission: Yes; 3.2 on 4.0 scale

Foreign Language Proficiency Evaluated: No

Financial Aid to First Year Students: 80% MA; 100% PhD

Graduates Placed: 50% MA; 100% PhD

DESCRIPTION OF GRADUATE PROGRAMS AND RESEARCH FACILITIES: The MA program includes work in the three divisions of Western Traditions, Eastern Traditions, and Critical Issues in Religion, and either a thesis, a language study project, or comprehensive examination. The PhD program offers preparation for research and teaching in four areas: Critical and Ethical Studies, Cross-Cultural Studies, Biblical Interpretation, and Historical Studies. The program is designed to prepare for teaching in college and university settings, drawing on more than 40 adjunct faculty members from related departments. The IU library contains over four million books and 25,000 serials. The university also houses the Folklore Institute, the Lilly Library of rare books and manuscripts, and the Kinsey Institute for Research in Sex, Gender and Reproduction. Interdisciplinary opportunities are enhanced by departments and institutes such as Anthropology, Sociology, Psychology, Comparative Literature, History, East Asian and Near Eastern Languages and Cultures; American, Central Eurasian, Jewish, Medieval, Russian and East European, Cultural, West European, and Women's Studies.

ACADEMIC PLAN, ADMISSION REQUIREMENTS, FINANCIAL AID: Applicants for graduate programs require transcripts of previous academic work, three letters of recommendation, a personal statement, GRE scores and, for PhD admission, samples of written work. The university offers graduate fellowships, and the department offers associate instructorships, graderships and teaching stipends to qualified candidates. Usually such awards are accompanied by full tuition scholarship. Applications for fall semester are due by January 15.

FACULTY:

Ackerman, James S., PhD, Harvard University (1966), 1969, Emeritus Professor—religion and literature of Israel and the ancient Near East, Bible as literature

Alexander, Scott C., PhD, Columbia University (1993), 1990, Assistant Professor—Islamic studies

Bokenkamp, Stephen R., (East Asian Lang & Lit), PhD, University of California, Berkeley (1986), 1989, Associate Professor—classical Chinese language/Chinese literature, texts of the Taoist tradition

Brakke, David, PhD, Yale University (1992), 1993, Assistant Professor—New Testament, early church history

Campany, Robert F., PhD, University of Chicago (1988), 1988, Associate Professor—history of religions in China and Japan, theories of religion and culture

Choksy, Jamsheed, (Near Eastern Lang & Lit), PhD, Harvard University (1991), 1993—Near Eastern religions, Zoroastrianism

Conkle, Daniel O., (Law), JD, The Ohio State University (1979), Religious liberty, religion and law, and the role of religion in American politics and public life

Dixie, Quinton, PhD, Union Theological Seminary, New York (1999), 1997, Visiting Lecturer—African-American religious history

Elliott, Dyan, (History), PhD, University of Toronto (1989), 1988, Associate Professor—Medieval, social and intellectual history, women/spirituality/sexuality

Haberman, David L., PhD, University of Chicago (1984), 1993, Associate Professor—history of South Asian religions, Indian arts and aesthetics, ritual studies, theories of religion, Native American religions

Hart, James G., PhD, University of Chicago (1972), 1972, Professor—philosophy of religion, philosophical theology, peace and conflict studies

Larson, Gerald J., PhD, Columbia (1966), 1995, Tagore Professor—philosophy and history of religion (India), Sanskrit, India studies

Manring, Rebecca, PhD, University of Washington (1995), 1996, Lecturer—Hindi, Sanskrit, Asian religions

Marks, Herbert J., (Comparative Literature), PhD, Yale University (1985), 1984, Associate Professor—Hebrew Bible, history and theory of biblical interpretation, Bible in western literature

McRae, John, PhD, Yale University (1983), 1996, Associate Professor—history of Chinese Buddhism religions of China and Japan

Miller, Richard B., PhD, University of Chicago (1985), 1985, Professor—methods in religious ethics, history of Christian ethics, social and political theory

Mongoven, Ann M., PhD, University of Virginia (1996), 1996, Assistant Professor—history of Christian ethics, methods in religious and philosophical ethics, comparative ethics

Nattier, Jan, PhD, Harvard University (1988), 1992, Associate Professor—religions of China, Japan, Tibet and Mongolia, history and interpretation of Buddhist tradition in Central Asia, South Asia, and North America

Orsi, Robert A., PhD, Yale University (1982), 1988, Professor—religion in America, popular religion, social theory

Preus, J. Samuel, ThD, Harvard University (1967), 1973, Professor Emeritus—religious thought and theories of religion in early modern Europe, history of the Bible in Europe

Satlow, Michael L., PhD, Jewish Theological Seminary of America (1993), 1999, Associate Professor—Judaism in antiquity, rabbinics

Smith, David H., PhD, Princeton University (1967), 1967, Professor—professional ethics, ethics and governance, theological ethics, teaching ethics

Stein, Stephen J., PhD, Yale University (1970), 1970, Chancellors' Professor—history of religions in America, American studies, eighteenth century studies

Weaver, Mary Jo, PhD, University of Notre Dame (1973), 1975, Professor—contemporary Christian religious thought, theology and literature, Roman Catholic and feminist studies

Weitzman, Steven P., PhD, Harvard University (1993), 1993, Assistant Professor—Hebrew Bible, early Judaism

Indiana University of Pennsylvania

Indiana PA 15705-1087

Phone: 412-357-2310
Fax: 412-357-4039
E-mail: bouffard@grove.uip.edu
URL: www.uip.edu/rs/

TYPE OF INSTITUTION: Public
EXECUTIVE OFFICER: Brenda Carter, Dean
CHAIRPERSON: Albert Bouffard
COORDINATOR: Theresa Smith
UNDERGRADUATE ENROLLMENT: 14,000
GRADUATE ENROLLMENT: 1,500

Indiana University Purdue University Indianapolis

Dept of Religious Studies
425 University Blvd, Room 335
Indianapolis IN 46202-5140

Phone: 317-274-1465
Fax: 317-274-2347

TYPE OF INSTITUTION: Public
EXECUTIVE OFFICER: Herman Saatkamp, Jr., Dean School of Liberal Arts
CHAIRPERSON: Rowland A. Sherrill
UNDERGRADUATE ENROLLMENT: 23,500
GRADUATE ENROLLMENT: 5,000

Indiana Baptist College, Heritage

1301 W County Line Rd, Greenwood IN 46142

Indiana Bible College

3350 Carson Ave, Indianapolis IN 46227

Indiana Christian University

530 E Ireland Rd
South Bend IN 46614

Phone: 219-291-3292
Fax: 219-299-4248

TYPE OF INSTITUTION: Private, Multi-Denominational: Charismatic
EXECUTIVE DIRECTOR: Delron Shirley, Dean
UNDERGRADUATE ENROLLMENT: 100
GRADUATE ENROLLMENT: 20

Indiana State University

Terre Haute IN 47809

Phone: 812-237-3121
Fax: 812-237-3062
E-mail: hujenn@root.indstate.edu
URL: web.indstate.edu:80/humanities

TYPE OF INSTITUTION: Public
CHAIRPERSON: Donald L. Jennermann

Indiana Wesleyan University

4201 S Washington Street
Marion IN 46953

Phone: 765-677-2241
Fax: 765-677-2766
E-mail: slennox@indwes.edu
URL: www.indwes.edu

TYPE OF INSTITUTION: Private, Wesleyan Church
EXECUTIVE OFFICER: By Baylis, Academic Dean
CHAIRPERSON: Stephen Lennox
COORDINATOR: Ken Schenck
UNDERGRADUATE ENROLLMENT: 1,900
GRADUATE ENROLLMENT: 120
DEGREES OFFERED: AA, AS, BA, BS
UNDERGRADUATE MAJORS: 275
DEGREES CONFERRED: 60

DESCRIPTION OF UNDERGRADUATE PROGRAM: Indiana Wesleyan is an evangelical liberal arts institution with close denominational ties to The Wesleyan Church while endeavoring to serve a broad constituency of students in traditional and non-traditional (degree completion) programs. The Division of Religion and Philosophy provides general education courses (nine hours) for all traditional students as well as pre-professional and professional programs for those planning careers in Christian ministry. Most graduates for this division enter directly into parish or para-church ministry. However, seminary or graduate study is encouraged. Faculty are involved in scholarly research and writing, but give primary attention to classroom teaching and mentoring of students.

GRADUATE PROGRAM

Graduate Advisor: Ken Schenck

Graduate Degrees Offered: MA

Degrees Conferred: 15 MA

Graduate Students in Residence: 0 MA

Not in Residence: 120 MA

Average No. of New Students Enrolled: 20 MA

Women Students: 7 MA

Minority Students: 1 MA

Foreign Students: 17 MA

Minimum GRE Score Requisite to Admission: No

Minimum GPA Score Requisite to Admission: Yes, 3.0 on 4.0 scale

Foreign Language Proficiency Evaluated: Yes

Financial Aid to First Year Students: 90% MA

Financial Aid to Other Students: 90% MA

Attrition Among Students: 10% MA

Graduates Placed: 95% MA

DESCRIPTION OF GRADUATE PROGRAM AND RESEARCH FACILITIES: This 36-hour Master's program is specifically designed to serve the working professional. Classes are taught in one-week modules with pre and post lecture assignments. Considerable freedom is given in choosing courses within several predescribed areas of study (Biblical, Doctrinal, Historical, and Practical). A Capstone thesis, ministry-related project, or CPE experience is required. Students have access to the University library and are encouraged to use library/research facilities near their place of employment. On-line and E-mail access to faculty members is available and encouraged.

ACADEMIC PLAN, ADMISSION REQUIREMENTS, FINANCIAL AID: The program consists of ten 3-hour classes selected by the student, a one-hour course in Research Methods, and a five-hour thesis, project, or clinical practicum. Admission to the program is through application to the Graduate committee by person holding a baccalaureate degree from an accredited college. A minimum GPA of 3.0 on a 4.0 scale and 24 hours of college credit in religious studies is also required. Language proficiency required for students with English as a second language. Tuition discounts available for persons serving on full-time parish ministry

FACULTY:

Bence, Clarence L., PhD, Emory University (1991), 1992, Professor of Religion, 765-677-2247, Fax: 765-677-2766, E-mail: bbence@indwes.edu.

Drury, Keith, LHD, Indiana Wesleyan University (1996), 1996, Assistant Professor of Religion, 765-677-2249, Fax: 765-677-2766, E-mail: kdrury@indwes.edu

Kierstead, Melanie, PhD, Drew University (1996), 1997, Assistant Professor of Religion, 765-677-2248, Fax: 765-677-2766, E-mail: mkierste@indwes.edu

Lennox, Stephen J., PhD, Drew University (1992), 1993, Chairperson, Division of Religion and Philosophy, andAssociate Professor of Religion, 765-677-2241, Fax: 765-677-2766, E-mail: slennox@indwes.edu

Lo, James, PhD, University of South Africa,1996, Assistant Professor of Intercultural Studies, 765-677-2246, Fax: 765-677-2766, E-mail: jlo@indwes.edu

Schenck, Kenneth, PhD, University of Durham (1997), 1997, Assistant Professor of Religion, 765-677-2258, Fax: 765-677-2766, E-mail: kschenck@indwes.edu

Springer, Keith, MDiv, Nazarene Theological Seminary (1972), 1990, Assistant Professor of Religion, 765-677-2243, Fax: 765-677-2766, E-mail: kspringe@indwes.edu

Williams, Wilbur G., DD, Bartlesville Wesleyan College (1992), 1967, Associate Professor of Biblical Literature and Archaeology, 765-677-2244, Fax, 765-677-2766, E-mail: wwilliam@indwes.edu

---

University of Indianapolis

1400 East Hanna Avenue
Indianapolis IN 46227

Phone: 317-788-3233
Fax: 317-788-3300
E-mail: mcartrwight@uindy.edu
URL: www.uindy.edu/~prel/relmain.htm

TYPE OF INSTITUTION: Private, United Methodist

EXECUTIVE OFFICER: Jerry Israel, President

CHAIRPERSON: Michael G. Cartwright

UNDERGRADUATE ENROLLMENT: 3,000
GRADUATE ENROLLMENT: 1,000

Inter-American University

San German PR 00753

Inter-Lutheran Theological Seminary

11015-A County Rd 15, Minneapolis MN 55441

Interdenominational Theological Center

700 MLK Jr Drive
Atlanta GA 30314

Phone: 404-527-7700
Fax: 404-527-0901

TYPE OF INSTITUTION: Private, Interdenominational
EXECUTIVE OFFICER: Robert M. Franklin, President
GRADUATE ENROLLMENT: 424

International Bible College

PO Box IBC
3625 Helton Dr
Florence AL 35630

Phone: 205-766-6610
Fax: 205-760-0981
E-mail: sgoldman@i-b-c.edu

TYPE OF INSTITUTION: Private, Church of Christ
EXECUTIVE OFFICER: George E. Goldman, Dean of the College
UNDERGRADUATE ENROLLMENT: 165

International Bible College

1218 Fair Fax Ave, Los Angeles CA 90019

International Bible College

2369 Benrus Blvd
San Antonio TX 78228

Phone: 210-434-5541
Fax: 210-434-1111

TYPE OF INSTITUTION: Private
EXECUTIVE OFFICER: David Cook, President
UNDERGRADUATE ENROLLMENT: 70

International Christian Institute

11931 Seventh St, Houston TX 77072

International College and Graduate School

20 Dowsett Ave, Honolulu HI 96817

International School of Theology

24600 Arrowhead Springs Rd, San Bernardino CA 92414-0001

International Seminary

PO Box 1208, Plymouth FL 32768

Iona College

Religious Studies, New Rochelle NY 10801

University of Iowa

School of Religion
314 Gilmore Hall
Iowa City IA 52242-1376

Phone: 319-335-2164
Fax: 319-335-3716
E-mail: religion@uiowa.edu
URL: www.uiowa.edu/~religion/

TYPE OF INSTITUTION: Public

EXECUTIVE OFFICER: Robert D. Baird, Director

COORDINATORS: Janine Sawada (Undergraduate); J. Kenneth Kuntz (Graduate)

UNDERGRADUATE ENROLLMENT: 18,000

GRADUATE ENROLLMENT: 6,500

DEGREES OFFERED: BA

DESCRIPTION OF UNDERGRADUATE PROGRAM: The School of Religion at the University of Iowa is the oldest academic department of its kind in a state university. The aim of the undergraduate program of the School of Religion is to clarify and deepen the student's understanding of the religious dimensions of human culture and experience across the world using diverse academic approaches and methods. The religion major at Iowa is a flexible yet focused program of study. A total of thirty hours of coursework at three levels is required. Preliminary requirements include 15 hours of foundational studies in historical religious traditions of the world. Advanced requirements include 12 hours of continuing studies in one of four areas of concentration: Western Religion and Religious Thought; Asian Religious Traditions, Religious Texts and Their Historical Backgrounds; and Contemporary Religious Issues. A 3 hour Senior Seminar is also required for majors.

GRADUATE PROGRAM

Member of the Council on Graduate Studies in Religion

Graduate Advisor: J. Kenneth Kuntz

Graduate Degrees Offered: MA; PhD

Degrees Conferred: 3 MA; 4 PhD

Graduate Students in Residence: 6 MA; 35 PhD

Not in Residence: 0 MA; 11 PhD

Average No. of New Students Enrolled: 5 MA; 5 PhD

Women Students: 2 MA; 18 PhD

Minority Students: 1 PhD

Foreign Students: 1 MA; 2 PhD

Minimum GRE Score Requisite to Admission: Yes; 1050 MA,1100 PhD

Minimum GPA Score Requisite to Admission: Yes; 3.0 MA; 3.2 PhD on 4.0 scale

Foreign Language Proficiency Evaluated: Yes

Financial Aid to First Year Students: 80% PhD

Financial Aid to Other Students: 12% MA; 51% PhD

Attrition Among Students: 3% MA; 6% PhD

Graduates Placed: 50% PhD

DESCRIPTION OF GRADUATE PROGRAM AND RESEARCH FACILITIES: Masters and doctoral work is available in four areas: History of Asian Religions, History of Religious Thought in the West, Theology, Ethics, and Culture; and Comparative or Interdisciplinary Studies in Religion. Evidence of the ability to write scholarly papers, a cumulative GPA of at least 3.2 (on a scale of 4.0), and satisfactory progress in meeting language requirements are the main factors that determine the admission of PhD students to candidacy prior to the end of their second year of residence. All graduate degree students submit a program of study (course work, seminars, languages, and other research tools) for the approval of their advisory committee. In addition to Greek, Latin, and modern European languages, the University offers courses in Chinese, Japanese, Sanskrit, and Hindi. The School of Religion offers Biblical Hebrew, Aramaic, and other Semitic languages as needed. MA students may choose a thesis or non-thesis program; all are required to take written final exams. PhD students are required to take written and oral comprehensive examinations and to write and defend a dissertation. They also have an excellent opportunity to gain valuable experience as teaching assistants in the department's general education courses for undergraduate students. University Libraries contain more than three million volumes; the Main Library has open stacks, and carrels are available for graduate students.

ACADEMIC PLAN, ADMISSION REQUIREMENTS, FINANCIAL AID: The University of Iowa is on the semester system, with 3 summer sessions. Admission requirements: transcripts, a statement of purpose, 3 letters of recommendation, GRE Verbal-Quantitative-Analytical scores, a writing sample demonstrating the ability to engage in critical thinking. Fall admissions deadline: May 1. A number of teaching and research assistantships are available. Exceptionally qualified doctoral students may be nominated for a University of Iowa Fellowship (tuition plus substantial, full year stipend, with two service-free fellowship years). Students interested in the relationship among religion, the visual arts, and humanistic values may apply for the Gilmore Scholarship. Deadline for fall financial aid application: February 1.

FACULTY:

Adamek, Wendi L., PhD, Stanford (1998), 1998, Assistant Professor—Chinese religions

Baird, Robert D., PhD, Iowa (1964), 1966, Professor—history of religions, methodology, religion in modern India, E-mail: robert-baird@uiowa.edu

Bozeman, T. Dwight, PhD, Duke (1974), 1974, Professor (joint appointment, Department of History)—American religious history, E-mail: d-bozeman@uiowa.edu

Cates, Diana Fritz, PhD, Brown University (1990), 1990, Associate Professor—religious ethics, E-mail: diana-cates@uiowa.edu

Holstein, Jay A., PhD, Hebrew Union College (1970), 1970, Professor—Judaic and biblical studies

Keen, Ralph, PhD, University of Chicago (1990), 1993, Assistant Professor—medieval and Reformation, theology, religion and social thought, E-mail: ralph-keen@uiowa.edu

Klemm, David E., PhD, Iowa (1980), 1982, Professor—philosophical theology, nineteenth and twentieth century religious thought, E-mail: david-klemm@uiowa.edu

Kuntz, J. Kenneth, PhD, Union, New York (1963), 1967, Professor—Old Testament, Hebrew Bible, E-mail: ken-kuntz@uiowa.edu

McCue, James F., PhD, Wisconsin (1961), 1965, Professor—history of Christian thought, E-mail: james-mccue@uiowa.edu

Nickelsburg, George W. E., ThD, Harvard (1968), 1969, Professor—New Testament, post-biblical Judaism, inter-testamental Judaism, E-mail: george-nickelsburg@uiowa.edu

Sawada, Janine, PhD, Columbia University (1990), 1994, Assistant Professor—history of Japanese religions, E-mail: j-sawada@uiowa.edu

Smith, Frederick M., PhD, Pennsylvania (1984), 1990, Associate Professor (joint appointment, Department of Asian Languages and Literature)—classical Indians religions, Sanskrit language and literature, E-mail: frederick-smith@uiowa.edu

Weir, Robert F., PhD, Princeton (1972), 1988, Professor (joint appointment, College of Medicine)—biomedical ethics, E-mail: robert-weir@uiowa.edu

---

Iowa State University

Dept of Philosophy and Religious Studies
402 Carrie Chapman Catt Hall
Ames IA 50011

Phone: 515-294-2566
Fax: 515-294-0780
E-mail: sawyerm@iastate.edu

TYPE OF INSTITUTION: Public

EXECUTIVE OFFICER: Martin Jischke, President

PROFESSOR IN CHARGE: Mary R. Sawyer

UNDERGRADUATE ENROLLMENT: 20,000

GRADUATE ENROLLMENT: 5,000

DEGREES OFFERED: BA Major

UNDERGRADUATE MAJORS: 30

DEGREES CONFERRED: 0

DESCRIPTION OF UNDERGRADUATE PROGRAM: Religious Studies gives students the opportunity to investigate and reflect on religions in an objective, critical, and appreciative manner. Though there is emphasis in religious studies on the wide variety of religious phenomena as well as on the various methods in the study of religion, the aim is to help students develop their own integrated understanding of the nature of religion and its role in individual and social life.

FACULTY:

Avalos, Hector, PhD, Harvard (1991), 1994, Assistant Professor—Bible, Latino/a religious experience

Baum, Robert, PhD, Yale (1986), 1998, Assistant Professor—Islam, religions of Africa, religion and imperialism, methodology

Comstock, Gary L., PhD, University of Chicago (1983), 1982, Associate Professor—philosophy of religion, ethics

Gross, Lawrence, PhD, Stanford (1998), 1998, Assistant Professor—Buddhism, American Indian religions

Hunter, David, PhD, Notre Dame (1986), Professor—history of Christianity, patristics

McDuff, Elaine, PhD, University of Iowa (1998), Assistant Professor—religion in America, Judaism

Sanford, A. Whitney, PhD, University of Pennsylvania (1995), 1996, Assistant Professor—history of religions, religions of India, methodology

Sawyer, Mary R., PhD, Duke University (1986), 1986, Associate Professor—sociology of religion, religion in North America, religion and politics, African American religious experience

Iowa Wesleyan College

601 North Main
Mt Pleasant IA 52641

Phone: 319-385-8021
Fax: 319-385-6296

TYPE OF INSTITUTION: Denominational: United Methodist
EXECUTIVE OFFICER: Vance Yoder, Academic Dean
COORDINATOR: George E. LaMore, Jr.
UNDERGRADUATE ENROLLMENT: 1,000

Rabbi Isaac Elchanan Seminary

2540 Amsterdan Ave, New York NY 10033

Ithaca College

Dept of Philosophy and Religion
Ithaca NY 14850

Phone: 607-274-1378
Fax: 607-274-1538
E-mail: bailey@ithaca.edu
URL: www.ithaca.edu

TYPE OF INSTITUTION: Private
EXECUTIVE OFFICER: Peggy Williams, President
CHAIRPERSON: Lee Bailey
UNDERGRADUATE ENROLLMENT: 5,000

Jackson College of Ministries
1555 Beasley Rd, Jackson MS 39206

Jackson State College
Jackson MS 39203

Rabbi Jacob Joseph School
One Plainfield Ave, Edison NJ 08817

James Madison University
Harrisonburg VA 22807

Phone: 540-568-6394
Fax: 540-568-8072

TYPE OF INSTITUTION: Public
EXECUTIVE OFFICER: Richard Whitman, Dean College of Arts and Letters
CHAIRPERSON: Daniel E. Flage
UNDERGRADUATE ENROLLMENT: 12,000

Jamestown College
Dept of Religion and Philosophy, Jamestown ND 58401

Jarvis Christian College
Hawkins TX 75765

Jesuit School of Theology at Berkeley
1735 LeRoy Ave
Berkeley CA 94709

Phone: 510-841-8804
Toll Free: 800-824-0122
Fax: 510-841-8536
E-mail: admissions@jstb.edu

TYPE OF INSTITUTION: Private, Roman Catholic
EXECUTIVE OFFICER: George Griener, SJ, Dean
COORDINATOR: Linda A. Menes, Director of Admissions
GRADUATE ENROLLMENT: 200

The Jewish Theological Seminary of America
3080 Broadway
New York City NY 10027-4649

Phone: 212-678-8024
Fax: 212-678-8947
E-mail: gradschool@jtsa.edu

TYPE OF INSTITUTION: Denominational

EXECUTIVE OFFICERS: Stephen Garfinkel, Dean, Graduate School; Shuly Rubin Schwartz, Dean, List College

UNDERGRADUATE ENROLLMENT: 145

GRADUATE ENROLLMENT: 282

John Brown University

Box 3067, Siloam Springs AR 72761

John Carroll University

Dept of Religious Studies
20700 N Park Blvd
Cleveland OH 44118

Phone: 216-397-4708
Fax: 216-397-4518
E-mail: plauritzen@.jcu.edu
URL: 143.105.24.3/religion/

TYPE OF INSTITUTION: Private, Roman Catholic

CHAIRPERSON: Paul Lauritzen

UNDERGRADUATE ENROLLMENT: 3,519

GRADUATE ENROLLMENT: 807

DEGREES OFFERED: BA

UNDERGRADUATE MAJORS: 17

DEGREES CONFERRED: 4

DESCRIPTION OF UNDERGRADUATE PROGRAM: The study of human religious experience throughout history and in the contemporary world is an integral part of undergraduate liberal education and makes a distinctive contribution to the Core Curriculum at John Carroll University. Two courses in religious studies are required of all undergraduates. Majors and minors in the department explore religious issues at greater depth, either for their own enrichment or in preparation for careers in various ministries. The program for majors requires at least limited course work in several different areas of religious studies and allows the student considerable flexibility in the choice of further courses.

GRADUATE PROGRAM

Graduate Advisor: Joan Nuth

Graduate Degrees Offered: MA

Degrees Conferred: 11 MA

Graduate Students in Residence: 22 MA

Not in Residence: 13 MA

Average No. of New Students Enrolled: 7 MA

Women Students: 9 MA

Minority Students: 1 MA

Foreign Students: 1 MA

Minimum GRE Score Requisite to Admission: No

Minimum GPA Score Requisite to Admission: Yes; 2.5 on 4.0 scale

Foreign Language Proficiency Evaluated: Yes, by language departments

Financial Aid to First Year Students: 100% MA

Financial Aid to Other Students: 20% MA

Attrition Among Students: 10% MA

Graduates Placed: 100% MA

DESCRIPTION OF GRADUATE PROGRAM AND RESEARCH FACILITIES: Further training for careers in religious education, for traditional or emerging ministries within denominational or ecumenical contexts, and for various other activities is available through two graduate programs in the department. One leads to the Master of Arts Degree in one of four areas: a specialization in religious ethics, a specilization in philosophical or systematic theology, a concentration in pastoral theology, or a general religious studies format. The other graduate program leads to a Certificate of Advanced Studies for someone who already holds a Master's Degree or its equivalent. Graduate courses and workshops sheduled in the evening during each semester and at various timed during the summer provide many and varied opportunities for continuing education as well. The MA degree requires 30 semester hours. Option A requires a thesis (which counts for 6 hours) plus proficiency in a foreign language; Option B is a non-thesis degree, but it requires a research essay or a project essay. Comprehensive exams are required of all MA candidated. Grasselli Library at JCU has holdings of about 400,000 volumes; the holdings of area libraries are readily accessible to JCU graduate students; interlibrary loan services are well staffed.

ACADEMIC PLAN, ADMISSION REQUIREMENTS, FINANCIAL AID: JCU operates on the semester system with three five-week summer sessions. Graduate courses are given in the evenings during both semesters and during the daytime during the second summer session (mid-June to mid-July); graduate workshops are given for various periods of time during much of the summer. Prerequisites for the MA include at least 6 upper-division courses (18 semester hours) in theology or religious studies at the undergraduate or graduate level; those for the Certificate of Advanced Studies include an earned Master's Degree and at least 18 semester hours of undergraduate theology or religious studies (or their equivalent); deficiencies can be met at JCU or elsewhere. Documents required for admission to the MA program: GRE (general test) or MAT scores, 3 letters of recommendation, personal statement, and transcripts. Completed applications are processed as received. A few graduate assistantships and occasional appointments as dormitory head resident are available. Financial aid is available for all graduate students.

FACULTY:

Donnelly, Doris K., PhD, Claremont Graduate School (1971), 1989, Professor—sacramental theology, spirituality, 216-397-1651, E-mail: ddonnelly@jcu.edu

Kelly, Joseph F., PhD, Fordham University (1973), 1972, Professor—ancient and early medieval church history, 216-397-4713, E-mail: kelly@jcu.edu

Krupa, Stephen T., MA, University of Detroit Mercy (1975), 1997, Instructor—Amerian Christian spirituality, 216-397-1656, E-mail: skropa@jcu.edu

Lassiter, Valentino, DMin, Eden Theological Seminary (1975), 1995, Assistant Professor—African American studies, 216-397-4707, E-mail: vlassiter@jcu.edu

Lauritzen, Paul, PhD, Brown University (1985), 1985, Professor—religious ethics, 216-397-4706, E-mail: plauritzen@jcu.edu

Mason, David R., PhD, University of Chicago (1973), 1972, Professor—philosophical and systematic theology, 216-397-4700, E-mail: dmason@jcu.edu

McGinn, Sheila, PhD, Northwestern University (1989), 1992, Associate Professor—New Testament, 216-397-3087, E-mail: smcginn@jcu.edu

Nietupski, Paul, PhD, Columbia University (1993), 1993, Assistant Professor—East Asian religions, mysticism, 216-397-4704, E-mail: pnietupski@jcu.edu

Nuth, Joan M., PhD, Boston College (1988), 1987, Associate Professor—contemporary Catholic theology, 216-397-1678, E-mail: jnuth@jcu.edu

Schubeck, Thomas L., PhD, University of Southern Californai (1975), 1989, Associate Professor—religious ethics, liberation theology, 216-397-4703, E-mail: tschubeck@jcu.edu

Spencer, John R., PhD, University of Chicago (1980), 1977, Associate Professor—Old and New Testament, archeology, 216-397-4705, E-mail: spencer@jcu.edu

John F. Kennedy University

Program Information, Orinda CA 94563

John Wesley College

2314 N Centennial St
High Point NC 27265

Phone: 336-889-2262
Fax: 336-889-2261
URL: www.johnwesley.edu

TYPE OF INSTITUTION: Private, Interdenominational (Wesleyan)
EXECUTIVE OFFICER: Brian C. Donley, President
CHAIRPERSON: Mike McClure
UNDERGRADUATE ENROLLMENT: 200

Johns Hopkins University

Charles and 34th Sts, Baltimore MD 21218

Johnson Bible College

Knoxville TN 37998

Johnson C. Smith University

100 Beatties Ford Rd
Charlotte NC 28216

Phone: 704-378-1198
Fax: 704-378-3556

TYPE OF INSTITUTION: Private
EXECUTIVE OFFICER: Rosalyn Jones, Dean College of Arts and Sciences
UNDERGRADUATE ENROLLMENT: 1,500

University of Judaism

15600 Mulholland Dr
Bel Air CA 90077

Phone: 310-476-9777
Fax: 310-471-1278

TYPE OF INSTITUTION: Private, Jewish
EXECUTIVE OFFICER: Hanan Alexander, Vice President, Academic Affairs
CHAIRPERSONS: Aryeh Cohen (Undergraduate); Rabbi Daniel Gordis (Graduate)
UNDERGRADUATE ENROLLMENT: 94
GRADUATE ENROLLMENT: 85

Judson College

Box 120
Marion AL 36756

Phone: 334-683-5100
Fax: 334-683-5147
E-mail: scollier@future.judson.edu

TYPE OF INSTITUTION: Denominational: Southern Baptist
EXECUTIVE OFFICER: David Potts, President
CHAIRPERSON: Stuart G. Collier
UNDERGRADUATE ENROLLMENT: 400

Judson College

1151 North State St, Elgin IL 60120

Juniata College

Huntingdon PA 16652

Kalamazoo College

1200 Academy St, Kalamazoo MI 49007

Rabbinical College of Kamenitz Yeshiva

1650 56th St, Brooklyn NY 11204

University of Kansas

Dept of Religious Studies
102 Smith Hall
Lawrence KS 66045-2164

Phone: 785-864-4663
Fax: 785-864-5205
E-mail: rstudies@ukans.edu
URL: kuhttp.cc.ukans.edu/~rstudies

TYPE OF INSTITUTION: Public
EXECUTIVE OFFICER: Sally Frost-Mason, Dean
CHAIRPERSON: Timothy Miller
COORDINATOR: Paul A. Mirecki
UNDERGRADUATE ENROLLMENT: 30
GRADUATE ENROLLMENT: 25

Kansas City College Bible School

7401 Metcalf Ave
Overland Park KS 66204

Phone: 913-722-0272
Fax: 913-722-2135
E-mail: kccbslib@magic1.org

TYPE OF INSTITUTION: Denominational: Church of God (Holiness)
EXECUTIVE OFFICER: Gayle Woods, President
UNDERGRADUATE ENROLLMENT: 53

Kansas State University

Manhattan KS 66506

Kansas Wesleyan University

100 E Claflin
Salina KS 67401-6196

Phone: 785-827-5541, ext. 1415
Fax: 785-827-0927
E-mail: pcbube@kwu.edu
URL: www.kwu.edu/
religion

TYPE OF INSTITUTION: Private, United Methodist
EXECUTIVE OFFICER: Marshall Stanton, President
CHAIRPERSON: Paul Custodio Bube
UNDERGRADUATE ENROLLMENT: 650

GRADUATE ENROLLMENT: 30
DEGREES OFFERED: BA in Religion; BA in Family and Youth Ministries
UNDERGRADUATE MAJORS: 5
DEGREES CONFERRED: 2
DESCRIPTION OF UNDERGRADUATE PROGRAM: The department of Religion and Philosophy offers majors in Religion and Family and Youth Ministries. The religion manjor is designed to prepare students for advanced study toward ordained and diaconal ministries, or
for graduate study in most fields in religion. The Family and Youth Ministries major provides
professional training for those interested in careers serving in a local church setting. The major meets the certification requirements in Youth Ministry for the United Methodist Church.
Both majors offer a strong theological foundation for lay leadership. More information can be
found at http://www.kwu.edu/religion.

Kean College of New Jersey

Morris Ave, Union NJ 07083-7131

Kehilath Yakov Rabbinical Seminary

206 Wilson Ave, Brooklyn NY 11211

Kendall College

2408 Orrington Ave, Evanston IL 60201

Kenrick-Glennon Seminary

5200 Glennon Drive   **Phone: 314-644-0266**
St Louis MO 63119   **Fax: 314-644-3079**
TYPE OF INSTITUTION: Private, Roman Catholic
EXECUTIVE OFFICER: Rev. Msgr. George Lucas, President/Rector
UNDERGRADUATE ENROLLMENT: 30
GRADUATE ENROLLMENT: 67

Kent State University

Religious Studies   **Phone: 330-672-2315**
Bowman Hall   **Fax: 330-672-4867**
Kent OH 44242-0001   **E-mail: dodellsc@kent.edu**
TYPE OF INSTITUTION: Public
EXECUTIVE OFFICER: Carol A. Cartwright, President
COORDINATOR: David W. Odell-Scott
UNDERGRADUATE ENROLLMENT: 20,000
GRADUATE ENROLLMENT: 4,800

University of Kentucky

Lexington KY 40506

Kentucky Christian College

100 Academic Parkway
Grayson KY 41143

Phone: 606-474-3000
Fax: 606-474-3155
E-mail: jmetcalf@email.kcc.edu
URL: www.kcc.edu

TYPE OF INSTITUTION: Private, Christian Church/Church of Christ
EXECUTIVE OFFICER: Keith P. Keeran, President/CEO
UNDERGRADUATE ENROLLMENT: 560

Kentucky Mountain Bible College

Box 10
Vancleve KY 41385

Phone: 606-666-5000
Fax: 606-666-7744
E-mail: kmbc@kmbc.edu
URL: www.kmbc.edu

TYPE OF INSTITUTION: Private
EXECUTIVE OFFICER: Philip Speas, President
UNDERGRADUATE ENROLLMENT: 83

Kentucky Wesleyan College

3000 Frederica St
PO Box 1039
Owensboro KY 42302

Phone: 502-926-3111
Fax: 502-926-3196
E-mail: jeffreyf@kwc.edu

TYPE OF INSTITUTION: Denominational: United Methodist
EXECUTIVE OFFICER: Wesley Poling, President
CHAIRPERSON: Jeffrey Fager
UNDERGRADUATE ENROLLMENT: 730

Kenyon College

Dept of Religion
Gambier OH 43022

Phone: 740-427-5656
Fax: 740-427-5276
E-mail: adlerj@kenyon.edu
URL: www2.kenyon.edu/depts/religion

TYPE OF INSTITUTION: Private, Episcopal
EXECUTIVE OFFICER: Robert Oden, President
CHAIRPERSON: Joseph Adler
UNDERGRADUATE ENROLLMENT: 15

Keuka College

Keuka Park NY 14478

King College

1350 King College Rd   Phone: 423-968-1187
Bristol TN 37620 -2699
TYPE OF INSTITUTION: Private, Presbyterian (USA)
EXECUTIVE OFFICER: Richard John Stanislaw, President
CHAIRPERSON: James S. McClanahan, Jr.
UNDERGRADUATE ENROLLMENT: 600

King's College

Wilkes-Barre PA 18711   Phone: 570-208-5900
                                     Fax: 570-208-5988
                         E-mail: djgrimes@kings.edu
                         URL: www.kings.edu/

TYPE OF INSTITUTION: Private, Roman Catholic
EXECUTIVE OFFICER: Thomas J. O'Hara, President
CHAIRPERSON: Donald J. Grimes
UNDERGRADUATE ENROLLMENT: 1,850
GRADUATE ENROLLMENT: 175
DEGREES OFFERED: BA
UNDERGRADUATE MAJORS: 9
DEGREES CONFERRED: 6
FACULTY:

Cashore, J. Michael, PhD, McMaster University (1980), 1969, Associate Professor—scripture, systematic theology, philosophy of religion

Grimes, Donald J., PhD, Fordham University (1981), 1972, Chairman and Professor—history of Christianity, ecclesiology, scripture

Looney, Thomas P., PhD, Catholic University of America (1996), 1985, Assistant Professor—theology, ecclesiology, systematic theology, ecumenism

Muntzel, Philip A., PhD, Yale University (1984), 1972, Professor—Christian ethics, Protestant theology

Ribando, William R., STD, Catholic University of America (1970), 1966, Associate Professor—ecclesiology, scripture, systematic theology

King's College

266 Epworth Ave, London, Ontario N6A 2M3 Canada

K

Knox College

2 E South St
Galesburg IL 61401

Phone: 309-341-7000
Fax: 309-343-8921
URL: www.knox.edu

TYPE OF INSTITUTION: Private, Non-Denominational
EXECUTIVE OFFICER: Richard Millman, President
COORDINATOR: R. Lance Factor
UNDERGRADUATE ENROLLMENT: 1,100

Knox College

Toronto School of Theology
59 St George St
Toronto, Ontario M5S 2E6 Canada

Phone: 416-978-4500
Fax: 416-971-2133
E-mail: knox.college@utoronto.ca
URL: www.utoronto.ca/knox/

TYPE OF INSTITUTION: University Federated, Presbyterian
EXECUTIVE OFFICER: Arthur Van Seters, Principal
CHAIRPERSON: Arthur Van Seters
UNDERGRADUATE ENROLLMENT: 140

Knoxville College

901 College St NW, Knoxville TN 37921

Kol Yakov Torah Center

29 W Maple Ave, Monsey NY 10952

K P C A Presbyterian Theological Seminary

1721 N Broadway, Los Angeles CA 90031

Kutztown University

Philosophy Dept
PO Box 730
Kutztown PA 19530

Phone: 610-683-4230
E-mail: back@kutztown.edu
URL: www.kutztown.edu

TYPE OF INSTITUTION: Public
EXECUTIVE OFFICER: David McFarland, President
CHAIRPERSON: Allan Bäck

K

Lafayette College

Easton PA 18042

Phone: 610-3300-5520
Fax: 610-330-5585
URL: www.lafayette.edu~religion/
religion.htm

TYPE OF INSTITUTION: Private, Presbyterian

EXECUTIVE OFFICER: Arthur Rothkopf, President

CHAIRPERSON: Robert L. Cohn

UNDERGRADUATE ENROLLMENT: 2,000

DEGREES OFFERED: AB

UNDERGRADUATE MAJORS: 4

DEGREES CONFERRED: 1

DESCRIPTION OF UNDERGRADUATE PROGRAM: The Department of Religion at Lafayette College introduces students to the phenomenon of religion and to world religions. The approach is both systematic and historical, enabling students to understand religion from many different perspectives. Thus the department offers courses on various religious traditions, religion and society (including religious ethics), sacred texts, and religion and literature. Study for Religion majors is integrated into the larger academic life of the college. The college consists of four academic divisions, including humanities, social sciences, natural sciences, and engineering. Students from all four divisions regularly participate in the courses of the department and students in the religion department are encouraged to pursue the study of religion where it exists in other departments of the college.

FACULTY:

Cohn, Robert L., PhD, Stanford University (1974), 1987, Philip and Murial Berman Professor of Jewish Studies—biblical studies, history and literature of Judaism, Jewish-Christian relations, comparative religion, 610-330-5182, Fax: 610-330-5585, E-mail: cohnr@lafayette.edu

Lammers, Stephen E., PhD, Brown University (1971), 1969, Helen H.P. Manson Professor of the English Bible—Christian ethics, religion and society, war-peace questions, medical ethics, 610-330-5180, Fax: 610-330-5585, E-mail: lammerss@lafayette.edu

Opoku, Kofi Asare, STM, Yale University (1965), Visiting Professor—traditional African religion and culture, religious movements in West Africa, Islam in Africa, African religions in the Americas, 610-330-5183, Fax: 610-330-5585, E-mail: opokuk@lafayette.edu

Rinehart, Robin, PhD, University of Pennsylvania (1992), 1991, Associate Professor—Hinduism, Buddhism, Sikhism, religions of Asia, 610-330-5179, Fax: 610-330-5585, E-mail: rineharr@lafayette.edu

Ziolkowski, Eric J., PhD, University of Chicago (1987), 1988, Associate Professor—American religious history, religion and literature, religion and fantasy, philosophy of religion, 610-330-5181, Fax: 610-330-5585, E-mail: ziolkowe@lafayette.edu

La Grange College

La Grange GA 30240

Lake Forest College

555 N Sheridan Rd
Lake Forest IL 60045

Phone: 847-735-5175
Fax: 847-735-6291
E-mail: rmiller@lfmail.lfc.edu

TYPE OF INSTITUTION: Private, Non-Denominational
CHAIRPERSON: Ronald Miller
UNDERGRADUATE ENROLLMENT: 1,000
DEGREES OFFERED: Minor
UNDERGRADUATE MAJORS: 0
DEGREES CONFERRED: 0 (minor only)
DESCRIPTION OF UNDERGRADUATE PROGRAM: The department of religion serves to introduce students to the great spiritual traditions of the world: Judaism, Christianity, Islam, Hinduism, Buddhism, and Daoism. There are also courses on the ancient religions of Greece
and Rome and on the religions of indigenous peoples. Some of the courses also explore the
connections between religion and other disciplines: art, anthropology, environmental studies, history, literature, music, and philosophy. Through the academic study of the world's
great spiritual traditions students discuss religious issues in an atmosphere of free and serious inquiry, with a concern for the application of scholarly methods. The very nature of religious inquiry is such that deep human issues are dealt with on a regular basis: the nature of
ultimate reality, free will, the meaning of myths, the nature of mysticism, the function of
prayer and religious ritual, and the exploration of diverse paths of spiritual growth.
FACULTY:

Benton, Catherine, PhD, Columbia University, 1987, Lecturer—comparative religion, Asian,
cross-cultural studies, 847-735-5174, E-mail: benton@lfc.edu

Bronstein, Herbert, DD, Hebrew Union College, 1987, Lecturer—comparative religion, Judaic
studies, 847-735-5198, E-mail: bronstein@lfc.edu

Miller, Ronald H., PhD, Northwestern University, 1974, Associate Professor—comparative religion, biblical theology, Jewish-Christian dialogue, Coordinator of Campus Interfaith Center,
847-735-5175, E-mail: rmiller@lfc.edu

Lakehead University

Thunder Bay, Ontario P7B 5E1
Canada

Phone: 807-343-8293
Fax: 807-346-7764
E-mail: sandra.blackburn@lakeheadu.ca

TYPE OF INSTITUTION: Public
COORDINATOR: Richard A. Berg
UNDERGRADUATE ENROLLMENT: 210

Lakeland College

Sheboygan WI 53081

Lambuth University

705 Lambuth Blvd
Jackson TN 38301

Phone: 901-425-3329
Fax: 901-425-3499
E-mail: wilkerso@lambuth.edu
URL: www.lambuth.edu

TYPE OF INSTITUTION: Private, United Methodist
EXECUTIVE OFFICER: W. Ellis Arnold III, President
CHAIRPERSON: Kenneth Wilkerson
UNDERGRADUATE ENROLLMENT: 975

Lancaster Bible College

901 Eden Rd
Lancaster PA 17601

Phone: 717-569-7071, ext 8221
Fax: 717-560-8213
E-mail: collegerelations@lbc.edu
URL: www.lbc.edu

TYPE OF INSTITUTION: Private, Non-Denominational
EXECUTIVE OFFICER: Peter W. Teague, President
CHAIRPERSON: Robert D. Spender
UNDERGRADUATE ENROLLMENT: 728
GRADUATE ENROLLMENT: 65

Lancaster Theological Seminary

555 W James St
Lancaster PA 17603

Phone: 717-393-0654
Fax: 717-393-4254

TYPE OF INSTITUTION: Private, United Church of Christ
EXECUTIVE OFFICER: David M. Greenhaw, Dean of the Seminary
GRADUATE ENROLLMENT: 200

Lander College

Greenwood SC 29646

Landmark Baptist College

2222 E Hinson Ave
Haines City FL 33844

Phone: 941-422-6493
Fax: 941-422-0188

TYPE OF INSTITUTION: Denominational: Independent Baptist
EXECUTIVE OFFICER: Mickey P. Carter, Chancellor
UNDERGRADUATE ENROLLMENT: 84
GRADUATE ENROLLMENT: 10

Lane College

Jackson TN 38301

La Roche College

Pittsburgh PA 15237

La Salle University

Graduate Religion Program
1900 W Olney Ave
Philadelphia PA 19141

Phone: 215-951-1335
Fax: 215-951-1665
URL: www.lasalle.edu

TYPE OF INSTITUTION: Private, Roman Catholic
EXECUTIVE OFFICER: Michael J. McGinniss, FSC, President
CHAIRPERSON: Francis Berna, OFM
GRADUATE ENROLLMENT: 125

La Sierra University

School of Religion, Riverside CA 92515

Laurentian University of Sudbury

C/O Thorneloe University
Ramsey Lake Road
Sudbury, Ontario P3E 2C6
Canada

Phone: 705-673-1730, ext 0
Fax: 705-673-7979
E-mail: thorneprov@nickel.laurentian.ca
URL: www.laurentian.ca/www/jdr

TYPE OF INSTITUTION: Public
CHAIRPERSONS: Bruce Ward and Don Thompson
UNDERGRADUATE ENROLLMENT: 63

Université Laval

Faculté de théologie et de sciences religieuses
Bureau 846
Pavillon Félix-Antoine-Savard
Québec, Quebec G1K 7P4 Canada

Phone: 418-656-3576
Fax: 418-656-3273
E-mail: ftsr@ftsr.ulaval.ca
URL: www.ulaval.ca

TYPE OF INSTITUTION: Public, Roman Catholic affiliation
EXECUTIVE OFFICER: Marc Pelchat, Doyen
UNDERGRADUATE ENROLLMENT: 275
GRADUATE ENROLLMENT: 150
DEGREES OFFERED: CTh, CThJ, CPast, CShr, MJTh, MJThJ, BTh, BThJ, MaTh, PhD/ThD
UNDERGRADUATE MAJORS: 125
DEGREES CONFERRED: 100

DESCRIPTION OF UNDERGRADUATE PROGRAM: Le Baccalauréat en théologie (90 crédits) est un programme spécialisé en théologie, mais suffisamment flexible pour permettre une orientation scientifique ou professionnelle et des profils de formation personnalisés. Le Diplôme ou Majeure en théologie (60 crédits) offre une formation de base en théologie, jumelable avec d'autres disciplines (journalisme, sociologie, philosophie, psychologie, etc.). Le Diplôme ou Majeure en théologie juive (60 crédits) offre une initiation à la pratique de la théologie juive. Le Certificat ou Mineure en théologie (30 crédits) offre une initiation à la théologie, qui peut être combinée avec une majeure ou deux mineures dans d'autres disciplines. Le Certificat ou Mineure en études bibliques propose une initiation de base aux sciences bibliques. Le Certificat ou Mineure en études pastorales (30 crédits), prépare à l'animation pastorale et peut être combiné avec une majeure ou deux mineures dans d'autres disciplines. Le Certificat ou Mineure en sciences de la religion (30 crédits) offre une initiation critique au phénomène religieux selon les méthodes des sciences humaines (anthropologie, histoire, sociologie, psychologie, etc.). Le Certificat ou Mineure en théologie juive (30 crédits) offre un premier contact avec la théologie juive.

GRADUATE PROGRAM

Member of the Council on Graduate Studies in Religion

Graduate Advisor: Raymond Brodeur

Graduate Degrees Offered: MA; PhD/ThD

Degrees Conferred: 20 MA; 4 PhD; 1 Other

Graduate Students in Residence: 30 MA; 30 PhD/ThD

Not in Residence: 50 MA; 18 PhD/ThD

Average No. of New Students Enrolled: 21 MA; 6 PhD/ThD; 2 Other

Women Students: 35 MA; 10 PhD/ThD; 50 Other

Minority Students: 5 MA; 4 PhD/ThD

Foreign Students: 2 MA; 6PhD/ThD

Minimum GRE Score Requisite to Admission: No

Minimum GPA Score Requisite to Admission: Yes; 3 on 4.3 scale

Foreign Language Proficiency Evaluated: Yes

Financial Aid to First Year Students: 60% MA; 35% PhD

Financial Aid to Other Students: 40% MA; 28% PhD

Attrition Among Students: 8% MA; 5% PhD

Graduates Placed: 92% MA; 94% PhD; 100% Other

DESCRIPTION OF GRADUATE PROGRAMS AND RESEARCH FACILITIES: Le Doctorat en théologie (PhD) (90 crédits) est un programme de 3e cycle qui permet une spécialisation poussée dans un champ d'études particulier de la théologie (Écriture sainte, dogme, éthique, histoire, pastorale et sciences humaines des religions). La Maitrise en théologie (MA) (45 credits). Elle offre trois cheminements: 1) le cheminement axé sur la recherche (avec mémoire) prépare à la recherche dans les divers champs de la theologie (theologie systematique, éthique, Ecriture sainte, histoire du christianisme, theologie pratique); 2) le cheminement axé sur l'intervention (avec stages) offre une formation professionnelle (paroisses, hopitaux, écoles, prison, etc.); 3) le cheminement axé sur l'approfondissement théologique (avec essai) offre un apprentissage plus poussé de la reflexion theologique. La Maîtrise en sciences humaines de la religion (MA) (45 crédits). Ce programme multidisciplinaire vise à former à l'analyse scientifique du phénomène religieux sous ses différents aspects (anthropologique, philosophique, psychologique, sociologique, etc.). Les principaux domaines d'excellence de la Faculté sont le christianisme ancien, la gnose et le manichéisme; l'histoire des catéchismes; la théologie systématique; l'éthique; la théologie pratique et les sciences humaines des religions. L'Université Laval possède une vaste bibliothèque en théologie et en sciences religieuses. De plus, elle a un centre de documentation spécialisé en patristique (BIBP).

ACADEMIC PLAN, ADMISSION REQUIREMENTS, FINANCIAL AID: Pour être admis aux programmes de premier cycle, il faut normalement être détenteur d'un Diplôme d'études collégiales. Pour être admis à la maîtrise en théologie, il faut être détenteur d'un Baccalauréat en théologie. Les bacheliers d'autres disciplines auront à satisfaire à des exigences propédeutiques. Pour être admis à la maîtrise en sciences humaines de la religion, il faut posséder un baccalauréat dans l'une ou l'autre des sciences humaines. Pour être admis au PhD (en théologie), il faut posséder une maîtrise en théologie ou en sciences humaines des religions. Les détenteurs d'autres maîtrises en sciences humaines devront se soumettre à une démarche propédeutique avant d'être admis. Les étudiants gradués reçoivent une aide financière moyenne de 2000$ par année. De plus, la Fondation de l'Université Laval accorde plusieurs bourses de plus de 10 000$ par année.

FACULTY:

Aubert, Marcel, Professeur de formation des maîtres en enseignement religieux, 418-656-2131 poste 5021, Fax: 418-656-3273, E-mail: marcel.aubert@ftsr.ulaval.ca

Brodeur, Raymond, Doctorat en sciences théologiques, Sorbonne, Professeur de formation des maîtres en enseignment religieux, 418-656-2131 poste 5513, Fax: 418-656-3273, E-mail: raymond.brodeur@ftsr.ulaval.ca

Chénard, Gabriel, Doctorat en théologie, Université Laval, Professeur de théologie morale, 418-656-2131 poste 7975, Fax: 418-656-3273, E-mail: gabriel.chenard@ftsr.ulaval.ca

Côté, Laurent, Licence en liturgie, Institut Saint-Anselme, Rome, Professeur de dogmatique, 418-656-2131 poste 2426, Fax: 418-656-3273, laurent.cote@ftsr.ulaval.ca

Côté, Pierre-René, Licence en Écriture sainte, Institut pontifical biblique, Rome, Professeur d'exégèse du Nouveau Testament, 418-656-2131 poste 2774, Fax: 418-656-3273, E-mail: pierre-rene.cote@ftsr.ulaval.ca

Couture, André, DScRel, Sorbonne, Professeur en histoire des religions, 418-656-2131 poste 5037, Fax: 418-656-3273, E-mail: andré.couture@ftsr.ulaval.ca

Farrell, Shannon-Élisabeth, Licence en Écriture sainte, Institut pontifical biblique, Rome, Professeure d'exégèse de l'Ancien Testament, 418-656-2131 poste 3944, Fax: 418-656-3273

Faucher, Alain, Licence en Écriture sainte, Institut pontifical biblique, Rome, Professeur d'exégèse de l'Ancien Testament, 418-656-2131 poste 7668, Fax: 418-656-3273, E-mail: alain.faucher@ftsr.ulaval.ca

Filteau, Jean-Claude, Doctorat en théologie, Université Laval, Professeur d'exégèse de l'Ancien Testament et d'histoire de la littérature biblique, 418-656-2131 poste 8039, Fax: 418-656-3273, E-mail: jean-claude.filteau@ftsr.ulaval.ca

Fortin, Anne, Doctorat en histoire des religions et anthropologie religieuse, Sorbonne, Professeure de théologie fondamentale et de théologie systématique, 418-656-2131 poste 5529, Fax: 418-656-3273, E-mail: anne.fortin.melkevik@ftsr.ulaval.ca

Gaudette, Pierre, Doctorat en théologie, Université du Latran, Rome, Professeur de théologie morale fondamentale, 418-656-2131 poste 7309, Fax: 418-656-3273, E-mail: pierre.gaudette@ftsr.ulaval.ca

Gervais, Michel, Doctorat en théologie, Université Angelicum, Rome, Professeur de dogmatique, 418-656-2131, Fax: 418-656-3273, E-mail: michel.gervais@rec.ulaval.ca

Giguère, Hermann, Doctorat en théologie, Université Grégorienne, Rome, Professeur de théologie spirituelle et d'histoire de la spiritualité, 418-656-2131 poste 7650, Fax: 418-656-3273, E-mail: herman.giguere@ftsr.ulaval.ca

Gosselin, Pauline, Maîtrise en pédagogie catéchétique et en pastorale, Université de Louvain, Dipl]4mde l'Institut supérieur catéchétique, Paris, Professeure de formation des maîtres en enseignement religieux, 418-656-2131 poste 3581, Fax: 418-656-3273, E-mail: pauline.gosselin@ftsr.ulaval.ca

Hurley, Bob J., PhD, Université McGill, Professor de formation des maîtres en enseignement religieux, 418-656-2131 poste 2947, Fax: 418-656-3273, E-mail: robert.hurley@ftsr.ulaval.ca

Keating, Bernard, Doctorat en théologie, Université Laval, Professeur d'éthique, 418-656-2131 poste 7236, Fax: 418-656-3273, E-mail: bernard.keating@ftsr.ulaval.ca

Langevin, Paul-Émile, Doctorat en théologie, Université Grégorienne, Rome, Professeur d'exégèse du Nouveau Testament, 418-656-2131 poste 5025, Fax: 418-656-3273

Laugrand, Frédéric, Doctorat en anthropologie, Université Laval, Professeur en sciences des religions, 418-656-2131 poste 8530, Fax: 418-656-3273, E-mail: laugrand@ftsr.ulaval.ca

Lemay, Benoit, Maîtrise en pédagogie, Maîtrise en théologie, Université Laval, Professeur de formation des maîtres en enseignement religieux, 418-656-2131 poste 5425, Fax: 418-656-3273, E-mail: benoit.lemay@ftsr.ulaval.ca

Lemieux, Raymond, Maîtrise en sciences sociales, Université Laval, Professeur de sociologie et d'histoire de la religion, 418-656-2131 poste 3399, Fax: 418-656-3273, E-mail: raymond.lemieux@ftsr.ulaval.ca

Painchaud, Louis, Doctorat en théologie, Université Laval, Professeur de littérature chrétienne ancienne, 418-656-2131 poste 4743, Fax: 418-656-3273, E-mail: louis.painchaud@ftsr.ulaval.ca

Pasquier, Anne, Doctorat en théologie, Université Laval, Professeure de patrologie, 418-656-2131 poste 2417, Fax: 418-656-3273, E-mail: anne.pasquier@ftsr.ulaval.ca

Pelchat, Marc, Doctorat en théologie, Université Grégorienne, Rome, Professeur de théologie pratique et d'ecclésiologie, 418-656-2131 poste 7823, Fax: 418-656-3273, E-mail: marc.pelchat@ftsr.ulaval.ca

Poirier, Paul-Hubert, Doctorat en théologie, Université de Strasbourg, Professeur de patrologie et d'histoire de l'Église, 418-656-2131 poste 5324, Fax: 418-656-3273, E-mail: paul-hubert.poirier@ftsr.ulaval.ca

Racine, Jacques, Licence en théologie, Maîtrise en sociologie (scolarité) Université Laval, Professeur de théologie pastorale et d'éthique sociale, 418-656-2131 poste 8184, Fax: 418-656-3273, E-mail: jacques.racine@ftsr.ulaval.ca

Richard, Jean, Doctorat en théologie, Université Angelicum, Rome, Professeur de dogmatique, 418-656-2131 poste 2789, Fax: 418-656-3273, E-mail: jean.richard@ftsr.ulaval.ca

Roberge, Michel, Licence en Écriture sainte, Institut Pontifical biblique, Rome, Licence en théologie, en philosophie, Université Laval, Professeur d'exégèse du Nouveau Testament, 418-656-2131 poste 5815, Fax: 418-656-3273, E-mail: michel.roberge@ftsr.ulaval.ca

Roberge, René-Michel, Doctorat en théologie, Université Laval, Professeur en théologie fondamentale et d'histoire de la pensée chrétienne, 418-656-2131 poste 8299, Fax: 418-656-3273, E-mail: rene.michel.roberge@ftsr.ulaval.ca

Routhier, Gilles, Doctorat en théologie, Institut catholique de Paris, Professeur de théologie dogmatique et pratique, 418-656-2131 poste 7510, Fax: 418-656-3273, E-mail: gilles.routhier@ftsr.ulaval.ca

Viau, Marcel, PhD, Montréal, Professeur de théologie pratique, 418-656-2131 poste 2826, Fax: 418-656-3273, E-mail: marcel.viau@ftsr.ulaval.ca

---

La Verne College

La Verne CA 91750

Lawrence University

Religious Studies Dept
115 S Drew St
Appleton WI 54912-0599

Phone: 920-832-6669
Fax: 920-832-6944
E-mail: karen.1.carr@lawrence.edu
URL: www.cwis.lawrence.edu

TYPE OF INSTITUTION: Private
EXECUTIVE OFFICER: Richard A. Harrison, Dean of the Faculty
CHAIRPERSON: Karen L. Carr
UNDERGRADUATE ENROLLMENT: 13,000

Lebanon Valley College

101 N College Ave
Annville PA 17003

Phone: 717-867-6310
Fax: 717-867-6124
E-mail: heffner@lvc.edu
URL: www.lvc.edu

TYPE OF INSTITUTION: Private
EXECUTIVE OFFICER: Stephen C. MacDonald, Vice President and Dean of the Faculty
CHAIRPERSON: John H. Heffner
UNDERGRADUATE ENROLLMENT: 1,350
GRADUATE ENROLLMENT: 80
DEGREES OFFERED: BA, majors in religion, philosophy
UNDERGRADUATE MAJORS: 16
DEGREES CONFERRED: 5
FACULTY:

Achtermann, Mark E., MA, Chicago Theological Seminary (1990), 1993, Adjunct Assistant Professor (part-time)—comparative philosophy, Asian religions, 717-867-6130, Fax: 717-867-6124, E-mail: achterma@lvc.edu

Bain-Selbo, Eric W., PhD, University of Chicago (1997), 1997, Assistant Professor—social ethics, continental European philosophy, inter-religious dialogue, 717-867-6133, Fax: 717-867-6124, E-mail: selbo@lvc.edu

Byrne, Donald E., Jr., PhD, Duke University (1972), 1971, Professor—American studies, ethics, religion and literature, 717-867-6356, Fax: 717-867-6124, E-mail: byrne@lvc.edu

Cantrell, Voorhis C., PhD, Boston University (1967), 1968, Professor Emeritus

Crockett, Clayton, PhD, Syracuse University (1998), 1997, Adjunct Assistant Professor (part-time)—modern religious philosophical and religious thought, hermeneutics, methodology, 610-268-0302, E-mail: cvcrock@bellatlantic.net

Ehrhart, Carl Y., PhD, Yale University (1954), 1947, Professor Emeritus

Fogle, Jon A., DMin, Princeton Theological Seminary (1997), 1998, Adjunct Assistant Professor (part-time), 717-838-4236, E-mail: jfogle@ezonline.com

Heffner, John H., Ph.D., Boston University (1976), 1972, Professor—history of philosophy, philosophy of religion, religion and science, 717-867-6132, Fax: 717-867-6124, E-mail: heffner@lvc.edu

Hoepfer, Donald C., MA, Pennsylvania State University (1990), 1992 Adjunct Instructor (part-time)—applied ethics, logic, Fax: 717-867-6124, E-mail: hoepfer@lvc.edu

Hubler, J. Noel, PhD, University of Pennsylvania (1995), 1995, Assistant Professor—history of Christianity, ethics, world religions, 717-867-6131, Fax: 717-867-6124, E-mail: hubler@lvc.edu

Layman, David W., PhD, Temple University (1994), 1993, Adjunct Assistant Professor (part-time)—religion in America, Jewish-Christian dialogue, world religions, 717-867-6130, Fax: 717-861-6124

McArdle, James W., MA (1997), 1995, Adjunct Instructor (part-time)—American philosophy, logic, ethics, 610-370-5276

Sanagorski, Thomas H., MDiv, United Theological Seminary (1974), 1997, Adjunct Instructor (part-time)—religion in America, 717-867-6130, Fax 717-867-6124

Schroepfer, Helen D., MA, St Mary's Seminary and University (1993), 1994, Adjunct Instructor (part-time)—world religions, 717-291-4191

Thompson, Warren K. A., MA, University of Texas (1963), 1967, Professor Emeritus, E-mail: thomp@lebmofo.com

Troutman, Perry J., PhD, Boston University (1964), 1960, Professor Emeritus, E-mail: troutman@lvc.edu

Wethington, L. Elbert, PhD, Duke University (1949), 1963, Professor Emeritus

Woomer, Darrell, PhD, Duquesne University (1996), 1992, Chaplain—biblical studies, Buddhism, spirituality, 717-867-6135, Fax: 717-867-6124, E-mail: woomer@lvc.edu

Zivic, Louis, MA, Jewish Theological Seminary of America (1975), 1998, Adjunct Assistant Professor (part-time)—religion in America, 717-273-2669

Lee University

1120 North Ocoee	**Phone: 423-614-8140**
PO Box 3450	**Fax: 423-614-8155**
Cleveland TN 37320-3450	**URL: www.leeuniversity.edu**

TYPE OF INSTITUTION: Denominational: Church of God

EXECUTIVE OFFICER: R. Jerome Boone, Dean, School of Religion

UNDERGRADUATE ENROLLMENT: 3,100

GRADUATE ENROLLMENT: 80

DEGREES OFFERED: BA, BS, and MA

UNDERGRADUATE MAJORS: 471

DEGREES CONFERRED: 72

DESCRIPTION OF UNDERGRADUATE PROGRAM: Lee University is a Christian institution which offers liberal arts and professional education on both the baccalaureate and master's levels. It seeks to provide education that integrates biblical truth as revealed in the Holy Scriptures with truth discovered through the study of the arts and sciences and in the practice of various professions. A personal commitment to Jesus Christ as Lord and Savior is the controlling perspective from which the educational enterprise is carried out. The foundational purpose of all educational programs is to develop within the students knowledge, appreciation, understanding, ability and skills which will prepare them for responsible Christian living in the modern world. The School of Religion at the university offers biblical and theological studies from an Evangelical, Pentecostal Christian perspective. Undergraduate degrees prepare students for ministerial vocations and graduate work.

FACULTY:

Bayles, Bob R., MDiv, Church of God School of Theology (1992), 1994, Instructor—Christian education, 423-614-8152, E-mail: bbayles@leeuniversity.edu

Blackmon, Andrew, MCE, Reformed Theological Seminary (1977), 1989, Assistant Professor of Christian Education, 423-614-8153, E-mail: ablackmon@leeuniversity.edu

Boone, R. Jerome, DMin, Columbia Theological Seminary (1995), 1976, Professor of Old Testament and Christian Formation, 423-614-8144, E-mail: jboone@leeuniversity.edu

Bowdle, Donald N., PhD, Bob Jones University (1961), ThD, Union Theological Seminary in Virginia, 1962, Professor of History and Religion, 423-614-8146, E-mail: dbowdle@leeuniversity.edu

Coulter, Dale M., DPhil (cand.), University of Oxford (1999), Instructor in Theology, E-mail: dcoulter@leeuniversity.edu

Cross, Terry L., PhD, Princeton Theological Seminary (1992), 1997, Associate Professor of Theology, 423-614-8142, E-mail: tcross@leeuniversity.edu

Daffe, Jerald J., DMin, Western Conservative Baptist Seminary (1983), 1987, Professor of Pastoral Ministries, 423-614-8145

Fuller, Michael E., PhD (cand.), University of Durham (2000), Instructor in Biblical Studies, E-mail: mfuller@leeuniversity.edu

Johns, Terry L., DMin, Columbia Theological Seminary (1997), 1993, Assistant Professor of Theology, 423-614-8373, E-mail: tjohns@leeuniversity.edu

Moodley, Edley, PhD (cand.), Asbury Seminary (1999), Instructor in Intercultural Studies, E-mail: emoodley@leeuniversity.edu

Powery, Emerson, PhD, Duke University (1999), 1996, Assistant Professor of New Testament, 423-614-8146, E-mail: epowery@leeuniversity.edu

Roebuck, David G., PhD, Vanderbilt University (1997), 1991, Assistant Professor of Religion, 423-614-8576, E-mail: droebuck@leeuniversity.edu

Searcy, Barbara J., ThM, Princeton Theological Seminary (1997), 1997, Instructor of Religion, 423-614-8149, E-mail: bsearcy@leeuniversity.edu

Simmons, William A., PhD, University of St Andrews, Scotland, (1990), 1986, Associate Professor of New Testament, 423-614-8150, E-mail: wsimmons@leeuniversity.edu

Sims, John, PhD, Florida State University, (1975), 1971, Professor of Religion and History

Smith, Henry, DMin, California Graduate School of Theology, (1979), 1986, Professor of Pastoral Ministries, 423-614-8370, E-mail: hsmith@leeuniversity.edu

Usherwood, Ridley N., DMin, Columbia Theological Seminary (1995), 1991, Associate Professor of Intercultural Studies, 423-614-8143

Lees-McRae College

PO Box 128
Banner Elk NC 28604

Phone: 828-898-5241
Fax: 828-898-8814
URL: www.lmc.edu

TYPE OF INSTITUTION: Private, Presbyterian Church USA
EXECUTIVE OFFICER: Earl Robinson, President
CHAIRPERSON: Dwaine Greene
UNDERGRADUATE ENROLLMENT: 470

Lehigh University

Dept of Religion Studies
9 W Packer Ave
Bethlehem PA 18015

Phone: 610-758-3353
Fax: 610-758-3391
E-mail: meg4@lehigh.edu
URL: www.lehigh.edu/~inrel/inrel.html

TYPE OF INSTITUTION: Private

CHAIRPERSON: Kenneth L. Kraft

UNDERGRADUATE ENROLLMENT: 4,400

GRADUATE ENROLLMENT: 1,200

DEGREES OFFERED: BA, Major in Religion Studies

UNDERGRADUATE MAJORS: 17

DESCRIPTION OF UNDERGRADUATE PROGRAM: Founded by A. Roy Eckardt, the religion studies department at Lehigh University is committed to the academic investigation of religion as an intrinsic and vital dimension of human culture. The scholarly study of religion is an integral facet of a liberal arts education. The student of religion is engaged in the critical and interpretive task of understanding patterns of religious thought and behavior as aspects of the human cultural experience. The department traditionally has had strength in the area of interreligious dialogue, particularly Jewish-Christian studies, and in recent years the department has grown in interdisciplinary breadth and in the balanced coverage of major world religions. Especially complementary to these pursuits at Lehigh are such programs as the Science, Technology, and Society program, and the East Asian studies program. The department also benefits from the active cross-fertilization of faculty and students from other religion departments at regional institutions that are a part of the Lehigh Valley Association of Independent Colleges.

FACULTY:

Girardot, Norman J., PhD, Chicago (1974), 1980, Professor—history of religions, Taoism, Chinese religions, mythology and folklore, religion and art, 610-758-3364, E-mail: njg0@lehigh.edu

Kraft, Kenneth, PhD, Princeton (1984), 1990, Associate Professor—religions of Japan, Buddhist studies, engaged Buddhism, 610-758-3370, E-mail: klk2@lehigh.edu

Raposa, Michael L., PhD, Pennsylvania (1987), 1985, Professor—philosophy of religion and culture, 610-758-3354, E-mail: mlr0@lehigh.edu

Silberstein, Laurence, PhD, Brandeis (1972), 1984, Professor and Director of Philip and Muriel Berman Center for Jewish Studies—Jewish studies, modern Jewish thought, Martin Buber, methodology in study of religion, gender studies, 610-758-4870, E-mail: ljs2@lehigh.edu

Steffen, Lloyd, PhD, Brown University (1984), 1990, Professor and University Chaplain—ethics, modern Christian thought, religion and psychology, 610-758-3876, E-mail: lhs1@lehigh.edu

Weissler, Chava, PhD, Pennsylvania (1982), 1988, Professor and Philip and Muriel Berman Chair of Jewish Civilization—Jewish studies, folklore, folk religion, gender studies, 610-758-3372, E-mail: lew1@lehigh.edu

Wright, Benjamin, III, PhD, Pennsylvania (1988), 1990, Associate Professor—early Judaism, Christian origins, 610-758-3344, E-mail: bgw1@lehigh.edu

Le Moyne College

Dept of Religious Studies
Syracuse NY 13214-1399

Phone: 315-445-4345
Fax: 315-445-4540

TYPE OF INSTITUTION: Private
EXECUTIVE OFFICER: Robert A. Mitchell, SJ, President
CHAIRPERSON: Nancy Ring
UNDERGRADUATE ENROLLMENT: 2,177

Le Moyne-Owen College

807 Walker Ave, Memphis TN 38126

Lenoir Rhyne College

Hickory NC 28601

LeTourneau University

Biblical Studies   Phone: 903-233-3300
PO Box 7001   Fax: 903-233-3263
Longview TX 75607-7001
CHAIRPERSON: Hobert Farrell

Lewis University

Religious Studies Dept   Phone: 815-838-0500, ext 5324
Route 53   Fax: 815-838-9456
Romeoville IL 60446-2298   E-mail: mcvannma@cs.lewisu.edu

TYPE OF INSTITUTION: Private, Catholic
EXECUTIVE OFFICER: K. Delaney, Dean, College of Arts and Sciences
CHAIRPERSON: Mark McVann, FSC
UNDERGRADUATE ENROLLMENT: 2,916
GRADUATE ENROLLMENT: 790

Lewis and Clark College

0615 SW Palatine Hill Rd   Phone: 503-768-7451
Box 41   Fax: 503-768-7447
Portland OR 97219   E-mail: rbaugh@lclark.edu
                                     URL: www.lclark.edu/~religion/

TYPE OF INSTITUTION: Private
CHAIRPERSON: Richard Rohrbaugh
UNDERGRADUATE ENROLLMENT: 1,850
DEGREES OFFERED: BA
UNDERGRADUATE MAJORS: 17
DEGREES CONFERRED: 9
DESCRIPTION OF UNDERGRADUATE PROGRAM: The religious studies department provides
    the opportunity for disciplined reflection on religious texts/traditions within the context of the

college humanities program. A major and a minor are offered, with a strong emphasis on both interdisciplinary and international perspectives.

FACULTY:

Cole, Alan, PhD, University of Michigan (1994), Assistant Professor—East Asian religions, Buddhism, methodology, 503-768-7484, E-mail: cole@lclark.edu

Frankel, Sylvia, PhD, University of Oregon (1981), Adjunct Professor—Judaism, Holocaust literature, Jewish history, 503-768-7452, E-mail: frankel@lclark.edu

Rohrbaugh, Richard L., STD, San Francisco Theological Seminary (1977), Professor—New Testament, Greek, social world of early Christianity, 503-768-7486, E-mail: rbaugh@lclark.edu

Wheeler, Rachel, PhD, Yale University (1998), Assistant Professor—religion in American history, 503-768-7481, E-mail: rwheeler@lclark.edu

---

Lexington Baptist College

3440 Versailles Rd   **Phone: 606-252-1130**
Lexington KY 40510   **Fax: 606-252-5649**
E-mail: lexbapcol@aol.com

TYPE OF INSTITUTION: Private, Baptist
EXECUTIVE OFFICER: David Adams, President
UNDERGRADUATE ENROLLMENT: 133

Lexington Theological Seminary

631 S Limestone St   **Phone: 606-252-0361**
Lexington KY 40508   **Fax: 606-281-6042**

TYPE OF INSTITUTION: Private, Christian Church (Disciples of Christ)
EXECUTIVE OFFICER: Richard L. Harrison, Jr., President
GRADUATE ENROLLMENT: 200

Liberty University

Box 20000, Lynchburg VA 24506

Liberty Baptist Theological Seminary

Box 20000, Lynchburg VA 24506

Life Bible College

1100 Covina Blvd   **Phone: 909-599-5433**
San Dimas CA 91773   **Fax: 909-599-6690**
E-mail: info@lifebible.edu

TYPE OF INSTITUTION: Private, Foursquare
UNDERGRADUATE ENROLLMENT: 495

Life Bible College East

900 Life Dr, Christiansburg VA 24073

Lima Technical College

Lima OH 45804

Limestone College

Gaffney SC 29340

Lincoln University

Dept of Religion
Lincoln PA 19352-0999

Phone: 610-932-8300, ext 3295 or 3258
Fax: 610-932-1217

TYPE OF INSTITUTION: Private
CHAIRPERSON: Gwinyai Muzorewa
UNDERGRADUATE ENROLLMENT: 2,000
GRADUATE ENROLLMENT: 300

Lincoln Christian College and Seminary

100 Campus View Dr, Lincoln IL 68656-2111

Lincoln Christian College-East Coast

2410 Creswell Road
PO Box 629
Bel Air MD 21014

Phone: 410-836-2000
Fax: 410-734-4271
E-mail: lccec@aol.com

TYPE OF INSTITUTION: Private, Christian Church
EXECUTIVE OFFICER: Robin Underhill, Dean of College
UNDERGRADUATE ENROLLMENT: 65

Lincoln Christian Seminary

100 Campus View Dr
Lincoln IL 68656

Phone: 217-732-3168, ext 2245
Fax: 217-732-1821
E-mail: semadmis@lccs.edu
URL: www.lccs.edu

TYPE OF INSTITUTION: Private, Christian Churches
EXECUTIVE OFFICER: Keith Ray, President
GRADUATE ENROLLMENT: 280

Linda Vista Baptist College and Seminary
2075 E Madison Ave, El Cajon CA 92019

Lindewood College
2090 S Kings Hwy, St Charles MO 63301

Lindsey Wilson College
210 Lindsey Wilson St, Columbia KY 42728

Linfield College
McMinnville OR 97128

Lipscomb University
3901 Granny White Pike
Nashville TN 37204-3951

Phone: 615-269-1000, ext 2451
Fax: 615-269-1808
E-mail: gary.holloway@lipscomb.edu
URL: www.dlu.edu

TYPE OF INSTITUTION: Private, Church of Christ
EXECUTIVE OFFICER: Stephen F. Flatt, President
CHAIRPERSON: Gary Holloway
UNDERGRADUATE ENROLLMENT: 190
GRADUATE ENROLLMENT: 115

Livingston College
701 W Monroe St, Salisbury NC 28144

Livingston University
Livingston AL 35470

Living Word Bible College
2495 E Mountain St, Pasadena CA 91104

Loma Linda University
Loma Linda CA 92350

Loma Linda University

Riverside CA 92505

Rabbinical College of Long Island

201 Magnolia St, Long Beach NY 11561

Long Island Seminary of Jewish Studies

444 Beach 6th St, Far Rockaway NY 11691

Loras College

Dubuque IA 52001

Louisiana College

Dept of Religion and Philosophy
Pineville LA 71359

Phone: 318-487-7254
Fax: 318-487-7191
E-mail: winbery@andria.lacollege.edu
URL: www.lacollege.edu/depart/religion/
religion.home

TYPE OF INSTITUTION: Private, LA Baptist Convention
EXECUTIVE OFFICER: Rory Lee, President
CHAIRPERSON: Carlton L. Winbery
UNDERGRADUATE ENROLLMENT: 947

Louisiana State University

Religious Studies Program
Coates Hall
Baton Rouge LA 70803

Phone: 225-388-2220
Fax: 225-388-4897
E-mail: tguidry@lsu.edu
URL: www.artsci.lsu.edu/phil/

TYPE OF INSTITUTION: Public
COORDINATOR: Rodger Payne
UNDERGRADUATE ENROLLMENT: 25,000
GRADUATE ENROLLMENT: 5,000
DEGREES OFFERED: BA (Religious Studies Concentration)
UNDERGRADUATE MAJORS: 30
DEGREES CONFERRED: 10
DESCRIPTION OF UNDERGRADUATE PROGRAM: The Religious Studies Program is currently part of the Philosophy Department in the College of Arts and Sciences. Begun in 1980 the program has nine professors of its own and shares the services of approximately 12 professors from related departments. A religious studies major requires 27 hours in the depart-

ment. Currently, the department offers one scholarship to an outstanding junior or senior majoring in religion. The department also participates in the University's Masters of Arts in Liberal Arts Program.

FACULTY:

Buehler, Arthur, PhD, Harvard University (1993), 1998, Assistant Professor—Islam

Burkett, Delbert, PhD, Duke University (1989), 1996, Associate Professor—New Testament and early Christianity

Harned, David B., PhD, Yale University (1963), 1986, Professor Emeritus—history of Christian thought

Henderson, John B., PhD, University of California, Berkeley (1977), 1995, Professor (joint appointment)—religions of China and Japan

Irvine, Stuart, PhD, Emory University (1989), 1986, Associate Professor—Hebrew Bible, Israelite history

Jones, Carolyn, PhD, University of Virginia (1991), 1988, Associate Professor—religion and literature

Kamenetz, Rodger, MA, Stanford University (1975), 1998, Professor (joint appointment)—Jewish studies

May, John R., PhD, Emory University (1971), 1994, Professor (joint appointment)—religion and film

Payne, Rodger, PhD, University of Virginia (1989), 1991, Associate Professor—religion in America, modern Catholic history

Seynaeve, Jaak, DDiv, University of Louvain (1948), 1987, Visiting Professor (part-time)—New Testament

Sutherland, Gail, PhD, University of Chicago (1987), 1987, Associate Professor—Asian religions, religions and gender

Whittaker, John H., PhD, Yale University (1974), 1980, Professor—philosophy of religion, western religions, psychology of religion

University of Louisville

South Third St, Louisville KY 40292

Louisville Bible College

PO Box 91046
Louisville KY 40291-0046

Phone: 502-231-5221
Fax: 502-231-5222
E-mail: loubibcol@juno.com

TYPE OF INSTITUTION: Private, Non-Denominational
EXECUTIVE OFFICER: Tommy Mobley, President
UNDERGRADUATE ENROLLMENT: 177
GRADUATE ENROLLMENT: 28

Louisville Presbyterian Theological Seminary

1044 Alta Vista Rd
Louisville KY 40205-1798

Phone: 502-895-3411
Fax: 502-895-1096

TYPE OF INSTITUTION: Denominational: Presbyterian
EXECUTIVE OFFICER: W. Eugene March, Dean of Seminary
GRADUATE ENROLLMENT: 246

Lourdes College

6832 Convent Blvd
Sylvania OH 43560

Phone: 419-885-3211
Fax: 419-882-3987
E-mail: ggrubb@lourdes.edu
URL: www.lourdes.edu

TYPE OF INSTITUTION: Private, Roman Catholic
EXECUTIVE OFFICER: Ann Francis Klimkowski, OSF, President
CHAIRPERSON: Geoffrey J. Grubb
UNDERGRADUATE ENROLLMENT: 1,350

Loyola College in Maryland

4501 North Charles Street
Baltimore MD 21210-2699

Phone: 410-617-2219
Fax: 410-617-2628
E-mail: szy@loyola.edu
URL: www.loyola.edu

TYPE OF INSTITUTION: Private, Roman Catholic
CHAIRPERSON: James J. Buckley
UNDERGRADUATE ENROLLMENT: 3,236
GRADUATE ENROLLMENT: 3,128
DEGREES OFFERED: BA
UNDERGRADUATE MAJORS: 20
DEGREES CONFERRED: 4
DESCRIPTION OF UNDERGRADUATE PROGRAM: The department of theology aims to engage in and teach Christian theology in the context of a Catholic liberal arts college. All students must take two theology courses; students may also take their required ethics course in theology. The practice of theology requires study of the origins and uses of Jewish and Christian scriptures, the history of Christianity (Eastern and Western, Catholic and Protestant), contemporary theologies, and theological ethics. It also requires studying the multiple relationships between theology and contemporary philosophies, religions, and cultures. Thus, our introductory courses in theology aim to help students to interpret the Bible, to understand the history of Christianity, and to become the sort of persons who can respond intelligently to the way these texts and traditions challenge (and are challenged by) modernity and post-modernity. A theology major requires ten further courses (including a senior seminar). Students interested in majoring in theology construct their curriculum in consultation with faculty advisors.

FACULTY:

Bauerschmidt, Frederick, PhD, Duke University (1996), 1994, Assitant Professor—medival theology, 410-617-2042, Fax: 410-617-2628, E-mail: fcb@loyola.edu

Buckley, James J., PhD, Yale University (1977), 1980, Professor—systematic theology, 410-617-2657, Fax: 410-617-2628, E-mail: buckley@loyola.edu

Christman, Angela Russell, PhD, University of Virginia (1995), 1994, Assistant Professor—patristic theology, 410-617-2359, Fax: 410-617-2628, E-mail: christman@loyola.edu

Driver, Steven D., PhD, University of Toronto (1995), 1995, Adjunct Faculty (part-time)—medieval studies, 410-617-2372, Fax: 410-617-2628

Fowl, Stephen E., PhD, University of Sheffield (1988), 1989, Associate Professor—New Testament, ethics, 410-617-2878, Fax: 410-617-2628, E-mail: fowl@loyola.edu

Guroian, Vigen, PhD, Drew University (1978), 1981, Professor—Christian ethics, 410-617-2214, Fax: 410-617-2628

Healy, Joseph M., PhD, Fordham University (1961), 1980, Adjunct Faculty (part-time)—philosophical theology, 410-617-2910, Fax: 410-617-2034, E-mail: healy@loyola.edu

Herman, Floyd L., Hebrew Union College (1964), 1981, Adjunct Faculty (part-time)—Judaism, 410-617-2519, Fax: 410-617-2628, E-mail: herman@loyola.edu

Kreidler, Mary Jane, PhD, Marquette University (1987), 1988, Adjunct Faculty—history of Christianity, 410-617-2444, Fax: 410-617-2052, E-mail: kreidler@loyola.edu

Marsh, Charles R., Jr., PhD, University of Virginia (1989), 1990, Associate Professor—philosophical theology, 410-617-2218, Fax: 410-617-2628, E-mail: marsh@loyola.edu

Mathews-McGuiness, Claire R., PhD, Yale University (1994), 1992, Assistant Professor—Hebrew scriptures, 410-617-2356, Fax: 410-617-2628, E-mail: mathews@loyola.edu

Miles, Stephen, PhD (cand.), Boston College, Instructor—Christian ethics, 410-617-2043, E-mail: smiles@loyola.edu

Patterson, Webster T., STD, Gregorian University (1956), 1969, Emeritus Professor—systematic, biblical theology, 410-617-2519, Fax: 410-617-2628

Rossi, Joseph Samuel, PhD, Catholic University (1989), 1989, Associate Professor—American Catholic life and thought, 410-617-2371, Fax: 410-617-2628, E-mail: rossi@loyola.edu

Ryan, Peter F., SJ, ThD, Gregorian University (1994), Assistant Professor—moral theology, 410-617-2705, Fax: 410-617-2628

Loyola University of Chicago

6525 N Sheridan Rd
Chicago IL 60626

Phone: 312-508-2350
Fax: 312-508-2386
URL: www.luc.edu/depts/theology/grad

TYPE OF INSTITUTION: Private, Jesuit, Catholic

EXECUTIVE OFFICER: John J. Piderit, SJ, President

CHAIRPERSON: John P. McCarthy

DEGREES OFFERED: BA

UNDERGRADUATE MAJORS: 72

DEGREES CONFERRED: 4

DESCRIPTION OF UNDERGRADUATE PROGRAM: The program of the Department of Theology provides students with resources for analysis of religion; for investigation of the historical development and contemporary practice of particular religious traditions; and for critical appreciation of personal faith and sympathetic appreciation of the beliefs of others. These resources are drawn principally from the Roman Catholic tradition. However, attention is directed to other Christian traditions as well as Judaism, Islam and Eastern Religions. Core Curriculum in theology is divided into four areas: doctrine, biblical literature, religious traditions, and Christian life and practice. A student selects three courses from at least two of the fours areas to complete the core requirement of nine hours in theology. Major in Theology is declared by application to the director of undergraduate programs. A concentration in theology develops analytical and interpretive skills as well as techniques of effective communication. Because religion touches some of the deepest aspirations and values of humanity, theological study offers insight to some of the most profound critical and spiritual currents in history. Minor in Theology requires six courses, each student's program is individually tailored to fit his/her plans in consultation with the director of minors.

GRADUATE PROGRAM

Graduate Advisor: Robert A. DiVito

Graduate Degrees Offered: MA; PhD

Degrees Conferred: 5 MA; 4 PhD

Graduate Students in Residence: 20 MA; 32 PhD

Not in Residence: 1 MA; 3 PhD

Average No. of New Students Enrolled: 8 MA; 8 PhD

Women Students: 4 MA; 9 PhD

Minority Students: 1 MA; 8 PhD

Foreign Students: 0 MA; 4 PhD

Minimum GRE Score Requisite to Admission: Yes

Minimum GPA Score Requisite to Admission: Yes; 3.0 on 4.0 scale

Foreign Language Proficiency Evaluated: No

Financial Aid to First Year Students: 75% PhD

Financial Aid to Other Students: 97% PhD

Graduates Placed: 100% PhD

DESCRIPTION OF GRADUATE PROGRAM AND RESEARCH FACILITIES: The program is designed both for students seeking a Master's Degree as their final graduate degree and for those students who will pursue the doctoral degree in Theology at Loyola. Admission to the PhD program is limited to ten full-time students each Fall semester, and the deadline for applications is April 1. Applicants with no previous graduate work take 60 hours of course work and then enroll in 6 hours of directed readings aimed at the research and writing of a doctoral dissertation. Students who already possess an MA in theology/religious studies or an MDiv degree can request advanced standing during the first semester after admission. The program offers a specialization in New Testament and Early Christianity, in Christian Ethics, or in Constructive Theology. Students are eligible to take the comprehensive examinations after the completion of 27 hours of doctoral courses and after all language requirements have been fulfilled. Those applicants who seek the MA as their final graduate degree can be admitted to the program on a part-time basis. Thirty hours of course work are taken for the MA degree. Facilities include a library which houses over 1.3 million volumes, 121,00 serial and journal subscriptions, audio-visual materials CD-ROMs and Internet access.

ACADEMIC PLAN, ADMISSION REQUIREMENTS, FINANCIAL AID: All applicants to the graduate programs should meet the following requirements: possess an accredited baccalaureate degree that is strong in the liberal arts and sciences, with at least nine credit hours in theology or religious studies; have earned a grade point average (GPA) of at least 3.0 (B); and have achieved acceptable scores in the General Test of the Graduate Record Examination. Applicants to the MA program who have not been engaged in a degree program for three years prior to application may substitute the results of the Miller Analogy Test for the GRE scores. Candidates applying to the PhD program with an MA in theology/religious studies or MDiv degree may be required to take prerequisite courses before being admitted to doctoral level courses. Applicants are required to submit: a completed application form along with the required fee; all undergraduate and graduate transcripts; the results of either the Graduate Record Examination taken with the last three years (MA or PhD) or the Miller Analogy Test (MA applicants only`sahd three letters of recommendation from former graduate and/or undergraduate professors. Research Assistantships and tuition scholarships are available on a competitive basis to new and continuing full-time students. A limited number of Fellowships are also available to qualified students. Applications for these awards are due in the Graduate School by February 1.

FACULTY:

Breuer, Edward, PhD, Harvard University (1990), 1997, Associate Professor—Jewish Studies

Chmielewski, Philip J., PhD, Yale (1987), 1989, Associate Professor—Christian ethics

Costigan, Richard F., PhD, University of Ottawa (1972), 1975, Associate Professor—history of ecclesiology, ecclesio-political history

Cotter, Wendy, PhD, St Michael's College (1991), Associate Professor—New Testament, synoptics

DiVito, Robert A., PhD, Harvard University (1986), 1991, Associate Professor—semitic and Hellenistic civilization

French, William C., PhD, University of Chicago (1985), 1984, Associate Professor—Catholic and Protestant ethics, environmental ethics, war and peace issues

Haughey, John C., STD, Catholic University of America (1967), 1991, Professor—Christian ethics

Hermansen, Marcia K., PhD, University of Chicago (1982), 1997, Associate Professor—Islamic studies, world religions, mysticism

Jung, Patricia Beattie, PhD, Vanderbilt University (1979), 1995, Associate Professor—sexual ethics, moral theology

Martin, Dennis D., PhD, University of Waterloo (1982), 1991, Associate Professor—late medieval and reformation studies

McCarthy, John P., PhD, University of Chicago (1985), 1986, Chairperson and Associate Professor—systematic theology, fundamental theology, hermeneutics

McCulloh, Gerald W., PhD, University of Chicago (1973), 1968, Associate Professor—history and structure of religious thought, nineteenth-century theology, American religious experience, Protestant theology, philosophical theology, philosophy of religion

McGinty, Mary Peter, PhD, Marquette University (1967), 1973, Assistant Chairperson and Associate Professor—sacramental theology, eucharist, contemporary theology

McIntosh, Mark A., PhD, University of Chicago (1993), 1993, Assistant Professor—spiritual theology, contemporary systematic theology

Nilson, Jon, PhD, University of Notre Dame (1975), 1975, Associate Professor—contemporary theology, theological method

Overbeck, T. Jerome, PhD, University of California, Berkeley (1983), 1990, Adjunct Professor—liturgy

Phelps, Jamie T., PhD, Catholic University of America (1989), 1998, Visiting Associate Professor—systematics, ecclesiology, liberation/contextual theologies

Pintchman, Tracy, PhD, University of California, Santa Barbara (1992), 1992, Associate Professor—religious traditions of South Asia

Ranck, Thomas E., PhD, Drew University (1969), 1970, Associate Professor—scripture studies, Pentateuchal studies, New Testament images of Jesus

Ross, Susan A., PhD, University of Chicago, (1982), 1985, Associate Professor—contemporary systematic theology, feminism

Schuck, Michael J., PhD, University of Chicago (1988), 1986 Associate Professor—ethics

Szarek, Eugene, PhD, Marquette University (1975), 1991, Assistant Professor, New Testament, Christian marriage

Tobin, Thomas H., PhD, Harvard University (1980), 1980, Associate Professor—New Testament, Hellenistic Judaism, Hellenistic philosophy, gnosticism

Viviano, Pauline A., PhD, St Louis University (1981), 1980, Associate Professor—Old Testament, methodology, New Testament

Wahlde, Urban C. von, PhD, Marquette University (1975), 1981, Professor—Johannine literature, New Testament studies

Walter, James J., PhD, Catholic University of Louvain (1974), 1984, Professor—Christian ethics

White, John L., PhD, Vanderbilt University (1970), 1981, Professor—New Testament, Hellenistic society, Hellenistic Judaism, Pauline literature, Ancient epistolography

Williams, Daniel H., PhD, University of Toronto (1991), 1994, Assistant Professor—patristics, Early Christian history

---

Loyola University New Orleans

6363 St Charles Avenue
New Orleans LA 70118-6195

Phone: 504-865-3943
Fax: 504-865-3179
URL: www.loyno.edu/religious.studies

TYPE OF INSTITUTION: Private, Catholic

EXECUTIVE OFFICER: Frank Scully, Dean

CHAIRPERSON: Catherine Wessinger

UNDERGRADUATE ENROLLMENT: 4,950

GRADUATE ENROLLMENT: 650

DEGREES OFFERED: BA (World Religions Track, Christianity Track)

UNDERGRADUATE MAJORS: 15

DEGREES CONFERRED: 5

DESCRIPTION OF UNDERGRADUATE PROGRAM: The undergraduate program offers the opportunity to study the human person as a religious believer, and the impact of religion on human existence. The department is an ecumenically diverse community of learners studying within the Roman Catholic tradition. Majors must complete 30 or 33 semester hours of Religious Studies courses, depending on the major track chosen.

GRADUATE PROGRAM

Graduate Advisor: Stephen Duffy

Graduate Degrees Offered: MA; JD/MA (in conjunction with Loyola Law School)

Degrees Conferred: 4 MA

Graduate Students in Residence: 33 MA

Average No. of New Students Enrolled: 5 MA

Minimum GRE Score Requisite to Admission: No

Minimum GPA Score Requisite to Admission: Yes; 3.0 on 4.0 scale

Foreign Language Proficiency Evaluated: No

DESCRIPTION OF GRADUATE PROGRAM AND RESEARCH FACILITIES: The MA degree is intended both as a terminal degree and as preparation for the PhD. Areas of concentration are available in biblical studies, ethics, systematic theology, the history of christianity, and world religions. Required: 30 semester hours of course work, or 24 semester hours and a thesis; proficiency in a foreign language; comprehensive exam. For the JD/MA program (offered in conjunction with Loyola Law School): 21 semester hours of course work in religious studies is required. The combined libraries of the universities and seminaries in New Orleans offer excellent resouces.

ACADEMIC PLAN, ADMISSION REQUIREMENTS, FINANCIAL AID: Loyola operates on a semester system. A BA or its equivalent from an accredited institution is required for admission to the graduate program. Preparation for graduate study should include an adequate background in undergraduate religion and philosophy. Applicants with a background in the humanities or the sciences may also be admitted but may be expected to do preliminary work in religious studies for undergraduate credit. Financial aid and scholarships are available.

FACULTY:

Allik, Tiina, PhD, Yale University (1982), Associate Professor—systematic theology, 504-865-3059, Fax: 504-865-3179, E-mail: allik@loyno.edu

Bernardi, Peter, SJ, PhD, Catholic University (1997), Assistant Professor—systematic theology, 504-865-3941, Fax: 504-865-3179, E-mail: bernardi@loyno.edu

Cahill, Timothy, PhD, Pennsylvania (1995), Assistant Professor—history of religions, 504-865-3183, Fax: 504-865-3179, E-mail: tccahill@loyno.edu

Duffy, Stephen, STD, Catholic University (1970), Professor—systematic and historical theology, 504-865-3060, Fax: 504-865-3179, E-mail: sjduffy@loyno.edu

Gnuse, Robert, PhD, Vanderbilt University (1980), Professor—Hebrew Scriptures, 504-865-3057, Fax: 504-865-3179, E-mail: rkgnuse@loyno.edu

Gregson, Vernon, PhD, Marquette University (1978), J.D. Loyola University New Orleans (1993), Professor—systematic theology and psychology of religion, 504-865-3942, Fax: 504-865-3179, E-mail: vgregson@loyno.edu

Janz, Denis, PhD, University of Toronto (1979), Professor—history of Christianity, 504-865-3061, Fax: 504-865-3179, E-mail: drjanz@loyno.edu

Keulman, Kenneth, PhD, University of Toronto (1979), Professor—ethics, 504-865-2652, Fax: 504-865-3179, E-mail: kkeulman@loyno.edu

Richard, Earl, PhD, Catholic University, (1976), Professor—Christian scriptures, 504-865-3058, Fax: 504-865-3179, E-mail: richard@loyno.edu

Smith, Thomas, PhD, University of Notre Dame (1988), Associate Professor—historical theology, 504-865-3679, Fax: 504-865-3179, E-mail: tsmith@loyno.edu

Wessinger, Catherine, PhD, University of Iowa (1985), Professor—history of religions and women's studies, 504-865-3182, Fax: 504-865-3179, E-mail: wessing@loyno.edu

---

Loyola Marymount University

7900 Loyola Blvd
Los Angeles CA 90045-8400

Phone: 310-338-7670
Fax: 310-338-1947
E-mail: cturner@lmumail.lmu.edu
URL: www.lmu.edu

TYPE OF INSTITUTION: Private, Roman Catholic

EXECUTIVE OFFICER: Robert B. Lawton, SJ, President

CHAIRPERSON: Thomas P. Rausch, SJ, Dept of Theological Studies

UNDERGRADUATE ENROLLMENT: 4,000

GRADUATE ENROLLMENT: 2,000

DEGREES OFFERED: BA, MA

UNDERGRADUATE MAJORS: 30

DEGREES CONFERRED: 7

DESCRIPTION OF UNDERGRADUATE PROGRAM: Loyola Marymount is a comprehensive university which combines the educational tradition of the Society of Jesus (Jesuits) and the

Religious of the Sacred Heart of Mary (Marymount Sisters). The department of theological studies offers both a major and a minor as well as a wide range of course offerings for the two course core requirement in theology.

GRADUATE PROGRAM

Graduate Advisor: Jeffrey Siker

Graduate Degrees Offered: MA

Degrees Conferred: 2 MA

Graduate Students in Residence: 0

Not in Residence: 30

Average No. of New Students Enrolled: 17

Women Students: 14 MA

Minority Students: 16 MA

Foreign Students: 3 MA

Minimum GRE Score Requisite to Admission: Yes; 500 verbal

Minimum GPA Score Requisite to Admission: Yes; 3.0

Foreign Language Proficiency Evaluated: No

Financial Aid to First Year Students: 70% MA

Financial Aid to Other Students: 70% MA

Attrition Among Students: 5% MA

Graduates Placed: 90% MA

DESCRIPTION OF GRADUATE PROGRAM AND RESEARCH FACILITIES: The department of theological studies offers graduate programs in theology and pastoral studies on a full or part-time basis. Courses are scheduled in the late afternoons, evenings, and in two summer sessions. Graduate students receive personal attention from both staff and a full-time faculty. The university library has over 355,000 books and bound periodicals, including 150 plus theological periodicals.

ACADEMIC PLAN, ADMISSION REQUIREMENTS, FINANCIAL AID: A Baccalaureate degree from an accredited institution, sufficient background in theology or religious studies, and the demonstrated ability to do graduate studies are required. This last requirement can be fulfilled by providing a range of information including: graduate work completed or advanced degree obtained; evidence of undergraduate work, including GPA and submission of written academic work (e.g., a term paper); scores received on the GRE, the Miller Analogy, or other standardized tests (recommended but not required); a personal interview.

FACULTY:

Au, Wilkie, PhD, California, Santa Barbara (1976), 1989, Adjunct Professor—spirituality

Burton-Christie, Douglas, PhD, Graduate Theological Union (1989), 1994, Associate Professor—spirituality

Butler, Anthea D., PhD (cand.), Vanderbilt University (2000), Assistant Professor—church history with emphasis in American and African-American Christianity

Chapple, Christopher Key, PhD, Fordham (1980), 1985, Professor—religions and philosophies of South Asia, history of religions, Sanskrit

Coleman, John A., SJ, PhD, University of California, Berkeley (1974), 1997, Professor, Casassa Chair of Social Justice—sociology and theology, sociology of religion, social ethics, social theory

Connolly, John R., PhD, Marquette (1971), 1971, Professor—systematic theology, revelation, faith, liberation theology

Deck, Allan Figueroa, SJ, PhD, Saint Louis (1974), STD, Gregorian, Rome (1988), 1992, Adjunct Professor—Hispanic theology and ministry

Fredericks, James, SS, PhD, Chicago (1988), 1992, Associate Professor—systematic and comparative theology

Horan, Michael P., PhD, Catholic University (1989), 1994, Associate Professor—religious education, pastoral theology

Just, Felix, SJ, STL, Jesuit School of Theology, Berkeley (1990), 1996, Assistant Professor—New Testament studies, Christian origins

Matovina, Timothy M., PhD, Catholic University (1993), 1995, Assistant Professor—religion and culture

Mayeski, Marie Anne, PhD, Fordham (1973), 1974, Professor—history of Christianity, New Testament, patristics, feminist studies

Popiden, John R., PhD, Notre Dame (1980), 1977, Associate Professor—ethics, moral theology

Rausch, Thomas P., SJ, PhD, Duke (1976), 1976, Professor—systematic theology, ecclesiology, New Testament, ecumenical studies

Ryan, Herbert J., SJ, STD, Gregorian, Rome (1967), 1974, Professor—history of Christianity, Roman Catholic-Anglican studies, ecumenism, liturgy, patristics and medieval theology

Siker, Jeffrey S., PhD, Princeton Theological Seminary (1989), 1987, Associate Professor—New Testament studies, patristics, Christian origins, history of interpretation

Smith-Christopher, Daniel L., DPhil, Oxford University (1986), 1989, Associate Professor—Old Testament, Hebrew Bible, peace studies, Bible and cultural diversity

van Wensveen, Louke, PhD, Princeton Theological Seminary (1987), 1991, Assistant Professor—theological/philosophical ethics, social ethics, business ethics, feminist ethics, philosophical hermeneutics

VanderWilt, Jeffrey, PhD, University of Notre Dame (1996), 1998, Assistant Professor—liturgical and sacramental theology

Walter, James J., PhD, Katholieke Universiteit te Leuven, Belgium (1974), O'Malley Chair of Bio-Ethics—bio-ethics, moral theology

---

Lubbock Christian University

5601 19th St
Lubbock TX 79407

Phone: 806-796-8800, ext 353
E-mail: steve.joiner@lcu.edu
URL: www.lcu.edu

TYPE OF INSTITUTION: Private, Church of Christ
EXECUTIVE OFFICER: L. Ken Jones, President
CHAIRPERSON: Steve Joiner
UNDERGRADUATE ENROLLMENT: 70
GRADUATE ENROLLMENT: 20

Luther College

Dept of Religion and Philosophy
700 College Drive
Decorah IA 52101-1045

Phone: 319-387-2000
Fax: 319-387-2158
E-mail: sieberjo@luther.edu
URL: www.luther.edu

TYPE OF INSTITUTION: Denominational: Evangelical Lutheran Church in America

EXECUTIVE OFFICER: Carolyn Mottley, Acting Dean

CHAIRPERSON: John H. Sieber

UNDERGRADUATE ENROLLMENT: 2,450

DEGREES OFFERED: BA

UNDERGRADUATE MAJORS: 18

DEGREES CONFERRED: 3-4 year

DESCRIPTION OF UNDERGRADUATE PROGRAM: Luther College is a private liberal arts college associated with the Evangelical Lutheran Church in America. It seeks to be at once a community of faith and a community of learning. All students are required to take at least two religion courses plus an upper level interdisciplinary course dealing with values. The Religion faculty offer courses in biblical studies, historical theology, religious history, theology, ethics and world religions. Biblical Hebrew and classical and biblical Greek are offered by the Classics Department.

FACULTY:

Hanson, Bradley, PhD, Princeton Theological Seminary, 1970, Professor—systematic theology, 319-387-1184, Fax: 319-387-2158, E-mail: hansonbr@luther.edu

Kopf, Gereon, PhD, Temple, 1996, Assistant Professor—Asian religions, 319-387-1497, Fax: 319-387-2158, E-mail: kopfg@luther.edu

Kraabel, A. Thomas, PhD, Harvard Divinity, 1968, Professor—biblical studies, 319-387-1004, Fax: 319-387-2158, E-mail: kraabela@luther.edu

Martin-Schramm, James, PhD, Union Theological Seminary in New York City, 1996, Assistant Professor—Christian ethics, 319-387-1251, Fax: 319-387-2158, E-mail: marschja@luther.edu

Rue, Loyal, PhD, Hartford Seminary Foundation, 1974, Professor—philosophical theology, 319-387-1138, Fax: 319-387-2158, E-mail: rueloyal@luther.edu

Schroeder, Joy, PhD, Notre Dame, 1999, Assistant Professor—biblical and feminist studies, 319-387-1276, Fax: 319-587-2158

Sieber, John H., PhD, Claremont Graduate School, 1966, Professor—biblical studies, 319-387-1273, Fax: 319-387-2158, E-mail: sieberjo@luther.edu

Sparkes, Terry E., PhD, University of Chicago, 1993, Assistant Professor—religious history, 319-387-2165, Fax: 319-387-2158, E-mail: skarkete@luther.edu

Swanson, Kristin A., ABD, Vanderbilt, Assistant Professor—biblical studies, 319-387-1054, Fax: 319-387-2158

Weiss, David, ABD, Notre Dame, Instructor—biblical studies, 319-387-1127, Fax: 319-387-2158, E-mail: weissdav@luther.edu

Wrightsman, Bruce, PhD, University of Wisconsin, 1970, Professor—biblical studies and theology, 319-387-1277, Fax: 319-387-2158, E-mail: wrightsm@luther.edu

---

Luther Seminary

2481 Como Avenue
St Paul MN 55108

Phone: 651-641-3456
Fax: 651-641-3354
E-mail: rbrusic@luthersem.edu
URL: www.luthersem.edu

TYPE OF INSTITUTION: Private, Lutheran (ELCA)

EXECUTIVE OFFICER: David Tiede, President

GRADUATE ENROLLMENT: 779

Lutheran Bible Institute of Seattle

4221 228th Ave SE
Issaquah WA 98029

Phone: 206-392-0400
Fax: 206-392-0404

TYPE OF INSTITUTION: Private, Multi-Denominational: Lutheran, but open to all
EXECUTIVE OFFICER: James A. Bergquist, President
CHAIRPERSON: Jean E. C. Wahlstrom, Academic Dean
UNDERGRADUATE ENROLLMENT: 180

Lutheran School of Theology at Chicago

1100 East 55th St
Chicago IL 60615-5199

Phone: 773-256-0700
Fax: 773-256-0782
E-mail: lstcadms@mcs.com

TYPE OF INSTITUTION: Denominational: Lutheran-ELCA
EXECUTIVE OFFICER: James Kenneth Echols, President
CHAIRPERSON: Ralph W. Klein
GRADUATE ENROLLMENT: 70

Lutheran Theological Seminary

61 N West Confederate Ave
Gettysburg PA 17325

Phone: 717-334-6286
Fax: 717-334-3469

TYPE OF INSTITUTION: Denominational: Lutheran
EXECUTIVE OFFICER: Darold H. Beekmann, President
GRADUATE ENROLLMENT: 231

Lutheran Theological Seminary

7301 Germantown Ave
Philadelphia PA 19119-1794

Phone: 800-286-4616
Fax: 215-248-4577
E-mail: mtairy@ltsp.edu
URL: www.ltsp.edu

TYPE OF INSTITUTION: Private, ELCA
EXECUTIVE OFFICER: Robert G. Hughes, President

Lutheran Theological Seminary

114 Seminary Crescent
Saskatoon SK S7N OX3 Canada

Phone: 306-966-7850
Fax: 306-966-7852

TYPE OF INSTITUTION: Private
EXECUTIVE OFFICER: Faith E. Rohrbough, President

CHAIRPERSON: Roger W. Uitti
UNDERGRADUATE ENROLLMENT: 85

Lutheran Theological Southern Seminary

4201 North Main St
Columbia SC 29203

Phone: 803-786-5150
Fax: 803-786-6499
E-mail: freisz@ltss.edu

TYPE OF INSTITUTION: Private, Evangelical Lutheran Church in America
EXECUTIVE OFFICER: H. Frederick Reisz, Jr., President
GRADUATE ENROLLMENT: 182

Luther Rice Seminary

3038 Evans Mill Rd, Lithonia GA 30038

Lycoming College

700 College Place
Williamsport PA 17701-5192

Phone: 570-321-4022
Fax: 570-321-4090
E-mail: hughes@lycoming.edu
URL: www.lycoming.edu

TYPE OF INSTITUTION: Private, United Methodist
EXECUTIVE OFFICER: John F. Piper, Academic Dean
CHAIRPERSON: Richard A. Hughes
UNDERGRADUATE ENROLLMENT: 1,500

Lynchburg College

Lynchburg VA 24501

Lyndon State College

Lyndonville VT 05851

Lyon College

PO Box 2317
Batesville AR 72503

Phone: 501-698-4348
Fax: 501-698-4622
E-mail: rkholyer@lyon.edu
URL: www.lyon.edu

TYPE OF INSTITUTION: Private, Presbyterian Church (USA)
EXECUTIVE OFFICER: Walter B. Roettger, President
CHAIRPERSON: Robert Holyer
UNDERGRADUATE ENROLLMENT: 431

Macalester College

1600 Grand Ave	Phone: 651-696-6141
St Paul MN 55105	Fax: 651-696-6430
	E-mail: laine@macalester.edu

TYPE OF INSTITUTION: Private, United Presbyterian

EXECUTIVE OFFICER: Michael MacPherson, President

CHAIRPERSON: James W. Laine

UNDERGRADUATE ENROLLMENT: 1,760

DEGREES OFFERED: BA

UNDERGRADUATE MAJORS: 39

DEGREES CONFERRED: 19

DESCRIPTION OF UNDERGRADUATE PROGRAM: Working within the humanities and social sciences, the department offers courses examining both the historical and contemporary expressions of religion. The curriculum includes courses in the religions of Asia, as well as Judaism, Christianity, and Islam. Concentrations are offered in religion in America, African-American religion, women in religion, and technology and ethics. A senior seminar on approaches to the study of religion is required of all majors.

FACULTY:

Braude, Anne D., PhD, Yale University (1987), 1994, Associate Professor—religion in America, Native American traditions, women in religion (on leave 1999-2000)

Cooey, Paula M., PhD, Harvard University (1981), 1999, Professor—Christian theology and culture, religion and the arts, women and religion, 651-696-6596, Fax: 651-696-6430, E-mail: cooey@macalester.edu

Laine, James W., ThD, Harvard University (1984), 1985, Professor—religions of India, China and Japan, Islam, 651-696-6789, Fax: 651-696-6430, E-mail: laine@macalester.edu

Pinn, Anthony B., PhD, Harvard University (1994), 1994, Associate Professor—African-American religion, liberation theology, religion and popular culture, 651-696-6141, Fax: 651-696-6430, E-mail: pinn@macalester.edu

Roetzel, Calvin J., PhD, Duke University (1968), 1969, Professor—biblical studies, 651-696-6150, Fax: 651-696-6430, E-mail: roetzel@macalester.edu

PART-TIME FACULTY:

Cytron, Barry D., PhD, Iowa State University (1982), 1989, Lecturer in Religious Studies—Jewish life and thought, Jewish-Christian dialogue

Hopper, David H., ThD, Princeton Theological Seminary (1959), 1959, Professor—contemporary Christian thought, science and religion, technology and ethics, 651-696-6152, Fax: 651-696-6430, E-mail: hopper@macalester.edu

Raskas, Bernard S., BD, Jewish Theological Seminary of America (1949), 1985, Visiting Distinguished Professor of Religious Studies—Jewish ethics and Holocaust, 651-696-6024, Fax: 651-696-6430

Machzikei Hadath Rabbinical College

5407 16th Ave, Brooklyn NY 11219

MacMurray College

447 E College Ave
Jacksonville IL 62650

Phone: 217-479-7000, ext 140
Fax: 217-479-7147
E-mail: rstewart@mac.edu
URL: www.mac.edu

TYPE OF INSTITUTION: Private, United Methodist
EXECUTIVE OFFICER: Larry Bryan, President
CHAIRPERSON: R. J. Stewart
UNDERGRADUATE ENROLLMENT: 700

Madonna College

36600 Schoolcraft Rd, Livonia MI 48150

Magdalen College

Tory Hill Rd, RFD #2 Box 375, Warner NH 03278-9206

Magnolia Bible College

PO Box 1109
822 South Huntington
Kosciusko MS 39090

Phone: 662-289-2896
Fax: 662-289-1850

TYPE OF INSTITUTION: Private, Non-Denominational
EXECUTIVE OFFICER: Gary Kirkendall, President
UNDERGRADUATE ENROLLMENT: 60

Malone College

515 25th St NW
Canton OH 44709

Phone: 216-471-8100
Fax: 216-454-6977

TYPE OF INSTITUTION: Private, Evangelical Friends
EXECUTIVE OFFICER: Ronald G. Johnson, President
CHAIRPERSON: Duane F. Watson
UNDERGRADUATE ENROLLMENT: 1,900
GRADUATE ENROLLMENT: 150

Manchester College

Dept of Religion and Philosophy, North Manchester IN 46962

Manhattan College

| Dept of Religious Studies | Phone: 718-862-7442 |
| Bronx NY 10471 | Fax: 718-862-7513 |

E-mail: jwilcox@.manhattan.edu
URL: www.manhattan.edu/arts/rls/rls.html

TYPE OF INSTITUTION: Private, Roman Catholic

EXECUTIVE OFFICER: Mary Ann O'Donnell, Dean

CHAIRPERSON: John R. Wilcox

UNDERGRADUATE ENROLLMENT: 2,317

DEGREES OFFERED: BA Major, Minor

UNDERGRADUATE MAJORS: 7

DEGREES CONFERRED: 3

DESCRIPTION OF UNDERGRADUATE PROGRAM: Manhattan's approach to the academic study of religion is two-fold. One dimension focuses on religious traditions, including the systematic examination of scriptures, theologies, the history of religions, and the phenomenology of religion. The second dimension focuses on religion as an element of human experience and in relationship to contemporary issues—death, marriage and sexuality, peace and social justice, science and society, and urban problems. Religious studies is taught by an ecumenically oriented faculty who assist students in developing an understanding of and appreciation for the traditions and teachings of the great religions and religious movements of the world. The introductory course is a study of the nature and experience of religion. Upon completion of this course, students may select from a wide variety of elective courses, including specialized seminars, to complete their study of religion. A Roman Catholic (RC) concentration is offered, and an RC cluster in cooperation with other departments may be elected. For the catalogue and further information: John R. Wilcox, chairperson.

FACULTY:

Babre, Claude, PhD (cand.), Union Theological Seminary (1999), 1999, Adjunct Lecturer—psychology and religion, 718-862-7430, E-mail: cbabre@manhattan.edu

Berger, Robert, DMin, Drew (1990), 1991, Associate Professor—Catholicism, 718-862-7419, E-mail: rberger@manhattan.edu

Fahey, Joseph J., PhD, New York University (1974), 1966, Professor—social ethics, 718-862-7305, E-mail: faheyjj@peacenet.org

Ferguson, Thomas, PhD, Fordham University (1993), 1991, Associate Professor—Islam, ecumenics, 718-862-7137, E-mail: tferguson@manhattan.edu

Fish, Tamara, PhD (cand.), Columbia University and Union Theological Seminary (2000), 1995, Adjunct Lecturer—comparative religion, 718-862-7419, E-mail: tfish@manhattan.edu

Gides, David, PhD (cand.), Fordham University (2000), 1999, Adjunct Lecturer—modern historical theology, 718-862-7430, E-mail: dgides@manhattan.edu

Gray, Donald P., PhD, Fordham (1968), 1962, Professor—Christian systematic theology, 718-862-7114, E-mail: dgray@manhattan.edu

Harr, Lois, MA, St Joseph's Seminary (1991), Professional Diploma in Religious Education, Fordham University (1994), 1998, Adjunct Lecturer—Catholic social teaching, liberation theology, service learning programs, 718-862-7142, E-mail: lharr@manhattan.edu

Kaplan, Stephen, PhD, Temple (1981), 1981, Professor—Asian religions, history of religions, 718-862-7113, E-mail: skaplan@manhattan.edu

Kauta, John B., PhD, Fordham (1992), 1995, Adjunct Assistant Professor—African traditional religions, 718-862-7430

Keber, John W., MA, Fordham University (1970), 1969, Associate Professor—scripture, science and religion, 718-862-7347, E-mail: jkeber@manhattan.edu

Knox, E. Richard, PhD (cand.), Union Theological Seminary (1999), 1994, Adjunct Lecturer—business ethics and engineering ethics, 718-862-7430

Plaskow, Judith E., PhD, Yale (1975), 1979, Professor—systematic theology, women and religion, 718-862-7123, E-mail: jplaskow@manhattan.edu

Ryan, John Barry, STD, Institut Catholique (1973), 1972, Professor—liturgy, Native American religions, 718-862-7459, E-mail: jryan@manhattan.edu

Setzer, Claudia J., PhD, Columbia University (1990), 1990, Associate Professor—New Testament, world religions, 718-862-7123, E-mail: csetzer@manhattan.edu

Wilcox, John R., PhD, Union Theological Seminary (1977), 1974, Professor—Christian ethics, ethics for the professions, Roman Catholic higher education, 718-862-7442, E-mail: jwilcox@manhattan.edu

Zyla, Roy T., PhD (cand.), University of California at Santa Barbara (2000), 1998, Adjunct Lecturer—history and philosophy of antiquity, 718-862-7430, E-mail: 6500zyla@ucsbuxa.ucsb.edu

Manhattan Christian College

1415 Anderson Avenue
Manhattan KS 66502-4081

Phone: 785-539-3571
Fax: 785-539-0832
E-mail: wmwatt@mccks.edu
URL: www.mccks.edu

TYPE OF INSTITUTION: Private, Non-Denominational
EXECUTIVE OFFICER: Kenneth Cable, President
CHAIRPERSON: T. Scott Caulley
UNDERGRADUATE ENROLLMENT: 400

Manhattan School of Music

120 Claremont Ave, New York NY 10027

Manhattanville College

Purchase NY 10577

University of Manitoba

Department of Religion
Winnipeg, Manitoba R3T 2N2 Canada

Phone: 204-474-9516
Fax: 204-474-7601

TYPE OF INSTITUTION: Public
EXECUTIVE OFFICER: Raymond Currie, Dean of Arts
CHAIRPERSON: Dawne McCance
UNDERGRADUATE ENROLLMENT: 1,000
GRADUATE ENROLLMENT: 38
DEGREES OFFERED: BA General, BA Advanced, BA Honors, pre-MA, MA, PhD

Manna Bible Institute
PO Box 21464, Philadelphia PA 19141-0464

Mansfield State College
Mansfield PA 16933

Maranatha Baptist Bible College Inc
745 W Main St, Watertown WI 53094

Marian College
3200 Cold Spring Rd, Indianapolis IN 46222

Marian College
45 S National Ave, Fond Du Lac WI 54935

Marietta College
215 Fifth St
Marietta OH 45750

Phone: 740-376-4653
Fax: 740-376-4923
E-mail: machaffb@marietta.edu
URL: www.marietta.edu

TYPE OF INSTITUTION: Private
EXECUTIVE OFFICER: Larry Wilson, President
CHAIRPERSON: Barbara MacHaffie

Marietta Bible College Inc
Muskingum Dr, Box 32, Marietta OH 45750

Marin Bible College
1370 S Navato Blvd, Navato CA 94947

Marist College
Religious Studies Dept, Poughkeepsie NY 12601

Marlboro College

College Rd, Marlboro VT 05344

Marquette University

Dept of Theology, 100 Coughlin Hall
PO Box 1881
Milwaukee WI 53201-1881

Phone: 414-288-7170
Fax: 414-288-5548
E-mail: mutheology@marquette.edu
URL: www.theo.mu.edu

TYPE OF INSTITUTION: Private

EXECUTIVE OFFICER: Thomas E. Hachey, Dean College of Arts and Sciences

CHAIRPERSON: Patrick Carey

COORDINATOR: Thaddeus J. Burch, SJ, Dean Graduate School

UNDERGRADUATE ENROLLMENT: 7,590

GRADUATE ENROLLMENT: 2,161

DEGREES OFFERED: BA in Theology, BA, Teaching Major in Religious Studies

UNDERGRADUATE MAJORS: 32

DEGREES CONFERRED: 9

DESCRIPTION OF UNDERGRADUATE PROGRAM: The undergraduate program is predominantly Catholic, but includes courses and teachers from other Christian and non-Christian traditions. Courses in scripture, systematic theology, religious ethics, and the history of thought throughout the Christian era give opportunities for a fully-rounded knowledge of the total Judeo-Christian theological enterprise. Along with a regular academic major, there is also available a teaching major, which leads to certification by the State of Wisconsin and which includes material from allied areas of sociology, history, anthropology, and the like.

GRADUATE PROGRAM

Graduate Advisor: Bradford Hinze

Graduate Degrees Offered: MA; PhD

Degrees Conferred: 4 MA; 10 PhD

Graduate Students in Residence: 14 MA; 84 PhD/ThD

Not in Residence: 3 MA; 30 PhD/ThD

Average No. of New Students Enrolled: 5 MA; 14 PhD/ThD

Women Students: 11 MA; 25 PhD

Minority Students: 2 MA; 3 PhD/ThD

Foreign Students: 3 PhD/ThD

Minimum GRE Score Requisite to Admission: Yes; 600 verbal, PhD; 510 verbal, MA

Minimum GPA Score Requisite to Admission: Yes; 3.0 on 4.0 scale

Foreign Language Proficiency Evaluated: No

Financial Aid to First Year Students: 70% MA; 90% PhD

Financial Aid to Other Students: 33% MA; 40% PhD

Attrition Among Students: 5-6% MA

Graduates Placed: 85% MA; 95% PhD

DESCRIPTION OF GRADUATE PROGRAM AND RESEARCH FACILITIES: Roman Catholic in orientation, with ecumenical commitment to the whole Christian theological tradition. PhD specializations: Biblical, Historical, Systematics/Ethics, Theology and Society (interdisciplinary). The department offers a focus on Luther Studies in a Roman Catholic Context. MA: 30 semester hours (including 18 core hours and MA project); proficiency in French or German prior to qualifying examinations. Doctoral candidacy requires passing a qualifying examination (written and oral) after course work. A dissertation is written under a director of one's choice. The Marquette Library has more than 800,000 volumes and 7,000 serials, and access to electronic data bases. There is a basic reference section in theology, extensive holdings in the biblical area, patristics, conciliar documents and a collection of primary sources, commentaries, translations, and critical monographs of the best medieval, modern, and contemporary authors.

ACADEMIC PLAN, ADMISSION REQUIREMENTS, FINANCIAL AID: Marquette University operates on the semester system. Preparation for graduate study should preferably be an undergraduate major in theology or religious studies or another appropriate field (e.g., philosophy, classics). Ample opportunities for supplementing incomplete undergraduate preparation in religious studies are available. Ideally, all students should have some familiarity with scripture and basic Christian teachings. Documents required: GRE scores (aptitude); transcripts; two letters of recommendation (three if financial aid is requested); a statement of foreign language proficiency; for those without graduate degrees, a list of undergraduate theology courses taken; a brief statement of purpose for beginning graduate study in theology. A number of tuition scholarships are awarded each year by the Graduate School. These vary from 3 to 18 hours of tuition remission and are awarded on the recommendation of the department. A number of fellowships are available. Competition for teaching and research assistantships is open to all graduate students; assistantship awards involve free tuition and an annual stipend (presently ca. $8,590-$10,000). Applicants for financial aid must submit a special financial aid application, in addition to the regular application for admission. Financial aid deadline: February 15.

FACULTY:

Barnes, Michel René, PhD, University of St Michael's College, Toronto (1992), 1991, Associate Professor—history and theology of early Christianity, 414-288-3735, E-mail: barnesm@vms.csd.mu.edu

Caldwell, Thomas, SSL, Pontifical Biblical Institute, Rome (1964), 1965, Assistant Professor—Old Testament and intertestamental periods, 414-288-5508, E-mail: caldwellt@vms.csd.mu.edu

Carey, Patrick, PhD, Fordham (1975), 1978, Professor—American Protestant and Catholic religious life and thought, 414-288-7170, E-mail: careyp@vms.csd.mu.edu

Coffey, David, STD, Catholic Institute of Sydney (1960), 1995, Presidential Chair in Catholic Theology—Trinity, Christology, grace, 414-288-1967, E-mail: coffeyd@marquette.edu

Copeland, M. Shawn, PhD, Boston College (1991), 1994, Associate Professor—systematic theology, locating her work at the level of foundations with particular attention to method, theological anthropology, liberation and political theologies, and African-American religious experience and culture, 414-288-3746, E-mail: copelands@vms.csd.mu.edu

Dabney, D. Lyle, DrTheol, Eberhard-Karls Universitat, Tubingen (1989), 1994, Assistant Professor—Protestant systematic theology with particular attention to the areas of the contemporary German theological discussion, Wesleyan theology, the question of nature and graca, and pneumatology, 414-288-3744, E-mail: dabneyd@vms.csd.mu.edu

Dempsey, Deirdre, PhD, The Catholic University of America (1989), 1994, Assistant Professor—Northwest Semitic languages and literatures, with a specialty in biblical Hebrew, 414-288-7647, E-mail: dempseyd@vms.csd.mu.edu

Duffey, Michael K., PhD, Notre Dame (1981), 1980, Associate Professor—theological ethics, 414-288-3748, E-mail: duffeym@vms.csd.mu.edu

Edwards, Richard, PhD, Chicago (1968), 1978, Associate Professor—New Testament, Christian origins, 414-288-7156, E-mail: edwardsr@vms.csd.mu.edu

Fahey, Michael A., SJ, Theol, University of Tubingen, Germany (1970) Professor—Contemporary Catholic theology, Eastern Orthodox theology, Vatican II, World Council of churches, modern German theology, 3rd century north African theology, medieval eucharistic controversies, Email: michael.fahey@marquette.edu

Gawronski, Raymond, STD, Gregorian University (1992), 1993, Assistant Professor—systematic theology with a strong focus on the mystical, 414-288-3745, E-mail: gawronskir@vms.csd.mu.edu

Golitzin, Alexander, DPhil, Oxford (1980), 1989, Assistant Professor—Orthodox church history and thought, 414-288-7510, E-mail: golitzina@vms.csd.mu.edu

Hagen, Kenneth, ThD, Harvard University (1967), 1967, Professor—medieval and Reformation theology, 414-288-6961, E-mail: hagenk@vms.csd.mu.edu

Hills, Julian V., ThD, Harvard University (1985), 1985, Associate Professor—New Testament, Christian origins, 414-288-3776, E-mail: hillsj@vms.csd.mu.edu

Hinze, Bradford E., PhD, Chicago (1989), 1989, Assistant Professor—systematic and foundational theology, 414-288-3743, E-mail: hinzeb@vms.csd.mu.edu

Hinze, Christine Firer, PhD, University of Chicago Divinity School (1989), 1990, Associate Professor—theological ethics, 414-288-6802, E-mail: hinzec@vms.csd.mu.edu

Hughson, D. Thomas, PhD, University of St Michael's College, Toronto (1981), 1979, Associate Professor—Catholic systematic theology, fundamental theology, 414-288-7323, E-mail: hughsont@vms.csd.mu.edu

Johnson, Mark F., PhD, University of Toronto (1990), 1996, Assistant Professor—Christian ethics, 414-288-7646, E-mail: johnsonmar@vms.csd.mu.edu

Kelly, William, STD, Institut Catholique (1963), 1961, Associate Professor—contemporary Catholic systematic theology and its historical roots, 414-288-3747, E-mail: kellysj@vms.csd.mu.edu

Kurz, William, PhD, Yale (1976), 1975, Associate Professor—New Testament and Christian origins, 414-288-7148, E-mail: kurzw@vms.csd.mu.edu

Lambeck, Robert, STL, St Louis University (1951), 1966, Assistant Professor—Far Eastern religious studies, 414-288-3742, E-mail: lambeckr@vms.csd.mu.edu

Laurance, John, PhD, University of Notre Dame (1983), 1991, Associate Professor—history and theology of Christian liturgy, 414-288-3734, E-mail: laurancej@vms.csd.mu.edu

Maguire, Daniel, STD, Gregorian (1969), 1971, Professor—Christian ethics, 414-288-3749, E-mail: maguired@vms.csd.mu.edu

Masson, Robert, PhD, Fordham (1978), 1980, Associate Professor—foundational and systematic theology, philosophical theology, 414-288-6952, E-mail: massonr@vms.csd.mu.edu

Misner, Paul, DrTheol, Munich (1969), 1979, Associate Professor—history of Christian life and thought in Europe since the seventeenth century, 414-288-3737, E-mail: misnerp@vms.csd.mu.edu

Mueller, Joseph G., STL, Centre Sèvres, Paris (1995), 1999, Assistant Professor—early Christian theology and ecclesiology, 414-288-7647, E-mail: joseph.mueller@marquette.edu

Pace, Sharon, PhD, Notre Dame (1985), 1985, Associate Professor—Old Testament (Hebrew Bible/Judaica), 414-288-7503, E-mail: paces@vms.csd.mu.edu

Rossi, Philip J., PhD, Texas (1975), 1975, Associate Professor—Christian ethics, moral philosophy, philosophy of religion, 414-288-3738, E-mail: rossip@vms.csd.mu.edu

Schmitt, John J., PhD, Chicago (1977), 1980, Associate Professor—Old Testament, ancient Israel, 414-288-3739, E-mail: schmittj@vms.csd.mu.edu

Stockhausen, Carol, PhD, Marquette University (1984), 1984, Associate Professor—New Testament, Christian origins, 414-288-3736, E-mail: stockhausenc@vms.csd.mu.edu
Zemler-Cizewski, Wanda, PhD, Centre for Medieval Studies, Toronto (1983), 1985, Associate Professor—history of medieval theology, 414-288-3741, E-mail: cizewski@vms.csd.mu.edu

Mars Hill College

Mars Hill NC 28754
Phone: 828-689-1238
Fax: 828-689-1474
E-mail: pfender@mhc.edu

TYPE OF INSTITUTION: Private, Baptist
EXECUTIVE OFFICER: Robert Knott, Executive Vice President
CHAIRPERSON: W. Thomas Sawyer
UNDERGRADUATE ENROLLMENT: 30

Marshall University

Dept of Religious Studies, Huntington WV 25701

Martin Luther College

1995 Luther Ct
New Ulm MN 56073-3300
Phone: 507-354-8221
Fax: 507-354-8225
URL: www.mlc-wels.edu

TYPE OF INSTITUTION: Private, Wisconsin Evangelical Lutheran Synod
EXECUTIVE OFFICER: Theodore B. Olsen, President
CHAIRPERSON: Joel D. Fredrich
UNDERGRADUATE ENROLLMENT: 850

Mary College

Bismark ND 58501

Mary Baldwin College

Dept of Religion
Staunton VA 24401
Phone: 540-887-7065
Fax: 540-887-7137
E-mail: jegilman@cit.mbc.edu

EXECUTIVE OFFICER: Cynthia Tyson, President
CHAIRPERSON: James E. Gilman
UNDERGRADUATE ENROLLMENT: 11

University of Mary Hardin-Baylor

Dept of Religion
UMHB Station 900 College
Belton TX 76513

Phone: 254—295-4568
Fax: 254-295-4535
E-mail: swyrick@umhb.edu

TYPE OF INSTITUTION: Denominational: Baptist

CHAIRPERSON: Stephen Von Wyrick

UNDERGRADUATE ENROLLMENT: 2,093

GRADUATE ENROLLMENT: 219

DEGREES OFFERED: BA Religion

UNDERGRADUATE MAJORS: 97

DESCRIPTION OF UNDERGRADUATE PROGRAM: The Religion Department's biblically based curriculum addresses several objectives. First, the curriculum provides the necessary preparation for graduate study in Religion. Second, the Department provides a foundation for seminary education. Third, the Department provides an education for individuals with a general interest in the study of Religion. Fourth, the Religion curriculum provides continuing education for persons currently in ministry. Fifth, it offers courses that will enable the student to be an effective member of a local church. Sixth, the curriculum provides foundation for individuals directly entering the ministry upon graduation from UMHB.

FACULTY:

Holcomb, Carol Crawford, PhD, Baylor University (1999), 1999, Assistant Professor—church history, 254-295-4569, E-mail: cholcomb@umhb.edu

Kemp, Leroy, ThD, Southwestern Baptist Theological Seminary (1966), 1987, Professor—theology, ministry, 254-295-4622, E-mail: lkemp@umhb.edu

Martin, Tony, PhD, Southwestern Baptist Theological Seminary (1979), 1981, Professor—New Testament, Greek, 254-295-4570, E-mail: tmartin@umhb.edu

Reynolds, J. A., ThD, New Orleans Baptist Theological Seminary (1962), 1962, Professor—church history, 254—295-4569, E-mail: jreynolds@umhb.edu

Wyrick, Stephen Von, PhD, Southwestern Baptist Theological Seminary (1981), 1994, Professor—Hebrew Bible, Hebrew, archaeology, 254-295-4568, E-mail: swyrick@umhb.edu

Mary Washington College

1301 College Avenue
Fredericksburg VA 22401-5358

Phone: 540-654-1343
Fax: 540-654-1080
E-mail: jgoehrin@mwc.edu
URL: mwc.edu

TYPE OF INSTITUTION: Public

EXECUTIVE OFFICER: William M. Anderson, President

CHAIRPERSON: Craig Vasey

UNDERGRADUATE ENROLLMENT: 3,800

Marycrest International University

1607 West 12th St
Davenport IA 52804

Phone: 319-326-9512
Fax: 319-326-9347
E-mail: gmonnard@mcrest.edu
URL: www.mcrest.edu/

TYPE OF INSTITUTION: Private
EXECUTIVE OFFICER: Laurence Conner, President
CHAIRPERSON: Gary Monnard
UNDERGRADUATE ENROLLMENT: 400
GRADUATE ENROLLMENT: 412

Marygrove College

8425 W McNichols
Detroit MI 48221-2599

Phone: 313-927-1200
Fax: 313-927-1345

TYPE OF INSTITUTION: Private, Roman Catholic
EXECUTIVE OFFICER: John E. Shay, Jr., President
CHAIRPERSON: George P. Alcser
COORDINATOR: Anthony R. Kosnik
UNDERGRADUATE ENROLLMENT: 1,090
GRADUATE ENROLLMENT: 1,430

Maryknoll School of Theology

N 4, Maryknoll NY 10545

Marylhurst College

Marylhurst OR 97036

Marymount College

Tarrytown NY 10591

Marymount College

2897 N Glebe Rd, Arlington VA 22207

Marymount-Manhattan College

221 E 71st St, New York NY 10021

Maryville College

13550 Conway Rd, St Louis MO 63141

Maryville College

Maryville TN 37801

Marywood College

Religious Studies Dept
2300 Adams Ave
Scranton PA 18509-1598

Phone: 717-348-6211
Fax: 717-961-4769
E-mail: frm@ac.marywood.edu

TYPE OF INSTITUTION: Private, Roman Catholic
EXECUTIVE OFFICER: Mary Reap, IHM, President
CHAIRPERSON: Michael A. Fuchs, Undergraduate
COORDINATOR: Frances R. McCormick, Graduate
UNDERGRADUATE ENROLLMENT: 2,000
GRADUATE ENROLLMENT: 1,200

University of Massachusetts

Amherst MA 01003

Phone: 413-545-6770

TYPE OF INSTITUTION: Public
EXECUTIVE OFFICER: David Scott, Chancellor
COORDINATOR: William M. Johnston
UNDERGRADUATE ENROLLMENT: 14,000
GRADUATE ENROLLMENT: 3,000

The Master's College

21726 Placerita Canyon Rd
Newhall CA 91321-0878

Phone: 805-259-3540
Fax: 850-259-5006

TYPE OF INSTITUTION: Private, Non-Denominational
EXECUTIVE OFFICER: John Hughes, Academic Dean
CHAIRPERSON: Tom Halstead, Chair, Bible Department
UNDERGRADUATE ENROLLMENT: 850

McCormick Theological Seminary

5555 South Woodlawn Ave
Chicago IL 60637

Phone: 773-947-6307
Fax: 773-288-2612
URL: www.mccormick.edu

TYPE OF INSTITUTION: Private, Presbyterian (USA)

EXECUTIVE OFFICER: David Esterline, Interim Dean/Vice President for Academic Affairs
GRADUATE ENROLLMENT: 400
FACULTY:

Ashby, Homer U., Jr., PhD, Northwestern University (1978), 1979 Professor—pastoral care, health and wellness, ministry with older adults and spiritual dimensions of professional practice. 773-947-6300, Fax: 773-288-2612, E-mail: hashby@mccormick.edu

Brawley, Robert L., PhD, Princeton Theological Seminary (1978), 1992, Professor—New Testament, Luke-Acts, ethics, 773-947-6300, Fax: 773-288-2612, E-mail: rbrawley@mccormick.edu

Caldwell, Elizabeth Francis, PhD, Northwestern University (1990), 1984, Professor—pastoral theology, religious education, 773-947-6300, Fax: 773-288-2812, E-mail: caldwell@mccormick.edu

Campbell, Cynthia McCall, PhD, Southern Methodist University (1981), 1995, Professor—church and ministry, theology and worship, 773-947-6300, Fax: 773-288-2612, E-mail: ccampbell@mccormick.edu

Cary, Charles M., DMin, McCormick Theological Seminary (1984), 1999, Professor—ministry, stewardship and parish administration, 773-947-6300, Fax: 773-288-2612, E-mail: ccary@mccormick.edu

Case-Winters, Anna, PhD, Vanderbilt University (1988), 1986, Professor—theology, 773-947-6300, Fax: 773-288-2612, E-mail: acasewinters@mccormick.edu

Cathey, Robert, PhD, Duke University (1989), 1998, Professor—theology, theology: dogmatic, systematic, and ecumenical 773-947-6300, Fax: 773-288-2612, E-mail: rcathey@mccormick.edu

Chun, Hearn, ThM, Princeton Seminary (1972), 1989, Assistant Professor—ministry and theological studies, 773-947-6300, Fax: 773-288-2612, E-mail: hchun@mccormick.edu

Cortes-Fuentes, David, ThM, Union Theological Seminary (1990), 1993, Director of Hispanic Ministries—biblical interpretation/New Testament, 773-947-6300, Fax: 773-288-2612, E-mail: dcortes@mccormick.edu

Daniels, David, III, PhD, Union Theological Seminary (1992), 1987, Associate Professor—church history, 773-947-6300, Fax: 773-288-2612, E-mail: ddaniels@mccormick.edu

Edwards, Sandra, MA, Florida State University (1972h), 1996, Director of the African-American Ministries Program—African-American/urban studies, 773-947-6300, Fax: 773-288-2612, E-mail: sedwards@mccormick.edu

Esterline, David V., PhD, Graduate Theological Union (1986), 1997 Director of Doctoral Programs & Continuing Education—ministry & education, 773-947-6300, Fax: 773-288-2612, E-mail: desterline@mccormick.edu

Finney, Leon D., Jr., DMin, McCormick Theological Seminary (1990), 1993, Director—African-American Leadership Partnership Program, urban economic and social development, 773-753-2470, Fax: 773-753-2480, E-mail: 104227,733@compuserve.com

Hadsell, Heidi, PhD, University of Southern California (1979), 1988, Professor—christian social ethics, environmental ethics, E-mail: hhn@wcc-coe.org

Halverstadt, Hugh, PhD, Northwestern University (1973), 1979, Professor—ministry, practical theology, 773-947-6300, Fax: 773-288-2612, E-mail: hhalverstadt@mccormick.edu

Hiebert, Theodore, PhD, Harvard University (1984), 1995, Professor—Old Testament and biblical studies, 773-947-6300, Fax: 773-288-2612, E-mail: thiebert@mccormick.edu

Holper, J. Frederick, (1988), 1998, Professor—preaching and worship, 773-947-6300, Fax: 773-288-2612, E-mail: fholper@mccormick.edu

Kapp, Deborah, MA, Loyola University (1999), 1995, Assistant Professor—congregational ministry, 773-947-6300, Fax: 773-288-2612, E-mail: dkapp@mccormick.edu

Knowles, Melody D. G., MDiv, Princeton Theological Seminary (1994), 1999, Assistant Professor—Hebrew scriptures, 773-947-6300, Fax: 773-288-2612, E-mail: mknowles@mccormick.edu

Livezey, Lois Gehr, PhD, University of Chicago (1983), 1988, Professor—Christian ethics, 773-947-6300, Fax: 773-288-2612, E-mail: llivezey@mccormick.edu

Mullen, Deborah Flemister, MDiv, Colgate Rochester Divinity School (1982), 1989, Assistant Professor—ministry & Historical Studies, 773-947-6300, Fax: 773-288-2612, E-mail: dmullen@mccormick.edu

Rivera, Luis, ThD, Harvard Divinity School (1993), 1995, Associate Professor—theology, systematic theology, ecclesiology, theological anthropology, Latino and Latin-American theology 773-947-6300, Fax: 773-288-2612, E-mail: lrivera@mccormick.edu

Rodriguez-Diaz, Daniel, PhD, National University of Mexico (1979), 1988, Professor—church history, Hispanic ministries, 773-947-6300, Fax: 773-288-2612, E-mail: drodriguez@mccormick.edu

Sawyer, Kenneth, PhD, University of Chicago Divinity School (1992), 1993, Assistant Professor—church history, 773-947-6300, Fax: 773-288-2612, E-mail: ksawyer@mccormick.edu

Tanzer, Sarah, PhD, Harvard University (1987), 1986, Associate Professor—Judaism and Christian origins, 773-947-6300, Fax: 773-288-2612, E-mail: stanzer@mccormick.edu

Wendorf, Mark W., MDiv, (1979), 1996, Assistant Professor—urban ministry, 773-974-6300, Fax: 773-288-2612, E-mail: mwendorf@mccormick.edu

Yoon, Victor S., ThD, Graduate Theological Union (1986), 1997, Associate Professor—Asian studies, Korean American ministry, 773-947-6300, Fax: 773-288-2612, E-mail: vyoon@mccormick.edu

---

McGill University

Faculty of Religious Studies	**Phone: 514-398-4121**
Birks Building, 3520 University St	**Fax: 514-398-6665**
Montreal, Quebec H3A 2A7 Canada	**URL: www.mcgill.ca/religion**

TYPE OF INSTITUTION: Public, Inter-Denominational

EXECUTIVE OFFICER: B. Barry Levy, Dean of the Faculty of Religious Studies

UNDERGRADUATE ENROLLMENT: 101

GRADUATE ENROLLMENT: 90

DEGREES OFFERED: BA Major, BA Honors, BA Jt Honors, BA Minor, BTh

DEGREES CONFERRED: 2 BTh, 23 BA

DESCRIPTION OF UNDERGRADUATE PROGRAM: Honors, Major and Minor Programs in Religious Studies (given as part of the BA curriculum): Instruction available in major religious traditions (i.e., Christianity, Islam, Hinduism, Buddhism), including such areas as history, languages, theology, ethics, psychology, art, methodology, contemporary issues, (e.g., women in religion). The Honors program offers a high degree of concentration and analysis through course work, intensive research, and peer group discussion. It requires 66 credits (out of a total of 90) in Religious Studies and approved related courses in other departments and faculties. The Major program requires 36 credits in such courses. BTh Program: A program in Theology intended primarily for candidates for ministry or those proceeding to higher degrees in Theology. Both programs are normally of three years duration.

GRADUATE PROGRAM

Member of the Council on Graduate Studies in Religion

Graduate Degrees Offered: MA; PhD; STM

Degrees Conferred: 8 MA; 3 PhD; 0 STM

Graduate Students in Residence: 24 MA; 15 PhD/ThD; 1 Other

Not in Residence: 7 MA; 42 PhD/ThD; 1 Other

Average No. of New Students Enrolled: 8 MA; 8 PhD/ThD; 6 Other

Women Students: 12 MA; 16 PhD/ThD; 4 Other

Minority Students: 7 MA; 3 PhD/ThD

Foreign Students: 7 MA; 9 PhD/ThD

Minimum GRE Score Requisite to Admission: No

Minimum GPA Score Requisite to Admission: Yes; 3.30 MA; 3.50 PhD

Financial Aid to First Year Students: 10% MA; 50% PhD

Financial Aid to Other Students: 5% MA; 5% PhD; 5% Other

DESCRIPTION OF GRADUATE PROGRAM AND RESEARCH FACILITIES: The Faculty of Graduate Studies and Research, located in Dawson Hall, directs and controls all programs leading to higher degrees and recommends candidates to the Senate for these degrees. As a Department within it, the Faculty of Religious Studies offers courses leading to the degrees of Master of Sacred Theology, Master of Arts, and Doctor of Philosophy. The purpose of the MA degree is to encourage advanced study and research in religious studies and theology, especially for those who wish to become scholars or teachers and those who are already engaged in some field of religious service. The STM is meant primarily for those who intend to enter the ministry of the Christian church or another religious institution, or proceed to teaching in schools or to some form of social work. The purpose of the PhD program is to engage students in academic studies at the highest level and to enable them if they so wish to prepare for an academic career. It normally requires three years of research beyond the bachelor's degree and two beyond the master's. There are four areas of study: 1) Biblical (including Old Testament and New Testament), 2) Christian Theology (including Church History and Christian Theology), 3) Religion and Culture (including Religion and the Arts, Theological Ethics, Philosophy of Religion), 4) Comparative Study (including Hindu, Buddhist, Muslim, and other traditions). The Faculty has its own branch library of some 68,000 volumes of theology and comparative studies. Students also have access to all the resources of the McGill University Libraries System. For information concerning admission requirements contact the Department concerned.

ACADEMIC PLAN, ADMISSION REQUIREMENTS, FINANCIAL AID: For details on Academic Plans and Admissions please contact the individual responsible for the particular program in which you are interested (see beginning of entry). A limited amount of financial aid in the form of scholarships, bursaries, loans, teaching assistantships is available. For information contact the Dean.

FACULTY:

Baum, G., DTh, Fribourg (1956), 1986, Professor Emeritus—ethics

Boutin, M., DTh, Munich (1973), 1991, Professor—philosophy of religion

Farrow, D. B., PhD, King's, London (1994), 1998, Assistant Professor—Christian theology

Hall, D. J., ThD, Union Seminary, New York (1963), 1975, Professor Emeritus—Christian theology

Hayes, R. P., PhD, Toronto (1982), 1987, Associate Professor—Asian religions

Henderson, I. H., DPhil, Oxford (1989), 1988, Associate Professor—New Testament

Hori, V. S., PhD, Stanford (1976), Assistant Professor—Japanese religions

Kirby, T., DPhil, Oxford, Assistant Professor—church history
Kirkpatrick, P. G., DPhil, Oxford (1985), 1984, Associate Professor—Old Testament
Levy, B. B., PhD, NYU (1978), 1997, Professor—Jewish and biblical studies
McLelland, J. C., PhD, Edinburgh (1953), 1959, Professor Emeritus—philosophy of religion
Runnalls, D. R., PhD, Toronto (1971), 1971, Professor—Old Testament, Judaism
Sharma, A., PhD, Harvard (1978), 1987, Professor—Asian religions
Simons, J., PhD, Georgetown (1980), 1995, Faculty Lecturer—philosophical theology
Wisse, F., PhD, Claremont (1968), 1980, Professor—New Testament
Young, K. K., PhD, McGill (1978), 1978, Professor—Asian religions

---

McKendree College

Dept of Religious Studies
701 College Rd
Lebanon IL 62254

Phone: 618-537-6961
Fax: 618-537-6259
E-mail: mmcguire@atlas.mckendree.edu
URL: www.mckendree.edu

TYPE OF INSTITUTION: Private, United Methodist
EXECUTIVE OFFICER: James Dennis, President
CHAIRPERSON: Marilyn McGuire
UNDERGRADUATE ENROLLMENT: 2,047

McMaster University

Dept of Religious Studies
University Hall
Hamilton, Ontario L8S 4K1 Canada

Phone: 905-525-9140
Fax: 905-525-8161
E-mail: westerho@mcmaster.ca
URL: www.socsci.mcmaster.ca/relstud/

TYPE OF INSTITUTION: Public
CHAIRPERSON: Stephen Westerholm
UNDERGRADUATE ENROLLMENT: 13,500
GRADUATE ENROLLMENT: 1,500
DEGREES OFFERED: BA, MA, PhD
UNDERGRADUATE MAJORS: 100
DESCRIPTION OF UNDERGRADUATE PROGRAM: Brief description of department and its institutional setting: The undergraduate program in religious studies provides students with in-depth study of the texts, themes, and traditions of the major religions of the world through a variety of approaches. It requires that students gain a twofold expertise, one in understanding a particular religious tradition, another in comprehending the scope of religious phenomena. Courses are offered in four general areas: Biblical, Asian Religions, Western Religious Traditions, and Thematic and Comparative.
GRADUATE PROGRAM
Member of the Council on Graduate Studies in Religion
Graduate Advisor: E. Schuller
Graduate Degrees Offered: MA; PhD
Degrees Conferred: 6 MA; 2 PhD

Graduate Students in Residence: 13 MA; 35 PhD

Not in Residence: 1 MA; 8 PhD

Average No. of New Students Enrolled: 7 MA; 8 PhD

Women Students: 7 MA; 13 PhD

Foreign Students: 1 MA; 7 PhD

Minimum GRE Score Requisite to Admission: No

Minimum GPA Score Requisite to Admission: Yes; B+

Foreign Language Proficiency Evaluated: Yes

Financial Aid to First Year Students: 100% MA; 100% PhD

Financial Aid to Other Students: 36% MA; 55% PhD

Attrition Among Students: 10% PhD

DESCRIPTION OF GRADUATE PROGRAM AND RESEARCH FACILITIES: The Department offers a graduate program dealing with religion and the religious experience of humankind, past and present, in East and West. The scope of the program is indicated by the variety of methods drawn on in the effort to understand religion and religious phenomena. These are philosophical, philological, literary, historical, anthropological, sociological. The goal of the program might be expressed by reference to three habits: openness both to the great religious traditions and to modern resources and methods for understanding them; independence of judgment, which bespeaks a critical mind; and reflection by which one who is critical within a particular horizon learns to become critical also of that self same horizon. The Department as such has no confessional ties nor does it aim at providing a theological education. Concentrations are possible in Judaism and Christianity in the Greco-Roman period, Western Religious Traditions (religion and politics, religion and the social sciences and Western religious thought), and Asian Religions (Buddism and East Asian Religions, and Hinduism and Jainism). Mills Library has holdings of over 1.3 million volumes with comprehensive collections in relevant areas and currently receives 9,000 titles of periodicals. Toronto, Ontario, and U.S. libraries are accessible through a loan system.

ACADEMIC PLAN, ADMISSION REQUIREMENTS, FINANCIAL AID: McMaster operates on a two-term system. The normal requirement for admission to graduate studies is graduation with upper second-class standing in an Honours program which includes religion as a major subject and a beginning in study of relevant languages. Applications from related fields may also be considered. Documents required: official transcripts, two letters of recommendation, statement of interest. Numerous fellowships and awards are available, ranging in value from $2,000 to $15,000, including teaching assistantships.

FACULTY:

Arapura, J. G., PhD, Columbia (1960), 1965, Professor Emeritus—Indian philosophies of religion

Badone, E., PhD, Berkeley (1985), 1987, Associate Professor—religion, anthropology, 905-525-9140 ext 23395, Fax: 905-525-8161, E-mail: badone@mcmaster.ca

Combs, A. E., PhD, Columbia (1963), 1962, Professor Emeritus—Hebrew Bible, 905-525-9140 ext 23386, Fax: 905-525-8161

Granoff, P., PhD, Harvard (1973), 1976, Professor—Sanskrit, Hindu religious history, Asian art, 905-525-9140 ext 24210, Fax: 905-525-8161, E-mail: shinohar@mcmaster.ca

Greenspan, L. I., PhD, Brandeis (1973), 1965, Professor—religion and modern social and political thought, 905-525-9140 ext 24597, Fax: 905-525-8161, E-mail: greenspn@mcmaster.ca

Jan, Y.-h, PhD, Visva-Bharati (1964), 1967, Professor Emeritus—Buddhism, history of Chinese religions

Kinsley, D. R., PhD, Chicago (1970), 1969, Professor—medieval Hinduism, 905-525-9140 ext 24759, Fax: 905-525-8161, E-mail: kinsleyd@mcmaster.ca

Kroeker, P. T., PhD, University of Chicago (1989), 1988, Associate Professor—religion and social ethics, 905-525-9140 ext 23385, Fax: 905-525-8161, E-mail: kroekert@mcmaster.ca

MacQueen, G., PhD, Harvard (1979), 1977, Associate Professor—Buddhist scriptural tradition, 905-525-9140 ext 23388, Fax: 905-525-8161, E-mail: macqueen@mcmaster.ca

Mendelson, A., PhD, Chicago (1971), 1976, Professor—Hellenistic Judaism, 905-525-9140 ext 23389, Fax: 905-525-8161, E-mail: mendelsn@mcmaster.ca

Mol, J. J., PhD, Columbia (1960), 1970, Professor Emeritus—sociology of religion

Planinc, Z., PhD, Harvard University (1989), 1988, Associate Professor—religion and political philosophy, 905-525-9140 ext 23394, Fax: 905-525-8161, E-mail: planincz@mcmaster.ca

Reinhartz, A., PhD, McMaster (1983), 1987, Professor—history of Early Judaism and Christianity, 905-525-9140 ext 24239, Fax: 905-525-8161, E-mail: reinhart@mcmaster.ca

Robertson, J. C., PhD, Yale (1967), 1968, Professor—contemporary philosophy and Christian thought, 905-525-9140 ext 23392, Fax: 905-525-8161, E-mail: robrtsnj@mcmaster.ca

Schuller, E., PhD, Harvard University (1984), 1990, Professor—Hebrew Bible and early Palestinian Judaism, 905-525-9140 ext 23390, Fax: 905-525-8161, E-mail: schuller@mcmaster.ca

Shinohara, K., PhD, Columbia (1976), 1972, Professor—Buddhist religious history, East Asian religions, 905-525-9140 ext 23393, Fax: 905-525-8161, E-mail: shinohar@mcmaster.ca

Vallée, G., DTheol, Münster (1971), 1972, Professor Emeritus—history of Christian thought, 905-525-9140 ext 23386, Fax: 905-525-8161

Westerholm, S., DTh, Lund (1978), 1984, Associate Professor—New Testament, exegesis, 905-525-9140 ext 24734 or 24363, Fax: 905-525-8161, E-mail: westerho@mcmaster.ca

Whillier, W. K., PhD, McMaster (1973), 1970, Associate Professor (part-time)—Rg Veda, philosophy of language, 905-525-9140 ext 23773, Fax: 905-525-8161, E-mail: whillier@mcmaster.ca

Widdicombe, P., DPhil, Oxford (1990), 1993, Associate Professor—patristic and systematic theology, 905-525-9140 ext 22220, Fax: 905-525-8161, E-mail: widdicom@mcmaster.ca

Younger, P., PhD, Princeton University (1965), 1964, Professor Emeritus—Indian religious tradition and contemporary India, 905-525-9140 ext 23397, Fax: 905-525-8161

McMaster Divinity College

1280 Main St W
Hamilton, Ontario L8S 4K1
Canada

Phone: 905-525-9140 ext 24401
Fax: 905-577-4782
E-mail: divinity@mcmaster.ca
URL: www.mcmaster.ca/divinity

EXECUTIVE OFFICER: William H. Brackney, Principal and Dean

McMurry College

Abilene TX 79605

McPherson College

PO Box 1402
1600 E Euclid Ave
McPherson KS 67460

Phone: 316-241-0731
Fax: 316-241-8443

TYPE OF INSTITUTION: Private, Church of the Brethren
EXECUTIVE OFFICER: Gary Dill, President
CHAIRPERSON: A. Herbert Smith
UNDERGRADUATE ENROLLMENT: 500

Meadville Lombard Theological School

5701 South Woodlawn Avenue
Chicago IL 60637

Phone: 773-256-3000
Fax: 773-753-1323
URL: www.meadville.edu

TYPE OF INSTITUTION: Private, Unitarian Universalist
EXECUTIVE OFFICER: William R. Murry, President and Academic Dean
GRADUATE ENROLLMENT: 42

Memorial University of Newfoundland

St Johns, Newfoundland A1C 5S7
Canada

Phone: 709-737-8166
Fax: 709-737-8059
E-mail: dhawkin@morgan.ucs.mun.ca
URL: www.mun.ca/rels/

TYPE OF INSTITUTION: Public, Non-Denominational
CHAIRPERSON: David J. Hawkin
UNDERGRADUATE ENROLLMENT: 14,042
GRADUATE ENROLLMENT: 1,623
DEGREES OFFERED: BA, BA (Hons.)
UNDERGRADUATE MAJORS: 65
DEGREES CONFERRED: 22
DESCRIPTION OF UNDERGRADUATE PROGRAM: The undergraduate major in Religious Studies is a component of the offerings of the Faculty of Arts and allows students to select courses from four areas of concentration: Biblical Studies, Christian Thought and History, World Religions, or Religion, Ethics, and Modern Culture. A wide choice of courses is available, including courses in Canadian religious history. Courses in religious education methodology are offered by the Faculty of Education. Students doing degrees in Arts, Education, or Physical Education may complete a minor in Religious Studies as part of their programs. The first two years of the undergraduate program may be taken at the Sir Wilfred Grenfell College, Corner Brook, an integral part of the University.
GRADUATE PROGRAM
Graduate Advisor: Jennifer Porter
Graduate Degrees Offered: MA
Degrees Conferred: 2 MA
Graduate Students in Residence: 12 MA

Average No. of New Students Enrolled: 4 MA

Women Students: 7 MA

Minimum GRE Score Requisite to Admission: No

Minimum GPA Score Requisite to Admission: No

Foreign Language Proficiency Evaluated: No

DESCRIPTION OF GRADUATE PROGRAM AND RESEARCH FACILITIES: Memorial University offers a program leading to the degree of Master of Arts. The program requires completion of at least four graduate courses and an original thesis. A working knowledge of any language necessary for the thesis will be required. The University Library has extensive holdings in Religious Studies generally, and more especially in those areas of specialization in which the MA is offered. This collection includes considerable bodies of material in French, German, and Latin. A careful acquisitions policy, pursued for almost a decade before the inception of an MA program, has built a collection well suited to the likely needs of graduate students in religion.

ACADEMIC PLAN, ADMISSION REQUIREMENTS, FINANCIAL AID: For full-time students, the MA in Religious Studies should take two years. Part-time students will be considered for admission; in their case the duration of the program will be from three to five years. Applicants should normally hold an honors degree in Religious Studies (or its equivalent) and as a minimum requirement must have completed with high standing at least 15 semester courses (8 full-year courses) in Religious Studies. Candidates without honors degrees may be required to complete additional undergraduate courses. Candidates for full-time studies are eligible to be considered for fellowships and assistantships.

FACULTY:

Bell, David N., DPhil, Oxford (1975), 1970, University Research Professor—world religions, patristic and medieval thought, 709-737-8172, E-mail: dbell@morgan.ucs.mun.ca

DeRoche, Michael, PhD, McMaster (1986), 1995, Associate Professor—Early Judaism, biblical studies, Western world religions, 709-737-3539, E-mail: mderoche@morgan.ucs.mun.ca

Hawkin, David J., PhD, McMaster (1974), 1974, Professor—biblical studies, 709-737-8173, E-mail: dhawkin@morgan.ucs.mun.ca

Murphy, Terrence M., PhD, Newcastle-upon-Tyne (1977), 1975, Professor—history of Christian thought, Canadian religious history, 709-737-8254, E-mail: tmurphy@morgan.ucs.mun.ca

Newton, Michael C., PhD, McMaster (1981), 1978, Professor—biblical studies, Christian thought, world religions, 709-637-6279, E-mail: mnewton@morgan.ucs.mun.ca

Parker, Kim I., PhD, McMaster (1988), 1985, Associate Professor—biblical studies, 709-737-8594, E-mail: kparker@morgan.ucs.mun.ca

Porter, Jennifer, PhD, McMaster (1995), 1995, Assistant Professor—religion and modern culture, social scientific theory of religion, 709-737-2469, E-mail: jporter@morgan.ucs.mun.ca

Rainey, Lee, PhD, Toronto (1990), 1990, Associate Professor—Asian religions, Chinese philosophy, women in religion, 709-737-8285, E-mail: lrainey@morgan.ucs.mun.ca

Rollmann, Hans, PhD, McMaster (1979), 1981, Professor—history of Christian thought, religious history of Newfoundland and Labrador, 709-737-8171, E-mail: hrollman@morgan.ucs.mun.ca

Shute, Michael, ThD, Toronto (1991), 1988, Associate Professor—ethics, philosophy of religion, 709-737-4538, E-mail: mshute@morgan.ucs.mun.ca

Memphis Theological Seminary

168 East Parkway South at Union
Memphis TN 38104

Phone: 901-458-8232
Fax: 901-452-4052
E-mail: banderson@mtscampus.edu
URL: www.mtscampus.edu

TYPE OF INSTITUTION: Private, Cumberland Presbyterian
EXECUTIVE OFFICER: Larry Blakeburn, President
GRADUATE ENROLLMENT: 281

Associated Mennonite Biblical Seminary

3003 Benham Ave
Elkhart IN 46517

Phone: 219-295-3726
Fax: 219-295-0092
E-mail: admissions@ambs.edu
URL: www.ambs.edu

TYPE OF INSTITUTION: Private, Mennonite

EXECUTIVE OFFICER: J. Nelson Kraybill, President

GRADUATE ENROLLMENT: 173

Graduate Advisor: Willard M. Swartley, Dean

Graduate Degrees Offered: MA; MDiv

Degrees Conferred: 12 MA; 28 MDiv

Graduate Students in Residence: 40 MA; 80 MDiv

Not in Residence: 0 MA; 4 MDiv

Average No. of New Students Enrolled: 12 MA; 30 MDiv

Women Students: 20 MA; 50 MDiv

Minority Students: 2 MA; 2 MDiv

Foreign Students: 11 MA; 12 MDiv

Minimum GRE Score Requisite to Admission: No

Minimum GPA Score Requisite to Admission: Yes; 2.0 on 4.0 scale

Foreign Language Proficiency Evaluated: No

Financial Aid to First Year Students: 75% MA

Financial Aid to Other Students: 75% MA

DESCRIPTION OF GRADUATE PROGRAM AND RESEARCH FACILITIES: AMBS is a bi-national (US and Canada) educational institution for Mennonite and Anabaptist related denominations that seeks to prepare pastors, missionaries, teachers, evangelists and other church leaders for ministries throughout the world. Other denominations are also welcome. Degrees offered are the 1) MDiv, with concentrations in Primary Program (pastoral ministry), Pastoral Care and Counseling, and Theological Studies; 2) MA: Peace Studies: 3) MA: Theological Studies, with concentrations in Biblical Studies, Church History, and Theology and Ethics; 4) Master of Arts in Christian Formation; 5) Master of Arts in Mission and Evangelism. The MDiv program requires 90.0 semester hours and normally takes three years. The MA programs require 60.0 semester hours and normally take two years. The Institute of Mennonite Studies, on-location, is the research agency of AMBS. The library includes over 100,000 books, and has on-line links to other libraries.

ACADEMIC PLAN, ADMISSION REQUIREMENTS, FINANCIAL AID: AMBS operates on a modified semester plan with a Fall Semester (September-December), Interterm (January) and Spring Semester (February-May). Also operates Summer School. Entrance to degree programs requires a BA degree from an accredited college/university or its equivalent. All applicants are asked to express a commitment to or interest in Christian faith, ministry and witness. An application for admission must be supported by academic transcripts of previous study and three letters of recommendation. Financial aid is available on the basis of demonstrated need and the limits of budget available. Application forms are available for both admission and financial aid on request from the Director of Admissions.

FACULTY:

Elias, Jacob W., ThD, Toronto School of Theology (1978), 1977, Professor—New Testament, 219-296-6201, Fax: 219-295-0092, E-mail: jelias@ambs.edu

Koontz, Gayle Gerber, PhD, Boston University (1985), 1982, Professor (part-time)—theology and ethics, 219-296-6232, Fax: 219-295-0092, E-mail: ggkoontz@ambs.edu

Koontz, Theodore J., PhD, Harvard University (1985), 1982, Professor (part-time)—ethics and peace studies, 219-296-6219, Fax: 219-295-0092, E-mail: tkoontz@ambs.edu

Koop, Karl, PhD, Toronto School of Theology, 1997, Assistant Professor—theology and Anabaptist-Mennonite studies, 219-296-6242, Fax: 219-295-0092, E-mail: kkoop@ambs.edu

Kraybill, J. Nelson, PhD, Union Theological Seminary (1992), 1997, President— New Testament, 219-296-6243, Fax: 219-295-0092, E-mail: nkraybill@ambs.edu

Kropf, Marlene, DMin, Graduate Theological Foundation (1997), 1984, Assistant Professor (part-time)—spiritual formation and worship, 219-296-6265, Fax: 219-295-0092, E-mail: mkropf@ambs.edu

McPhee, Art, PhD (cand.), Asbury Theological Seminary, 1997, Assistant Professor—mission and evangelism, 219-296-6210, Fax: 219-295-0092, E-mail: amcphee@ambs.edu

Ollenburger, Ben C., PhD, Princeton Theological Seminary (1982), 1987, Professor—biblical studies, 219-296-6205, Fax: 219-295-0092, E-mail: bco@@ambs.edu

Sawatsky, Walter W., PhD, University of Minnesota (1976), 1990, Professor (part-time)—church history and mission, 219-296-6209, Fax: 219-295-0092, E-mail: wsawatsky@ambs.edu

Sawatzky, Erick, DMin, St Steven's College (1985), 1985, Director of Field Education and Associate Professor—pastoral ministry, 219-296-6235, Fax: 219-295-0092, E-mail: esawatzky@ambs.edu

Schertz, Mary H., PhD, Vanderbilt University School of Religion (1993), 1988, Associate Professor—New Testament, 219-296-6218, Fax: 219-295-0092, E-mail: mschertz@ambs.edu

Schipani, Daniel S., PhD, Princeton Theological Seminary (1981), 1985, Professor—Christian education and personality, 219-296-6237, Fax: 219-295-0092, E-mail: dschipani@ambs.edu

Slough, Rebecca, PhD, Graduate Theological Union (1989), 1998, Assistant Professor—church music, 219-296-6238, Fax: 219-295-0092, E-mail: rslough@ambs.edu

Swartley, Willard M., PhD, Princeton Theological Seminary (1973), 1978, Professor—New Testament, 219-296-6228, Fax: 219-295-0092, E-mail: wswartley@ambs.edu

Yoder, June Alliman, DMin, Bethany Theological Seminary (1991), 1981, Associate Professor (part-time)—communication and preaching, Fax: 219-295-0092, E-mail: jayoder@ambs.edu

Yoder, Perry, PhD, University of Pennsylvania (1970), 1985, Professor—Old Testament, 219-296-6248, Fax: 219-295-0092, E-mail: pyoder@ambs.edu

Mennonite Brethern Biblical Seminary

4824 E Butler Ave
Fresno CA 93727-5097

Phone: 209-251-8628
Fax: 209-251-7212
E-mail: mbseminary@aol.com

TYPE OF INSTITUTION: Private, Mennonite Brethren
EXECUTIVE OFFICER: Henry J. Schmidt, President
GRADUATE ENROLLMENT: 171

Mercer University

Roberts Dept of Christianity
1400 Coleman Ave
Macon GA 31207

Phone: 912-752-2755
Fax: 912-752-2384
URL: www.mercer.edu

TYPE OF INSTITUTION: Private, Baptist
EXECUTIVE OFFICER: R. Kirby Godsey, President
CHAIRPERSON: Walter B. Shurden
UNDERGRADUATE ENROLLMENT: 4,045

Mercy College

Dobbs Ferry NY 10522

Mercyhurst College

501 East 38th St, Erie PA 16546

Meredith College

3800 Hillsborough St
Raleigh NC 27607

Phone: 919-760-8313
Fax: 919-760-2305
E-mail: vanceb@meredith.edu

TYPE OF INSTITUTION: Private
EXECUTIVE OFFICER: Maureen Hartford, President
CHAIRPERSON: Robert L. Vance
UNDERGRADUATE ENROLLMENT: 2,400

Merrimack College

315 Turnpike Street
North Andover MA 01845

Phone: 978-837-5188
Fax: 978-837-5078

TYPE OF INSTITUTION: Private, Roman Catholic
EXECUTIVE OFFICER: Richard J. Santagati, President
CHAIRPERSON: Thomas M. Casey, OSA

UNDERGRADUATE ENROLLMENT: 2,500

DEGREES OFFERED: BA Major

UNDERGRADUATE MAJORS: 5; 7 Minors

DESCRIPTION OF UNDERGRADUATE PROGRAM: The study of religion at Merrimack College is not designed to elicit particular confessional commitments from the student body. The academic study of religion transcends rather than supplants individual confessional commitments. The program for a major in religious studies is therefore designed to promote an understanding and intellectual grasp of religion as an important human concern and an influential force in history. Besides majors there are double majors who combine religious studies with a tangent discipline. Many students take Religious Studies as electives.

FACULTY:

Bishop, R. Steven, MA, Boston University, 1996, Adjunct Lecturer—American religions, 978-837-5000 ext 4168

Casey, Thomas M., OSA, PhD, Ottawa (1976), 1977, Professor—psychology of religion, sociology of religion, 978-837-5188, E-mail: tcasey@merrimack.edu

Choi, Anna S., PhD (cand.), Boston University, 1992, Adjunct Lecturer—Old Testament, Near Eastern studies, 978-837-5000 ext 4168, E-mail: achoi@merrimack.edu

Dwyer, Kevin F., OSA, MA, Villanova (1962), 1963, Professor—ecclesiology, church history, 978-837-5164, E-mail: kdwyer@merrimack.edu

Huber, Elaine C., PhD, Graduate Theological Union (1984), 1981, Associate Professor—contemporary search for God, feminist theology, 978-837-5000 ext 4537

Kay, Warren A., DrTheol, University of Zurich (1991), 1989, Associate Professor—systematic theology, 978-837-5000 ext 4522, E-mail: wkay@merrimack.edu

Kimball, Virginia M., ABD, University of Dayton, Adjunct Lecturer—Marian Theology 978-837-5000 ext 4166

Kitts, Margo, PhD, UCLA-Berkeley and Graduate Theological Union-Berkeley (1994), 1996, Assistant Professor—eastern religions, history and phenomenology of religions, 978-837-5000 ext 4521

O'Hare, Padraic, EdD, Union Theological Seminary, Columbia University (1974), 1988, Professor—Jewish-Christian relations, moral theology, 978-837-5000 ext 4524

Mesivta Eastern Parkway Rabbinical Seminary

510 Dahill Rd, Brooklyn NY 11218

Rabbinical Academy Mesivta Rabbi

1593 Coney Island Ave, Brooklyn NY 11230

Mesivta Torah Vodaath Rabbinical Seminary

425 E 9th St, Brooklyn NY 11218

Mesivtha Tifereth Jer Amr

145 E Broadway, New York NY 10002

Messiah College

Grantham PA 17027

Phone: 717-766-2511
Fax: 717-697-6040
E-mail: jyeatts@mcis.messiah.edu

TYPE OF INSTITUTION: Denominational: Brethren in Christ
EXECUTIVE OFFICER: Rodney Sawatsky, President
CHAIRPERSON: John R. Yeatts
UNDERGRADUATE ENROLLMENT: 2,400

Methodist College

Dept of Phil and Religion
5400 Ramsey St
Fayetteville NC 28311

Phone: 910-630-7077
Fax: 910-630-2356
E-mail: jxwalsh@aol.com

TYPE OF INSTITUTION: Private, United Methodist
EXECUTIVE OFFICER: Anthony DeLapa, Vice President Academic
CHAIRPERSON: Richard G. Walsh
UNDERGRADUATE ENROLLMENT: 1,700

Methodist Theological School in Ohio

3081 Columbus Pike
PO Box 8004
Delaware OH 43015

Phone: 740-363-1146
Fax: 740-362-3135
E-mail: pres@mtso.edu
URL: www.mtso.edu

TYPE OF INSTITUTION: Denominational: United Methodist
EXECUTIVE OFFICER: Norman E. Dewire, President
GRADUATE ENROLLMENT: 281

University of Miami

PO Box 248264
Coral Gables FL 33124-4672

Phone: 305-284-4733
Fax: 305-284-2772
E-mail: ssapp@miami.edu
URL: www.miami.edu/oldas/rs.html

TYPE OF INSTITUTION: Private
EXECUTIVE OFFICER: Kumble R. Subbaswamy, Dean of the College of Arts and Sciences
CHAIRPERSON: Stephen Sapp
UNDERGRADUATE ENROLLMENT: 7,902
GRADUATE ENROLLMENT: 4,850
DEGREES OFFERED: BA Major
UNDERGRADUATE MAJORS: 7 Majors; 17 Minors
DEGREES CONFERRED: 29 Majors; 46 Minors

DESCRIPTION OF UNDERGRADUATE PROGRAM: The University regards the academic study of religion as an integral part of liberal, humane learning and seeks to assist students in understanding the role religion plays in human existence and culture. Instruction in the Department of Religious Studies is non-sectarian and seeks an open analysis of all points of view. Courses are designed to provide a general orientation to the academic study of religion for the undergraduate student, as well as more advanced exposure for those who wish to pursue professional careers where a study of religious ideas and institutions would be helpful. The department also sponsors the Society for the Study of Religion and Cultures, a student group whose mission is to increase students' knowledge and understanding (beyond what they can gain in the classroom) of the world's religions and the cultures in which they exist. This mission is supported by a faculty advisor, Dr. Dexter E. Callender.

FACULTY:

Callender, Dexter E., Jr., PhD, Harvard University (1995), 1995, Assistant Professor—Hebrew Bible, Near Eastern traditions and civilizations, 305-284-4733, Fax: 305-284-2772 E-mail: dec@miami.edu

Dickens, W. T., PhD, Yale University (1997), 1997, Visiting Assistant Professor—contemporary religious issues, Catholic theology and ethics, history of Christianity, 305-284-4733, Fax: 305-284-2772, E-mail: tdickens@miami.edu

Fitzgerald, John T., PhD, Yale University (1984), 1981, Associate Professor—New Testament, Greco-Roman philosophy and religion, 305-284-4733, Fax: 305-284-2772, E-mail: jtfitz@umiami.ir.miami.edu

Green, Henry A., PhD, St Andrews University, Scotland (1982), 1984, Professor—Gnosticism, sociology of religion, American Jewry, ethnicity and religion, 305-284-4375, Fax: 305-284-4686, E-mail: hgreen@miami.edu

Kling, David W., PhD, University of Chicago (1985), 1993, Associate Professor—history of Christianity, revivalism, fundamentalism, 305-284-4733, Fax: 305-284-2772, E-mail: dkling@miami.edu

Sapp, Stephen, PhD, Duke University (1975), 1979, Professor—biomedical ethics, religious gerontology, 305-284-4733, Fax: 305-284-2772, E-mail: ssapp@miami.edu

Schuld, J. Joyce, PhD, Yale University (1995), 1995, Assistant Professor—ethics, philosophy of religion, history of Christianity, women's studies, 305-284-4733, Fax: 305-284-2772, E-mail: schuld@umiami.ir.miami.edu

Takim, Liyakatali, PhD, School of Oriental and African Studies in London (1990), 1999, Visiting Assistant Professor—Messianism and Jurisprudence in Islam, Judaism, Christianity, 305-284-4733, Fax: 305-284-2772, E-mail: ltakim@miami.edu

Zohar, Zion, PhD, New York University (1999), 1999, Visiting Assistant Professor—Sephardic studies, Jewish thought, Jewish philosophy and mysticism, 305-284-4733, Fax: 305-284-2772, E-mail: relstudies@miami.edu

---

Miami University

Dept of Religion
7 Old Manse
Oxford OH 45056

Phone: 513-529-4300
Fax: 513-529-529-1774
E-mail: forsheho@muohio.edu
URL: www.muohio.edu/~relcwis

TYPE OF INSTITUTION: Public
EXECUTIVE OFFICER: Ronald A. Crutcher, Provost
CHAIRPERSON: Harold O. Forshey
UNDERGRADUATE ENROLLMENT: 16,000

GRADUATE ENROLLMENT: 2,000

DEGREES OFFERED: BA, MA

UNDERGRADUATE MAJORS: 35

DEGREES CONFERRED: 9

DESCRIPTION OF UNDERGRADUATE PROGRAM: The undergraduate major in religion focuses on the study of beliefs and symbolic behavior as they relate to the sacred and through which groups of people have tried to make sense of their common experiences in the world. The curriculum includes a variety of methodologies and an array of religious traditions in particular cultures.

GRADUATE PROGRAM

Graduate Advisor: Elizabeth L. Wilson

Graduate Degrees Offered: MA

Degrees Conferred: 2 MA

Graduate Students in Residence: 12 MA

Not in Residence: 3 MA

Average No. of New Students Enrolled: 4 MA

Women Students: 4 MA

Minority Students: 2 MA

Minimum GRE Score Requisite to Admission: No

Minimum GPA Score Requisite to Admission: Yes; 2.75 on 4.0 scale

Foreign Language Proficiency Evaluated: No

Financial Aid to First Year Students: 75% MA

Financial Aid to Other Students: 90% MA

Attrition Among Students: 10% MA

Graduates Placed: 85% MA

DESCRIPTION OF GRADUATE PROGRAM AND RESEARCH FACILITIES: The primary purpose of the MA program in religion is to prepare students for doctoral level work in religion or cognate disciplines. All graduate students must successfully complete a comprehensive examination, written and oral, on specified books of major significance in the study of religion. Thirty semester credit hours including 6 hours of thesis credit are required. Areas of specialization for the MA thesis include History and Phenomenology of Religion, South and East Asian Religions, Religion of Ancient Israel, Modern Jewish Studies, Contemporary Islam, Early Christianity, Religion and American Culture, African Religions, and Women's Studies. The MA program draws on the resources of faculty in related departments, especially Anthropology, Classics, English, History, Philosophy, Psychology, and Sociology. The King Library currently holds approximately 2,000,000 volumes with basic collections in the fields of religion and a broad range of current journals.

FACULTY:

Cayton, Mary Kupiec, PhD, Brown (1981), Faculty Affiliate—history and American studies, American religious, social and intellectual history, 513-529-5140, E-mail: caytonmk@muohio.edu

Elzey, Wayne D., PhD, Chicago (1974), 1970 Associate Professor—history and phenomenology of religions, Mesoamerican religions, American popular religions, 513-529-4309

Forshey, Harold O., ThD, Harvard (1973), 1966, Professor—religion of ancient Israel, religions of the ancient Near East, archaeology, 513-529-1727, E-mail: forsheho@muohio.edu

Goldy, Charlotte Newman, PhD, Suny, Binghamton, (1978), Faculty Affiliate—medieval European history, 513-529-5123, E-mail: goldycn@muohio.edu

Hanges, James C., PhD, Chicago (1999), 1997, Assistant Professor—history of religions, early Christianity and the religions of the Graeco-Roman world, 513-529-2029, E-mail: hangesjc@muohio.edu

Idinopulos, Thomas A., PhD, Chicago (1965), 1966, Professor—history of Jewish thought and culture, the Holocaust, Judaism in modern Israel, 513-529-4306, E-mail: idinopta@muohio.edu

Miller, Alan L., PhD, Chicago (1968), 1979, Professor—East Asian religions, history of religions, 513-529-4304, E-mail: milleral@muohio.edu

Williams, Peter W., PhD, Yale (1970), 1970, Distinguished Professor—religion and American studies, American studies, history of Christianity, 513-529-4305, E-mail: williapw@muohio.edu

Wilson, Elizabeth, PhD, Chicago (1992), 1992, Associate Professor—South Asian religion, history of religions, women's studies, 513-529-4307, E-mail: wilsone@muohio.edu

Miami Bible Institute

9775 SW 87th Ave
Miami FL 33176

Phone: 305-595-5314
Fax: 305-596-4564
E-mail: revrickx.netcom.com

TYPE OF INSTITUTION: Private, Non-Denominational
EXECUTIVE OFFICER: Rickey L. Patterson, President

Miami Christian College

500 NE First Ave, PO Box 019674, Miami FL 33132

University of Michigan

3064 Frieze Bldg
Ann Arbor MI 48109-1285

Phone: 734-764-4475
Fax: 734-936-4835
E-mail: astrid.beck@umich.edu

TYPE OF INSTITUTION: Public
EXECUTIVE OFFICER: Ralph G. Williams, Director of Program on Studies in Religion
COORDINATOR: Astrid B. Beck
UNDERGRADUATE ENROLLMENT: 35,000

Michigan Christian College

800 West Avon Rd, Rochester Hills MI 48307

Michigan State University

Dept of Religious Studies
116 Morrill Hall
East Lansing MI 48824-1036

Phone: 517-353-2930
Fax: 517-432-1460
E-mail: religstu@pilot.msu.edu
URL: www.pilot.msu.edu/user/religstu

TYPE OF INSTITUTION: Public
CHAIRPERSON: John T. Hinnant
UNDERGRADUATE ENROLLMENT: 38,000
GRADUATE ENROLLMENT: 10,000

Mid-America Baptist Theological Seminary

2216 Germantown Rd South
Germantown TN 38138-3815

Phone: 901-751-8453
Fax: 901-751-8454
E-mail: info@mabts.edu

TYPE OF INSTITUTION: Private, Southern Baptist
EXECUTIVE OFFICER: Michael R. Spradlin, President
UNDERGRADUATE ENROLLMENT: 44
GRADUATE ENROLLMENT: 299

Mid-America Bible College

3500 SW 119th St, Oklahoma City OK 73170

Mid-America Nazarene University

2030 East College Way
Olathe KS 66062

Phone: 913-782-3750, ext 250
Fax: 913-791-3406
E-mail: wwood@mnu.edu
URL: www.mnu.edu/religion

TYPE OF INSTITUTION: Private, Church of the Nazarene
EXECUTIVE OFFICER: Richard Spindle, President
CHAIRPERSON: Jim Edlin
UNDERGRADUATE ENROLLMENT: 103

Mid-American Baptist Theological Seminary/Northeast Campus

2810 Curry Rd
Schenectady NY 12303

Phone: 518-355-4000
Fax: 518-355-8298
E-mail: ne_info@mabtsne.edu
URL: www.mabts.edu

TYPE OF INSTITUTION: Private
EXECUTIVE OFFICER: Michael R. Spradlin, President
CHAIRPERSON: Jeffery B. Ginn, Director

Mid-Continent Baptist Bible College

PO Box 7010, Mayfield KY 42066

Mid Tennessee State University
Murfreesboro TN 37130

Middlebury College

Dept of Religion
Monroe Hall
Middlebury VT 05753

Phone: 802-443-5289
Fax: 802-443-2084
E-mail: yarbrough@middlebury.edu
URL: www.middlebury.edu/~rel

CHAIRPERSON: Larry Yarbrough

UNDERGRADUATE ENROLLMENT: 20

DEGREES OFFERED: BA

UNDERGRADUATE MAJORS: 20

DEGREES CONFERRED: 7

DESCRIPTION OF UNDERGRADUATE PROGRAM: The Religion Department at Middlebury College seeks to acquaint students with the world's major religious traditions, the varieties of religious experience, and with religious approaches to a wide range of topics and questions. Though emphasizing the study of individual religious traditions, holding that a solid understanding of one is crucial for developing appreciation of other traditions and of religion as a fundamental human experience, the Religion faculty also seeks to make students aware of comparative and interdisciplinary approaches to the study of religion. Among the latter, Middlebury has particular strengths in religion and the environment. Many members of the Religion Department also have ties to the College's International Studies Program. The Department's Scott Fund underwrites biannual symposia, which have dealt with religion and the arts and religious pluralism in America. The topic for the symposium in 2000 is religion and international affairs.

FACULTY:

Bakhos, Carol A., MPhil, Jewish Theological Seminary (1996), 1998, Lecturer—Jewish studies and biblical Hebrew, 802-443-2547, Fax: 802-443-2084, E-mail: cbakhos@middlebury.edu

Ferm, Robert L., PhD, Yale University (1958), 1969, Professor—history of American religion, 802-443-5293, Fax: 802-443-2084, E-mail: ferm@middlebury.edu

Gould, Rebecca Kneale, PhD, Harvard University (1997), 1998, Assistant Professor—religion and nature and environmental ethics in both Western and Non-Western cultural contexts, 802-443-2548, Fax: 802-443-2084, E-mail: rgould@middlebury.edu

Keenan, John, PhD, University of Wisconsin (1980), 1986, Professor—Asian religions, 802-443-5020, Fax: 802-443-2084, E-mail: keenan@middlebury.edu

Saleh, Walid, MPhil, Yale University (1996), 1999, Lecturer—Islamic studies, 802-443-3255, E-mail: saleh@middlebury.edu

Schine, Robert S., PhD, Jewish Theological Seminary of America (1990), 1985, Professor—Jewish studies and biblical Hebrew, 802-443-5391, E-mail: schine@middlebury.edu

Sonderegger, Katherine, PhD, Brown University (1990), 1987, Professor—Western religious thought with emphasis on Christianity and Judaism, 802-443-5292, Fax: 802-443-2084, E-mail: sondereg@middelbury.edu

Waldron, William S., PhD, University of Wisconsin (1990), 1996, Assistant Professor—Asian religious traditions, Buddhism, and comparative issues of East-West psychology and philosophy of mind, 802-443-2040, Fax: 802-443-2084, E-mail: wwaldron@middlebury.edu

Yarbrough, O. Larry, PhD, Yale University (1984), 1983, Professor—biblical studies (both Jewish and Christian scriptures), the orgins of Christianity and religion and literature, 802-443-5294, Fax: 802-443-2084, E-mail: yarbrough@middlebury.edu

Midland Lutheran College

Fremont NE 68025

Midway College

512 Stephens St
Midway KY 40347

Phone: 606-846-4421
Fax: 606-846-5333
URL: www.midway.edu

TYPE OF INSTITUTION: Denominational: Christian Church (Disciples of Christ)
EXECUTIVE OFFICER: Allyson Handley, President
COORDINATOR: Robert J. Miller
UNDERGRADUATE ENROLLMENT: 5

Midwestern Baptist Theological Seminary

5001 Oak Trafficway N, Kansas City MO 64118

Miles College

PO Box 3800, Birmingham AL 35208

Milligan College

Milligan TN 37682

Millikin University

Dept of Religion
Decatur IL 62522

Phone: 217-424-6277
Fax: 217-424-3993

CHAIRPERSON: Edward A. Yonan

Millsaps College

1701 N State St
Jackson MS 39210

Phone: 601-974-1334
E-mail: smithsg@okra.millsaps.edu
URL: www.millsaps.edu/www/religion/

TYPE OF INSTITUTION: Private, United Methodist
EXECUTIVE OFFICER: Richard A. Smith, Academic Vice President
CHAIRPERSON: Steven G. Smith
UNDERGRADUATE ENROLLMENT: 1,197

GRADUATE ENROLLMENT: 164
DEGREES OFFERED: BA, BS
UNDERGRADUATE MAJORS: 15
DEGREES CONFERRED: 6
DESCRIPTION OF UNDERGRADUATE PROGRAM: Eight courses (32 credit hours equivalent) are required for the major. Double majoring at Millsaps is not uncommon. Various concentrations draw on religious studies courses, including European studies, women's studies, and Christian education. Department faculty also design and teach core humanities courses with a religious studies focus.
FACULTY:
Ray, Darby K., PhD, Vanderbilt University (1996), 1996, Assistant Professor—Christian thought, biblical studies, 601-974-1337, Fax: 601-974-1324, E-mail: raydk@millsaps.edu
Smith, Steven G., PhD, Duke University (1980), 1985, Professor—philosophy of religion, Western religious thought, 601-974-1334, Fax: 601-974-1324, E-mail: smithsg@millsaps.edu
Thatamanil, John J., PhD (cand.), Boston University, 1998, Assistant Professor—comparative religion, Hinduism, 601-974-1333, Fax: 601-974-1324, E-mail: thatajj@millsaps.edu

University of Minnesota

Dept of Classical and Near Eastern Studies
9 Pleasant St SE
Minneapolis MN 55455

Phone: 612-625-5353
Fax: 612-624-4894
E-mail: cnes@maroon.tc.umn.edu
URL: cnes.cla.umn.edu

TYPE OF INSTITUTION: Public
EXECUTIVE OFFICER: Steven J. Rosenstone, Dean-College of Liberal Arts
CHAIRPERSON: William W. Malandra
UNDERGRADUATE ENROLLMENT: 26,148
GRADUATE ENROLLMENT: 8,288

Minnesota Bible College

920 Mayowood Rd SW
Rochester MN 55902

Phone: 507-288-4563
Fax: 507-288-9046
E-mail: academic@mnbc.edu
URL: www.mnbc.edu

TYPE OF INSTITUTION: Private, Non-Denominational
EXECUTIVE OFFICER: Christopher A. Davis, Vice President of Academics
UNDERGRADUATE ENROLLMENT: 130
DEGREES OFFERED: AA, BA, BS
UNDERGRADUATE MAJORS: 6
DEGREES CONFERRED: 39
DESCRIPTION OF UNDERGRADUATE PROGRAM: Two-year AA in the lower division includes 24 semester hour Biblical Studies and Theology core with the possibility of an additional 8 hours of Biblical and Classical Languages in the Language track. Upon completion of the AA, students may pursue specialized education for vocational ministry in the BA or BS programs. To receive a bachelor's degree from MBC, students must complete 1) the 22 hour up-

per division general core, 2) the mandatory 40 hour Biblical Studies and Theology major, and 3) either a 36 hour second major (Pastoral Leadership [BA track only; requires 2 years of Greek and 1 year of Hebrew], Christian Education, Music, Youth and Family Ministries or General Studies) or 2 minors (Biblical and Classical Languages, Christian Education, Counseling, History, Media in Ministry, Missions, Music and Youth Ministries).

FACULTY:

Davis, Christopher A., PhD, Union Theological Seminary in Virgina (1992), 1992, Professor and Vice President of Academics—New Testament, Greek, 507-288-4563, Fax: 507-288-9046, E-mail: academic@mnbc.edu

Mangano, Mark J., PhD, Hebrew Union College (1990), 1990, Professor—Old Testament, Hebrew, biblical criticism, 507-288-4563, Fax: 507-288-9046, E-mail: mmangano@mnbc.edu

McAlister, Paul K., DMin, Bethel Theological Seminary (1978), 1972, Professor—Theology, New Testament, missions, ethics, 507-288-4563, Fax: 507-288-9046, E-mail: pmcal@mnbc.edu

Penniston, Joyce K., PhD, University of Minnesota (1980), 1981, Instructor (part-time)—Greek, humanities, 507-288-4563, Fax: 507-288-9046, E-mail: jpenn@mnbc.edu

Mirrer Yeshiva Central Institute

1791-5 Ocean Pkwy, Brooklyn NY 11223

College Misericordia

301 Lake St
Dallas PA 18612

Phone: 717-675-2441
E-mail: sranne@miseri.edu

TYPE OF INSTITUTION: Private, Roman Catholic
EXECUTIVE OFFICER: Michael MacDowell, President
COORDINATOR: Anne E. McLaughlin, RSM

Missionary Baptist Seminary

5224 Stagecoach Rd
Little Rock AR 72204

Phone: 501-455-4588
Fax: 501-455-4589
E-mail: seminary@aristotle.net

TYPE OF INSTITUTION: Private
EXECUTIVE OFFICER: David Robinson, Chancellor
UNDERGRADUATE ENROLLMENT: 100
GRADUATE ENROLLMENT: 20

Mississippi College

PO Box 4012
Clinton MS 39058

Phone: 601-925-3218
Fax: 601-925-3960
E-mail: christian-studies@mc.edu
URL: www.mc.edu

TYPE OF INSTITUTION: Private, Southern Baptist

EXECUTIVE OFFICER: Howell Todd, President
CHAIRPERSON: Les Hughes
UNDERGRADUATE ENROLLMENT: 2,451
GRADUATE ENROLLMENT: 1,083

Mississippi University for Women

Box W 299, Columbus MS 39701

Mississippi State University

State College MS 39762

University of Missouri

405 General Classroom Bldg
Columbia MO 65211-4140

Phone: 573-882-4769
Fax: 573-884-5438
E-mail: rsinfo@missouri.edu
URL: www.missouri.edu/~religwww

TYPE OF INSTITUTION: Public
EXECUTIVE OFFICER: Richard Wallace, Chancellor
CHAIRPERSON: Jill Raitt
UNDERGRADUATE ENROLLMENT: 16,000
GRADUATE ENROLLMENT: 6,000
DEGREES OFFERED: BA, MA
UNDERGRADUATE MAJORS: 30
DEGREES CONFERRED: 20

DESCRIPTION OF UNDERGRADUATE PROGRAM: Begun in 1981, the department of religious studies at MU is dedicated to the academic study of religion. Its place in the college of arts and science is assured by the appreciation of religious studies as a partner necessary for a balanced undergraduate curriculum. Courses satisfy a humanities requirement and also offer a more specialized study of religion for majors in religious studies. The program offers courses in the religions of Asia, of the West, and of indigenous societies. It emphasizes study of the various kinds of religious expression: art, literature, action, text and speech.

DESCRIPTION OF GRADUATE PROGRAM: The master's program in religious studies is designed to achieve two goals that reflect the distinct educational aims of two different kinds of students. The first goal is preparation of students for PhD programs. Increasingly, doctoral programs in religious studies expect applicants to have a master's or similar advanced degree. The degree is designed to prepare students for entry into such programs. It therefore emphasizes appropriate language study, the recognized, scholarly approaches to the study of religion, history of the discipline, research methods, and knowledge of the range of religious experience and expression. The second goal is to provide graduate study of religions for those who desire it in order to enrich their educational lives, to prepare for seminary study, or to strengthen work in other allied disciplines, such as journalism, education, history, literature, anthropology or art history.

FACULTY:

Brereton, Joel P., PhD, Yale University (1975), 1982, Associate Professor—South Asian religions, 573-882-4760, E-mail: breretonj@missouri.edu

Clart, Philip, PhD, University of British Columbia (1997), 1998, Assistant Professor, East Asian religions, 573-882-8830, E-mail: clartp@missouri.edu

Flanagan, John Robert, PhD, University of Iowa (1979), 1983, Lecturer (part-time)—religion and psychology, 573-882-0059, E-mail: flanaganj@missouri.edu

Friesen, Steve, PhD, Harvard University (1990), 1993, Associate Professor—Christian origins, 573-822-0033, E-mail: friesens@missouri.edu

Johnson, Paul, PhD, University of Chicago, (1996), 1996, Assistant Professor—indigenous religions, 573-882-0058, E-mail: johnsonpc@missouri.edu

Raitt, Jill, PhD, University of Chicago (1970), 1981, Chair—history of Christianity, 573-882-0057, E-mail: raittj@missouri.edu

Welch, Sharon, PhD, Vanderbilt University (1982), 1992, Professor—women and religion, theological ethics, 573-882-8831, E-mail: welchs@missouri.edu

---

University of Missouri-Kansas City

Center for Religious Studies
203 Cockefair Hall
5100 Rockhill Road
Kansas City MO 64110-2499

Phone: 816-235-1631
Fax: 816-235-5723
URL: www.umkc.edu/history

TYPE OF INSTITUTION: Public

EXECUTIVE OFFICER: Gordon Lamb, Acting Chancellor

CHAIRPERSON: Gary Ebersole

GRADUATE ENROLLMENT: 14

GRADUATE PROGRAM

Graduate Advisors: Joseph P. Schultz, Gary Ebersole

Graduate Degrees Offered: PhD

Degrees Conferred: 0

Graduate Students in Residence: 14 PhD

Average No. of New Students Enrolled: 6 PhD

Minority Students: 1 PhD

Minimum GRE Score Requisite to Admission: Yes, 1500

Minimum GPA Score Requisite to Admission: Yes, 3.5 on 4.0 scale

Foreign Language Proficiency Evaluated: Yes

Financial Aid to First Year Students: 0% PhD; 10% Other

Financial Aid to Other Students: 10% PhD

Attrition Among Students: 7% PhD

DESCRIPTION OF GRADUATE PROGRAM AND RESEARCH FACILITIES: The UMKC Center for Religious Studies is a consortium of six educational institutions that have agreed to pool their academic resources in establishing a religious studies discipline in UMKC's interdisciplinary PhD program. Representatives from UMKC, Central Baptist Theological Seminary, Nazarene Theological Seminary, Park College, Rockhurst College, and William Jewell College comprise a steering committee that, together with the director of the center, determines curriculum, sets academic standards, interviews applicants and decides on their eligibility, and oversees other administrative matters. Professors from the participating institutions in the consortium serve as adjunct doctoral faculty at UMKC and, along with UMKC faculty, supervise doctoral dissertations and teach graduate courses. UMKC is the doctoral degree-granting institution.

ACADEMIC PLAN, ADMISSION REQUIREMENTS, FINANCIAL AID: Students entering the Interdisciplinary PhD Program who select religious studies as a coordinaitng discipline (a coordinating discipline is the principal discipline of study and the codiscipline is the secondard discipline) work under a supervisory committee whose chairman is in regular contact with the student and along with the committee sets up a plan of study consisting of courses, written and oral exams and dissertation. Each student must work in a minimum of two disciplines whose faculty are on the supervisory committee. Applicants must possess a master of religious studies, a master of theology or a masters degree in any of the disciplines of the humanities or social sciences. Under certain conditions a master of divinity degree is acceptable. Teaching fellowships and research scholarships are available but competitive.

FACULTY:

Ebersole, Gary L., PhD, University of Chicago (1981), 1981, Professor—history of religions, Japanese religion and literature, 816-235-5704, Fax: 816-235-5723

Hattaway, Herman M., PhD, Louisiana State University (1969), 1972, Professor—American history, American religious history, 816-235-2549, Fax: 816-235-5723

Klausner, Carla L., PhD, Harvard University (1963), Professor—Middle East studies, Islamic civilization, 816-235-2540, Fax: 816-235-5723

Schultz, Joseph, PhD, Brandeis University (1962), 1963, Professor—Judaic studies, history of religions, 816-235-2538, Fax: 816-235-5723

Spatz, Lois S., PhD, Indiana University (1968), 1973, Professor—classics, 816-235-2563, Fax: 816-235-1308

ADJUNCT DOCTORAL FACULTY:

Chance, Bradley, PhD—New Testament studies, phenomenology of religion

Coleson, Joseph E., PhD—biblical and Near Eastern studies

Duke, David, PhD—ethics and religion

Edwards, Paul, PhD—philosophy of religion, theology

Gall, Robert, PhD—philosophy of religion

Lyon, William S., PhD—Native American studies

Raser, Harold, PhD—American religious history

Schwartz, Howard, MA—Judaic studies

Wheeler, David, PhD—theology

Missouri Baptist College

12542 Conway Rd, Saint Louis MO 63141

Missouri Valley College

PO Box 1000, Marshall MO 65340

Rabbinical Seminary of M'Kor Chaim

1571 55th St, Brooklyn NY 11219

University of Mobile

PO Box 13220
Mobile AL 36663-0220

Phone: 334-675-5990
Fax: 334-675-9816
E-mail: drcrt@aol.com

TYPE OF INSTITUTION: Private, Southern Baptist
EXECUTIVE OFFICER: Cecil Taylor, Dean, School of Religion
UNDERGRADUATE ENROLLMENT: 135
GRADUATE ENROLLMENT: 40

Molloy College

1000 Hempstead Ave
PO Box 5002
Rockville Centre NY 15271-5002

Phone: 516-678-5000 Ext 6146
Fax: 516-256-2243
E-mail: afargnoli@molloy.edu

TYPE OF INSTITUTION: Private
EXECUTIVE OFFICER: Valerie Collins, Acting President
CHAIRPERSON: A. Nicholas Fargnoli
UNDERGRADUATE ENROLLMENT: 2,023
GRADUATE ENROLLMENT: 275

Monmouth College

700 E Broadway
Monmouth IL 61462-1998

Phone: 309-457-2311
Fax: 309-457-2152
E-mail: chenyang@monm.edu
URL: www.monm.edu

TYPE OF INSTITUTION: Private, Presbyterian Church (USA)
EXECUTIVE OFFICER: Richard F. Giese, President
CHAIRPERSON: Chenyang Li
UNDERGRADUATE ENROLLMENT: 1,041

Monmouth College

West Long Br NJ 07764

University of Montana

Dept of Religious Studies, Missoula MT 59812

Montana Bible College

PO Box 6070
Bozeman MT 59771

Phone: 406-586-3585
E-mail: mbc@avicom.net
URL: www.link-usa.com/mbc

TYPE OF INSTITUTION: Private, Non-Denominational
EXECUTIVE OFFICER: Mark Amunrud, Board Chairman
COORDINATOR: Steven D. Mathewson
UNDERGRADUATE ENROLLMENT: 25

Montana State University

Bozeman MT 59715

Montclair State University

Upper Montclair NJ 07043

Phone: 973-655-5144
URL: www.msu.org/deptweb/

TYPE OF INSTITUTION: Public
EXECUTIVE OFFICER: Susan Cole, President
CHAIRPERSON: Michael S. Kogan
UNDERGRADUATE ENROLLMENT: 53

Université de Montréal

Faculté de théologie
CP 6128, Succursale Centreville
Montréal, Québec H3C 3J7 Canada

Phone: 514-343-7080
Fax: 514-343-5738
E-mail: theologie@ere.umontreal.ca
URL: mistral.ere.umontreal.ca/davidrob/theo

TYPE OF INSTITUTION: Private, Catholic
EXECUTIVE OFFICER: Jean-Marc Charron, Dean
CHAIRPERSONS: Robert David, Biblical Studies; Michel-M. Campbell, Practical Theology; Michel Beaudin, Theological Studies; Guy-Robert St Arnaud, Religious Science
UNDERGRADUATE ENROLLMENT: 545
GRADUATE ENROLLMENT: 143

Montreal Diocesan Theological College

3473 University St
Montreal, Quebec H3A 2A8
Canada

Phone: 514-849-3004
Fax: 514-849-4113
E-mail: diocoll@netrover.com
URL: www.montreal.anglican.org/mdtc

TYPE OF INSTITUTION: Private, Anglican/Episcopal
EXECUTIVE OFFICER: Andrew Hutchison, President

Montreat College

PO Box 1267
Montreat NC 28711

Phone: 828-669-8012, ext 3813
Fax: 828-669-9554
E-mail: dglassford@montreat.edu
URL: www.montreat.edu

TYPE OF INSTITUTION: Denominational: Presbyterian Church (USA)
EXECUTIVE OFFICER: Don King, Vice-President and Dean of Academic Affairs
CHAIRPERSON: Darwin K. Glassford
UNDERGRADUATE ENROLLMENT: 30

Moody Bible Institute

820 North La Salle St, Chicago IL 60610

Moravian College

Dept of Religion
1200 Main St
Bethlehem PA 18018

Phone: 610-861-1300
E-mail: medps01@moravian.edu
URL: www.moravian.edu

TYPE OF INSTITUTION: Private, Moravian
EXECUTIVE OFFICER: Ervin Rokke, President
CHAIRPERSON: Donald P. St. John
UNDERGRADUATE ENROLLMENT: 1,200

Moravian Theological Seminary

1200 Main Street
Bethlehem PA 18018

Phone: 610-861-1516
Fax: 610-861-1569
E-mail: seminary@moravian.edu
URL: www.moravian.edu

TYPE OF INSTITUTION: Denominational: Moravian
EXECUTIVE OFFICERS: Ervin J. Rokke, President
CHAIRPERSON: David A. Schattschneider, Vice President
GRADUATE ENROLLMENT: 100
GRADUATE PROGRAM
Graduate Degrees Offered: MA
Degrees Conferred: 5 MA; 1 Other
Graduate Students in Residence: 2 MA
Not in Residence: 31 MA
Average No. of New Students Enrolled: 4 MA; 1 Other
Women Students: 23 MA; 1 Other
Minority Students: 2 MA
Foreign Students: 2 MA
Minimum GRE Score Requisite to Admission: No

Minimum GPA Score Requisite to Admission: Yes; 2.50 on 4.0 scale

Foreign Language Proficiency Evaluated: Yes

Financial Aid to First Year Students: 25%MA

Financial Aid to Other Students: 54% MA

Attrition among Students: 14% MA

Graduates Placed: 86% MA; 94% Other

DESCRIPTION OF GRADUATE PROGRAM AND RESEARCH FACILITIES: Master of Arts in Pastoral Counseling: The Master of Arts in Pastoral Counseling degree (MAPC) seeks to integrate the biblical and theological perspective of the Jewish/Christian tradition with the practice of counseling and psychotherapy. It thus combines a spiritual and theological understanding of humanity with knowledge of psycho dynamics and treatment issues, with the goal of ministering to the whole person. The MAPC degree is appropriate for clergy who wish to focus on a counseling ministry, mental health professionals who wish to achieve a more holistic perspective in their ongoing work, or lay persons who wish to provide counseling in a parish or institutional setting. Master of Arts in Theological Studies: The Master of Arts in Theological Studies degree (MATS) is designed to introduce persons to the theological disciplines. Some MATS students remain in their current career while others pursue theological vocations. The degree assists persons to integrate a Christian perspective into their current vocation. For those seeking a career in teaching in the theological areas, the degree will be exploratory for a PhD degree. The degree also will help those who are seeking a theological vocation in the area of Christian education or as lay leaders in their denomination. Students are introduced to the classical theological disciplines (biblical studies, history and doctrine) but can specialize in any area of interest, including courses in pastoral theology.

Library Collections: Reeves Library offers seminary students and faculty an excellent collection of over 240,000 volumes and 1,395 periodicals within and supported by a total liberal arts collection of 225,000 volumes and 1,350 periodicals. All major on-line and CD-ROM databases are available for research purposes and the library has a number of specialized microform collections in theology, ecumenism, and hymnology. As the library for the graduate theological seminary of the Moravian Church in America, it features a research collection of Hussite and Moravian materials in many languages. Included are unpublished materials, theses, and dissertations. Materials about countries in which there are and have been Moravian churches are also added to the collection. The resources available in Reeves Library are greatly enhanced by the Library's cooperative agreements with other seminaries, colleges and universities. A cooperative agreement with other Lehigh Valley Association of Independent Colleges institutions makes over two million volumes available by direct loan or daily courier service. In addition, the sixteen cooperating libraries of the Southeastern Pennsylvania Theological Library Association share over 1,750,000 volumes in theology and related disciplines.

ACADEMIC PLAN, ADMISSION REQUIREMENTS, FINANCIAL AID: Admission to the Seminary: All students who desire to enter Moravian Theological Seminary as degree candidates must submit an application form accompanied by a $25.00 application fee, transcripts, letters of reference, and an admissions essay (to be received no later than April 1st of the academic year preceding matriculation). Applicants must hold a baccalaureate degree. Generally, a 2.5 undergraduate record is considered minimum for entry into the Seminary. The Seminary may require entering students to complete a variety of psychological and vocational tests prior to admission. Candidates commit themselves to fulfill their respective degree requirements within a 2-6 year period.

Transfer Students: The Seminary requires that the cumulative grade point average of transferred courses be 2.67 or better. Courses with grades below a B- are not transferable. These policies apply only to courses taken at accredited seminaries. Transfer students will be required to take a minimum of 30 on-campus credit hours at Moravian Theological Seminary and meet all degree requirements.

Financial Aid: The basic responsibility for financing educational costs and living expenses belongs to the student, who is expected to rely on personal and family resources. A student's resources may include savings, earnings, gifts, private loans, and if the student is married, earnings of a spouse. Students are encouraged to seek additional financial assistance from other resources including their local congregations and/or denominations, civic groups, and foundations.

Resources: Each year, many students at the Seminary receive financial assistance which may consist of tuition grant, grants-in-aid, scholarships, and loans. Most of these funds have been created by alumni and friends of the Seminary to honor the achievements of distinguished individuals. Other resources are available through supervised ministry placements, denominational agencies, and outside employment. In keeping with its ecumenical tradition, Moravian Theological Seminary provides assistance to all students who qualify. Policies: Aid is awarded on the basis of demonstrated need. Students who desire financial aid are required to file an application substantiating need and provide full information on potential resources and indebtedness. A new application must be filed each year. Eligibility for financial aid is limited to matriculated students who are enrolled for at least six credit hours per term. Other limitations may apply according to the conditions governing each source. Preference is given to full-time resident students. Financial aid awarded in the first term is normally renewable for up to three terms for students enrolled in a two-year degree program, provided that the evidence of need remains, that funds continue to be available, and that enrollment eligibility is maintained. Employment opportunities are available on campus and in the community. Students or spouses make their own arrangements for employment. Faculty approval of a student's academic load is necessary when the student's outside workload exceeds twenty hours per week.

FACULTY:

Appler, Deborah A., MDiv, Southern Methodist University, 1999, Assistant Professor—Old Testament

Asquith, Glenn H., Jr., PhD, Southern Baptist Theological Seminary, 1978, Professor of Pastoral Theology on the Van and Katherine Merle-Smith Fund

Crouch, Frank L., PhD, Duke University, 1996, Assistant Professor—New Testament

Dreydoppel, Otto, Jr., PhD (cand.), University of Chicago, 1989, Director of Moravian Studies and Assistant Professor—church history

Hargis, Charles L., PhD, Union Theological Seminary, Virginia, 1978, 1993, Professor of Doctrinal Theology on the J. Taylor Hamilton Chair of Doctrinal Theology

Harstine, Willard R., DMin, Drew University, 1982, Associate Professor of Pastoral Theology on the Edward Rondthaler Chair of Practical Theology

Minor, John Thomas, MS, University of North Carolina, Chapel Hill, 1984, Library Director with rank of Professor

Schattschneider, David A., PhD, University of Chicago, 1968, Dean and Vice President of the Seminary and The S. Morgan Smith and Emma Fahs Smith Professor of Historical Theology

Ward, Kay, DMin, Claremont School of Theology, 1990, Director of Advancement and Assistant Professor—pastoral theology

ADJUNCT FACULTY:

Bly, Lois L., MDiv, Garrett Evangelical Theological Seminary

Clemens, Deborah Rahn, PhD, Drew University

DeRemer, David H., MDiv, Princeton Theological Seminary

Dungan, F. Alvin, MDiv, Trinity Lutheran Seminary

Dwyer, Patricia, DMin, Eastern Baptist Theological Seminary
Gilbert, Emily Jean, MDiv, Union Theological Seminary
Johanson, Andrew H., Jr., DMin, Eastern Baptist Theological Seminary
Kleintop, Douglas H., MDiv, Moravian Theological Seminary
Krentz, Michael E., DMin, Northwestern University
Lewis, Roy, DMin, Drew University
Patterson, L. Dale, PhD, Drew University
Wagner, Walter H., PhD, Drew University
Yrigoyen, Charles, Jr., PhD, Temple University

Morehouse College

830 Westview Dr SW, Atlanta GA 30314

Morgan State University

PO Box 155
Baltimore MD 21239

Phone: 443-885-3436/3245
Fax: 410-319-3119
E-mail: obegus@morgan.edu

TYPE OF INSTITUTION: Public
EXECUTIVE OFFICERS: Earl Richardson, President; Clara Adams, Vice President for Academic Affairs; Burney Hollis, Dean College of Liberal Arts
CHAIRPERSON: Otto Begus
UNDERGRADUATE ENROLLMENT: 58

Morningside College

Dept of Religious Studies, Sioux City IA 51106

Morris College

Sumter SC 29150

Morris Brown College

Atlanta GA 30314

Mount Allison University

Dept of Religious Studies
Hart Hall, 63D York St
Sackville NB E4L 1G9 Canada

Phone: 506-364-2556
Fax: 506-364-2645
URL: www.mta.ca/faculty/humanities/
religious/

TYPE OF INSTITUTION: Private, Non-Denominational
CHAIRPERSON: M. Colin Grant

UNDERGRADUATE ENROLLMENT: 2,250

Mount Angel Seminary

Division of Theology
St Benedict OR 97373

Phone: 503-845-3951
Fax: 503-845-3126

TYPE OF INSTITUTION: Private, Roman Catholic
EXECUTIVE OFFICERS: Patrick S. Brennan, President-Rector; Ernest Skublics, Academic Dean
UNDERGRADUATE ENROLLMENT: 90
GRADUATE ENROLLMENT: 108

Mount Holyoke College

South Hadley MA 01075

Phone: 413-538-2233
Fax: 413-538-2512 or 2579
E-mail: amdion@mhc.mtholyoke.edu
URL: www.mtholyoke.edu/acad/relig/

TYPE OF INSTITUTION: Private, Non-Denominational
EXECUTIVE OFFICER: Joanne V. Creighton, President
CHAIRPERSON: Jane F. Crosthwaite
UNDERGRADUATE ENROLLMENT: 2,000

Mount Marty College

1105 W 8th St
Yankton SD 57078

Phone: 605-668-1011
Fax: 605-668-1607
E-mail: mfrigge@rs6.mtmc.edu
URL: www.mtmc.edu

TYPE OF INSTITUTION: Private, Catholic
EXECUTIVE OFFICER: Michael Kaelke, Academic Dean
COORDINATOR: Sr. Marielle Frigge
UNDERGRADUATE ENROLLMENT: 942
GRADUATE ENROLLMENT: 62

Mount Mary College

2900 N Menomonee River Pkwy
Milwaukee WI 53222-4597

Phone: 414-258-4810
Fax: 414-256-1205
E-mail: penzenj@mtmary.edu

TYPE OF INSTITUTION: Private, Roman Catholic
EXECUTIVE OFFICER: Patricia Drogos O'Donoghue, President
CHAIRPERSON: Joan Penzenstadler, SSND
UNDERGRADUATE ENROLLMENT: 15

Mount Mercy College

1330 Elmhurst Dr NE   Phone: 319-363-8213, ext 1385
Cedar Rapids IA 52402   E-mail: davidard@mmc.mtmercy.edu

TYPE OF INSTITUTION: Private, Roman Catholic
EXECUTIVE OFFICER: Thomas Feld, President
CHAIRPERSON: David J. Ard

Mount Olive College

209 N Breazeale Ave, Mount Olive NC 28365

College of Mount Saint Joseph

Religious Pastoral Studies Dept   Phone: 513-244-4272
5701 Delhi Rd   Fax: 513-244-4788
Cincinnati OH 45233-1670

TYPE OF INSTITUTION: Private, Roman Catholic
EXECUTIVE OFFICER: Francis Marie Thrailkill, OSU, President
CHAIRPERSON: John Trokan
UNDERGRADUATE ENROLLMENT: 1,300
GRADUATE ENROLLMENT: 30
DEGREES OFFERED: Religious Studies, Pastoral Ministries, Religious Education
UNDERGRADUATE MAJORS: 50
DEGREES CONFERRED: 3
DESCRIPTION OF UNDERGRADUATE PROGRAM: The religious pastoral studies department
   at the Mount provides students with the resources to appreciate and analyze religion; to in-
   vestigate the sources, development and practice of religious faith; and to develop their own
   faith while appreciating that of others. The department offers a major in academic theology
   as well as majors preparing students to meet the growing need in the church for religious
   educators and lay pastoral ministers.
GRADUATE PROGRAM
Graduate Advisor: John Trokan
Graduate Degrees Offered: MA
Degrees Conferred: 6 MA
Graduate Students in Residence: 30 MA
Average No. of New Students Enrolled: 15 MA
Women Students: 25 MA
Minority Students: 1 MA
Minimum GRE Score Requisite to Admission: No
Minimum GPA Score Requisite to Admission: Yes; 2.75 on 4.0 scale
Foreign Language Proficiency Evaluated: No
Attrition Among Students: 10% MA
Graduates Placed: 100% MA

DESCRIPTION OF GRADUATE PROGRAM AND RESEARCH FACILITIES: The graduate program has a specific goal: to meet the needs of people active in a variety of fields of pastoral ministry and religious education who desire specialized training in the field of family studies in order to integrate a family life perspective into their particular forms of religious ministry.

ACADEMIC PLAN, ADMISSION REQUIREMENTS, FINANCIAL AID: Application for admission form. Three letters of recommendation from employers/professors/colleagues. Official transcripts for all college credits (minimum G.P.A of 2.7). A short (5 page) essay explaining why the student is applying to the program and what his/her goals are in pastoral ministry. An interview with the Graduate Admissions Committee

FACULTY:

Akers, Louise, SC, DMin, Episcopal Divinity School, Cambridge, MA, Adjunct Professor—systematics, ethics and spirituality

Bookser, Mary, SC, PhD, The Union Institute (1997), Adjunct Professor—Hebrew scriptures, feminist theology, spirituality, 513-347-5471, Fax: 513-244-4788

Bourg, Florence, PhD, Boston College (1998), Associate Professor—systematic theology, Christian ethics, social justice, theology of human sexuality and marriage, 513-244-4212, Fax: 513-244-4788

deCourcy, Alan, DMin, United Theological Seminary, Dayton, Ohio (1992), 1991, Assistant Professor—introduction to theology, marital and family therapy, 513-523-4774, Fax: 513-244-4788

Foley, J. Thomas, PhD, University of Strasbourg, France, 1977, Associate Professor—new trends in theology, theology of human sexuality and marriage, 513-244-4200, Fax: 513-244-4788

Jansen, Mary Ann, OSU, MA, PhD (cand.), Graduate Institute, Adjunct Professor—spirituality, theology and anthropology

Kenney, Robert B., PhD, Southern Baptist Theological Seminary (1994), 1994, Adjunct Instructor—Christian ethics, business ethics, world religions, 513-451-4296, Fax: 513-244-4788

Kloos, Marge, SC, DMin (cand.), United Theological Seminary, Associate Professor—Christology, ecclesiology, feminist theology, theology and ecology, theology and anthropology, family religion and community, new trends in theology, 513-244-4245, Fax: 513-244-4788

Metz, Judith, SC, PhD (cand.), The Union Institute, Adjunct Professor—historical theology, Christian beginnings, the Reformation, American religious experience, women's religious experience, 513-244-4496, Fax: 513-244-4788

Obach, Robert E., PhD, Syracruse University (1982), 1991, Adjunct Instructor—faith and technology, Johannine literature, 513-253-3069, Fax: 513-244-4788

Trokan, John T., DMin, St Mary of the Lake College, Mundelein, Illinois (1987), 1987, Associate Professor—Christian scripture, theology of human sexuality and marriage, family ministry, 513-244-4272, Fax: 513-244-4222

Mount St Mary College

330 Powell Ave
Newburgh NY 12550

Phone: 914-561-0800
Fax: 914-562-6762
URL: www.msmc.edu

TYPE OF INSTITUTION: Private, Catholic
EXECUTIVE OFFICER: Sr. Anne Sakac, President

CHAIRPERSON: Edwin Teall
UNDERGRADUATE ENROLLMENT: 520
GRADUATE ENROLLMENT: 1,600

Mount Saint Mary's College

10 Chester Place
Los Angeles CA 90007-2598

Phone: 213-477-2650
Fax: 213-477-2649
URL: www.msmc.la.edu

TYPE OF INSTITUTION: Private, Roman Catholic
EXECUTIVE OFFICER: Karen Kennelly, CSJ, President
CHAIRPERSON: Marie Egan, IHM, Religious Studies
COORDINATOR: M. Alexis Navarro, IHM, Director of Graduate Religious Studies
UNDERGRADUATE ENROLLMENT: 1,685
GRADUATE ENROLLMENT: 50

Mount Saint Mary's College

Emmitsburg MD 21727

Phone: 301-447-5370
Fax: 301-447-5755
E-mail: mcdonald@msmary.edu
URL: www.msmary.edu

TYPE OF INSTITUTION: Private, Roman Catholic
EXECUTIVE OFFICER: Carol L. Hinds, Vice President and Dean of the College
CHAIRPERSON: Patricia M. McDonald, SHCJ
UNDERGRADUATE ENROLLMENT: 1,300
GRADUATE ENROLLMENT: 300

College of Mount Saint Vincent

Religious Studies Liaison, Riverdale NY 10471

Mount St Vincent University

Dept of Religious Studies, Halifax, Nova Scotia B3M 2J6 Canada

---

Mount Union College

Alliance OH 44601

Mount Vernon Nazarene College

Martinsburg Rd, Mount Vernon OH 43050-9500

Mountain States Baptist College

824 Third Ave N
Great Falls MT 59401

Phone: 406-761-0308
E-mail: msbcjonas@montana.com
URL: www.montana.com/fairview

TYPE OF INSTITUTION: Private, Independent Baptist
EXECUTIVE OFFICER: Richard Jonas, Vice President
UNDERGRADUATE ENROLLMENT: 25

Muhlenberg College

2400 Chew St
Allentown PA 18104

Phone: 484-664-3435
Fax: 484-664-5627
E-mail: mittlema@muhlenberg.edu
URL: hal.muhlberg.edu/depts/religion/

TYPE OF INSTITUTION: Private, Lutheran
EXECUTIVE OFFICER: Arthur Taylor, President
CHAIRPERSON: Alan Mittleman
UNDERGRADUATE ENROLLMENT: 1,950
DEGREES OFFERED: Religion Major/Minor, Jewish studies minor
UNDERGRADUATE MAJORS: 6
DEGREES CONFERRED: 6
DESCRIPTION OF UNDERGRADUATE PROGRAM: Religious Studies are understood to be an integral part of the liberal arts. From this two purposes follow: The Department endeavors to foster a critical appreciation of the student's own religious tradition and the religious traditions of others. The Department, secondly, emphasizes interdisciplinary studies which explore the relationship between religion and the other areas of life where students pursue their primary vocations. Because of the location and constituency of the College, Jewish-Christian relations receive considerable attention.

FACULTY:

Campagna-Pinto, Stephen, PhD (cand.), Harvard University (1999), Assistant Visiting Professor—history of Christian thought

Gorman, Jill, PhD (cand.), Temple University (1999), Assistant Visiting Professor—biblical studies

Hardy, Julia, PhD, Duke University (1990), Assistant Professor—religions of China and Japan, E-mail: jhmardy@muhlenberg.edu

Jennings, William H., PhD, Yale University (1966), 1969, Professor—Christian social ethics, religions of Japan, E-mail: jennings@muhlenberg.edu

Mittleman, Alan, PhD, Temple University (1985), 1988, Associate Professor—Jewish studies, E-mail: mittlema@muhlenberg.edu

Pettit, Peter, PhD, Claremont Graduate University (1993), 1999, Director of the Institute for Jewish and Christian Understanding, E-mail: papettit@muhlenberg.edu

Schwartz, Susan, PhD, Syracuse University (1982), 1986, Associate Professor—religions of India, religion and literature, E-mail: sschwart@muhlenberg.edu

Multnomah Bible College and Biblical Seminary

8435 NE Glisan St   Phone: 503-255-0332
Portland OR 97220   Fax: 503-254-1268
                                                E-mail: udub@multnomah.edu
                                                   URL: www.multnomah.edu

TYPE OF INSTITUTION: Private, Interdenominational
EXECUTIVE OFFICER: Daniel Lockwood, President
UNDERGRADUATE ENROLLMENT: 590
GRADUATE ENROLLMENT: 206

Rabbinical Seminary of Munkacs

1377 42nd St, Brooklyn NY 11219

Murray State University

Dept of Philosophy and Religious Studies   Phone: 502-762-2405
Murray KY 42071   Fax: 502-762-3424
                                            E-mail: terry.foreman@murraystate.edu
                                          URL: www.mursuky.edu/qacd/chs/phirgs
                                                                     /home.htm

TYPE OF INSTITUTION: Public
EXECUTIVE OFFICER: Kern Alexander, President
COORDINATOR: Terry Foreman

Muskingum College

Dept of Religion and Philosophy   Phone: 740-826-8125
Brown Chapel   Fax: 740-826-8404
New Concord OH 43762   E-mail: rnutt@muskingum.edu
                                                    URL: muskingum.edu

TYPE OF INSTITUTION: Private, Presbyterian USA
CHAIRPERSON: Rick Nutt
UNDERGRADUATE ENROLLMENT: 5

The Naropa Institute

2130 Arapahoe Ave
Boulder CO 80302-6697

Phone: 303-444-0202
Fax: 303-444-0410
E-mail: info@naropa.edu
URL: naropa.edu

TYPE OF INSTITUTION: Private
EXECUTIVE OFFICER: John Whitehouse Cobb, President
CHAIRPERSON: Judith Simmer-Brown
UNDERGRADUATE ENROLLMENT: 364
GRADUATE ENROLLMENT: 483

Nashotah House

2777 Mission Road
Nashotah WI 53058

Phone: 414-646-6500
Fax: 414-646-6504
E-mail: nashotah@nashotah.edu
URL: www.nashotah.edu

TYPE OF INSTITUTION: Private, Episcopal Church
EXECUTIVE OFFICER: Gary W. Kriss, President and Dean
GRADUATE ENROLLMENT: 30

National College of Education

Evanston IL 60201

Nazarene Theological Seminary

1700 E Meyer Blvd
Kansas City MO 64131

Phone: 816-333-6254
Fax: 816-333-6271
URL: www.nts.edu

TYPE OF INSTITUTION: Denominational: Church of the Nazarene
EXECUTIVE OFFICER: A. Gordon Wetmore, President
COORDINATORS: Roger Hahn (MDiv), Alex Deasley (MA), Ed Robinson (MRE, DMin), Charles
  Gailey (MA in Missiology)
GRADUATE ENROLLMENT: 265

Nazarene Indian Bible College

2315 Markham Rd SW, Albuquerque NM 87195

Nazareth College of Rochester

4245 East Avenue
Rochester NY 14618-3790

Phone: 716-389-2729
Fax: 716-586-2452
E-mail: thdonlin@naz.edu
URL: www.naz.edu/dept/religious_studies/

TYPE OF INSTITUTION: Private
EXECUTIVE OFFICER: Robert Miller, President
CHAIRPERSON: Thomas Donlin-Smith
UNDERGRADUATE ENROLLMENT: 1,900
GRADUATE ENROLLMENT: 1,000

University of Nebraska

Department of Classics and Religious Studies
237 Andrews Hall
Lincoln NE 68588-0337

Phone: 402-472-2460
Fax: 402-472-4481
E-mail: jturner@unlserve.unl.edu
URL: www.unl.edu/classics

TYPE OF INSTITUTION: Public
EXECUTIVE OFFICER: James Moeser, Chancellor
CHAIRPERSON: Sidnie White Crawford
COORDINATOR: John D. Turner
UNDERGRADUATE ENROLLMENT: 19,000
GRADUATE ENROLLMENT: 4,800
DEGREES OFFERED: Arts and Sciences Undergraduate Minor in Religious Studies or BA in
    Classics with concentration in Religious Studies
UNDERGRADUATE MAJORS: 20 Classics; 24 Minors in Religious Studies
DEGREES CONFERRED: 10
DESCRIPTION OF UNDERGRADUATE PROGRAM: The interdisciplinary program in religious
    studies provides a flexible curriculum that will introduce undergraduates to several distinct
    areas of religious study by combining appropriate courses from a variety of disciplines in the
    humanities and social sciences. The aim of the program is to give the student a knowledge of
    religion as a phenomenon of human life.
FACULTY:
Adkin, Neil, PhD, Universities of Glasgow, (1982), 1986, Associate Professor—classics, classi-
    cal and Medieval Latin language, Latin patristic and Latin Medieval literature, Jerome, Eras-
    mus, 402-472-4483, Fax: 402-472-4481/9771, E-mail: nadkin@unlserve.unl.edu
Burnett, Stephen G., PhD, University of Wisconsin-Madison (1990), 1997, Lecturer—history,
    classics, and Judaic studies, 402-472-2417, Fax: 402-472-4481/9771, E-mail:
    sburneft@unlserve.unl.edu
Cahan, Jean, PhD, Johns Hopkins University (1983), 1987, Director, Center for Judaic
    Studies—Spinoza, modern Jewish philosophy, philosophy of religion, 402-472-5915, Fax:
    402-472-4481/9771, E-mail: jcahan@unlserve.unl.edu
Crawford, Dan D., PhD, Pittsburgh (1972), 1997, Senior Lecturer—philosophy, philosophy of
    religion, 402-472-4392, Fax: 402-472-4481, E-mail: dcrawford@unlserve.unl.edu

Crawford, Sidnie White, PhD, Harvard University (1988), 1997, Associate Professor—Hebrew Bible, classics, history and literature of Second Temple Judaism, 402-472-4475, Fax: 402-472 4481/9771, E-mail: scrawfor@unlserve.unl.edu

Gorman, Robert J., PhD, University of Pennsylvania (1995), 1995, Lecturer—Cicero Hellenistic philosophy, classical tradition, 402-472-4485, Fax: 402-472-4481/9771, E-mail: rgorman@unlserve.unl.edu

Leinieks, Vaidis, PhD, Princeton University (1962), 1966, Professor—classics, Homer, Greek tragedy, structural linguistics, 402-472-4481, Fax: 402-472-4481/9771

Rinkevich, Thomas E., PhD, Ohio State University (1973), 1967, Associate Professor—classics, Greek and Latin language and poetry, Egyptian language, 402-472-4482, Fax: 402-4724481/9771, E-mail: ter@unlserve.unl.edu

Turner, John D., PhD, Duke University (1970), 1976, Cotner Professor of Religious Studies, Professor—classics and history, New Testament, Hellenistic/Graeco-Roman religion and philosophy, Gnosticism, later Platonism and Neoplatonism, Coptic language and literature, 402- 472-7008, Fax: 402-472-4481/9771, E-mail: jturner@unlserve.unl.edu

Winter, Thomas N., PhD, Northwestern (1968), 1970, Associate Professor—classics, 402-472-4480, Fax: 402-472-4481/9771, E-mail: twinter@unlserve.unl.edu

AFFILIATED FACULTY:

Ide, Harry, PhD, Cornell University (1988), Associate Professor—philosophy, ancient Hellenistic, and Medieval philosophy

Whift, Hugh P., PhD, University of North Carolina at Chapel Hill, Professor—sociology, deviance (especially violence), sociology of religion, and quantitative methods

---

University of Nebraska

60th and Dodge Streets
Omaha NE 68182

Phone: 402-554-2629
Fax: 402-554-2949
E-mail: rfreund@unomaha.edu

TYPE OF INSTITUTION: Public
CHAIRPERSON: Richard A. Freund
UNDERGRADUATE ENROLLMENT: 17,000

Nebraska Christian College

1800 Syracuse Ave
Norfolk NE 68701

Phone: 402-379-5000
Fax: 402-379-5100
E-mail: ddonaldson@nechristian.edu
URL: www.nechristian.edu

TYPE OF INSTITUTION: Private, Christian Churches/Churches of Christ
EXECUTIVE OFFICER: Daniel J. Donaldson, Academic Dean
UNDERGRADUATE ENROLLMENT: 152

Nebraska Wesleyan University

Dept of Religion and Philosophy
5000 Saint Paul Avenue
Lincoln NE 68504-2796

Phone: 402-466-2371
Fax: 402-465-2179
E-mail: dbp@calvin.nebrwesleyan.edu
URL: www.nebrwesleyan.edu/religion.html

TYPE OF INSTITUTION: Private, United Methodist related
EXECUTIVE OFFICER: Jeanie Watson, President; Richard H. Quinn, Vice President for Academic Affairs
CHAIRPERSON: David B. Peabody
UNDERGRADUATE ENROLLMENT: 1,600

Ner Israel Rabbinical College

Mount Wilson Ln, Baltimore MD 21208

Neumann College

Aston PA 19014

New Brunswick Theological Seminary

17 Seminary Place
New Brunswick NJ 08901

Phone: 732-247-5241
Fax: 732-249-5412

TYPE OF INSTITUTION: Denominational: Reformed Church in America
EXECUTIVE OFFICER: Norman J. Kansfield, President
CHAIRPERSON: Paul R. Fries, Dean of the Seminary
GRADUATE ENROLLMENT: 225

Academy of the New Church

Bryn Athyn PA 19009

New College for Advanced Christian Study

2600 Dwight Way, Berkeley CA 94704

University of New England

11 Hills Beach Rd, Biddeford ME 04005

New England Bible College

PO Box 2886
So Portland ME 04116-2886

Phone: 207-799-5979
Fax: 207-799-6586
E-mail: info@nebc.edu
URL: www.nebc.edu

TYPE OF INSTITUTION: Non-Denominational
EXECUTIVE OFFICER: William E. Inman, President
UNDERGRADUATE ENROLLMENT: 60

University of New Hampshire

Durham NH 03824

Phone: 603-862-3015
Fax: 603-862-0178
E-mail: davidtf@hopper.unh.edu
URL: www.unh.edu/history/rsmain.html

TYPE OF INSTITUTION: Public
EXECUTIVE OFFICER: Marilyn Hoskin, Dean, College of Liberal Arts
COORDINATOR: David Frankfurter
UNDERGRADUATE ENROLLMENT: 10,434

New Jersey City University

2039 Kennedy Boulevard
Jersey City NJ 07305

Phone: 201-200-3220
Fax: 201-200-2228
E-mail: hhochsmann@njcu.edu
URL: www.hjcu.edu

TYPE OF INSTITUTION: Public
EXECUTIVE OFFICER: Carlos Hernandez, President
CHAIRPERSON: Hyun Hochsmann
UNDERGRADUATE ENROLLMENT: 6,412
GRADUATE ENROLLMENT: 2,132

University of New Mexico

Religious Studies Program
Albuquerque NM 87131

Phone: 505-277-4009
Fax: 505-277-6362

TYPE OF INSTITUTION: Public
EXECUTIVE OFFICER: Dean W. Gordon, College of Arts and Sciences
COORDINATOR: Andrew J. Burgess
UNDERGRADUATE ENROLLMENT: 18,998
GRADUATE ENROLLMENT: 5,346

New Mexico State University

Las Cruces NM 88003

New Orleans Baptist Theological Seminary

3939 Gentilly Blvd, New Orleans LA 70126

College of New Rochelle

New Rochelle NY 10801

New York University

19 University Place, 501A
New York NY 10012

Phone: 212-998-3756
Fax: 212-993-4827
E-mail: religious studies@nyu.edu
URL: www.nyu.edu

TYPE OF INSTITUTION: Private
EXECUTIVE OFFICER: L. Jay Oliva, President
COORDINATOR: Elliot Wolfson
UNDERGRADUATE ENROLLMENT: 30
GRADUATE ENROLLMENT: 17

State University of New York at Albany

Dept of Classics and Humanities 376, Albany NY 12222

State University of New York at Buffalo

Buffalo NY 14214

State University of New York at Cortland

Cortland NY 13045

State University of New York at New Paltz

75 South Manheim Blvd
Suite 6
New Paltz NY 12561-2440

Phone: 914-257-2980
Fax: 914-257-2735

TYPE OF INSTITUTION: Public
EXECUTIVE OFFICER: Roger Bowen, President
COORDINATOR: J. David Blankenship
UNDERGRADUATE ENROLLMENT: 400

State University of New York at Oswego

Oswego NY 13126

New York Theological Seminary

5 W 29th Street
New York NY 10001

Phone: 212-532-4012
Fax: 212-684-0757

TYPE OF INSTITUTION: Private, Non-Denominational
EXECUTIVE OFFICERS: M. William Howard, President; T. Richard Snyder, Academic Dean
GRADUATE ENROLLMENT: 330

Newberry College

2100 College Street
Newberry SC 29108

Phone: 803-321-5197
Fax: 803-321-5627
E-mail: rkleckley@newberry.edu
URL: www.newberry.edu

TYPE OF INSTITUTION: Private, Evangelical Lutheran Church in America
EXECUTIVE OFFICERS: Peter French, President; Jonathan Franz, Dean
CHAIRPERSON: Garth Kemerling
UNDERGRADUATE ENROLLMENT: 700

Newman Theological College

15611 St Albert Trail NW
Edmonton, Alberta T5L 4H8
Canada

Phone: 403-447-2993
Fax: 403-447-2685
E-mail: admin@newman.edu
URL: www.newman.edu

TYPE OF INSTITUTION: Private, Roman Catholic
EXECUTIVE OFFICERS: Kevin Carr, President; Martin Moser, Academic Vice President and
    Dean of Theology
CHAIRPERSON: Kevin Carr
UNDERGRADUATE ENROLLMENT: 101
GRADUATE ENROLLMENT: 154

Newman University

3100 McCormick
Wichita KS 67213

Phone: 316-942-4291
Fax: 316-942-4483

TYPE OF INSTITUTION: Private, Roman Catholic
EXECUTIVE OFFICER: Sr. Tarcisia Roths, ASC, President
CHAIRPERSON: Rev. Richard A. Boever, CSSR
UNDERGRADUATE ENROLLMENT: 117

Niagara University

Department of Religious Studies	Phone: 716-286-8460
Ozanam House	Fax: 716-286-8454
Niagara University NY 14109	E-mail: jhubbert@niagara.edu
	URL: www.niagara.edu

TYPE OF INSTITUTION: Private, Catholic

EXECUTIVE OFFICER: Joseph L. Levesque, President

CHAIRPERSON: Joseph G. Hubbert

UNDERGRADUATE ENROLLMENT: 2,335

North American Baptist Seminary

1321 W 22nd St, Sioux Falls SD 57105

University of North Carolina, Chapel Hill

Dept of Religious Studies	Phone: 919-962-5666
College of Arts and Sciences	Fax: 919-962-1567
101 Saunders Hall, CB#3225	E-mail: religion@email.unc.edu
Chapel Hill NC 27599-3225	URL: www.unc.edu/depts/rel_stud

TYPE OF INSTITUTION: Public

EXECUTIVE OFFICER: Risa Palm, Dean

CHAIRPERSON: Carl Ernst

COORDINATORS: David J. Halperin, Bart D. Ehrman

UNDERGRADUATE ENROLLMENT: 15,300

GRADUATE ENROLLMENT: 6,800

University of North Carolina at Charlotte

Dept of Religious Studies	Phone: 704-547-4598
9201 University City Blvd	Fax: 704-547-3002
Charlotte NC 28223-0001	E-mail: estclair@email.uncc.edu
	URL: www.uncc.edu/rels

TYPE OF INSTITUTION: Public

EXECUTIVE OFFICER: James H. Woodward, Chancellor

CHAIRPERSON: Edward B. St. Clair

UNDERGRADUATE ENROLLMENT: 14,400

GRADUATE ENROLLMENT: 2,600

DEGREES OFFERED: BA

UNDERGRADUATE MAJORS: 60

DEGREES CONFERRED: 15

DESCRIPTION OF UNDERGRADUATE PROGRAM: The curriculum for the religious studies major covers the three general areas of Western religions, Asian religions, and religion and contemporary culture. An integrative seminar for senior majors is required. The Department is housed in the College of Arts and Sciences and makes an explicit commitment to inquiry in the traditions of the liberal arts. UNC Charlotte is a large and growing comprehensive university in the largest urban center of the Carolinas.

FACULTY:

Cohen, Richard A., PhD, State University of New York, Stoney Brook (1980), 1994, Isaac Swift Distinguished Professor of Judaic Studies—contemporary Jewish thought, ethics and religion, 704-547-4599, Fax: 704-547-3002, E-mail: richacohen@aol.com

Gestwicki, Ronald A., PhD, Syracuse (1971), 1972, Associate Professor—religion and culture, holistic depth psychology, 704-547-4603, E-mail: ragesti@email.uncc.edu

Getz, Lorine M., PhD, University of St Michael's College, Toronto (1979), 1989, Associate Professor of Religious Studies—women and religion; art, literature, and religion; 704-547-2784, Fax: 704-547-3002, E-mail: drlmgetz@juno.com

Johnson, Kathryn V., PhD, Harvard (1985), 1986, Assistant Professor—Islamic and Near Eastern studies, 704-547-4586, Fax: 704-547-3002, E-mail: kvjohnso@email.uncc.edu

Marshall, Celia B., MA, Yale (1978), 1992, Lecturer—biblical studies, 704-547-3378, Fax: 704-547-3002, E-mail: acmssm@aol.com

Meyer, Jeffrey F., PhD, Chicago (1973), 1973, Professor—religions of China and East Asia, 704-547-4602, Fax: 704-547-3002, E-mail: jfmeyer@email.uncc.edu

Reeves, John C., PhD, Hebrew Union College, Cincinnati (1989), 1996, Blumenthal Professor of Judaic Studies, 704-547-3070, Fax: 704-547-3002, E-mail: jcreeves@email.uncc.edu

Robinson, Joanne Maguire, PhD, University of Chicago (1996), 1996, Assistant Professor—history of Christianity, the Medieval period in the West, Christianity and art, 704-547-2888, Fax: 704-547-2888, E-mail: jmaguire@email.uncc.edu

St. Clair, Edward B., PhD, Duke (1970), 1970, Chairperson—religion and culture, philosophy of religion, 704-547-4604, Fax: 704-547-3002, E-mail: estclair@email.uncc.edu

Tabor, James D., PhD, University of Chicago (1981), 1989, Professor—Christian origins, first century Mediterranean religions, 704-547-2783, Fax: 704-841-3828 or 704-547-3002, E-mail: jdtabor@email.uncc.edu

Thomas, Herman E., PhD, Hartford (1978), 1974, Associate Professor—religion in American culture, Black religion in America, 704-547-4605, Fax: 704-547-3002, E-mail: hethomas@email.uncc.edu

White, J. Daniel, PhD, Pennsylvania (1972), 1971, Associate Professor—religions of South Asia, 704-547-4601, Fax: 704-547-3002, E-mail: jdwhite@email.uncc.edu

Witherspoon, Loy H., PhD, Boston (1962), Professor Emeritus—biblical studies, 704-547-4600, Fax: 704-547-3002

University of North Carolina, Greensboro

1000 Spring Garden Street
109 Foust Bldg
Greensboro NC 27412-5001

Phone: 910-334-5762
Fax: 910-334-4258
E-mail: bowdenp@uncg.edu

TYPE OF INSTITUTION: Public

EXECUTIVE OFFICER: Walter Beale, Dean

CHAIRPERSON: Charles D. Orzech

UNDERGRADUATE ENROLLMENT: 10,000

GRADUATE ENROLLMENT: 2,500

University of North Carolina, Wilmington

Dept of Philosophy and Religion
601 S College Road
Wilmington NC 28403-3297

Phone: 910-962-3406
Fax: 910-962-7070
URL: www.uncwil.edu/p&r

TYPE OF INSTITUTION: Public

CHAIRPERSON: Joe B. Wilson

UNDERGRADUATE ENROLLMENT: 9,000

North Carolina State University

Dept of Philosophy and Religion
Campus Box 8103
Raleigh NC 27695-8103

Phone: 919-515-3214
Fax: 919-515-7856
E-mail: phil_rel@ncsu.edu

TYPE OF INSTITUTION: Public

CHAIRPERSON: Harold D. Levin (Interim Head)

UNDERGRADUATE ENROLLMENT: 21,000

DEGREES OFFERED: BA in Religious Studies

UNDERGRADUATE MAJORS: 35

DEGREES CONFERRED: 27

DESCRIPTION OF UNDERGRADUATE PROGRAM: Courses in Religious Studies have been offered at North Carolina State University since 1928 and today constitute an integral part of the curriculum of the College of Humanities and Social Sciences. In fall 1993 the Department of Philosophy and Religion inaugurated a new BA in Religious Studies, which replaced a hybrid BA in Philosophy with Concentration in Religious Studies. The new degree program in Religious Studies consists of 33 credit hours in the study of religion, with limited distribution requirements to ensure core instruction in a variety of religious traditions, in comparative and cross-cultural religious themes, and in the methods for the academic study of religion. The course of instruction is predicated on the proposition that religion is a category of human experience that is *sui generis* and fundamental to the creation of human meaning, hence its humanistic orientation. The program retains sufficient flexibility through elective classes to allow each student to personalize his or her course of study. The BA can be taken with an Honors track, and is complemented by a Minor in Religious Studies for non-majors from any other discipline within the university.

FACULTY:

Adler, William, PhD, Pennsylvania (1982), 1984, Professor—early Christian literature, 919-515-6334, Fax: 919-515-7856, E-mail: william_adler@ncsu.edu

Cunningham, Mary Kathleen, PhD, Yale (1988), 1983, Associate Professor—modern Western religious thought; history of Christian thought, E-mail: mk_cunningham@ncsu.edu, 919-515-6105, Fax: 919-515-7856

Dohrmann, Natalie Bosworth, PhD, Chicago (1999), 1999, Assistant Professor—early Judaism, Hebrew Bible, 919-515-6194, Fax: 919-515-7856, E-mail: nb_dohr@ncsu.edu

Fitzgerald, W. Curtis, BD, Southern Seminary (1952), 1956, Associate Professor Emeritus—history of Western religions

Highfill, W. Lawrence, PhD, Duke (1955), 1956, Associate Professor Emeritus—Asian religions

Jaffe, Richard, PhD, Yale (1995), 1994, Assistant Professor—Buddhist studies, Japanese religions, East Asian religions, 919-515-6195, Fax: 919-515-7856, E-mail: richard_jaffe@ncsu.edu

Stewart, Tony K., PhD, Chicago (1985), 1986, Associate Professor—history of religions, methods for the study of religion, South Asian religions, 919-515-6335, Fax: 919-515-7856, E-mail: tony_stewart@ncsu.edu

North Carolina Wesleyan College

3400 N Wesleyan Blvd
Rocky Mount NC 27804

Phone: 919-985-5100
Fax: 919-977-3701
E-mail: ccreegan@ncwc.edu

TYPE OF INSTITUTION: Private, United Methodist
EXECUTIVE OFFICER: John B. White, President
DISCIPLINE CONTACT: Charles L. Creegan
UNDERGRADUATE ENROLLMENT: 1,500

North Central College

30 N Brainard St
PO Box 3063
Naperville IL 60566-7063

Phone: 630-637-5316
Fax: 630-637-5121
E-mail: hem@noctrl.edu

TYPE OF INSTITUTION: Private, United Methodist
EXECUTIVE OFFICER: R. Devadoss Pandian, Dean of Faculty
CHAIRPERSON: Howard E. Mueller
UNDERGRADUATE ENROLLMENT: 1,950
GRADUATE ENROLLMENT: 310

North Central Bible College

910 Elliot Ave, Minneapolis MN 55404

University of North Dakota

Box 7128
Grand Forks ND 58202

Phone: 701-777-4236
URL: www.und.nodak.edu/dept/philrel

TYPE OF INSTITUTION: Public
EXECUTIVE OFFICER: Charles Kupchella, President
CHAIRPERSON: Scott Lowe
UNDERGRADUATE ENROLLMENT: 40

North Dakota State University

402 Minard Hall
Fargo ND 58105

Phone: 701-231-7026
Fax: 701-231-1047
E-mail: helgelan@plains.nodak.edu

TYPE OF INSTITUTION: Public
COORDINATOR: John Helgeland, Director of the School of Religion
UNDERGRADUATE ENROLLMENT: 9,500
GRADUATE ENROLLMENT: 500

North Park University

3225 W Foster Ave
Chicago IL 60625-4895

Phone: 773-244-6200
E-mail: admission@northpark.edu
URL: www.northpark.edu

TYPE OF INSTITUTION: Private, Evangelical Covenant Church
EXECUTIVE OFFICER: David G. Horner, President
UNDERGRADUATE ENROLLMENT: 1,304
GRADUATE ENROLLMENT: 630

North Park Theological Seminary

3225 West Foster Ave
Chicago IL 60625

Phone: 773-244-6210
Fax: 773-244-6244
URL: www.northpark.edu

TYPE OF INSTITUTION: Denominational: Evangelical Covenant Church
EXECUTIVE OFFICER: John E. Phelan, Jr., President and Dean of the Seminary
GRADUATE ENROLLMENT: 133

North Texas State University

Denton TX 76203

Northeastern University

360 Huntington Ave
Boston MA 02115

Phone: 617-373-3636
Fax: 617-373-4359
E-mail: ssetta@neu.edu
URL: www.casdn.neu.edu/-philosop

TYPE OF INSTITUTION: Private
EXECUTIVE OFFICER: Richard Freeland, President
CHAIRPERSON: Michael R. Lipton
UNDERGRADUATE ENROLLMENT: 41

Northeastern Illinois University

5500 N St Louis Ave, Chicago IL 60625

Northern Arizona University

Dept of Humanities, Arts, & Religion
Box 6031
Flagstaff AZ 86011

Phone: 520-523-3881
Fax: 520-523-1881
E-mail: dennis.rusche@nau.edu
URL: www.nau.edu/~human/

TYPE OF INSTITUTION: Public, Non-Denominational
CHAIRPERSON: Dennis Rusché
COORDINATOR: Arne Hassing
UNDERGRADUATE ENROLLMENT: 15,000
GRADUATE ENROLLMENT: 3,000

Northern Baptist Theological Seminary

660 E Butterfield Road
Lombard IL 60148

Phone: 708-620-2103
Fax: 708-620-2194

TYPE OF INSTITUTION: Denominational: ABC (USA)
EXECUTIVE OFFICER: Douglas R. Sharp, Vice President for Academic Affairs and Dean of
Seminary
GRADUATE ENROLLMENT: 64

Northern California Bible College

4455 Stoneridge Dr
Pleasanton CA 94588

Phone: 925-846-6464
Fax: 925-846-3462
URL: www.ncbc.net

TYPE OF INSTITUTION: Private, Non-Denominational
EXECUTIVE OFFICER: Ernest Gentile, President
UNDERGRADUATE ENROLLMENT: 90

Northern California Bible College

1532 McLaughlin Ave, San Jose CA 95122

Northern Illinois University

DeKalb IL 60115

University of Northern Iowa

Dept of Philosophy and Religion
Cedar Falls IA 50614-0501

Phone: 319-273-6221
Fax: 319-273-7095
E-mail: betty.deberg@uni.edu
URL: www.uni.edu

TYPE OF INSTITUTION: Public

EXECUTIVE OFFICER: Aaron Podalefsky, Vice President and Provost

CHAIRPERSON: Betty A. DeBerg

UNDERGRADUATE ENROLLMENT: 13,000

DEGREES OFFERED: BA Phil, Study of Religion

UNDERGRADUATE MAJORS: 55

DEGREES CONFERRED: 15

DESCRIPTION OF UNDERGRADUATE PROGRAM: The Department of Philosophy and Religion offers undergraduate majors in Philosophy and the Study of Religion, minors in those disciplines and in Ethics. It also serves all the students of the University as a source of electives and General Education options in philosophy and religion and the humanities. It is possible for students majoring in this department to proceed directly to the Master of Business Administration program, if they have completed the requirements of a minor in the College of Business Administration.

FACULTY:

Atkinson, Kenneth, PhD, Temple University (1999), 1999, Assistant Professor of Religion—biblial studies, archeology, world religions, 319-273-6221

Blackwell, Michael D., PhD, Boston University (1994), 1995, Adjunct Assistant Professor—Christian social ethics, African American religious experience, race relations, 319-273-2250, E-mail: michael.blackwell@uni.edu

Brod, Harry, PhD, University of California, San Diego (1981), 1999, Associate Professor of Philosophy and Humanities—feminist theory and gender studies, continental philosophy, 319-273-6221

Clayton, Scharron A., PhD, University of Iowa (1980), 1991, Associate Professor—African American culture, human relations, ethnic studies, 319-273-2248, E-mail: scharron.clayton@uni.edu

Clohesy, William W., PhD, New School for Social Research (1981), 1987, Associate Professor—moral and political philosophy, German philosophy, American pragmatism, existential phenomenology, 319-273-6123, E-mail: william.clohesy@uni.edu

DeBerg, Betty A., PhD, Vanderbilt University (1988), 1997, Professor and Department Head—religion in America, history of Christianity, 319-273-6221, E-mail: betty.deberg@uni.edu

Feuerhak, Donald L., MDiv, Wartburg Seminary (1972), 1980, Adjunct Assistant Professor (part-time)—death and dying, 319-273-6221

Hill, Susan E., PhD, University of Chicago (1993), 1994, Assistant Professor—religion and literature, history of Christianity, modern religious thought, gender studies, 319-273-7177, E-mail: susan.hill@uni.edu

Holland, Margaret G., PhD, SUNY, Buffalo (1991), 1991, Assistant Professor—ethics, history of philosophy, philosophy and literature, feminist theory, 319-273-5975, E-mail: margaret.holland@uni.edu

Keeley, Brian Lee, PhD, University of California, San Diego (1997), 1999, Assistant Professor of Philosophy—philosophy of science, philosophy of mind, metaphysics, and epistemology, 319-273-6221

Morgan, David L., MA, Washington University (1966), 1969, Assistant Professor—logic, philosophy of science, Marxism, 319-273-6449, E-mail: david.morgan@uni.edu

Reineke, Martha J., PhD, Vanderbilt University (1983), 1984, Associate Professor—women's studies in religion, religion and society, philosophy of religion, 319-273-6233, E-mail: martha.reineke@uni.edu

Reitan, Eric H., PhD, SUNY-Buffalo, Instructor—ethics, philosophy, 319-273-2181, E-mail: eric.reitan@uni.edu

Robinson, James B., PhD, University of Wisconsin (1975), 1970, Associate Professor—Tibetan Buddhism, Indian religions, history of religions, 319-273-2507, E-mail: james.robinson@uni.edu

Soneson, Jerome P., PhD, Harvard University (1990), 1991, Associate Professor—theological ethics, process philosophy and theology, American pragmatism, environmental ethics, 319-273-2990, E-mail: jerome.soneson@uni.edu

---

Northern Kentucky University

University Dr
Highland KY 41099

Phone: 606-572-5259
Fax: 606-572-6080
E-mail: pence@nku.edu
URL: www.nku.edu

TYPE OF INSTITUTION: Public
EXECUTIVE OFFICER: Rodgers, Redding, Provost
COORDINATOR: Terry G. Pence
UNDERGRADUATE ENROLLMENT: 12,000

Northland College

Ashland WI 54806

Phone: 715-682-1241
E-mail: lalldritt@wheeler.northland.edu
URL: bobb.northland.edu

TYPE OF INSTITUTION: Private, UCC
EXECUTIVE OFFICER: Robert Parsonage, President
CHAIRPERSON: Leslie D. Alldritt

Northland Baptist Bible College

WI0085 Pike Plains Road
Dunbar WI 54119-9285

Phone: 715-324-6900
Fax: 715-324-6133
E-mail: info@nbbc.edu

TYPE OF INSTITUTION: Denominational: Baptist
EXECUTIVE OFFICER: Sam Horn, Vice President for Academic Affairs
CHAIRPERSON: William Arndt, Registrar/Academic Dean

UNDERGRADUATE ENROLLMENT: 650
GRADUATE ENROLLMENT: 150

Northwest College of the Assemblies

PO Box 579, Kirkland WA 98083

Northwest Baptist Seminary

4301 N Stevens
Tacoma WA 98407

Phone: 253-759-6104
Fax: 253-759-3299
URL: www.nbs.edu

TYPE OF INSTITUTION: Private, Baptist
EXECUTIVE OFFICERS: Mark D. Wagner, President
GRADUATE ENROLLMENT: 58

Northwest Baptist Seminary

See Associated Canadian Theological Schools (ACTS)

Northwest Christian College

Eugene OR 97401

Northwest Missouri State University

800 University Dr, Maryville MO 64468

Northwest Nazarene University

623 Holly St
Nampa ID 83686

Phone: 208-467-8538
Fax: 208-467-8469
E-mail: admissions@nnc.edu
URL: www.nnc.edu

TYPE OF INSTITUTION: Private, Church of the Nazarene
EXECUTIVE OFFICER: Richard A. Hagood, President
CHAIRPERSON: Ralph Neil
COORDINATOR: Gary Waller
UNDERGRADUATE ENROLLMENT: 110
GRADUATE ENROLLMENT: 15

Northwestern College

Orange City IA 51041

Northwestern College

3003 Snelling Ave N, Saint Paul MN 55113

Northwestern University

Dept of Religion
1940 Sheridan Rd
Evanston IL 60208-4050

Phone: 847-491-5488
Fax: 847-467-2062
E-mail: kieckhefer@nwu.edu

TYPE OF INSTITUTION: Private
EXECUTIVE OFFICER: Eric Sundquist, Dean
CHAIRPERSON: Richard Kieckhefer (Undergraduate); Manfred Vogel (Graduate)
UNDERGRADUATE ENROLLMENT: 8,000
GRADUATE ENROLLMENT: 4,000

Norwich University

Northfield VT 05663

College of Notre Dame

Ralston Ave, Belmont CA 94002

College of Notre Dame at Maryland

4701 N Charles St, Baltimore MD 21210

Notre Dame College

2321 Elm St, Manchester NH 03104

Notre Dame College

4545 College Rd
South Euclid OH 44121

Phone: 216-381-1680 ext 334
Fax: 216-381-3802
E-mail: lprochaska@ndc.edu
URL: www.ndc.edu

TYPE OF INSTITUTION: Private (women), Catholic
EXECUTIVE OFFICER: Anne Deming, President
CHAIRPERSON: Louise Prochaska, SND
UNDERGRADUATE ENROLLMENT: 650

University of Notre Dame

Department of Theology
Notre Dame IN 46556

Phone: 219-631-7811
Fax: 219-631-4268
E-mail: cavadini.1@nd.edu
URL: www.nd.edu: 80˜theo/

TYPE OF INSTITUTION: Private, Roman Catholic

EXECUTIVE OFFICER: Edward A. Malloy, President; Mark Roche, Dean

CHAIRPERSON: John C. Cavadini

UNDERGRADUATE ENROLLMENT: 7,838

GRADUATE ENROLLMENT: 2,500

DEGREES OFFERED: BA in Theology, MA, MTS, MDiv, PhD

UNDERGRADUATE MAJORS: 118

DEGREES CONFERRED: 53

DESCRIPTION OF UNDERGRADUATE PROGRAM: Students in the University are required to take two courses (6 credits) in Theology. The Department offers three kinds of majors: the first and second major, and joint major with Philosophy. The three majors share the same formal requirements: a two-semester sequence in the history of Christian thought, an upper-level scripture course, and a 1-credit Proseminar that introduces undergraduates to the range of disciplines and topics covered in Theology. The joint major in addition incorporates the requirements of a first major in Philosophy as well as a senior thesis and work in classical Greek (up to 12 hours). The remaining credits for each kind of major are given over to electives, taken at the upper-level: 15 additional credits for the first major, 9 for the second. Theology is a strong liberal arts major; students graduating with a minor in Theology are well prepared to teach high school religion or to go into graduate or professional studies.

GRADUATE PROGRAM

Member of the Council on Graduate Studies in Religion

Member of The Association of Theological Schools

Graduate Advisors: Gregory Sterling; Michael Connors; Randall Zachman

Graduate Degrees Offered: MA; MTS; PhD; MDiv

Degrees Conferred: 32 MA; 10 PhD; 11 MDiv

Graduate Students in Residence: 30 MA; 416 MTS; 76 PhD; 30 MDiv

Not in Residence: 4 MA; 2 PhD; 14 MDiv

Average No. of New Students Enrolled: 18 MA; 10 MTS; 12 PhD; 25 MDiv

Women Students: 13 MA; 5 MTS; 43 PhD; 15 MDiv

Minority Students: 2 MA; 9 PhD; 1 MDiv

Foreign Students: 2 MA; 1 MTS; 9 PhD

Minimum GRE Score Requisite to Admission: Yes; 500 v&a MA, MDiv; 600 v&q MTS, PhD

Financial Aid to Other Students: 100% MA; 100 MTS; 100% PhD; 100% MDiv

Attrition Among Students: 5% MA; 1% PhD; 25% MDiv

Graduates Placed: 100% MA; 100% PhD; 100% MDiv

DESCRIPTION OF GRADUATE PROGRAM AND RESEARCH FACILITIES: The MA Program offers three areas of specialization: Biblical Studies, Liturgical Studies, and Theological Studies. For admission to the MA, a potential student should have GRE scores of at least 500, and an undergraduate minor in theology or religious studies, or the equivalent. The Master of Theological Studies is a two year program designed specifically for students desiring to go on for doctoral work in one of the theological disciplines. The MTS has five areas of concentration: Biblical Studies with a concentration in ancient languages, History of Christianity, Liturgical Studies, Moral Theology, and Systematic Theology. The MTS includes a modern language requirement in all areas, and an ancient language requirement in Biblical Studies and History of Christianity. Applicants to the MTS should have GRE scores of at least 600, and undergraduate work in theology, philosophy, or cognate fields. The Master of Divinity program is professional as well as academic since it is designed to prepare students for learned and effective ministry in today's church. The 3 year, 75-credit hour program incorporates scripture, the history of Christian tradition, systematic theology, Christian ethics, field experience, and ministerial skills courses. The MDiv program includes a variety of students: members of the Congregation of Holy Cross studying for the priesthood, lay men and lay women, and sisters and brothers of religious congregations. Through this community of students, the University furthers the expansion and diversification of ministry, presents a realistic and helpful context for ministerial education, and also offers a full preparation for lay ministry and the priesthood in the Roman Catholic Church. The PhD program offers five major areas of specialization: Christianity and Judaism in Antiquity, which includes the four disciplines traditionally defined as Old Testament, New Testament, Judaism, and Early Church; the History of Christianity, with special strengths in the early church and the Medieval period; Liturgical Studies, with particular strengths in the History of the Liturgy Moral Theology/Christian Ethics, which provides a balanced mix of foundational and applied themes, and encourages a strong relationship to philosophical ethics; and Systematic Theology, in which the study of fundamental doctrinal themes, such as Christology, Trinity, or ecclesiology, may be pursued. For admission to the PhD program potential students should have a Master's degree in theology or equivalent, GRE scores of at least 600, and facility in some of the following languages: French, German, Greek, and Latin. Only a limited number of applicants, selected competitively, are admitted to the program each year, but all successful applicants will receive a tuition scholarship and usually also a stipend for the first five years of study if they have no other sources of funding. Two years of course work are generally required, followed by a year of independent study leading to candidacy examinations, prior to the writing of the dissertation.

FACULTY:

Ashley, J. Matthew, PhD, University of Chicago (1993), 1993, Assistant Professor—systematic theology, 219-631-7077, E-mail: james.m.ashley.2@nd.edu

Aune, David E., PhD, University of Chicago (1970), 1999, Professor—New Testament, E-mail: david.aune.1@nd.edu

Baxter, Michael, CSC, PhD, Duke University (1996), 1999, Assistant Professor—Christian ethics, E-mail: michael.j.baxter.6@nd.edu

Blenkinsopp, Joseph, DPhil, University of Oxford (1967), 1970, John A. O'Brien Professor Emeritus—Old Testament, E-mail: joseph.blenkinsopp.1@nd.edu

Bradshaw, Paul, PhD, King's College, University of London (1971), 1985, London Program Undergraduate Director and Professor—liturgy, E-mail: paul.bradshaw.1@nd.edu

Burrell, David, CSC, PhD, Yale University (1965), 1964, Theodore M. Hesburgh Professor of Arts and Letters—philosophical theology, 219-631-7094, E-mail: david.b.burrell.1@nd.edu (on leave 1998-99)

Cavadini, John, PhD, Yale University (1988), 1990, Associate Professor and Chair—early Christianity/patristics, 219-631-6662, E-mail: john.c.cavadini.1@nd.edu

Coll, Regina, CSJ, EdD, Columbia University (1984), 1984, Professional Specialist—pastoral education, 219-631-6493, E-mail: regina.a.coll.1@nd.edu

Connors, Michael E., CSC, ThD, Toronto School of Theology (1997), 1999, Assistant Professor—pastoral theology, E-mail: michael.e.conners.9@nd.edu

Cunningham, Lawrence S., PhD, Florida State University (1969), 1988, Professor—systematic theology, E-mail: lawrence.s.cunningham.1@nd.edu

Daley, Brian E., SJ, DPhil, Oxford University (1978), 1996, Catherine Huisking Professor of Theology—patristics, E-mail: brian.e.daley.3@nd.edu

D'Angelo, Mary Rose, PhD, Yale University (1976), 1993, Associate Professor—Christian origins, E-mail: mary.r.dangelo.2@nd.edu

Doak, Mary C., PhD, University of Chicago (1999), 1999, Assistant Professor—systematic theology, E-mail: mary.doak.5@nd.edu

Driscoll, Michael S., PhD, Sorbonne, Paris (1986), 1995, Tisch College Assistant Professor—sacramental theology, E-mail: michael.s.driscoll.7@nd.edu

Dunne, John S., CSC, STD, Gregorian University (1958), 1957, John A. O'Brien Professor—systematic theology, E-mail: john.s.dunne.1@nd.edu (on leave 1998-1999)

Ford, Josephine Massyngbaerde, PhD, Nottingham University (1965), 1965, Professor—New Testament, 219-631-5118, E-mail: josephine.m.ford.1@nd.edu

Gordon, Charles B., CSC, PhD, Cambridge University, England (1999), 1996, Assistant Professor—systematic theology, E-mail: charles.b.gordon20@nd.edu

Herdt, Jennifer A., PhD, Princeton University (1994), 1999, Assistant Professor—historical theology and Christian ethics, E-mail: jennifer.herdt.1@nd.edu

Hilkert, M. Catherine, OP, PhD, Catholic University of America (1996), Associate Professor—systematic theology, E-mail: m.c.hilkert.1@nd.edu

Jackson, Timothy D., PhD, Yale University (1984), 1999, Associate Professor—Christian ethics, E-mail: timothy.jackson.83@nd.edu

Johnson, Maxwell E., PhD, University of Notre Dame (1992), 1997, Associate Professor—liturgical studies, E-mail: maxwell.e.johnson.254@nd.edu

Krieg, Robert A., CSC, PhD, University of Notre Dame (1976), 1977, Professor—historical theology, systematic theology, 219-631-5129, E-mail: robert.a.krieg.1@nd.edu

Lahey, John, CSC, JCD, Catholic University of America (1988), 1984, P/T Assistant Professional Specialist—canon law, E-mail: john.f.lahey.3@nd.edu

Leyerle, S. Blake, PhD, Duke University (1991), 1990, Associate Professor—early Christianity, 219-631-7090, E-mail: blake.leyerle.1@nd.edu

Malkovsky, Bradley, PhD, University of Tübingen (1993), 1992, Assistant Professor—comparative theology, 219-631-7128, E-mail: bradley.j.malkovsky.1@nd.edu

Malloy, Edward A., CSC, PhD, Vanderbilt (1974), 1974, Professor and President—Christian ethics

McBrien, Richard P., STD, Pontifical Gregorian University (1967), 1980, Crowley-O'Brien-Walter Professor—systematic theology (ecclesiology), E-mail: richard.p.mcbrien.1@nd.edu

McCormick, Richard A., SJ, STD, Gregorian University (1957), 1986, John A. O'Brien Professor Emeritus—Christian ethics

Meier, John P., SSD, Biblical Institute, Rome (1976), 1998, Professor—New Testament, E-mail: john.p.meier.10@nd.edu

Melloh, John A., SM, PhD, University of St Louis (1974), 1978, Professional Specialist—liturgy and homiletics, E-mail: john.a.melloh.1@nd.edu

Mertensotto, Leon, CSC, STD, University of Fribourg (1961), 1961 Associate Professor—Christian ethics, E-mail: leon.j.mertensotto.1@nd.edu

Najman, Hindy, PhD, Harvard University (1998), 1998, Assistant Professor—Rabbinics, E-mail: hindy.najman.1@nd.edu

Neyrey, Jerome H., SJ, PhD, Yale University (1977), 1992, Professor—New Testament, 219-631-7469, E-mail: jerome.h.neyrey.1@nd.edu

O'Meara, Thomas F., OP, PhD, Ludwig-Maximillian University, Munich (1967), 1981, William K. Warren Professor—historical theology, systematic theology, E-mail: thomas.f.o'meara.1@nd.edu

O'Regan, Cyril J., PhD, Yale University (1989), 1999, Associate Professor—systematic theology, E-mail: cyril.j.o'regan.1@nd.edu

Page, Hugh R., Jr., PhD, Harvard University (1990), 1992, Associate Professor—Hebrew Bible, E-mail: hugh.r.page.6@nd.edu

Poorman, Mark, CSC, PhD, Graduate Theological Union (1990), 1990, Associate Professor—pastoral and moral theology, E-mail: mark.l.poorman.1@nd.edu

Porter, Jean, PhD, Yale University (1984), 1990, Professor—Christian ethics, E-mail: jean.porter.3@nd.edu

Ryan, Maura, PhD, Yale University (1992), 1993, Assistant Professor—Christian ethics, E-mail: maura.a.ryan.61@nd.edu

Signer, Michael A., PhD, University of Toronto (1978), 1992, Abrams Professor of Jewish Thought and Culture—Jewish studies, E-mail: michael.a.signer.1@nd.edu (on leave 1998-1999)

Sterling, Gregory E., PhD, Graduate Theological Union (1989), 1989, Associate Professor—New Testament, E-mail: gregory.e.sterling.1@nd.edu

Trembath, Kern R., PhD, University of Notre Dame (1984), 1991, Associate Professional Specialist and Assistant Chair—systematic theology, E-mail: kern.r.trembath.1@nd.edu

Ulrich, Eugene, PhD, Harvard University (1975), 1973, John A. O'Brien Professor—Old Testament, E-mail: eugene.c.ulrich.1@nd.edu (on leave spring 1999)

VanderKam, James C., PhD, Harvard University (1976), 1991, John A. O'Brien Professor—Hebrew Bible, E-mail: james.c.vanderkam.1@nd.edu

Wawrykow, Joseph P., PhD, Yale University (1987), 1986, Associate Professor—historical theology (medieval), E-mail: joseph.p.wawrykow.1@nd.edu (on leave 1998-1999)

White, James F., PhD, Duke University (1960), 1982, Professor—liturgy, E-mail: james.f.white.1@nd.edu (on leave spring 1999)

Whitmore, Todd D., PhD, University of Chicago (1990), 1990, Associate Professor—Christian ethics, E-mail: todd.d.whitmore.1@nd.edu

Zachman, Randall C., PhD, University of Chicago (1990), 1991, Associate Professor—Reformation theology, E-mail: randall.c.zachman.1@nd.edu

Notre Dame University

Nelson, British Columbia V1L 3C7 Canada

Notre Dame Graduate School of Christendom College

4407 Sano St　　　　　　　　　　　　　　　**Phone: 703-658-4304**
Alexandria VA 22312　　　　　　　　　　　 **Fax: 703-658-2318**

TYPE OF INSTITUTION: Public
EXECUTIVE OFFICER: Luther P. Niehoff, Administrative Director
GRADUATE ENROLLMENT: 80

Notre Dame Seminary and School of Theology

New Orleans LA 70118

Nyack College

Nyack NY 10960

Phone: 914-358-1710
Fax: 914-358-6429
E-mail: ruegsegr@nyack.com
URL: www.nyackcollege.edu

TYPE OF INSTITUTION: Private, Christian and Missionary Alliance
EXECUTIVE OFFICER: David Schroeder, President
CHAIRPERSON: Donal Nilsson
UNDERGRADUATE ENROLLMENT: 800

Oak Hills Christian College

1600 Oak Hills Rd SW
Bemidji MN 56601

Phone: 218-751-8670
Fax: 218-751-8825
URL: www.oakhills.edu

TYPE OF INSTITUTION: Private, Nondenominational
EXECUTIVE OFFICER: Thomas J. Bower, President
COORDINATOR: Gib Hoefakker
UNDERGRADUATE ENROLLMENT: 10

Oakland City College

Oakland City IN 47660

Oakwood College

Oakwood Rd NW, Huntsville AL 35896

Oberlin College

Religion Dept
10 N Professor St, Rice Hall
Oberlin OH 44074-1095

Phone: 440-775-8520
Fax: 440-775-8124
E-mail: brenda.snell@oberlin.edu
URL: www.oberlin.edu/~religion/

TYPE OF INSTITUTION: Private
EXECUTIVE OFFICER: Nancy Schrom Dye, President
CHAIRPERSON: James Dobbins
UNDERGRADUATE ENROLLMENT: 2,750
DEGREES OFFERED: BA
UNDERGRADUATE MAJORS: 72
DEGREES CONFERRED: 36

DESCRIPTION OF UNDERGRADUATE PROGRAM: The Department of Religion offers courses open to all students at introductory, intermediate, and advanced levels dealing with traditions and topics in the study of religion. The curriculum may serve as the focus of a liberal arts education for the general student and as pre-professional foundation for graduate study. The Major in Religion (27 hours) must include at least one course from four of the following areas offered by the Department: American Religious History; Christian History; East Asian Religions, Ethics; Hebrew and Christian Scriptures; Islam; Judaism; Modern Religion Thought; South Asian Religions. Students complete a concentration by taking additional courses, including an advanced seminar in one of these areas. An Honors Program in the major is available for qualified students. A number of cross-listed courses are offered with other programs, including African American Studies, Archeological Studies, Classics, Comparative Literature, East-Asian Studies, English, Judaic and Near Eastern Studies, Philosophy and Women's Studies.

FACULTY:

Dobbins, James, PhD, Yale University (1984), 1983, Professor—East Asian religions, Buddhism in China and Japan, Shin Buddhism, Taoism, 440-775-8533, E-mail: james.dobbins@oberlin.edu

Gibson, E. Leigh, PhD, Princeton University (1997), 1997, Assistant Professor—Hebrew scriptures, New Testament and Christian origins, social history of early Judaism and Christianity, Greco-Roman religions, 440-775-8531, E-mail: leigh.gibson@oberlin.edu

Kamitsuka, David, PhD, Yale University (1993), 1993, Associate Professor—modern religious thought, philosophy of religion, contemporary political theologies, 440-775-8475, E-mail: david.kamitsuka@oberlin.edu

Kamitsuka, Margaret D., MPhil, Yale University (1994); MA, Yale University (1990); 1996, Visiting Assistant Professor—feminist theology/religion and literature, 440-775-8201, E-mail: margaret.kamitsuka@oberlin.edu

Krassen, Miles, PhD, University of Pennsylvania (1990), 1992, Associate Professor—classical Judaism (Medieval to Modern), Hasidism, Jewish mysticism, 440-775-8521, E-mail: miles.krassen@oberlin.edu

McClure, Joyce Kloc, PhD, Yale University (1998), 1998, Assistant Professor—religious social ethics, 440-775-8534, E-mail: joyce.mcclure@oberlin.edu

Miller, Albert G., PhD, Princeton University (1994), 1991, Associate Professor—American religious history, African-American religion and experience, evangelicalism in America, African traditions, 440-775-8652, E-mail: albert.g.miller@oberlin.edu

Richman, Paula, PhD, University of Chicago (1983), 1985, Houck Professor—South Asian religions, religions of India, Hinduism, Tamil literature and traditions, 440-775-8532, E-mail: paula.richman@oberlin.edu

Zinn, Grover A., Jr., PhD, Duke University (1969), 1966, Danforth Professor—Christian history, medieval church and society, Christian mysticism and biblical literpretation, the Reformation, women and religious life in the Middle Ages, 440-775-8478, E-mail: grover.zinn@oberlin.edu

---

Oblate College

391 Michigan Ave, Washington DC 20017

Oblate School of Theology

285 Oblate Dr
San Antonio TX 78216-6693

Phone: 210-341-1366
Fax: 210-341-4519

TYPE OF INSTITUTION: Private, Roman Catholic
EXECUTIVE OFFICER: William Morell, President
UNDERGRADUATE ENROLLMENT: 18
GRADUATE ENROLLMENT: 118

Occidental College

1600 Campus Road
Los Angeles CA 90041

Phone: 213-259-2787
Fax: 213-341-4919
E-mail: naylor@oxy.edu
URL: www.oxy.edu

TYPE OF INSTITUTION: Private, Non-Denominational
EXECUTIVE OFFICER: John Slaughter, President
CHAIRPERSON: D. Keith Naylor
UNDERGRADUATE ENROLLMENT: 1,600

Oglethorpe College

Atlanta GA 30319

Ohio University

Dept of Philosophy
Ellis Hall, Rm 202
Athens OH 45701-2979

Phone: 740-593-4588
Fax: 740-593-4597
E-mail: phildept@ouvaxa.cats.ohiou.edu
URL: jupiter.phy.ohiouu.edu/
departments/philo

TYPE OF INSTITUTION: Public
EXECUTIVE OFFICER: Leslie Flemming, Dean, College of Arts and Sciences
CHAIRPERSON: Donald M. Borchert
UNDERGRADUATE ENROLLMENT: 15,950
GRADUATE ENROLLMENT: 2,900
DEGREES OFFERED: BA, MA
UNDERGRADUATE MAJORS: 50
DEGREES CONFERRED: 8
DESCRIPTION OF UNDERGRADUATE PROGRAM: Undergraduate major in philosophy requires a minimum of 40 quarter hours of courses including one each in ancient Greek thought, modern philosophy, and symbolic logic. Elective courses may include biblical literature, history of religions, and theoretical studies of religion. Minor in philosophy consists of 25 quarter hours of courses and can be entirely in religion studies.
GRADUATE PROGRAM
Graduate Advisor: John Bender
Graduate Degrees Offered: MA
Degrees Conferred: 5 MA
Graduate Students in Residence: 17 MA
Not in Residence: 3 MA
Average No. of New Students Enrolled: 15 MA
Women Students: 7 MA
Minority Students: 0 MA
Foreign Students: 1 MA

Minimum GRE Score Requisite to Admission: No

Minimum GPA Score Requisite to Admission: Yes, 3.0 on 4.0 scale

Foreign Language Proficiency Evaluated: Yes

Financial Aid to First Year Students: 50% MA

Financial Aid to Other Students: 75% MA

Attrition Among Students: 10% MA

Graduates Placed: 50% MA

DESCRIPTION OF GRADUATE PROGRAM AND RESEARCH FACILITIES: MA degree requires at least 45 quarter hours including five courses in history and subfields of Western philosophy. Elective courses and research may focus on studies of religious materials. Degree is completed by thesis.

ACADEMIC PLAN, ADMISSION REQUIREMENTS, FINANCIAL AID: Classes begin early September and end in June, plus two summer sessions and no classes in December. Studies in any Philosophy Department program can begin in any quarter. For graduate study, applicants must submit undergraduate transcripts, GRE scores, a writing sample, and three letters of reference. For unconditional admission a student must have achieved at least a 3.0 GPA on 4.0 scale.

FACULTY:

Bender, John, PhD, Harvard (1978), 1985, Professor and Graduate Chair—epistemology, aesthetics, 740-593-4599, Fax: 740-593-4597, E-mail: jbender1@ohiou.edu

Blocker, Gene, PhD, Berkeley (1966), 1972, Professor Emeritus—aesthetics, African and Chinese thought, 740-593-4641, Fax: 740-593-4597, E-mail: gblocker1@ohiou.edu

Borchert, Donald M., PhD, Princeton Theological Seminary (1966), 1967, Professor and Chair—Marxism, ethics, philosophy of religion, 740-593-4590, Fax: 740-593-4597, E-mail: dborchert1@ohiou.edu

Butrick, Richard, PhD, Columbia (1966), 1967, Professor Emeritus—logic, 740-593-4588, Fax: 740-593-4597, E-mail: butrick@ohiou.edu

Carson, Donald Scott, PhD, Duke (1996), 1996, Assistant Professor—ancient Greek, 740-593-0923, Fax: 740-593-4597, E-mail: cordond@ohiou.edu

Collins, Elizabeth, PhD, Berkeley (1991), 1991, Assistant Professor—culture theory, Hinduism, Buddhism, 740-593-0392, Fax: 740-593-4597, E-mail: ecollins1@ohiou.edu

Ehrlich, Philip, PhD, University of Illinois, Chicago (1979), 1993, Associate Professor—logic, philosophy of science, philosophy of math, 740-593-4595, Fax: 740-593-4597, E-mail: ehrlich@ohiou.edu

Lebar, Mark, PhD, Arizona (1999), 1999, Assistant Professor—ethics, E-mail: lebar@ohiou.edu

Mickunas, Algis, PhD, Emory (1969), 1974, Professor Emeritus—phenomenology, contemporary European philosophy, 740-593-4643, Fax: 740-593-4597, E-mail: mickunaa@ohiou.edu

Mosley, Albert G., PhD, Wisconsin (1967), 1990, Professor—ethics, philosophy of science, African philosophy, philosophy of racism, 740-593-4640, Fax: 740-593-4597, E-mail: amosley1@ohiou.edu

Petrik, James, PhD, Marquette (1992), 1992, Associate Professor—modern philosophy, 740-593-4593, Fax: 740-593-4597, E-mail: j petrik1@ohiou.edu

Ping, Charles, PhD, Duke (1961), 1975, President Emeritus of Ohio University and Professor of Philosophy—19th century philosophy, 740-593-4588, Fax: 740-593-4597, E-mail: ping@ohiou.edu

Trevas, Robert, PhD, Maryland (1970), 1968, Professor Emeritus—ethics, philosophy of sex and love, 740-593-4588, Fax: 740-593-4597, E-mail: trevas@ohiou.edu

Vatter, Miguel, PhD, New School for Social Research (1998), 1998, Assistant Professor—social and political philosophy, 740-593-4588, Fax: 740-593-4597

Weckman, George, PhD, Chicago (1969), 1968, Associate Professor, Assistant Chair—history of religions, 740-593-4594, Fax: 740-593-4597, E-mail: gweckman1@ohiou.edu

Zucker, Arthur, PhD, Minnesota (1990), 1985, Associate Professor and Director, Institute for Applied and Professional Ethics—ethics, philosophy of science, 740-593-4596, Fax: 740-593-4597, E-mail: azucker1@ohiou.edu

Ohio Dominican College

1216 Sunbury Rd
Columbus OH 43219

Phone: 614-253-2741
Fax: 614-252-0776
E-mail: finanb@odc.edu
URL: www.odc.edu

TYPE OF INSTITUTION: Private, Roman Catholic

EXECUTIVE OFFICER: Sr. Mary Andrew Matesich, OP, President

CHAIRPERSON: Barbara Finan

UNDERGRADUATE ENROLLMENT: 1,977

DEGREES OFFERED: AA, BA

UNDERGRADUATE MAJORS: 28

DEGREES CONFERRED: 7 BA

DESCRIPTION OF UNDERGRADUATE PROGRAM: Theology at Ohio Dominican College is done from within the context of the Roman Catholic tradition; however, members of other faith communities as well as non-believers can find meaning and personal enrichment through the academic study of theology at Ohio Dominican. The degree programs offered in theology can help to prepare students for a number of professional, ministerial, or educational opportunities—pastoral care positions, religion teachers and campus ministers, graduate studies, ordained ministry.

FACULTY:

Fatula, Mary Ann, OP, PhD, Catholic University of America (1981), 1974, Professor—systematic theology, 614-251-4795, Fax: 614-252-0776, E-mail: fatulam@odc.edu

Finan, Barbara, PhD, Marquette University (1986), 1979, Professor—systematic theology, 614-251-4721, Fax: 614-252-0776, E-mail: finanb@odc.edu

Madden, Leo, PhD, Pontifical Gregorian University (1999), 1991, Assistant Professor—biblical theology, 614-251-4720, Fax: 614-252-0776, E-mail: maddenl@odc.edu

Ohio Northern University

Dept of Philosophy and Religion
Ada OH 45810

Phone: 419-772-2195
Fax: 419-772-2467
URL: www.onu.edu/A+S/philosophy

TYPE OF INSTITUTION: Private, United Methodist

EXECUTIVE OFFICER: DeBow Freed, President

CHAIRPERSON: Raymond F. Person, Jr.

UNDERGRADUATE ENROLLMENT: 9

The Ohio State University

Division of Comparative Studies   Phone: 614-292-2559
308 Dulles Hall/230 W 17th Ave   Fax: 614-292-6707
Columbus OH 43210-1311
TYPE OF INSTITUTION: Public
EXECUTIVE OFFICER: Kermit Hall, Dean College of Humanities
COORDINATOR: Lindsay Jones
UNDERGRADUATE ENROLLMENT: 40,800

Ohio Valley College

4501 College Parkway   Phone: 304-485-7384, ext 140
Parkersburg WV 26101   Fax: 304-485-3106
     E-mail: bible@ovc.edu
     URL: www.ovc.edu

TYPE OF INSTITUTION: Private, Church of Christ
COORDINATOR: Robert J. Young
UNDERGRADUATE ENROLLMENT: 50

Ohio Wesleyan University

Delaware OH 43015

Talmudical Seminary of Oholei Torah

667 Eastern Pkwy, Brooklyn NY 11213

Ohr Hameir Theological Seminary

Box 2130, Peekskill NY 10566

Ohr Somayach Institutions

PO Box 334, Monsey NY 10952

University of Oklahoma at Norman

401 West Brooks St, Norman OK 73069

Oklahoma Baptist University

500 West University
Shawnee OK 74804-2590

Phone: 405-878-2377
Fax: 405-878-2378
E-mail: dick_rader@mail.okbu.edu
URL: www.okbu.edu

TYPE OF INSTITUTION: Private, Southern Baptist

EXECUTIVE OFFICER: Dick Rader, Dean School of Christian Service, Vice-President for Religious Life

UNDERGRADUATE ENROLLMENT: 2,171

GRADUATE ENROLLMENT: 23

DEGREES OFFERED: AA, BA

UNDERGRADUATE MAJORS: 260

DEGREES CONFERRED: 68

DESCRIPTION OF UNDERGRADUATE PROGRAM: The Joe L. Ingram School of Christian Service is composed of the Religion, Philosophy and Applied Ministry departments. The school provides basic instruction in philosophy and religion for the liberal arts curriculum and a full range of major concentrations specifically designed for persons preparing for Christian vocations and further study in Christian ministry.

GRADUATE PROGRAM

Graduate Advisor: Oscar Jeske

Graduate Degrees Offered: MA in Marriage and Family Therapy

Degrees Conferred: 10 MA

FACULTY:

Clarke, Robert Earl, ThD, Southwestern Baptist Theological Seminary (1965), 1968, Professor—philosophy and history of religion, 405-878-2222, Fax: 405-878-2233

Dawson, Robert A., PhD, Southwestern Baptist Theological Seminary (1982), 1985, Associate Professor—religious education and church administration, 405-878-2228, Fax: 405-878-2233, E-mail: robert_dawson@mail.okbu.edu

Hall, Kevin, PhD, Southwestern Baptist Theological Seminary (1993), 1994, Assistant Professor—Hebrew and biblical studies, 405-878-2218, Fax: 405-878-2233, E-mail: kevin_hall@mail.okbu.edu

Kelly, Bobby J., PhD, Southwestern Baptist Theological Seminary (1998), 1997, Assistant Professor—Greek and biblical studies, 405-878-2213, Fax: 405-878-2233, E-mail: bobby_kelly@mail.okbu.edu

McWilliams, Warren L., PhD, Vanderbilt (1974), 1976, Professor—theology and biblical studies, 405-878-2231, Fax: 405-878-2233, E-mail: warren_mcwilliams@mail.okbu.edu

Rader, Dick A., PhD, Southwestern Baptist Theological Seminary (1980), 1979, Professor—Christian ethics and missions, 405-878-2377, Fax: 405-878-2378, E-mail: dick_rader@mail.okbu.edu

Roark, C. Mack, DMin, Southwestern Baptist Theological Seminary (1977), 1984, Professor—Greek and biblical studies, 405-878-2232, Fax: 405-878-2233, E-mail: mack_roark@mail.okbu.edu

Wester, Donald Gray, PhD, University of Oklahoma (1979), 1968, Professor—philosophy, 405-878-2217, Fax: 405-878-2233, E-mail: don_wester@mail.okbu.edu

Wilks, Thomas M., DMin, Southern Baptist Theological Seminary (1977), 1984, Professor—in-service guidance and youth ministry, 405-878-2239, Fax: 405-878-2233, E-mail: tom_wilks@mail.okbu.edu

Yarbrough, Slayden A., PhD, Baylor University (1972), 1979, Professor—Christian history, 405-878-2227, Fax: 405-878-2233, E-mail: slayden_yarbrough@mail.okbu.edu

---

University of Oklahoma Christian Science and Art

Box 11000, Oklahoma City OK 73136-1100

Oklahoma City University

Wimberly School of Religion
2501 N Blackwelder
Oklahoma City OK 73106

Phone: 405-521-5284
Fax: 405-557-6046
E-mail: dgemler@.okcu.edu
URL: www.okcu.edu

TYPE OF INSTITUTION: Denominational: United Methodist

EXECUTIVE OFFICER: Stephen Jennings, President

DEAN: Donald G. Emler

UNDERGRADUATE ENROLLMENT: 2,000

GRADUATE ENROLLMENT: 2,400

DEGREES OFFERED: BA, MAR, MRE

UNDERGRADUATE MAJORS: 60

DEGREES CONFERRED: 16

DESCRIPTION OF UNDERGRADUATE PROGRAM: The School of Religion offers a BA with majors in religion, religion with an emphasis in religious education, and religion/philosophy. It provides courses for the University's foundation curriculum in the area of shared beliefs and values. A religion major consists of 30-36 hours, including two foundational courses, with a maximum of 42 hours. At least 15 hours must be in upper division courses and include one or more courses in the areas of Bible, church history, culture and ethics, and theology. A senior research paper is required. Internships are encouraged in the junior and senior year. A BA with an emphasis in church/sacred music is available through the OCU Petri School of Music and Performing Arts. The School of Religion cooperates with the Jewish Chautauqua Society to provide a course in Jewish studies each semester.

GRADUATE PROGRAM

Graduate Degrees Offered: MA; MRE

Degrees Conferred: 1 MAR

Graduate Students in Residence: 8 MA; 3 MRE

Average No. of New Students Enrolled: 2 MA; 1 MRE

Minority Students: 2 MA; 0 MRE

Foreign Students: 1 MA; 1 MRE

Minimum GRE Score Requisite to Admission: No

Minimum GPA Score Requisite to Admission: Yes, 2.5 on 4.0 scale

Financial Aid to First Year Students: 80% MA; 100% MRE

Financial Aid to Other Students: 80% MA; 100% MRE

Attrition Among Students: 25% MA

Graduates Placed: 100% MRE

DESCRIPTION OF GRADUATE PROGRAM AND RESEARCH FACILITIES: The Wimberly School of Religion is committed to the preparation of lay leadership for the church. The MRE degree is a professional degree for those who want to prepare for service in the church as a director of education, program director, and other ministries related to religious education. Studies involve examination of major sources of biblical theological, historical, ethical, and cultural studies. The MRE relates the theoretical to the practical. The degree normally coveres four to six semesters. The MAR requires 36 hours including a thesis. The MRE requires 59 hours. Research facilities include the William and Romayne Baily Library Collection, sustained by a permanent endowment. The archives of the Oklahoma Conference of the United Methodist Church are on the campus, as is a a collection of church school curriculum resources from different denominations.

ACADEMIC PLAN, ADMISSION REQUIREMENTS, FINANCIAL AID: Applicants should have a bachelor's degree from an accredited college or university, with at least a 2.5 grade point average. Undergraduate work in religion, humanities, and social sciences is recommended. Students who have an undergraduate major in Christian from schools recognized by the United Methodist Division of Diaconal Ministry may petition to take advanced studies in related courses upon recommendation by the Dean of the School of Religion. Financial aid and scholarships are available for United Methodist church professionals. One graduate assistanceship for a new student is available each year.

FULL-TIME FACULTY:

Dykes, Donna, PhD, Vanderbilt University, 1983, Professor/Professor of Hebrew Bible—biblical studies and theology, E-mail ddykes@okcu.edu

Emler, Donald G., EdD, Indiana University, 1989, Dean and Wimberly Professor of Christian Thought—Christian education, E-mail: dgemler@okcu.edu

Oden, Amy, PhD, Southern Methodist University, 1992, Associate Professor—church history, E-mail: aoden@okcu.edu

Starkey, John, PhD, Boston University, 1998, Assistant Professor—theology and New Testament, E-mail: jstarkey@okcu.edu

REGULAR ADJUNCT FACULTY:

Auxier, Randal, PhD, Emory University, 1992, Associate Professor—philosophy

Davies, Mark, MDiv, Candler School of Theology, 1996, Assistant Professor—philosophy, ethics

Packman, David, BHL, MA, Hebrew Union, 1977, Resident faculty under sponsorship of the Jewish Chautauqua Society—Judaism

Rusco, John, DMin, St Paul School of Thelogy, 1994, Dean of Chapel—internships

---

Oklahoma Mission Baptist College

PO Box 71, Marlow OK 73055

Oklahoma State University

226 Hanner **Phone: 405-744-6090**
Stillwater OK 74078-5064 **Fax: 405-744-4635**

TYPE OF INSTITUTION: Public

EXECUTIVE OFFICER: Bruce Crauder, Interim Dean of Arts and Sciences

CHAIRPERSON: Bruce Crauder

COORDINATOR: Bill Ivy

Old Dominion University

Dept of Philosophy and Religious Studies
BAL 401
Norfolk VA 23529-0083

Phone: 757-683-3861
Fax: 757-683-5345
URL: www.odu.edu

TYPE OF INSTITUTION: Public
EXECUTIVE OFFICER: James Koch, President
CHAIRPERSON: Lawrence J. Hatab

Olivet College

Olivet MI 49076

Olivet Nazarene University

Division of Religion and Philosophy
Kankakee IL 60901

Phone: 815-939-5264
Fax: 815-935-4992
URL: www.olivet.edu

TYPE OF INSTITUTION: Private, Church of the Nazarene
EXECUTIVE OFFICER: John C. Bowling, President
CHAIRPERSON: Robert Branson
DEGREES OFFERED: BA, BS
UNDERGRADUATE MAJORS: 120
DEGREES CONFERRED: 20
DESCRIPTION OF UNDERGRADUATE PROGRAM: The primary objective of the Division of Religion and Philosophy of Olivet Nazarene University is to educate for ministry within the Wesleyan-Arminian tradition (primarily within the Church of the Nazarene, the university's sponsoring institution), thus preparing clergy and laity for service to the church and the community and facilitating their personal spiritual development. The division offers 6 majors: religious studies, biblical studies, philosophy and religion, religion (Christian ministry), youth ministry, and Christian education. In addition, the division offers 6 minors: religion, biblical studies, philosophy, youth ministry, and Christian education.
GRADUATE PROGRAM
Graduate Advisor: Richard Thompson
Graduate Degrees Offered: MA
Degrees Conferred: 2 MA
Graduate Students in Residence: 15 MA
Not in Residence: 5 MA
Average No. of New Students Enrolled: 10 MA
Women Students: 3 MA
Minority Students: 2 MA
Foreign Students: 1 MA
Minimum GRE Score Requisite to Admission: No.

Minimum GPA Score Requisite to Admission: Yes, 2.5 on a 4.0 scale

Foreign Language Proficiency Evaluated: No.

Financial Aid to First Year Students: 30% MA

Financial Aid to Other Students: 10% MA

DESCRIPTION OF GRADUATE PROGRAM AND RESEARCH FACILITIES: The Master of Arts in Religion degree program offers the student advanced study in the areas of theology (systematic, philosophical, and historical) and biblical studies with the opportunity to concentrate in either area. The program offers the student the opportunity to develop spiritually and intellectually for the Christian ministry and for additional graduate work. Requirements for the program include 30 semester hours of graduate-level work in religion and a cumulative grade point average of 3.0 (based on a 4.0 grading system). Each course meets one afternoon or evening each week and are generally seminar-style in format.

ACADEMIC PLAN, ADMISSION REQUIREMENTS, FINANCIAL AID: The admission requirements are: an undergraduate degree from a regionally accredited college/university, a grade point average of 2.5 (based on a 4.0 grading system), a minimum of 15 junior or senior level courses in religion, and 3 recommendations. A limited number of scholarships are available to those who have been accepted into the program by March 15 prior to beginning the program.

FACULTY: DIVISION OF RELIGION AND PHILOSOPHY

Branson, Robert, PhD, Boston University (1976), 1992, Professor of Biblical Literature, Head, Division of Religion and Philosophy—Old Testament, 815-939-5190, Fax: 815-935-4992, E-mail: rbranson@olivet.edu

Bray, William H., DMin, Phillips University Graduate Seminary (1985), 1994, Chaplain to the University—preaching, pastoral counseling, 815-939-5236, E-mail: bbray@olivet.odu

Dalton, Ron, DMin, Vanderbilt University (1984), 1993, Associate Professor of Christian Ministry—Christian ministry, 815-939-5262, Fax: 815-935-4992, E-mail: rdalton@olivet.edu

Keen, Craig, PhD, Claremont Graduate School (1985), 1994, Professor of Theology—systematic and philosophical theology, philosophy, 815-939-5268, Fax: 815-935-4992, E-mail: ckeen@olivet.edu

Lovett, Russell, MDiv, Nazarene Theological Seminary (1977), 1992, Associate Professor of Biblical Literature—New Testament (Pauline letters), missions, 815-939-5279, Fax: 815-935-4992, E-mail: rlovett@olivet.edu

Murphy, Larry, PhD, Southern Baptist Theological Seminary (1988), 1992, Associate Professor of Biblical Literature—New Testament, 815-939-5269, Fax: 815-935-4992, E-mail: lmurphy@olivet.edu

Smith, Robert D., PhD, Baylor University (1981), 1982, Professor of Theology—history of Christianity, 815-939-5263, Fax: 815-935-4992, E-mail: rdsmith@olivet.edu

Thompson, Richard P., PhD, Southern Methodist University (1996), 1994, Associate Professor of Biblical Literature, Coordinator, MA in Religion Program—New Testament (Luke-Acts, synoptic gospels), literary criticism, 815-939-5270, Fax: 815-935-4992, E-mail: rthom@olivet.edu

Wine, David, MA, The Ohio State University (1977), 1995, Assistant Professor of Christian Education—Christian education. youth ministry, 815-939-5254, Fax: 815-935-4992, E-mail: dwine@olivet.edu

FACULTY: MASTER OF ARTS IN RELIGION PROGRAM

Branson, Robert, PhD, Boston University (1976), 1992, Professor of Biblical Literature, Head, Division of Religion and Philosophy—Old Testament, 815-939-5190, Fax: 815-935-4992, E-mail: rbranson@olivet.edu

Keen, Craig, PhD, Claremont Graduate School (1985), 1994, Professor of Theology—systematic and philosophical tieology, philosophy, 815-939-5268, Fax: 815-935-4992, E-mail: ckeen@olivet.edu

Murphy, Larry, PhD, Southern Baptist Theological Seminary (1988), 1992, Associate Professor of Biblical Literature—New Testament, 815-939-5269, Fax: 815-935-4992, E-mail: lmurphy@olivet.edu

Smith, Robert D., PhD, Baylor University (1981), 1982, Professor of Theology—history of Christianity, 815-939-5263, Fax: 815-935-4992, E-mail: rdsmith@olivet.edu

Thompson, Richard P., PhD, Southern Methodist University (1996), 1994, Associate Professor of Biblical Literature, Coordinator, MA in Religion Program—New Testament (Luke-Acts, synoptic gospels), literary criticism, 815-939-5270, Fax: 815-935-4992, E-mail: rthom@olivet.edu

Oral Roberts University

7777 S Lewis Ave   Phone: 918-495-6096
Tulsa OK 74171   Fax: 918-495-6033

TYPE OF INSTITUTION: Private, Non-Denominational
EXECUTIVE OFFICER: Paul G. Chappell, Dean
CHAIRPERSON: Kenneth Mayton
UNDERGRADUATE ENROLLMENT: 350
GRADUATE ENROLLMENT: 640

University of Oregon

Religious Studies Department   Phone: 541-346-4971
1294 University of Oregon   Fax: 541-346-2220
Eugene OR 97403-1294
TYPE OF INSTITUTION: Public
EXECUTIVE OFFICER: Joe Stone, Dean College of Arts and Science
CHAIRPERSON: Andrew Edmund Goble
UNDERGRADUATE ENROLLMENT: 13,300
GRADUATE ENROLLMENT: 3,300
DEGREES OFFERED: BA, BS
UNDERGRADUATE MAJORS: 27
DEGREES CONFERRED: 25

DESCRIPTION OF UNDERGRADUATE PROGRAM: The Department is a regular department within the College of Arts and Sciences and has been so since it was established in 1934. The study of religion at the University of Oregon involves a study of the history and philosophy of religions. Courses examine the origins, sacred texts, rituals and practices, beliefs, and subgroups of the world's major religions. The courses offered are intended to provide a broad understanding of the nature and role of religion in the world's different cultures, both present and past, for students in all fields, as well as integrated programs for majors in religious studies. Certain courses in other departments—such as Anthropology and History—are included in the major program.

FACULTY:

Earl, James W., PhD, Cornell (1971), 1987, Professor—Anglo-Saxon literature, 541-346-3960, Fax: 541-346-1509

Falk, Daniel K., PhD, University of Cambridge (1996), 1998, Assistant Professor—biblical studies, 541-346-4980, Fax: 541-346-2220

Goble, Andrew E., PhD, Stanford (1987), 1990, Associate Professor—premodern Japan, East Asia, 541-346-4800, Fax: 541-346-2220

Goldman, Marion Sherman, PhD, Chicago (1977), 1973, Professor—deviance, gender, new religious movements, 541-346-5167

Johnson, Benton, PhD, Harvard (1954), 1954, Professor Emeritus—sociology of religion, theory, 541-346-5009, Fax: 541-346-2220

Kim, Hee-Jin, PhD, Claremont Graduate School (1966), 1973, Professor Emeritus—Asian religions

Liberman, Kenneth B., PhD, University of California, San Diego (1981), 1983, Associate Professor—Tibetan Buddhism, yoga, 541-346-5008

Maddex, Jack P., PhD, North Carolina (1966), 1966, Professor—United States, Civil War, 541-346-4829

Reis, Elizabeth, PhD, University of California, Berkeley (1991), 1990, Adjunct Assistant Professor—early American, women's history, 541-346-5904, Fax: 541-346-4895

Rondeau, Jennifer, PhD, Cornell (1988), 1993, Assistant Professor—Italian Renaissance, 541-346-4821

Sanders, Jack T., PhD, Claremont Graduate School (1963), 1969, Professor Emeritus—biblical studies, 541-346-4997, Fax: 541-346-2220

Sherman, Sharon R., PhD, Indiana (1978), 1976, Professor—folklore, myth, 541-346-3966

Tokuno, Kyoko, PhD, University of California, Berkeley (1994), 1992, Assistant Professor—Asian religions, 541-346-4973, Fax: 541-346-2220

Weiss, Anita, PhD, University of California, Berkeley (1983), 1987, Associate Professor—South Asia, comparative Muslim societies, women in development, 541-346-3245

Wixman, Ronald, PhD, Chicago (1978), 1975, Professor—eastern Europe, former Soviet Union, cultural geography, 541-346-4568, Fax: 541-346-2067

Wojcik, Daniel, PhD, University of California, Los Angeles (1992), 1991, Professor—folklore, 541-346-3946

Ottawa University

2340 W Mission Ln, Phoenix AZ 85021

Ottawa University

1001 S Cedar
Ottawa KS 66067

Phone: 785-242-5000, ext 5472
Fax: 785-242-7429
E-mail: discher@ott.edu

TYPE OF INSTITUTION: Private, Non-Denominational
CHAIRPERSON: Mark R. Discher
UNDERGRADUATE ENROLLMENT: 500

Ottawa University at Kansas City

10865 Grandview Ste. 2000, Overland Park KS 66210

University of Ottawa

Classics and Religious Studies Department
70 Laurier Ave East
Ottawa, Ontario K1N 6N5 Canada

Phone: 613-562-5714
Fax: 613-562-5991
E-mail: cla-srs@uottawa.ca

TYPE OF INSTITUTION: Public

EXECUTIVE OFFICER: Peter Beyer, Director

UNDERGRADUATE ENROLLMENT: 5,800

GRADUATE ENROLLMENT: 3,700

DEGREES OFFERED: BA Honors Concentration, MA, PhD

UNDERGRADUATE MAJORS: 55

DEGREES CONFERRED: 21

DESCRIPTION OF UNDERGRADUATE PROGRAM: For the BA with Concentration or Honors in religious studies, the Department offers courses in English and in French, in the scientific study of the religious phenomenon: Doctrines, Institutions, Rituals, Religious Experience, Ethics, Symbolism, etc. The program deals with a variety of religious traditions and uses mainly historical, sociological, anthropological and psychological methods. No one tradition is regarded as normative.

GRADUATE PROGRAM

Graduate Degrees Offered: MA; PhD

Degrees Conferred: 2 MA; 6 PhD

Graduate Students in Residence: 6 MA; 24 PhD

Not in Residence: 1 MA; 12 PhD

DESCRIPTION OF GRADUATE PROGRAM: The programs leading to the MA or PhD in religious studies are also offered in English and in French, and take likewise the non-confessional normative approach. Using the above mentioned methods, the MA student can concentrate in the following areas: History of Religions; Psychology of Religion; Sociology of Religion; Early Christianity; Modern Christianity; Contemporary Christian Literature; Religion in Canada; Judaism; Samaritanism; Amerindian Religions; Women and Religion. The PhD student can concentrate in religions in comparative cultural context (contemporary and Late Roman Empire periods), Canadian Religion including Amerindian and Inuit Religions.

ACADEMIC PLAN, ADMISSION REQUIREMENTS, FINANCIAL AID: The Department offers a MA in religious studies with or without thesis. It consists of 18 or 27 credits respectively, and a comprehensive examination. For the PhD in religious studies the writing of a thesis is obligatory. Before being admitted to the MA program, candidates without a BA Honors in religious studies have to complete a qualifying year in which they have to fulfill the requirements of the Honors degree. To be admitted to the PhD program, candidates must have an MA in religious studies or the equivalent, conferred by a recognized university. Apart from Social Sciences and Humanities Research Council of Canada Fellowships, Ontario Graduate Scholarship program, and University of Ottawa Entrance Fellowships, students can obtain research and teaching assistantships in the Department. The Department holds two research centres: the Canadian Centre for Research on Women and Religion and the Research Centre for the Study of Religion.

FACULTY:

Beyer, Peter F., PhD, Toronto (1981), 1995, Associate Professor—sociologie de la religion/sociology of religion

Choquette, Robert, PhD, Chicago (1972), 1966, Professor—histoire religieuse canadienne/Canadian religious history

Dourley, John P., PhD, Fordham (1971), 1989, Adjunct—contemporary Christian thought, psychology of religion

Goldenberg, Naomi, PhD, Yale (1976), 1977, Full Professor—psychology of religion/psychologie de la religion, women and religion

Guédon, Marie-Françoise, PhD, Bryn Mawr (1972), 1989, Associate Professor—anthropolgie de la religion/anthropology of religion, études amérindiennes/native Indian and Inuit studies, chamanisme/shamanism

Kazmierski, Carl, DTh, Würzburg (1977), 1967, Associate Professor—New Testament, early Christianity

Piovanelli, Pierluigi, PhD, Turin (1991), 1999, Assistant Professor—Christianisme des origines/Early Christianity, Judaïsme ancien/Ancient Judaism, Christianisme de l'Éthiopien/Ethiopian Christianity

Pummer, Reinhard, DTh, Vienna (1965), 1967, Full Professor—history of religions, Judaism, Samaritanism

Tissot, Georges, PhD, Montreal (1978), 1964, Associate Professor—histoire des religions, religions amérindiennes/history of religions, Amerindian religions.

Otterbein College
Westerville OH 43081

Ouachita Baptist University

School of Christian Studies   **Phone: 870-245-5599**
Box 3787   **Fax: 870-245-5517**
Arkadelphia AR 71998-0001   **E-mail: admissions@alpha.obu.edu**
     URL: www.obu.edu

TYPE OF INSTITUTION: Private, Baptist

EXECUTIVE OFFICER: Andrew Westmoreland, President

CHAIRPERSON: J. Scott Duvall, Dean

UNDERGRADUATE ENROLLMENT: 1,604

DEGREES OFFERED: Biblical Studies/General, Biblical Studies/Language, Biblical Studies/Theology; Ministry/Pastoral, Ministry/Christian Education, Ministry/Youth, Ministry/Family Life Christian Counseling, Ministry/Missions and Cross Cultural Studies

UNDERGRADUATE MAJORS: 200

DEGREES CONFERRED: 49

DESCRIPTION OF UNDERGRADUATE PROGRAM: Ouachita Baptist University is a Southern Baptist church related liberal arts university known for its academic standard and Christian environment. The School of Christian Studies has three departments within the school: Biblical Studies & Theology, Christian Ministries, and Philosophy & Ethics. The School offers eight degree patterns with a distinguished history of combining academic and Christian excellence in preparation for ministry. Christian Studies students may participate in the Israel

Study Program at Hebrew University of Jerusalem for ten weeks during the summer. Ouachita also has a correlated education program with certain seminaries.

FACULTY:

Carter, Terry G., PhD, Southwestern Baptist Theological Seminary (1977), 1991, Associate Professor of Christian Ministries, Chair of the Department of Christian Ministries and Holder of the W. O. Vaught Chair, 870-245-5147, Fax: 870-245-5517, E-mail: carter@alpha.obu.edu

Duvall, J. Scott, PhD, Southwestern Baptist Theological Seminary (1984), 1989, Dean of the School of Christian Studies and J. C. and Mae Fuller Professor of Biblical Studies & Theology, 870-245-5520, Fax: 870-245-5517, E-mail: duvall@alpha.obu.edu

Elrod, Ben M., ThD, EdD, Southwestern Baptist Theological Seminary (1956), 1988, Chancellor of the University and Professor of Biblical Studies & Theology, 870-245-5410, Fax: 870-245-5500, E-mail: elrodb@alpha.obu.edu

Eubanks, Byron, PhD, University of Arkansas (1997), 1987, Associate Professor and Chair of the Department of Philosophy & Ethics, 870-245-5521, Fax: 870-245-5517, E-mail: eubanks@alpha.obu.edu

Hays, John Daniel, PhD, Southwestern Baptist Theological Seminary (1992), 1992, Associate Professor and Chair of the Department of Biblical Studies & Theology, 870-245-5526, Fax: 870-245-5517, E-mail: hays@alpha.obu.edu

Mwase, Isaac, PhD, Southwestern Baptist Theological Seminary (1993), 1994, Assistant Professor of Philosophy & Ethics, 870-245-5523, Fax: 870-245-5517, E-mail: mwase@alpha.obu.edu

Richards, E. Randolph, PhD, Southwestern Baptist Theological Seminary (1988), 1999, Associate Professor of Biblical Studies & Theology, 870-245-5527, Fax: 870-245-5517, E-mail: richardsr@alpha.obu.edu

Tucker, W. Dennis, Jr., PhD, Southern Baptist Theological Seminary (1997), 1997, Assistant Professor of Biblical Studies & Theology, Director of Academic Skills Development, and Director of External Programs, 870-245-5199, Fax: 870-245-5000, E-mail: tuckerd@alpha.obu.edu

Vang, Preben, PhD, Southwestern Baptist Theological Seminary `ÿ1994`ℕ97, Associate Professor of Biblical Studies & Theology, 870-245-5114, Fax: 870-245-5517, E-mail: vangp@alpha.obu.edu

Viser, William C., PhD, Southwestern Baptist Theological Seminary (1978), 1988, Associate Professor of Christian Ministries, 870-245-5524, Fax: 870-245-5517, E-mail: viser@alpha.obu.edu

---

College of Our Lady of the Elm

291 Springfield Street
Chicopee MA 01013

Phone: 413-594-2761
Fax: 413-592-4871
E-mail: pionm@elms.edu

TYPE OF INSTITUTION: Denominational: Catholic

EXECUTIVE OFFICER: Kathleen Kirley, SSJ, Dean of Graduate Studies

CHAIRPERSON: Eleanor Dooley, SSJ

COORDINATOR: Martin Pion

UNDERGRADUATE ENROLLMENT: 10

GRADUATE ENROLLMENT: 25

Our Lady of Holy Cross College
4123 Woodlawn Dr, New Orleans LA 70131

Our Lady of the Lake University
Dept of Religious Studies, San Antonio TX 78285

Oxford College of Emory University
Oxford GA 30267

Ozark Bible Institute
PO Box 398, Neosho MO 64850

Ozark Christian College
1111 N Main St   Phone: 417-624-2518
Joplin MO 64801   Fax: 417-624-0090
      E-mail: ozarkcc@aol.com

TYPE OF INSTITUTION: Private, Christian Churches/Churches of Christ
EXECUTIVE OFFICER: Ken Idleman, President
UNDERGRADUATE ENROLLMENT: 660

College of the Ozarks
Point Lookout MO 65726   Phone: 417-334-6411

TYPE OF INSTITUTION: Private, Presbyterian founding; many Protestant, R.C., et al
EXECUTIVE OFFICER: Kenton C. Olson, Dean of the College
CHAIRPERSON: Courtney Furman, Humanities Division, Dept of Philosophy and Religion
UNDERGRADUATE ENROLLMENT: 1,500

University of the Ozarks
415 College Ave, Clarksville AR 72830

O

Pace University of New York

41 Park Row, Room 310
New York City NY 10038

Phone: 212-346-1453
Fax: 212-346-1113
E-mail: tosullivan@pace.edu

TYPE OF INSTITUTION: Private
EXECUTIVE OFFICER: Gail Dinter-Gottlieb, Dean of Dyson College
CHAIRPERSON: Thomas D. O'Sullivan

Pace University at Pleasantville

Department of Philosophy and Religious
Studies
861 Bedford Rd
Pleasantville NY 10570

Phone: 914-773-3952
E-mail: hundersm@fsmail.pace.edu

TYPE OF INSTITUTION: Private
EXECUTIVE OFFICER: Gail Dinter-Gottlieb, Dean of Dyson College of Arts and Sciences
CHAIRPERSON: Thomas D. O'Sullivan

Pacific School of Religion

1798 Scenic Ave
Berkeley CA 94709

Phone: 510-848-0528
Fax: 510-845-8948
E-mail: wmckinney@psr.edu
URL: www.psr.edu

TYPE OF INSTITUTION: Multi-Denominational: United Church of Christ, United Methodist
    Church and Christian Church/Disciples
EXECUTIVE OFFICER: William McKinney, President
GRADUATE ENROLLMENT: 191

University of the Pacific

Religious Studies Dept
3601 Pacific Ave
Stockton CA 95211
TYPE OF INSTITUTION: Private
EXECUTIVE OFFICER: Donald DeRosa, President
CHAIRPERSON: Gilbert W. Schedler
UNDERGRADUATE ENROLLMENT: 2,758
GRADUATE ENROLLMENT: 547

Phone: 209-946-2161
E-mail: gschedle@uop.edu

Pacific University

Forest Grove OR 97116

Pacific Christian College

2500 E Nutwood Ave, Fullerton CA 92631

Pacific Coast Baptist Bible College

1100 S Valley Center, San Dimas CA 91773

Pacific Lutheran University

Department of Religion
Tacoma WA 98447

Phone: 253-535-7321
Fax: 253-536-5132
E-mail: oakmande@plu.edu

TYPE OF INSTITUTION: Private, ELCA

EXECUTIVE OFFICER: Loren J. Anderson, President

CHAIRPERSON: Douglas E. Oakman

UNDERGRADUATE ENROLLMENT: 3,600

GRADUATE ENROLLMENT: 200

DEGREES OFFERED: BA

UNDERGRADUATE MAJORS: 30

DEGREES CONFERRED: 10

DESCRIPTION OF UNDERGRADUATE PROGRAM: The Department of Religion is located in the Humanities Division of the College of Arts and Sciences. The Department stresses Christian studies. In addition it offers a full range of courses in the history of religions, social-scientific perspectives, and social ethics. The undergraduate major allows for concentration in several areas of study, including biblical, historical, theological, and comparative. It instills a critically appreciative approach to religion.

FACULTY:

Govig, Stewart D., PhD, New York University (1958), 1967, Professor—religious education, 253-535-7232, Fax: 253-536-5132

Howell, Nancy R., PhD, Claremont Graduate School (1990), 1991, Associate Professor—contemporary theology, 253-535-7238, Fax: 253-536-5132, E-mail: howellnr@plu.edu

Ingram, Paul O., PhD, Claremont Graduate School (1968), 1975, Professor—history of religions, 253-535-7319, Fax: 253-536-5132, E-mail: ingrampo@plu.edu

Killen, Patricia O'Connell, PhD, Stanford University (1987), 1989, Associate Professor—religion in North America, 253-535-7776, Fax: 253-536-5132, E-mail: killenpo@plu.edu

Lundeen, Lyman T., PhD, Union Theological Seminary, New York (1969), 1989, Professor—theology, 253-535-7321, Fax: 253-536-5132

Oakman, Douglas E., PhD, Graduate Theological Union (1986), 1988, Associate Professor—New Testament, 253-535-7317, Fax: 253-536-5132, E-mail: oakmande@plu.edu

Petersen, John, PhD, New York University (1970), 1967, Professor—Old Testament, 253-535-7320, Fax: 253-536-5132, E-mail: petersje@plu.edu

Pilgrim, Walter E., PhD, Princeton Theological Seminary (1971), 1971, Professor—New Testament, 253-535-7321, Fax: 253-536-5132

Stivers, Robert L., PhD, Columbia University and Union Theological Seminary, New York (1973), 1973, Professor—religion and society, 253-535-7318, Fax: 253-536-5132

Pacific Lutheran Theological Seminary

2770 Marin Ave
Berkeley CA 94708

Phone: 510-524-5264
Fax: 510-524-2408
URL: www.plts.edu

TYPE OF INSTITUTION: Private, Lutheran
EXECUTIVE OFFICER: Timothy F. Lull, President
GRADUATE ENROLLMENT: 195

Pacific Union College

Angwin CA 94508

Paine College

Augusta GA 30901

Palm Beach Atlantic College

PO Box 24708
West Palm Beach FL 33416

Phone: 561-803-2543
Fax: 561-803-2306
E-mail: mahanesk@pbac.edu
URL: www.pbac.edu/academ/ministry/
index.htm

TYPE OF INSTITUTION: Private
EXECUTIVE OFFICER: Ken Mahanes, Dean of School of Ministry and Vice President forReligious Life
UNDERGRADUATE ENROLLMENT: 150
GRADUATE ENROLLMENT: 20

Panhandle State College

Goodwell OK 73939

Park College

8700 River Park Drive
Parkville MO 64152

Phone: 816-714-2000
URL: www.park.edu

TYPE OF INSTITUTION: Private, Non-Denominational (undergraduate); Graduate school affiliated with RLDS church
EXECUTIVE OFFICER: Clara Brennan, Vice President for Academic Affairs
COORDINATORS: Robert S. Gall (Undergraduate); Wayne Ham (Graduate)

Park College

Graduate School of Religion
PO Box 1059
Independence MO 64051-1059

Phone: 816-833-1000

Patten College

2433 Coolidge Ave, Oakland CA 94601

Paul Quinn College

3837 Stuart Simpson Rd, Dallas TX 75261

Payne Theological Seminary

1230 Wilberforce-Clifton Rd
PO Box 474
Wilberforce OH 45384

Phone: 937-376-2946
Fax: 937-376-3330

TYPE OF INSTITUTION: Private, African Methodist Episcopal
EXECUTIVE OFFICER: Obery Hendricks, President; Wayne R. Davis, Academic Dean
GRADUATE ENROLLMENT: 55

Pembroke State University

Philosophy and Religion Dept, Pembroke NC 28372

University of Pennsylvania

Dept of Religious Studies
College Hall Box 36
Philadelphia PA 19104-6303

Phone: 215-898-7453
Fax: 215-898-6568
E-mail: rstudies@sas.upenn.edu
URL: ccat.sas.upenn.edu/rs

TYPE OF INSTITUTION: Private, Non-Denominational
EXECUTIVE OFFICER: Judith Rodin, President
CHAIRPERSON: Stephen N. Dunning
UNDERGRADUATE ENROLLMENT: 10,000
GRADUATE ENROLLMENT: 9,000

The Pennsylvania State University

108 Weaver Building
University Park PA 16802-5500

Phone: 814-865-3403
Fax: 814-863-7840
E-mail: wlp1@psu.edu
URL: www3.la.psu.edu/histrlst/

TYPE OF INSTITUTION: Public

EXECUTIVE OFFICER: Graham Spanier, President
COORDINATOR: William L. Petersen, Director
UNDERGRADUATE ENROLLMENT: 39,000
GRADUATE ENROLLMENT: 0
DEGREES OFFERED: BA
UNDERGRADUATE MAJORS: 25
DEGREES CONFERRED: 5

DESCRIPTION OF UNDERGRADUATE PROGRAM: The Religious Studies Program is an interdisciplinary unit in the College of the Liberal Arts. It includes a core of courses in Religious Studies and a wide variety of related courses in other departments within the College. The program includes courses in the major religious traditions, textual traditions, and diverse methodological approaches to the study of religion in the humanities and social sciences. As a matrix for integrating liberal studies, the Religious Studies Program provides for a) understanding historically, culturally, and sociologically a rich variety of religious issues, East and West, b) grasping the mutual interpenetration of religion and culture, and c) penetrating the ways in which religious language addresses, articulates, and informs human experience. Both a major and minor are offered.

DESCRIPTION OF GRADUATE PROGRAMS AND RESEARCH FACILITIES: The Religious Studies Program offers a graduate minor which can be taken at either the Masters or Doctoral level. It is also possible to include a emphasis in the Historical Study of Religion as a component of the graduate degree in History, again either at the Masters or Doctoral level. Application is made to the Department of History.

FACULTY:

Engel, David M., PhD, University of California, Berkeley (1997), 1997, Assistant Professor—classical Graeco-Roman philosophy, 814-865-3931, E-mail: dme8@psu.edu

Gianotti, Timothy J., PhD, University of Toronto (1997), 1997, Assistant Professor—classical Islamic religion, philosophy and mysticism, 814-863-4945, E-mail: tjg5@psu.edu

Halpern, Baruch, PhD, Harvard University (1978), 1992, Professor—Ancient history (social, intellectual, technological, military), archaeology, biblical studies, 814-865-0146, E-mail: bxh13@psu.edu

Jenkins, Philip, PhD, Cambridge University (1978), 1992, Distinguished Professor—new religious movements, sociology of religious problems, contemporary Catholic issues, 814-863-8946, E-mail: jpj1@psu.edu

Knoppers, Gary N., PhD, Harvard University (1988), 1987, Associate Professor—Hebrew Bible, early Judaism, New Testament, 814-865-3931, E-mail: gxk7@psu.edu

Petersen, William L., DTheol, State University of Utrecht, The Netherlands (1984), 1990, Professor—New Testament and early church, 814-865-7773, E-mail: wlp1@psu.edu

Poole, Thomas G., PhD, Penn State (1984), 1982, Affiliate Assistant Professor (part-time)—religious ethics, African-American religion, Black theology, American religion, 814-863-9755, E-mail: tgp1@psu.edu

Prebish, Charles S., PhD, University of Wisconsin, Madison (1971), 1971, Professor—Asian religions, Buddhist studies, 814-865-1121, E-mail: csp1@psu.edu

Roeber, A. Gregg, PhD, Brown (1977), 1996, Professor—religion in Colonial and early national America, German-American religious traditions, 814-865-1367, E-mail: agr2@psu.edu

Rose, Anne Carver, PhD, Yale University (1979), 1990, Associate Professor—American religious history, 814-863-0105, E-mail: acr5@psu.edu

Van Herik, Judith, PhD, University of Chicago (1978), 1977, Associate Professor—psychology and religion, comparative forms of healing, psychoanalytic theory, women and religion, 814-865-1686, E-mail: jxv4@psu.edu

Pensacola Bible Institute

PO Box 6235, Pensacola FL 32503

Pensacola Christian College

Box 18000, Pensacola FL 32523

Pepperdine University

Religion Division
24255 Pacific Coast Hwy
Malibu CA 90263-4352

Phone: 310-456-4352
Fax: 310-317-7271
E-mail: rmarrs@pepperdine.edu
URL:arachnid.pepperdine.edu/religiondiv/
home.htm

TYPE OF INSTITUTION: Private, Church of Christ

EXECUTIVE OFFICER: W. David Baird, Dean of Seaver College

CHAIRPERSON: Rick R. Marrs

UNDERGRADUATE ENROLLMENT: 2,700

GRADUATE ENROLLMENT: 150

DEGREES OFFERED: BA in Religion

UNDERGRADUATE MAJORS: 1

DEGREES CONFERRED: 7

DESCRIPTION OF UNDERGRADUATE PROGRAM: With emphasis on academic rigor and a spirit of genuine inquiry, the Religion Division seeks to lead students into a deeper understanding of religion and especially of Christianity. Further, these studies are encouraged by a faculty which is committed to the Christian faith. Academically, the division focuses principally on Biblical studies, Christian history, and Christian theology. At the same time, the division offers courses that introduce the student to the study of religion within a variety of human cultures, both ancient and modern. Through the undergraduate major, the division prepares students for a variety of undertakings. Some religion majors become ministers in local churches. Other majors view religion as a broad, liberal arts major and as desirable preparation for graduate work in psychology, business, law, or other fields. Other students go from a Seaver religion major to MA, MDiv, and PhD programs in religion, hoping to pursue a career in university teaching.

GRADUATE PROGRAM

Graduate Advisor: Rick R. Marrs

Graduate Degrees Offered: MA; MSMin; MDiv

Not in Residence: 3 MA

Average No. of New Students Enrolled: 4 MA

Women Students: 7 MA

Minimum GRE Score Requisite to Admission: Yes, 1050

Minimum GPA Score Requisite to Admission: No

Foreign Language Proficiency Evaluated: No

Financial Aid to First Year Students: 100% MA

Financial Aid to Other Students: 95% MA

Attrition Among Students: 5% MA

Graduates Placed: 100% MA

DESCRIPTION OF GRADUATE PROGRAM AND RESEARCH FACILITIES: The division offers three graduate programs: masters of arts, master of science in ministry and master of divinity. The division prepares students for the ministry, especially within Churches of Christ, and for further graduate studies in many other fields. Currently there are twenty students in the master of science in ministry program and eleven students in the master of divinity program. Eight master of science in ministry degrees and five master of divinity degrees have been conferred during the 1995-96 school year.

ACADEMIC PLAN, ADMISSION REQUIREMENTS, FINANCIAL AID: Applications for the degrees of master of arts in religion, master of divinity, and master of science in ministry, together with the necessary supporting documents, must be submitted to the Admission Office, Seaver College Graduate Programs, by March 1 for the following academic year. The Admission Committee meets periodically throughout the year, and applicants are notified as soon as is practicable after a decision has been reached. Students seeking financial aid for master's program will find it to their advantage to apply at an early date. Applicants must meet the admission requirements as specified. A personal conference with the chairperson of the Religion Division is advisable, and in certain instances an interview with the Admission Committee will be required.

FACULTY:

Chesnutt, Randall D., PhD, Duke University (1986), 1984, Professor—New Testament, 310-456-4180, E-mail: chesnutt@pepperdine.edu

Clark, W. Royce, PhD, University of Iowa (1973); JD, Pepperdine University (1985), 1970, Professor—religious thought and religion and law, 310-456-4354, E-mail: rclark@pepperdine.edu

Highfield, Ronald C., PhD, Rice University (1988), 1989, Associate Professor—religious thought and ethics, 310-456-4511, E-mail: rhighfie@pepperdine.edu

Hughes, Richard T., PhD, University of Iowa (1972), 1988, Distinguished Professor—history of Christianity, 310-456-4526, E-mail: rhughes@pepperdine.edu

Jolivet, Ira J., Jr., PhD, Baylor (1994), 1993, Associate Professor—New Testament, 310-456-4736, E-mail: ijolivet@pepperdine.edu

Love, Stuart, STD, San Francisco Theological Seminary (1979), 1979, Professor—ministry, 310-456-4163, E-mail: slove@pepperdine.edu

Marrs, Rick R., PhD, Johns Hopkins University (1982), 1987, Chair of Religion Division and Professor—Old Testament, 310-456-4179, E-mail: rmarrs@pepperdine.edu

Olbricht, Thomas H., PhD, University of Iowa (1959), STB, Harvard Divinity School (1962), 1986, Distinguished Professor Emeritus—theology, 310-456-4352, E-mail: olbricht@pepperdine.edu

Rodriguez, Daniel A., PhD (cand.), Fuller Theological Seminary, 1994, Assistant Professor—missions, 310-456-4767, E-mail: drodrigu@pepperdine.edu

Rushford, Jerry, PhD, University of California, Santa Barbara (1977), 1978, Professor—history of Christianity, 310-456-4270, Fax: 310-456-4227

Tyler, Ronald, PhD, Baylor University (1973), 1972, Professor—New Testament, 310-456-4144, E-mail: rtyler@pepperdine.edu

Willis, Timothy M., PhD, Harvard Graduate School of Arts and Sciences (1990), 1989, Associate Professor—Old Testament, 310-456-4511, E-mail: twillis@pepperdine.edu

Wilson, John F., PhD, University of Iowa (1967), 1983, Professor—archaeology and New Testament, 310-456-4281, Fax: 310-456-4227, E-mail: jwilson@pepperdine.edu

Winrow, Dewayne, PhD (cand.), University of Southern California, 1994, Irvine Visiting Professor—New Testament, 310-456-4759, E-mail: dwinrow@pepperdine.edu

Perkins School of Theology

Southern Methodist University
PO Box 750133
Dallas TX 75275-0133

Phone: 888-843-6564
Fax: 214-768-266

Pfeiffer College

Misenheimer NC 28109

Philadelphia College of Bible

200 Manor Ave, Langhorne PA 19047

Philadelphia Theological Seminary

7372 Henry Avenue
Philadelphia PA 19128-1401

Phone: 215-483-2480
Fax: 215-483-2484
E-mail: ptsofrec.edu
URL: www.PTSofREC.edu

TYPE OF INSTITUTION: Private, Reformed Episcopal
EXECUTIVE OFFICER: Wayne A. Headman, President
GRADUATE DEGREES OFFERED: MDiv
FACULTY:

Abboud, Jon W., MDiv, Philadelphia Theological Seminary (1983), Associate Professor—pastoral ministry, 215-483-2480, Fax: 215-483-2484, E-mail: jwa@ptsofrec.edu

Blackburn, Rollin J., PhD, Temple University (1998), Professor—biblical languages and literature, 215-483-2480, Fax: 215-483-2484, E-mail: rjb@ptsofrec.edu

Crouthamel, Dale H., ThM, Princeton (1983), Associate Professor—theology, 215-483-2480, Fax: 215-483-2484, E-mail: dhc@ptsofrec.edu

Harrah, Charles L., MDiv, Philadelphia Theological Seminary (1998), Instructor—Christian education, 215-483-2480, Fax: 215-483-2484, E-mail: clh@ptsofrec.edu

Headman, Wayne A., ThM, Princeton (1975), Instructor—New Testament studies, 215-483-2480, Fax: 215-483-2484, E-mail: wah@ptsofrec.edu

Hicks, David L., STM, Lutheran Theological Seminary (1998), Instructor—Greek, 215-483-2480, Fax: 215-483-2484, E-mail: dlh@ptsofrec.edu

Lillback, Peter A., PhD, Westminster (1985), Assistant Professor—church history, 215-483-2480, Fax: 215-483-2484, E-mail: pal@ptsofrec.edu

Riches, Leonard W., MDiv, Philadelphia Theological Seminary (1964), Professor—liturgics and theology, 215-483-2480, Fax: 215-483-2484, E-mail: lwr@ptsofrec.edu

Philander Smith College

812 West 13th Street
Little Rock AR 72202

Phone: 501-370-5236
E-mail: jrush@philandr.edu
URL: www.philander.edu

TYPE OF INSTITUTION: Private, United Methodist
EXECUTIVE OFFICER: William Thomas, Dean of Instruction
CHAIRPERSON: James E. Rush
UNDERGRADUATE ENROLLMENT: 900

Phillips University

100 S University
Enid OK 73701

Phone: 405-237-4433
Fax: 405-237-1607
E-mail: dpabbott@phillips.edu
URL: www.phillips.edu

TYPE OF INSTITUTION: Private, Christian Church (Disciples of Christ)
EXECUTIVE OFFICER: G. Curtis Jones, Jr., President
CHAIRPERSON: Dan Phillips Abbott
UNDERGRADUATE ENROLLMENT: 525

Phillips Theological Seminary

4242 S Sheridan
Tulsa OK 74145

Phone: 918-610-8303
Fax: 918-610-8404
E-mail: ptspres@fullnet.net

TYPE OF INSTITUTION: Private, Christian Church (Disciples of Christ)
EXECUTIVE OFFICER: William Tabbernee, President
GRADUATE ENROLLMENT: 175

Piedmont College

Philosophy and Religion Department
of Humanities
PO Box 10
Demorest GA 30535

Phone: 706-778-3000
Fax: 706-776-2811
E-mail: tlytle@piedmont.edu
URL: www.piedmont.edu

TYPE OF INSTITUTION: Private, National Association of Congregational Churches
EXECUTIVE OFFICER: W. Ray Cleere, President
COORDINATOR: Timothy F. Lytle
UNDERGRADUATE ENROLLMENT: 12

Piedmont Baptist College

716 Franklin St
Winston-Salem NC 27101

Phone: 910-725-8344
Fax: 910-725-5522
E-mail: luethyd@pbc.edu

TYPE OF INSTITUTION: Private, Independent Baptist
EXECUTIVE OFFICER: Howard Wilburn, President
CHAIRPERSON: David Luethy
UNDERGRADUATE ENROLLMENT: 280
GRADUATE ENROLLMENT: 20

Pikeville College

214 Sycamore St
Pikeville KY 41501-1194

Phone: 606-432-9200
Fax: 606-432-9328
URL: www.pc.edu

TYPE OF INSTITUTION: Private, Presbyterian
EXECUTIVE OFFICER: Wallace Campbell, Dean of the Faculty
CHAIRPERSON: Brigitte LaPresto
COORDINATOR: Carol Grizzard
UNDERGRADUATE ENROLLMENT: 750

Pillsbury Baptist Bible College

315 S Grove, Owatonna MN 55060

University of Pittsburgh

Dept of Religious Studies
2604 Cathedral of Learning
Pittsburgh PA 15260

Phone: 412-624-5990
Fax: 412-624-5994
E-mail: susief+@pitt.edu
URL:www.pitt.edu

TYPE OF INSTITUTION: Public
CHAIRPERSON: Tony Edwards
COORDINATOR: Paula M. Kane
UNDERGRADUATE ENROLLMENT: 27
GRADUATE ENROLLMENT: 22
DEGREES OFFERED: BA
UNDERGRADUATE MAJORS: 15
DEGREES CONFERRED: 3
DESCRIPTION OF UNDERGRADUATE PROGRAM: A major in religious studies includes possible fields of concentration in special religious traditions (Christian, Jewish, Hinduism and Buddhism) or in the focus on a particular time period (classical, medieval and modern). Further, joint programs can be designed with such foci as religion and fine arts, religion and politics, ritual studies, religion and philosophy, religion and literature, and religion and science.

The religious studies major consists of 27 credit hours in religious studies and 12 credit hours in a cognate discipline.

GRADUATE PROGRAM

Graduate Advisor: Paula Kane

Graduate Degrees Offered: MA; PhD

Degrees Conferred: 2 MA; 1 PhD

Graduate Students in Residence: 6 MA; 16 PhD

Not in Residence: 2 MA; 2 PhD

Average No. of New Students Enrolled: 3 MA; 3 PhD

Women Students: 6 MA; 8 PhD

Minority Students: 0 MA; 2 PhD

Foreign Students: 1 MA; 1 PhD

Minimum GRE Score Requisite to Admission: Yes, 575 verbal

Minimum GPA Score Requisite to Admission: Yes, 3.0 on 4.0 scale

Foreign Language Proficiency Evaluated: No

Financial Aid to First Year Students: 25% MA; 25% PhD

Financial Aid to Other Students: 25% MA; 25% PhD

Attrition Among Students: 12% MA; 5% PhD

Graduates Placed: 0% MA; 100% PhD

DESCRIPTION OF GRADUATE PROGRAM AND RESEARCH FACILITIES: At the University of Pittsburgh, religion is studied in the various contextual frames in which it is set, especially in its cultural and ecological settings. Students are systematically introduced to a variety of interdisciplinary approaches employed in the study of religion, and they are challenged to sharpen their own theoretical skills in tandem with the study of particular issues, problems, and cultural traditions. Resources for study and research are especially strong in specific areas of theoretical and thematic study, including religion and politics; religion and the arts; religious acculturation and ritual studies. Substantive study is also possible in the religions of East Asia and North America; the history of Judaism; religious thought and language and religion in contemporary society.

ACADEMIC PLAN, ADMISSION REQUIREMENTS, FINANCIAL AID: Applicants to both the MA and PhD programs should submit the application form and fee including a fully developed statement of purpose, official transcripts of all prior academic work, three letters of recommendation, a thesis or seminar paper, and GRE scores. (International applicants are asked to provide supplemental information including TOEFL scores.) The MA degree is a 27 credit program which requires a written comprehensive examination and a master's thesis. The PhD degree is 48 credits beyond the master's degree, 18 of which are drawn from a group of required courses. A PhD preliminary exam, competence in two foreign languages, PhD comprehensive examinations, and a dissertation are all required. Financial aid offered through the department consists of a number of part-time teaching assistantships providing a monthly stipend plus partial tuition remission. Students with superior records are placed into competition for numerous university-wide fellowships awarding stipends and tuition remission.

FACULTY:

Clothey, Fred W., PhD, University of Chicago (1968), 1975, Professor—history of religions, methodology, South Asian religions, 412-624-5977, Fax: 412-624-5994, E-mail: clothey+@pitt.edu

Edwards, Steven Anthony, PhD, Stanford (1981), 1981, Associate Professor—theory of religion, religious ethics, history of Christian thought, religious language, 412-624-2053, Fax: 412-624-5994, E-mail: tedwards+@pitt.edu

Goldstein, Bernard R., PhD, Brown University (1963), 1973, Professor—Jewish studies, religion and science, Hebrew Bible, Islam, 412-624-5989, Fax: 412-624-5994, E-mail: brg+@pitt.edu

Kane, Paula M., PhD, Yale University (1986), 1990, Associate Professor—religion in America, Catholicism in America, 412-624-2278, Fax: 412-624-5994, E-mail: pmk+@pitt.edu

Orbach, Alexander, PhD, University of Wisconsin (1975), 1977, Associate Professor—Jewish studies, modern Jewish history, 412-624-2279, Fax: 412-624-5994, E-mail: orbach+@pitt.edu

Penkower, Linda, PhD, Columbia University (1992), 1991, Assistant Professor—East Asian religious traditions, Buddhism in China and Japan, 412-624-2277, Fax: 412-624-5994, E-mail: penkower+@pitt.edu

Robertson, Roland, BSc, University of Southhampton, England (1960), 1968, Professor—sociology of religion, contemporary religion, 412-648-7118, Fax: 412-648-2799, E-mail: rolandr+@pitt.edu

Weisberg, Dvora E., PhD, Jewish Theological Seminary (1994), 1996, Visiting Assistant Professor—Judaism in antiquity, Rabbinics, women in Judaism, 412-624-5986, Fax: 412-624-5994, E-0mail: weisberg+@pitt.edu

ADJUNCT FACULTY:

Calian, S., Pittsburgh Theological Seminary—theology

Castillo-Cardenas, G., Pittsburgh Theological Seminary—Latin American religion

Gagnon, R., Pittsburgh Theological Seminary—early Christianity, Christian Bible

Kelly, D., Duquesne University—Catholic medical ethics

Partee, C., Pittsburgh Theological Seminary—church history

Stone, R., Pittsburgh Theological Seminary—ethics

Sutton, D., Carnegie Mellon University—Chinese popular religion

Wilson, J. E., Pittsburgh Theological Seminary—history of Christianity

---

Pittsburgh Theological Seminary

616 N Highland Ave
Pittsburgh PA 15206

Phone: 412-362-5610
Fax: 412-363-3260

TYPE OF INSTITUTION: Private, Presbyterian Church (USA)
EXECUTIVE OFFICER: Carnegie Samuel Calian, President
GRADUATE ENROLLMENT: 302

Pitzer College

1050 N Mills Ave, Claremont CA 91711

Platte Valley Bible College

305 E 16th St	Phone: 308-632-6933
PO Box 1227	Fax: 308-632-8599
Scottsbluff NE 69363-1227	E-mail: pvbc@prairieweb.com
	URL: www.pvbc.edu

TYPE OF INSTITUTION: Private
EXECUTIVE OFFICER: Lawrence D. Leathermon, President
UNDERGRADUATE ENROLLMENT: 76

Point Loma Nazarene College

3900 Lomaland Dr	Phone: 619-849-2200
San Diego CA 92106-2899	Fax: 619-849-7008
	E-mail: spowell@ptloma.edu
	URL: www.ptloma.edu

TYPE OF INSTITUTION: Denominational: Nazarene
EXECUTIVE OFFICER: Robert I. Brower, President
CHAIRPERSON: Samuel Powell
COORDINATOR: Samuel Powell, Director of Graduate Studies
UNDERGRADUATE ENROLLMENT: 2,050
GRADUATE ENROLLMENT: 400

Pomona College

Dept of Religious Studies	Phone: 909-607-3075
551 N College Ave	Fax: 909-621-8574
Claremont CA 91711-6337	E-mail: mdornish@pomona.claremont.edu
	URL: www.religious-studies.pomona.edu

TYPE OF INSTITUTION: Private
EXECUTIVE OFFICER: Peter W. Stanley, President
CHAIRPERSON: Margaret H. Dornish
UNDERGRADUATE ENROLLMENT: 1,430
DEGREES OFFERED: BA
UNDERGRADUATE MAJORS: 30
DEGREES CONFERRED: 17

DESCRIPTION OF UNDERGRADUATE PROGRAM: The concentration in Religious Studies is a cooperative program offered jointly by Claremont McKenna, Pitzer, Pomona, and Scirpps colleges. Eleven faculty teach full-time in the program. While offering a broadly based and inclusive program in the study of religion for all liberal arts students, the concentration in Religious Studies affords the opportunity for more specialized work at the intermediate and advanced levels in particular historic religious traditions, georgraphical areas, philosophical and critical approaches, and thematic and comparative studies. The following fields of specialized study are offered for concentrators in Religious Studies: 1) Historical Religious Traditions-Asian, 2) Historical Religious Traditions-Western; 3) Philosophy of Religion, Theology, and Ethics; and 4) Contemporary and Women's Studies in Religion.

FACULTY:

Dornish, Margaret H., PhD, The Claremont Graduate School, 1969, Professor—religious studies, Asian religions, Buddhist studies

Irish, Jerry A., PhD, Yale University, 1986, Professor—religious studies, philosophy of religion, theology, ethics,

Jackson, Howard, PhD, Claremont Graduate School, Lecturer—classics, Greek religion

Kassam, Zayn, PhD, McGill University, 1995, Assistant Professor—religious studies, Islamic studies, comparative philosophy

Whedbee, William, PhD, Yale University, 1966, Nancy M. Lyon Professor—biblical history and literature, biblical and Near Eastern religion, biblical hermeneutics, literary criticism

Wolf, Kenneth, PhD, Stanford University, Associate Professor—history, history of Christianity

Pontifical College Josephinum
7625 N High St, Columbus OH 43085

Pope John XXIII National Seminary

558 South Avenue
Weston MA 02193

Phone: 617-899-5500
Fax: 617-899-9057

TYPE OF INSTITUTION: Private, Roman Catholic
EXECUTIVE OFFICER: Francis D. Kelly, Rector/President
GRADUATE ENROLLMENT: 75

University of Portland

Dept of Theology
5000 N Willamette Blvd
Portland OR 97203-5798

Phone: 503-283-7274
Fax: 503-283-7399
E-mail: hosinski@uofport.edu
URL: www.uofport.edu

TYPE OF INSTITUTION: Private, Roman Catholic
EXECUTIVE OFFICER: David T. Tyson, CSC, President
CHAIRPERSON: Thomas E. Hosinski, CSC
UNDERGRADUATE ENROLLMENT: 2,500
GRADUATE ENROLLMENT: 350

Portland Christian School
2500 Portland Ave, Louisville KY 40212

Portland State University
Portland OR 97207

Presbyterian College

Clinton SC 29325

Phone: 864-833-2820
Fax: 864-833-8481
E-mail: phhobb@presby.edu
URL: www.presby.edu

TYPE OF INSTITUTION: Private, Presbyterian (USA)
EXECUTIVE OFFICER: John Griffith, President
CHAIRPERSON: Peter H. Hobbie
UNDERGRADUATE ENROLLMENT: 1,150

Presentation College

1500 N Main, Aberdeen SD 57401

University of Prince Edward Island

Dept of Religious Studies, Charlottetown, PEI C1A 4P3 Canada

Princeton University

Seventy-Nine Hall
Department of Religion
Princeton NJ 08544-1006

Phone: 609-258-4481
Fax: 609-258-2346
URL: www.princeton.edu/~religion

TYPE OF INSTITUTION: Private
EXECUTIVE OFFICER: John F. Wilson, Dean of Graduate School
CHAIRPERSON: Martha Himmelfarb
UNDERGRADUATE ENROLLMENT: 4,624
GRADUATE ENROLLMENT: 1,762

Princeton Theological Seminary

PO Box 821
Princeton NJ 08542-0803

Phone: 609-497-7818
Fax: 609-497-7819
E-mail: phd@ptsem.edu
URL: www.ptsem.edu

TYPE OF INSTITUTION: Private, Presbyterian Church, USA
EXECUTIVE OFFICER: Thomas W. Gillespie, President
CHAIRPERSON: Katharine Doob Sakenfeld, Director, PhD Studies
GRADUATE ENROLLMENT: 739
GRADUATE PROGRAM
Member of the Council on Graduate Studies in Religion
Graduate Advisor: Katharine Doob Sakenfeld
Graduate Degrees Offered: PhD
Degrees Conferred: 19 PhD

Graduate Students in Residence: 40 PhD

Not in Residence: 98 PhD

Average No. of New Students Enrolled: 20 PhD

Women Students: 54 PhD

Minority Students: 10 PhD

Foreign Students: 31 PhD

Minimum GRE Score Requisite to Admission: No

Minimum GPA Score Requisite to Admission: No

Foreign Language Proficiency Evaluated: No

Financial Aid to First Year Students : 100% PhD

Financial Aid to Other Students: 100% PhD

Attrition Among Students: 1% PhD

DESCRIPTION OF GRADUATE PROGRAM AND RESEARCH FACILITIES: The Princeton Seminary PhD program is designed to equip men and women for independent scholarship and for teaching in colleges and seminaries in various dimensions of the study of religion. Programs are offered in Biblical Studies, History and Ecumenics, Theology, Religion and Society, and Practical Theology. Individualized interdisciplinary programs are also sometimes permitted. Two years of full-time resident study are required; upon satisfactory completion of the comprehensive examinations and the dissertation, the candidate is recommended for the PhD degree. All degree requirements must normally be completed within six years of entry. Knowledge of French and German is required; ancient languages are required according to field of study. Speer and Luce Libraries offer substantial resources for theological study and research. Princeton Seminary students may use Firestone Library at Princeton University and, in consultation with their residence committees, may take a limited number of courses in the University's Graduate School.

ACADEMIC PLAN, ADMISSION REQUIREMENTS, FINANCIAL AID: Princeton Seminary operates on the semester system (two semesters a year). PhD students must hold the BA or equivalent from an approved college or university and the MDiv or equivalent from an approved theological or graduate institution. The MDiv is required of students in Practical Theology. In other fields of study, if the MDiv or its equivalent is lacking, a minimum of two years of graduate study in religion is required. Included in the two years must be a course each in Old Testament; New Testament; systematic theology, philosophy, or ethics; history of religions; a human science in relation to religion; and two courses in the history of Christianity. GRE General Test (or TOEFL for foreign students); transcripts; scholarly essay in intended field of study; letters of recommendation; letter of intent; autobiographical statement. Financial aid, fellowships, assistantships available.

FACULTY:

Allen, Diogenes, PhD, Yale University, Professor—philosophy, 609-497-7977, Fax: 609-497-7728, E-mail: diogenes.allen@ptsem.edu

Armstrong, James F., PhD, Princeton University, Professor—Old Testament language and exegesis, 609-497-7815, Fax: 609-497-7819, E-mail: james.armstrong@ptsem.edu

Bartow, Charles L., PhD, New York University, Professor—speech, 609-497-7963, Fax: 609-924-2973, E-mail: charles.bartow@ptsem.edu

Black, C. Clifton, PhD, Duke University, Professor—New Testament, 609-497-7762, Fax: 609-497-7728, E-mail: clifton.black@ptsem.edu

Blount, Brian K., PhD, Emory University, Associate Professor—New Testament, 609-497-7836, Fax: 609-497-7829, E-mail: brian.blount@ptsem.edu

Capps, Donald E., PhD, University of Chicago Divinity School, Professor—pastoral theology, 609-497-7988, Fax: 609-497-7728, E-mail: donald.capps@ptsem.edu

Charlesworth, James H., PhD, Duke University, Professor—New Testament language and literature, 609-497-7920, Fax: 609-497-7723, E-mail: james.charlesworth@ptsem.edu

Charry, Ellen T., PhD, Temple University, Associate professor—systematic theology, 609-497-7952, Fax: 609-497-7728, E-mail: ellen.charry@ptsem.edu

Crocco, Stephen D., PhD, Carnegie Mellon University, James Lenox Librarian, 609-497-7930, Fax: 609-497-1826, E-mail: stephen.crocco@ptsem.edu

Dean, Kendra Creasy, PhD, Princeton Theological Seminary, Assistant Professor—youth, church, culture, 609-497-7910 Fax: 609-279-9014, E-mail: kenda.dean@ptsem.edu

Deming, James C., PhD, University of Notre Dame, Associate Professor—modern European church history, 609-497-7844, Fax: 609-497-7829, E-mail: james.deming@ptsem.edu

Dobbs-Allsopp, Frederick William, PhD, Johns Hopkins University, Assistant Professor—Old Testament, 609-497-7924, Fax: 609-497-7829, E-mail: chip.dobbs-allsopp@ptsem.edu

Duff, Nancy J., PhD, Union Theological Seminary in New York, Associate Professor—Christian ethics, 609-497-7809, Fax: 609-497-7829, E-mail: nancy.duff@ptsem.edu

Dykstra, Robert C., PhD, Princeton Theological Seminary, Assistant Professor—pastoral theology, 609-252-2115, Fax: 609-279-9014, E-mail: robert.dykstra@ptsem.edu

Evans, Abigail Rian, PhD, Georgetown University, Professor—practical theology, 609-497-7970, Fax: 609-924-2973, E-mail: abigail.evans@ptsem.edu

Fenn, Richard K., PhD, Bryn Mawr Graduate School, Professor—Christianity and society, 609-497-7763, Fax: 609-924-2973, E-mail: richard.fenn@ptsem.edu

Gaventa, Beverly Roberts, PhD, Duke University, Professor—New Testament, 609-497-7765, Fax: 609-497-7728, E-mail: beverly.gaventa@ptsem.edu

Gillespie, Thomas W., PhD, Claremont Graduate School, President and Professor—New Testament, 609-497-7800, Fax: 609-924-2973, E-mail: president@ptsem.edu

Hanson, Geddes W., PhD, Princeton Theological Seminary, Professor—practical theology, 609-497-7843, Fax: 609-924-2973, E-mail: geddes.hanson@ptsem.edu

Hendrix, Scott Hampton, ThD, University of Tübingen, Professor—Reformation history and doctrine, 609-497-7854, Fax: 609-497-7829, E-mail: scott.hendrix@ptsem.edu

Hunsinger, Deborah van Deusen, PhD, Union Theological Seminary in New York, Assistant Professor—pastoral theology, 609-497-7884, Fax: 609-497-7728, E-mail: deborah.hunsinger@ptsem.edu

Jacks, G. Robert, PhD, Columbia University, Professor—speech, 609-497-7979, Fax: 609-924-2973, E-mail: robert.jacks@ptsem.edu

Johnson, W. Stacy, PhD, Harvard University, Associate Professor—systematic theology, 609-497-7922, Fax: 609-497-7728, E-mail: stacy.johnson@ptsem.edu

Juel, Donald H., PhD, Yale University, Professor—New Testament theology, 609-497-7832, Fax: 609-924-2973, E-mail: don.juel@ptsem.edu

Kay, James F., PhD, Union Theological Seminary in New York, Associate Professor—homiletics, 609-497-7941, Fax: 609-924-2973, E-mail: james.kay@ptsem.edu

Lapsley, Jacqueline Evangeline, Assistant Professor—Old Testament, 609-497-7855, Fax: 609-497-7728, E-mail: jacqueline.lapsley@ptsem.edu

LaRue, Cleophus J., Jr., PhD, Princeton Theological Seminary, Associate Professor—homiletics, 609-497-7874, Fax: 609-497-7829, E-mail: cleo.larue@ptsem.edu

Lee, Sang H., PhD, Harvard University, Professor—theology, 609-497-7885, Fax: 609-497-7870, E-mail: sang.lee@ptsem.edu

Loder, James E., PhD, Harvard University, Professor—philosophy of Christian education, 609-497-7914, Fax: 609-497-7829, E-mail: james.loder@ptsem.edu

McCormack, Bruce L., PhD, Princeton Theological Seminary, Professor]7systematictheology, 609-497-7987, Fax: 609-497-7728, E-mail: bruce.mccormack@ptsem.edu

McKee, Elsie A., PhD, Princeton Theological Seminary, Professor of Reformation Studies and the History of Worship—history of worship, 609-497-7989, Fax: 609-497-7829, E-mail: elsie.mckee@ptsem.edu

McVey, Kathleen E., PhD, Harvard University, Professor—church history, 609-497-7996, Fax: 609-497-7728, E-mail: kathleen.mcvey@ptsem.edu

Migliore, Daniel L., PhD, Princeton University, Professor—systematic theology, 609-497-7975, Fax: 609-497-7728, E-mail: daniel.migliore@ptsem.edu

Miller, Patrick D., PhD, Harvard University, Professor—Old Testament theology, 609-497-7985, Fax: 609-497-7728, E-mail: patrick.miller@ptsem.edu

Moorhead, James H., PhD, Yale University, Professor—American church history, 609-497-7984, Fax: 609-497-7728, E-mail: james.moorhead@ptsem.edu

Nichols, J. Randall, PhD, Princeton Theological Seminary, Lecturer—theology and communication, 609-497-7875, Fax: 609-924-2973, E-mail: randall.nichols@ptsem.edu

Olson, Dennis T., PhD, Yale University, Associate Professor—Old Testament, 609-497-7769, Fax: 609-497-7728, E-mail: dennis.olson@ptsem.edu

Osmer, Richard R., PhD, Emory University, Professor—Christian education, 609-497-7910, Fax: 609-497-7829, E-mail: richard.osmer@ptsem.edu

Paris, Peter J., PhD, University of Chicago, Professor—Christian social ethics, 609-497-7814, Fax: 609-497-7728, E-mail: peter.paris@ptsem.edu

Roberts, J. J. M., PhD, Harvard University, Professor—Old Testament, 609-497-7986, Fax: 609-924-2973, E-mail: jjm.roberts@ptsem.edu

Rorem, Paul, PhD, Princeton Theological Seminary, Professor—ecclesiastical history, 609-497-7998, Fax: 609-497-7829, E-mail: paul.rorem@ptsem.edu

Sakenfeld, Katharine Doob, PhD, Harvard University, Professor—Old Testament literature, exegesis, 609-497-7818, Fax: 609-497-7819, E-mail: katharine.sakenfeld@ptsem.edu

Seow, C. Leong, PhD, Harvard University, Professor—Old Testament, 609-497-7934, Fax: 609-924-2973, E-mail: leong.seow@ptsem.edu

Stackhouse, Max L., PhD, Harvard University, Professor—Christian ethics, 609-497-7898, Fax: 609-924-2973, E-mail: max.stackhouse@ptsem.edu

Stewart, John W., PhD, University of Michigan, Associate Professor—ministry and evangelism, 609-497-7976, Fax: 609-924-2973, E-mail: john.stewart@ptsem.edu

Taylor, Mark Lewis, PhD, University of Chicago Divinity School, Professor—theology and culture, 609-497-7918, Fax: 609-497-7728, E-mail: mark.taylor@ptsem.edu

Tel, Martin, Lecturer—church music, 609-497-7890, Fax: 609-497-7893, E-mail: martin.tel@ptsem.edu

Tisdale, Leonora Tubbs, PhD, Princeton Theological Seminary, Associate Professor—preaching and worship, 609-497-7963, Fax: 609-924-2973, E-mail: nora.tisdale@ptsem.edu

van Huyssteen, J. Wentzel, DTh, Free University of Amsterdam, Professor—theology and science, 609-497-7948, Fax: 609-924-2973, E-mail: wentzel.vanhuyssteen@ptsem.edu

Wagner, J. Ross, Jr., Assistant Professor—New Testament, 609-497-7856, Fax: 609-497-7829, E-mail: ross.wagner@ptsem.edu

Walls, Andrew R., Guest Professor of Ecumenics and Mission, 609-497-7798, Fax: 609-497-7728, E-mail: andrew.walls@ptsem.edu

Weathers, Janet L., PhD, University of Southern California, Assistant Professor—speech communication in ministry, 609-497-7889, Fax: 609-924-2973, E-mail: janet.weathers@ptsem.edu

Principia College

Elsah IL 62028

Phone: 618-374-5208
Fax: 618-374-5122
E-mail: csl@prin.edu
URL: www.prin.edu

TYPE OF INSTITUTION: Private, Christian Science
EXECUTIVE OFFICER: George Moffett, President
CHAIRPERSON: Christopher Scott Langton
UNDERGRADUATE ENROLLMENT: 570

Protestant-Episcopal Theological Seminary

3737 Seminary Rd, Alexandria VA 22304

Providence College

Theology Dept
Providence RI 02918

Phone: 401-865-2274
Fax: 401-865-2772

TYPE OF INSTITUTION: Private, Roman Catholic Dominican
CHAIRPERSON: James A. Driscoll, OP
UNDERGRADUATE ENROLLMENT: 3,600
GRADUATE ENROLLMENT: 1,009
DEGREES OFFERED: BA in Theology; MA in Biblical Studies, Religious Studies, Pastoral Ministries
UNDERGRADUATE MAJORS: 3
DEGREES CONFERRED: 3
DESCRIPTION OF UNDERGRADUATE PROGRAM: The program in Theology pursues two distinct objectives. 1) It provides all students fulfilling the two course general requirement with a large selection of courses dealing with a variety of pertinent areas and aspects of religion: Biblical literature, Roman Catholic theology, Protestant Christianity, and Jewish religious thought. 2) It provides majors in Theology with a program that is flexible and professional, designed to meet the particular and personal objectives of each student: professional, e.g., preparation for a career in religious education; or liberal, i.e., preparation for graduate study in religion or any other related discipline. Very popular with the students is our Minor program which provides an ordered and integral program under careful supervision for those whose interests are directed towards Theological Studies.
GRADUATE PROGRAM
Graduate Advisor: Robert J. Hennessey, OP
Graduate Degrees Offered: MA
Degrees Conferred: 23 MA
Graduate Students in Residence: 4 MA

Not in Residence: 40 MA

Average No. of New Students Enrolled: 44 MA

Women Students: 29 MA

Minority Students: 1 MA

Financial Aid to Other Students: Graduate Assistantships, 3

Attrition Among Students: 1% MA

Graduates Placed: 80% MA

DESCRIPTION OF GRADUATE PROGRAM AND RESEARCH FACILITIES: The objective of the graduate programs in religious studies is to offer a theological formation for a broad spectrum of students who are engaged professionally as teachers, religious education administrators, candidates to sacred orders, or those in formation, also for students and professors of literature, sociology, psychology, history or any other discipline to which theology might be related. The theological program emphasizes the continuity of theological tradition and the integration of contemporary theology into this tradition. Phillips Memorial Library contains 289,712 volumes and 64,860 bound periodicals.

ACADEMIC PLAN, ADMISSION REQUIREMENTS, FINANCIAL AID: Undergraduate: Theology majors follow a minimum of thirty-six hours in courses and/or seminar in Religious Studies. A minimum of nine hours of Philosophy are required, and a reading knowledge of one modern language is strongly advised. Admissions requirements: Applications must be received by February 1; for January admission the deadline is November 1. An official transcript of the secondary school record accompanied by two letters of recommendation from the applicant's secondary school teachers are needed. Applicants are required to submit the official results of the Scholastic Aptitude Test given by the College Entrance Examination Board. In lieu of the SAT the applicant may submit the test results of the American College Testing Program. Financial Aid: To be considered for financial aid all applicants must submit a Financial Aid Form (FAF) to the College Scholarship Service by February 15. Providence College financial aid is distributed on the basis of demonstrated need and the individual's ability to benefit from the educational opportunity the assistance offers. Graduate Requirements: For the MA in Religious Studies, at least 30 credits of graduate work of which 6 shall be in dogmatic theology, 6 in moral theology, 3 in Old Testament and 3 in New Testament. Also a three hour written comprehensive examination based on the required 18 credits specified above. For the MA in Biblical Studies, a reading proficiency in biblical Hebrew and Greek. Those who come unprepared in biblical languages are asked to pursue these courses on a priority basis. At least 30 credits of graduate level courses in sacred scripture of which 3 shall be on the historical aspects of the Old Testament, 3 shall be on the prophetic books, 3 on the wisdom literature, 3 on the synoptic gospels, 3 on the Pauline epistles and 3 on the Johannine literature. Also a three hour written comprehensive examination based on the required 18 credits specified above. For the MA in Pastoral Ministry, at least 30 credits of graduate work, of which 18 shall be in the areas specified for the MA in Religious Studies and 12 shall be in required Pastoral Ministry courses. Also, a three hour written comprehensive examination based on 3 credits in dogmatic theology, 3 credits in moral theology, 3 credits in scripture and 12 credits in pastoral ministry courses. Admissions Requirements: Bachelor's degree from a recognized college. Twenty-four credits in major with approximately a "B" average. This requirement may be fulfilled by twelve credits of undergraduate theology and twelve credits of philosophy, or their equivalent. Official transcripts and two written letters of recommendation must also be sent. Financial Aid: There is no financial aid on the graduate level. However, there are graduate assistantships.

FACULTY:

Azaro, Stanley, OP, ThD, Harvard University, 1989, Assistant Professor (on leave)

Barrera, Albino, OP, PhD, Yale, 1994, Assistant Professor

Barry, Robert, PhD, Boston College, 1996, Assistant Professor

Bonney, William, PhD, Fordham University, 1997, Assistant Professor

Collins, Raymond T. A., STD, University of Ottawa, 1959, Professor Emeritus

Conner, Paul, OP, STD, The Teresianum, Rome, Italy, 1992, Associate Professor (on leave)

Culpepper, Gary, PhD, Catholic University, 1994, Assistant Professor

Driscoll, James A., OP, STD, University of St Thomas Aquinas, Rome, 1967, Assistant Professor

Follmar, Mary Ann, STD, Gregorian University (Rome), 1986, Assistant Professor

Folsey, William D., OP, STD, University of St Thomas, Rome, 1966, Associate Professor

Gondreau, Paul, STD (cand.), University of Fribourg, Switzerland, 1997, Assistant Professor

Hall, Ralph T., OP, STD, University of St Thomas Aquinas, Rome, 1959, Associate Professor

Hennessey, Robert J., OP, STD, Dominican House of Studies, Washington, DC , 1992, Professor

Henritzy, Elias, OP, MA, STL, Dominican House of Studies,1993 (on leave)

Judd, Augustine, OP, MDiv, STL, Dominican House of Studies, Instructor

Keating, James, PhD, Catholic University (1998), Assistant Professor

Keegan, Terence J., OP, STD, University of St Thomas Aquinas, Rome, 1975, Professor (on leave)

Langlois, John A., OP, PhD (cand.), STL, Dominican House of Studies, 1992, Instructor

McPhail, J. Stuart, STLr, College of the Immaculate Conception, 1971, Instructor

Quigley, James F., OP, STD, University of St Thomas Aquinas, Rome, 1984, Associate Professor

Reid, John J., OP, STLr, College of the Immaculate Conception, 1974, Assistant Professor (on leave)

Reid, Patrick V., PhD, St Mary's University, 1977, Professor

Scully, M. Elaine, PhD, Boston University, 1977, Assistant Professor

Seaver, Paul W., OP, STLr, College of the Immaculate Conception, 1969, Professor

Stokes, David L., Jr., PhD, The Princeton Theological Seminary, 1999, Assistant Professor

Tkacik, Michael J., PhD, Duquesne University, 1998, Assistant Professor

Topel, Bernadette E., PhD, University of St Michael's College, Toronto, Canada (on leave)

Wagner, Walter, OP, JD, Duke University (1987); STL, Dominican House of Studies, 1994 (on leave)

Providence College and Seminary

Otterburne, Manitoba R0A 1G0
Canada

Phone: 204-433-7488
Fax: 204-433-7158
E-mail: dclimenhaga@providence.mb.ca

TYPE OF INSTITUTION: Private

EXECUTIVE OFFICER: Larry McKinney, President

University of Puget Sound

1500 N Warner
Tacoma WA 98416

Phone: 253-756-3745
Fax: 253-756-3500
E-mail: dedwards@ups.edu
URL: www.ups.edu/religion

TYPE OF INSTITUTION: Private
EXECUTIVE OFFICER: Susan Resneck Pierce, President
CHAIRPERSON: Douglas R. Edwards
UNDERGRADUATE ENROLLMENT: 2,800

Puget Sound Christian College

410 4th Ave N
Edmonds WA 98020

Phone: 425-775-8686
Fax: 425-775-8688

TYPE OF INSTITUTION: Private, Non-Denominational
EXECUTIVE OFFICER: Mark Krause, Academic Dean
UNDERGRADUATE ENROLLMENT: 200

Purdue University

Religious Studies, Dept of Philosophy
LAEB
West Lafayette IN 47907

Phone: 317-494-4276
Fax: 317-496-1616
E-mail: philosophy@sla.purdue.edu

TYPE OF INSTITUTION: Public
EXECUTIVE OFFICER: Steven Beering, President
COORDINATOR: Donald W. Mitchell
UNDERGRADUATE ENROLLMENT: 32,000
GRADUATE ENROLLMENT: 6,000
DEGREES OFFERED: BA Major
UNDERGRADUATE MAJORS: 7
DEGREES CONFERRED: 2

DESCRIPTION OF DEPARTMENT: Purdue's interdepartmental program offers the opportunity for the critical study of religion using a variety of methodologies from various disciplines within the University. This approach allows students to tailor the program to their special interests while broadening their understanding of the diversity of the religious life and thought of humankind. The program offers thirty courses through five departments.

FACULTY:

Astell, A. W., PhD, Wisconsin (1987), 1988, Professor—religious literature, medieval spirituality

Buckser, A. S., PhD, Berkeley (1993), 1995, Assistant Professor—anthropology of religion, religious movements

Curtis, S. K., PhD, Missouri (1986), 1989, Associate Professor—American religious history

Davidson, J. D., PhD, Notre Dame (1969), 1968, Professor—sociology of religion, congregational studies

Finke, R., PhD, Washington (1984), 1989, Associate Professor—sociology of religion

Goodhart, S. T., PhD, SUNY, Buffalo (1977), 1997, Associate Professor—biblical studies, modern Jewish and philosophy

King, R. J., PhD, Indiana (1994), 1996, Assistant Professor—ancient religions

Knudsen, D. D., PhD, North Carolina (1964), 1969, Professor—religion and society

Marina, J., PhD, Yale (1993), 1993, Assistant Professor—18th/19th century philosophy of religion

Mitchell, D. W., PhD, Hawaii (1971), 1971, Professor—Asian and comparative religion, Buddhist-Christian dialogue

Rowe, W. L., PhD, Michigan (1962), 1962, Professor—philosophy of religion

Rudolph, V. C., PhD, Iowa (1971), 1968, Associate Professor—Bible as literature

Ryba, T. W., PhD, Northwestern (1986), 1990, Adjunct Professor—method in the study of religion

Schrag, C. O., PhD, Harvard (1957), 1957, Distinguished Professor—phenomenology, existentialism, philosophy of religion

Young, G. D., PhD, Brandeis (1970), 1966, Associate Professor—ancient Israel and Semitic religions

Université du Québec à Chicoutimi

930 Jacques Cartier, Chicoutimi, Quebec G7H 2B1 Canada

Université du Québec à Montreal

Case Postale 8888
Succ. centre-ville
Montreal, Quebec H3C 3P8
Canada

Phone: 514-987-4497
Fax: 514-987-7856
E-mail: ribou.maryse@uqam.ca

TYPE OF INSTITUTION: Public
EXECUTIVE OFFICER: Paule Leduc, Rector
CHAIRPERSON: Marie-Andrée Roy
COORDINATOR: Gerard Rochais
UNDERGRADUATE ENROLLMENT: 160
GRADUATE ENROLLMENT: 40

Université du Québec à Rimouski

300 allée des Ursulines
Rimouski, Québec G5L 3A1
Canada

Phone: 418-723-1986, ext 1739
Fax: 418-724-1851
E-mail: monique_dumais@uqar.uquebec.ca

TYPE OF INSTITUTION: Public, Non-Denominational
EXECUTIVE OFFICER: Pierre Couture, Recteur
CHAIRPERSON: Monique Dumais
COORDINATORS: Renée DesRosiers (Undergraduate); Marie Beaulieu (Graduate)
UNDERGRADUATE ENROLLMENT: 149
GRADUATE ENROLLMENT: 76

Université du Québec à Trois-Rivieres

3351 Blvd Des Forges, Trois-Rivieres, Quebec G9A 5H7 Canada

Queens College

1900 Selwyn Ave, Charlotte NC 28274

Queens College of the City University of New York

Flushing NY 11367

Queen's University

Dept of Religious Studies
Kingston, Ontario K7L 3N6
Canada

Phone: 613-533-2106
Fax: 613-533-6879
E-mail: thomaslm@post.queensu.ca
URL: qsilver.queensu.ca/religion

TYPE OF INSTITUTION: Public

CHAIRPERSON: Pamela Dickey Young

UNDERGRADUATE ENROLLMENT: 8,000

DEGREES OFFERED: BA, BA(HON)

UNDERGRADUATE MAJORS: 106

DEGREES CONFERRED: 16

DESCRIPTION OF UNDERGRADUATE PROGRAM: The Department of Religious Studies is one among many departments within the Faculty of Arts and Science at Queen's. Students may take a three-year BA (15 courses) with a five-course Minor concentration in Religion, or a four-year Honours BA (19 courses) with either a seven-course Medial or a ten-course Major concentration. For all concentrators there is a combination of a core of required courses and flexibility of choice.

FACULTY:

Basser, Herbert W., PhD, Toronto (1983), 1980, Professor—Old Testament, Judaism

Goldberg, Ellen, PhD, Toronto (1995), 1997, Assistant Professor—history of religions, Hinduism, Buddism, women and religions

Hospital, Clifford G., PhD, Harvard (1973), 1971, Professor—history of religions, Hinduism

James, William C., PhD, Chicago (1974), 1973, Professor—religion and literature

Morrow, William S., PhD, Toronto (1988), 1987, Associate Professor—Hebrew scriptures

Schumaker, Millard K., PhD, Queen's (1970), 1969, Professor—ethics

Young, Pamela Dickey, PhD, Southern Methodist (1983), 1984, Professor—theology, women's studies

Zeidman, Reena L., PhD, Toronto (1992), 1992, Assistant Professor—Judaism

Quincy College

Dept of Theology and Religious Studies, Quincy IL 62301

Quinnipiac College

Hamden CT 06518

Radcliffe College

10 Garden St, Cambridge MA 02138 (See Harvard University)

Radford University

Dept of Philosophy/Religious Stds
Box 6943
Radford VA 24142

Phone: 540-831-5213
Fax: 540-831-5919
E-mail: kkipling@runet.edu
URL: www.runet.edu/~phre

TYPE OF INSTITUTION: Public
EXECUTIVE OFFICER: Douglas Covington, President
CHAIRPERSON: Kim J. Kipling
UNDERGRADUATE ENROLLMENT: 8,500

Ramapo College of New Jersey

Mahwah NJ 07430

Randolph-Macon College

Ashland VA 23005

Randolph-Macon Women's College

2500 Rivermont Ave, Lynchburg VA 24503

Reconstructionist Rabbinical College

Church Rd and Greenwood Ave, Wyncote PA 19095

Redemption Bible College

PO Box 519, Kaulua HI 96734

University of Redlands

1200 East Colton Avenue
PO Box 3080
Redlands CA 92373-0999

Phone: 909-793-2121 ext 3892
Fax: 909-793-2029
E-mial: bhuntley@uor.edu

TYPE OF INSTITUTION: Private
EXECUTIVE OFFICER: James Appleton, President
CHAIRPERSON: W. B. (Bill) Huntley
UNDERGRADUATE ENROLLMENT: 1,600
GRADUATE ENROLLMENT: 200

Reed College

Dept of Religion
3203 SE Woodstock Blvd
Portland OR 97202-8199
TYPE OF INSTITUTION: Private, Non-Denominational
EXECUTIVE OFFICER: Steven Koblik, President
CHAIRPERSON: Steven Wasserstrom
UNDERGRADUATE ENROLLMENT: 1,188

Phone: 503-771-1112
Fax: 503-777-7769

Reformed Bible College

3333 E Beltline Ave NE, Grand Rapids MI 49505

Reformed Presbyterian Theological Seminary

7418 Penn Ave, Pittsburgh PA 15208

Reformed Theological Seminary

1015 Maitland Center Commons, Maitland FL 32751

Reformed Theological Seminary

5422 Clinton Blvd, Jackson MS 39209

Regent College

5800 University Blvd
Vancouver, British Columbia V6T 2E4
Canada

Phone: 604-224-3245
Fax: 604-224-3097
E-mail: admissions@regent-college.edu
URL: www.regent-college.edu

TYPE OF INSTITUTION: Private
EXECUTIVE OFFICER: Walter Wright, Jr., President; Gordon T. Smith, Dean
UNDERGRADUATE ENROLLMENT: 45
GRADUATE ENROLLMENT: 1,305
DEGREES OFFERED: Certificate of Christian Studies
UNDERGRADUATE MAJORS: None
DEGREES CONFERRED: 1
DESCRIPTION OF UNDERGRADUATE PROGRAM: The CCS program is designed to give students from all walks of life a basic understanding of the Christian faith and to provide them with the tools for an ongoing life of Christian study, meditation and practical service. The Certificate allows students to attend Regent who may or may not have a university degree but who desire a goal-oriented program. Certificate students study along with Graduate students at the Vancouver Campus.
GRADUATE PROGRAM

Graduate Advisor: Wayne Heaslip (Registrar)

Graduate Degrees Offered: Other: MCS; ThM; DPCS

Degrees Conferred: 80 MCS; 4 ThM; 78 DPCS

Not in Residence: 1,305 Other

Average No. of New Students Enrolled: 240 Other

Women Students: 570 Other

Foreign Students: 749 Other

Minimum GRE Score Requisite to Admission: No

Minimum GPA Score Requisite to Admission: Yes, 2.8 on 4.0 scale

Foreign Language Proficiency Evaluated: No

Financial Aid to First Year Students: 25% Other

Financial Aid to Other Students: 21% Other

DESCRIPTION OF GRADUATE PROGRAM AND RESEARCH FACILITIES: The focus of Regent College programs is to provide students with a basic understanding of the Christian faith and to provide them with the tools for an ongoing life of Christian study, meditation and practical service. The Regent vision is for the integration of faith and life, that is, the need to bring the insights of faith to bear on personal, social and cultural issues. 1) The Diploma of Christian Studies is the foundational program of Regent College. Most students who enroll in the DpCS complete their studies and then return to secular vocations. 2) The Master of Christian Studies is designed to provide graduate theological education to those called to a vocation in the professions or to lay ministry in the church. It is also useful for those anticipating further graduate studies in prepartion for an academic career. There are three tracks to choose from: Thesis, Comprehensive Exam or Ministry Research Project. 3) The Master of Theology degree is the highest academic degree awarded at Regent College. The degree entails a one or two year program of advanced graduate level theological study. This degree has an inter-disciplinary approach to theological studies by way of the development of competence in theological research and writing, and the development of teaching and communication skills. The Library consists of a collection of over 110,000 items in paper, microform, and audio and visual formats, and thus is one of the largest theological libraries in Canada. The Library collects over 550 periodical titles in support of the course and programs offered at Regent College and Carey Theological College. Reference services are also available.

ACADEMIC PLAN, ADMISSION REQUIREMENTS, FINANCIAL AID: Regent has full semesters in Fall and Spring with shorter (one to three week) classes of more intense format offered in Winter and Summer School. 1) For the CCS the normal entrance requirement is a Grade 12 diploma or equivalent. Applicants should be 23 years of age or older. 2) For the Diploma of Christian Studies admission requirements are an undergraduate degree with a minimum grade point average of 2.8. 3) For the Masters of Christian Studies admission requirements are an undergraduate degree with a minimum of 2.8 grade point average and at least 12 credit of graduate level theological education with a minimum grade point average of 3.0 out of 4.0 for the comprehensive exam and ministry research project tract and 3.3 out of 4.0 for the thesis and arts thesis project. Several forms of financial assistance are made available to full-time students who have been admitted to a Regent program each year. They include Academic Entrance Scholarship, Endowment Scholarship and Awards, Bursaries, and Parachurch Youth Organization Tuition Reduction. There are also spousal tuition exemption programs for spouses of full time students. Canadian students can apply for Canada Student Loans and American students may apply for subsidized and unsubsidized Stafford student loans. Further information on any of these programs can be obtained from the Financial Aid Office.

FACULTY:

Adeney, Miriam, PhD, Washington State University (1980), 1980, Research Professor—missions and cross-cultural communication, 604-224-3245, Fax: 604-224-3097, E-mail: miriamsea@aol.com

Armerding, Carl, PhD, Brandies University (1968), 1970, Adjunct Professor—Old Testament

Ayers, Thena, EdD, University of Toronto (1992), 1991, Associate Dean of Students, Summer School Dean, Assistant Professor—adult education, 604-224-3245, Fax: 604-224-3097, E-mail: tayres@interchange.ubc.ca

Barnes, Craig, Adjunct Professor—spirituality

Barnett, Paul, PhD, University of London, Research Professor—biblical studies

Bell, Roy, DMin, Fuller, Professor Emeritus—family ministries

Collins, Philip, DMin, Fuller, Professor Emeritus

Crabb, Larry, Adjunct Professor—applied theology, psychology

Dawn, Marva, Adjunct Professor—spirituality

Dearborn, Timothy A., PhD, University of Aberdeen, Adjunct Professor—applied theology

Diewert, David, PhD, University of Toronto (1991), 1991, Associate Professor—biblical languages, 604-224-3245, Fax: 604-224-3097, E-mail: dt_diewert@bc.sympatico.ca

Fee, Gordon, PhD, University of Southern California (1966), 1986, Dean of Faculty, Professor—New Testament studies, 604-224-3245, Fax: 604-224-3097, E-mail: gfee@interchange.ubc.ca

Gaetz, Ivan, MEd, University of Alberta (1990), 1993, Librarian, 604-224-3245, Fax: 604-224-3097, E-mail: rgtig@unixg.ubc.ca

Gay, Craig M., PhD, Boston (1989), 1991, Associate Professor—interdisciplinary studies, 604-224-3245, Fax: 604-224-3097, E-mail: cmgay@regent-college.edu

Grenz, Stanley J., DTheo, Munich (1980), 1990, Pioneer McDonald Professor—Baptist Heritage, theology, ethics, 604-224-3245, Fax: 604-224-3097

Hancock, Maxine, PhD, University of Alberta (1992), 1993, Associate Professor—interdisciplinary studies, 604-224-3245, Fax: 604-224-3097, E-mail: mhancock@bordercity.com

Harris, Peter, DipHE, Trinity College, Bristol, Adjunct Professor—missions and conservation

Henkelman, Mark, PhD, Toronto, Adjunct Professor—philosophy of science

Houston, James M., DPhil, Oxford (1949), 1991, Board of Governors, 1970, Professor—spiritual theology, 604-224-3245, Fax: 604-224-3097

Hui, Edwin, PhD, University of British Columbia (1976), 1993, Associate Dean (Chinese Studies), 1995, Professor—medical ethics, spiritual theology, Chinese studies, 604-224-3245, Fax: 604-224-3097, E-mail: huicspbi@unixg.ubc.ca

Lewis, Donald M., DPhil, Ocford (1981), 1981, Professor—church history, 604-224-3245, Fax: 604-224-3097, E-mail: donlewis@unixg.ubc.ca

Ley, David, PhD, Pennsylvania State University, Adjunct Professor—urban and social geography

Lyon, David, PhD, University of Bradford, Adjunct Professor—sociology

Mogan, Peter, LLB, Faculty Associate—law

Mutch, Barbara, DMin, Princeton Theological Seminary, Assistant Professor—ministry, Director of Supervised Ministry Program

Packer, James I., DPhil, Oxford (1954), 1979, Board of Governors, Professor—theology, 604-224-3245, Fax: 604-224-3097

Peterson, Eugene H., Professor Emeritus—spiritual theology

Provan, Iain, PhD, Cambridge (1986), 1997, Marshal Sheppard Chair of Biblical Studies—Old Testament, 604-224-3245, Fax: 604-224-3097, E-mail: iprovan@interchange.ubc.ca

Ringma, Charles, PhD, Queensland (1991), 1997, Professor—missions and evangelism, 604-224-3245, Fax: 604-224-3097, E-mail: ringma@regent-college.edu

Schindell, Dallard W., DipCS, Regent College (1972), 1980, Director of Publications, Director of the Lookout Art Gallery, Instructor—Christianity and art, 604-224-3245, Fax: 604-224-3097, E-mail: dal@regent-college.edu

Shaw, Luci, BA, Wheaton College, Adjunct Professor—writer in residence, 604-224-3245, Fax: 604-224-3097

Smith, Gordon, PhD, Loyola School of Theology (1987), 1998, Academic Dean, Associate Professor—spiritual theology, 604-224-3245, Fax: 604-224-3097, E-mail: gordontsmith1@compuserve.com

Soderlund, Sven K., PhD, University of Glasgow (1978), 1988, Dean of Students, Associate Professor—biblical studies, 604-224-3245, Fax: 604-224-3097, E-mail: sks@unixg.ubc.ca

Stackhouse, John G., Jr., PhD, University of Chicago (1987), 1998, Sangwoo Youtong Chee Professor—theology, 604-224-3245, Fax: 604-224-3097, E-mail: jgs@regent-college.edu

Stelck, Brian F., PhD, University of Alberta (1994), 1994, Principal, Assistant Professor—applied theology, 604-224-3245, Fax: 604-224-3097, E-mail: stelck@unixg.ubc.ca

Stevens, R. Paul, DMin, Fuller (1987), 1997, Interim Academic Dean, 1996, Professor—applied theology, 604-224-3245, Fax: 604-224-3097

Thorson, Walter R., PhD, California Institute of Technology, Adjunct Professor—philosophy of science, 604-224-3245, Fax: 604-224-3097

Toews, John B., PhD, University of Colorado (1962), 1989, Professor—church history and Anabaptist studies, 604-224-3245, Fax: 604-224-3097, E-mail: jbtoews@interchange.ubc.ca

Towner, Philip, PhD, Aberdeen, Adjunct Professor—New Testament studies, missiology, Chinese studies, 604-224-3245, Fax: 604-224-3097

Waltke, Bruce K., PhD, Harvard (1965), 1991, Professor Emeritus—Old Testament studies, 604-224-3245, Fax: 604-224-3097

Watts, Rikk, PhD, Cambridge (1990), 1996, Associate Professor—New Testament, 604-224-3245, Fax: 604-224-3097, E-mail: rwatts@interchange.ubc.ca

Wilkinson, Loren, PhD, Syracuse University (1972), 1981, Professor ,7interdisciplinarystudies and philosophy, 604-224-3245, Fax: 604-224-3097

Wright, Walter C., Jr., PhD, Fuller (1977), 1988, President, Professor—Christian leadership and management, 604-224-3245, Fax: 604-224-3097, E-mail: wcwright@netcom.ca

Zimmerman, John C., DMin, San Francisco Theological Seminary (1977), 1986, Charles Bentall Professor—pastoral studies, 604-224-3245, Fax: 604-224-3097, E-mail: jczimmer@unixg.ubc.ca

---

Regent University

1000 Centerville Turnpike, Virginia Beach VA 23463

University of Regina

Religious Studies Program
Regina, Saskatchewan S4S 0A2
Canada

Phone: 306-585-5128
Fax: 306-585-4815
E-mail: religious.studies@uregina.ca
URL: www.uregina.ca/arts/rlst

TYPE OF INSTITUTION: Public
COORDINATOR: Leona Anderson
DEGREES OFFERED: BA, MA
UNDERGRADUATE MAJORS: 45
DEGREES CONFERRED: 5
GRADUATE PROGRAM
Graduate Degrees Offered: MA
Degrees Conferred: 18 MA
Graduate Students in Residence: 8 MA
Not in Residence: 4 MA
Average No. of New Students Enrolled: 3 MA
Women Students: 8 MA
Minority Students: 1 MA
Foreign Students: 0 MA
Minimum GRE Score Requisite to Admission: No.
Minimum GPA Score Requisite to Admission: Yes, 75 on a scale of 100
Foreign Language Proficiency Evaluated: No.
Financial Aid to First Year Students: 1% MA
Financial Aid to Other Students: 2% MA
Attrition Among Students: 10% MA
DESCRIPTION OF GRADUATE PROGRAM AND RESEARCH FACILITIES: The Religious
  Studies program offers students the opportunity to examine critically the realm of religion in
  its varied manifestations. Students can take courses in several religious traditions as well as
  thematic and methodological studies. The masters program requires a minimum of 15
  course credit hours and 15 credit hours of thesis research. Research from a comparative per-
  spective is especially encouraged.
FACULTY:
Anderson, Leona, PhD, McMaster University—Hinduism, Sanskrit literature, history of South
  Asia, popular religious movements in India, women and religion, new religions
Bolen, Don, DPhil (cand.), Oxford University—Christianity, ecumenical studies, Christology
Gorski, Isidore, STL—classical and contemporary Christology, gospel narratives of Jesus' suf-
  fering and death, gospel according to John
Greifenhagen, Volker, PhD, Duke University—Islam, Qur'an, images of Islam in the West, He-
  brew Bible, Pentateuch, emergent Judaism (Persian period), comparative scriptures and interpretations in Judaism, Christianity and Islam
Hillis, Bryan, PhD, University of Chicago—Christian denominationalism, religion in Canada,
  history of Christianity, Lutheran historiography, Lutheran/Evangelical relations, religious
  perspectives on death and dying.
Hordern, Richard, PhD, Union Theological Seminary, New York—Christianity, contemporary
  liberation theology, war and peace, English church history 15-19th centuries, biblical hermeneutics and interpretation, history of churches in Canada, especially on the prairies.
Kuikman, Jacoba, PhD, University of St Michael's College, Toronto School of Theology—history of antisemitism, first century Jewish-Christianity, Christology in the context of religious
  pluralism, historical Jesus studies, women in Judiasm and Christianity, contemporary
  Judiasm

Oh, Kang-nam, PhD, McMaster University—East Asian Buddhism, Hua-Yen Buddhism, mysticism, religious pluralism, Buddhist-Christian dialogue

---

Regis College

Religious Studies Dept, Weston MA 02193

Regis College

15 St Mary St
Toronto, Ontario M4Y 2R5
Canada

Phone: 416-922-5474
Fax: 416-922-2898
E-mail: regis.registrar@utoronto.ca

TYPE OF INSTITUTION: Denominational: Roman Catholic
EXECUTIVE OFFICERS: John E. Costello, President; Ronald A. Mercier, Dean
CHAIRPERSON: Carl Starkloff
GRADUATE ENROLLMENT: 203

Regis University

3333 Regis Blvd, Denver CO 80221-1099

Institute for Religious and Pastoral Studies

University of Dallas, Irving TX 75062-4799

Renison College

University of Waterloo, Waterloo, Ontario N2L 3G4 Canada

University of Rhode Island

Dept of Philosophy, Kingston RI 02881

Rhodes College

Dept of Religious Studies
200 N Parkway
Memphis TN 38112

Phone: 901-726-3664
Fax: 901-726-3727

TYPE OF INSTITUTION: Private, Presbyterian
EXECUTIVE OFFICER: William E. Troutt, President and Chief Executive Officer
CHAIRPERSON: Stephen R. Haynes
UNDERGRADUATE ENROLLMENT: 1,450
DEGREES OFFERED: BA
UNDERGRADUATE MAJORS: 26
DEGREES CONFERRED: 15

DESCRIPTION OF UNDERGRADUATE PROGRAM: The Department of Religious Studies has as its primary objective the academic study of religion in the context of a liberal arts education. The courses offered explore living religious traditions, especially the Judeo-Christian faith and its relevance for contemporary life and are a vital part of the basic requirement in humanities at Rhodes. There are twelve full-time and two part-time faculty members who present a wide spectrum of courses in biblical and theological studies, history of religions, and advanced rhetoric and methodology. The department also sponsors internships in Memphis area religious, social and health agencies. Majors in religious studies are fully qualified to enter seminary and prepare for a vocation in the church, or to pursue a post-graduate degree in the field.

FACULTY:

Armour, Ellen T., PhD, Vanderbilt University (1993), 1991, Assistant Professor—contemporary philosophy and theology, historical theology, feminist theory and religion, 901-843-3379, E-mail: armour@rhodes.edu

Bass, Diana B., PhD, Duke University (1991), 1997, Associate Professor—history of American religion, Evangelicalism and fundentalism, religion and society, 901-843-3262, E-mail: bass@rhodes.edu

Batey, Richard A., PhD, Vanderbilt University (1961), 1965, Professor—New Testament studies, 901-843-3909, E-mail: batey@rhodes.edu

Favazza, Joseph A., PhD, The Catholic University of Louvain, Belgium (1987), 1993, Assistant Professor—historical theology, Catholic studies, religion and ritual, 901-843-3907, E-mail: favazza@rhodes.edu

Haynes, Stephen R., PhD, Emory University (1989), 1989, Associate Professor—religion and politics, holocaust studies, religion and literature, 901-843-3583, E-mail: haynes@rhodes.edu

Ivory, Luther D., PhD, Emory University (1994), 1997, Assistant Professor—African-American religion and ethics, civil rights movement, 901-843-3379, E-mail: ivory@rhodes.edu

Kaltner, John C., PhD, Drew University (1993), 1996, Assistant Professor—Hebrew Bible, biblical languages, theology, Islamic studies, 901-843-3407, E-mail: kaltner@rhodes.edu

McKenzie, Steven L., ThD, Harvard University (1983), 1983, Associate Professor—Hebrew Bible, Hebrew, 901-843-3908, E-mail: mckenzie@rhodes.edu

McLain, F. Michael, PhD, Vanderbilt University (1966), 1967, Professor—philosophical theology, 901-843-3740, E-mail: mmclain@rhodes.edu

McNary-Zak, Bernadette, (1997), 1999, Assistant Professor—Early Christianity, Gnostic and Hellenstic thought, asceticism, Catholic studies, 901-843-3664, E-mail: mcnary@rhodes.edu

Muesse, Mark W., PhD, Harvard University (1987), 1988, Associate Professor—theology, comparative religions, 901-843-3589, E-mail: muesse@rhodes.edu

Streete, Gail P. C., PhD, Drew University (1983), 1990, Associate Professor—biblical studies, classics, women and religion, ascetical theology, 901-843-3742, E-mail: gstreete@rhodes.edu

Walsh, Carey E., ThD, Harvard University (1996), 1996, Assistant Professor—Hebrew Bible, 901-843-3578, E-mail: walsh@rhodes.edu

---

Rice University

Dept of Religous Studies, MS 15
PO Box 1892
Houston TX 77251-1892

Phone: 713-285-5201
Fax: 713-285-5486
E-mail: reli@rice.edu
URL: www.rice.edu/~religion/

TYPE OF INSTITUTION: Private

EXECUTIVE OFFICER: Malcolm Gillis, President

CHAIRPERSON: Gerald P. McKenny

UNDERGRADUATE ENROLLMENT: 2,700

GRADUATE ENROLLMENT: 1,400

DEGREES OFFERED: BA, MA, PhD

UNDERGRADUATE MAJORS: 19

DEGREES CONFERRED: 4

DESCRIPTION OF UNDERGRADUATE PROGRAM: The Department of Religious Studies, which was founded in 1968, has shaped its program to include a broad range of religious experiences, theories, and traditions. Its curriculum, both on the undergraduate and graduate level, is designed to educate students in the philosophical, theological, ethical, historical, textual and interdisciplinary approaches to religion, and to faciliate knowledge of different traditions. Nine full-time faculty members represent the following fields: African Studies, Biblical Studies (New Testament), Buddhism, Ethics (including biomedical ethics), Hebrew Bible, History of Christianity, Judaic Studies, Philosophy of Religion/Theology, and Psychology of Religion.

GRADUATE PROGRAM

Member of the Council on Graduate Studies in Religion

Graduate Advisor: Werner Kelber

Graduate Degrees Offered: MA; PhD

Degrees Conferred: 0 MA; 3 PhD

Graduate Students in Residence: 3 MA; 10 PhD

Not in Residence: 0 MA; 2 PhD

Average No. of New Students Enrolled: 2 MA; 0 PhD

Women Students: 1 MA; 4 PhD

Minority Students: 0 MA; 0 PhD

Foreign Students: 1 MA; 3 PhD

Minimum GRE Score Requisite to Admission: Yes

Minimum GPA Score Requisite to Admission: Yes

Foreign Language Proficiency Evaluated: No

Financial Aid to First Year Students: 100% MA; 100% PhD

Financial Aid to Other Students: 100% MA; 100% PhD

Attrition Among Students: 0% MA; 0% PhD

Graduates Places: 0% MA; 66% PhD

DESCRIPTION OF GRADUATE PROGRAM AND RESEARCH FACILITIES: The graduate program is designed to facilitate broad knowledge in Religious Studies and to permit flexibility as well as interdisciplinary pursuits within a framework of clearly defined fields. Students can major or minor in the following fields: AREA I. TRADITIONS: Historical and Textual Studies in the following Religious Traditions: 1) Christianity and/or Judaism in Antiquity; 2) Christianity and/or Judaism in the Modern World; 3) Buddhism: Focus On India And Tibet; 4) African Religions. AREA II. THEORIES AND METHODS: 1) Ethics/Biomedical Ethics; 2) Psychology of Religion; 3) Philosophy of Religion; 4) Religion and Contemporary Culture; 5) Comparative Studies; 6) Mysticism.

ACADEMIC PLAN, ADMISSION REQUIREMENTS, FINANCIAL AID: Graduate admission will be granted to a limited number of qualified students. A distinguished undergraduate record and high GRE scores are essential. An advanced degree in the humanities is desirable.

Within the limits of available funds fellowships and scholarships are awarded to qualified students. Fellowships include a stipend and a tuition waiver; scholarships provide a waiver of tuition only. Scholarships carry tuition grants of $16,100. MA students are eligible for stipend for two years and four years for PhD students.

FACULTY:

Bongmba, Elias, PhD, Joint Program at Iliff School of Theology and University of Denver (1995), 1995, Assistant Professor—African religions, 713-527-8750 ext 2759, Fax: 713-285-5486, E-mail: bongmba@rice.edu

Heitman, Elizabeth, PhD, Rice University (1987), 1988, Adjunct Associate Professor—medical and social ethics, emphasizing interaction of religion, culture, and medicine, ethics in professional relationships and communication, 713-500-9489, Fax: 713-500-9495, E-mail: sph0349@utsph.sph.uth.tmc.edu

Henze, Matthias, PhD, Harvard (1997), 1997, Assistant Professor—Hebrew Bible & history of interpretation, second temple studies, Aramaic/Syriac language and literature, 713-527-8750 ext 2754, E-mail: mhenze@rice.edu

Karff, Samuel E., PhD, Hebrew Union (1961), 1979, Lecturer—classic rabbinic theology, non-legal literature known as Agada, 713-771-6221, Fax: 713-771-5705

Kelber, Werner H., PhD, University of Chicago (1970), 1973, Turner Professor of Biblical Studies—early Christian literature (canonical and non-canonical), Christian origins, hermeneutics, and philosophy of language, 713-527-4995, Fax: 713-285-5486, E-mail: kelber@rice.edu

Klein, Anne C., PhD, University of Virginia (1981), 1989, Professor—Asian religions with strong emphasis on Indo-Tibetan Buddhist thought and practice, comparative and cross-cultural work on women and Buddhism incorporating contemporary feminist theory, 713-737-5612, Fax: 713-285-5486, E-mail: ack@rice.edu

Lobel, Diana, PhD, Harvard (1995), 1997, Assistant Professor—classical, Jewish & Islamic philosophy & religious thought; biblical interpretation; comparative religious thought (Eastern & Western), 713-527-8750 ext 2778, E-mail: dlobel@rice.edu

McKenny, Gerald P., PhD, University of Chicago (1989), 1989, Associate Professor and Chair—theological ethics in western traditions, theoretical and clinical health care ethics, comparative religious ethics, 713-737-5674, Fax: 713-285-5486, E-mail: mckenny@rice.edu

Parsons, William B., PhD, University of Chicago (1993), 1993, Associate Professor—psychology of religion and mysticism, 713-527-8750 ext 2440, Fax: 713-285-5486, E-mail: pars@rice.edu

Reiser, Stanley J., PhD, Harvard (1970), MD, State University of New York Downstate Medical Center (1963), 1983, Adjunct Professor—ethics and humanistic traditions of medicine, influence of technology on values and practice in medicine, 713-500-5080, Fax: 713-500-5088, E-mail: sreiser@heart.med.uth.tmc.edu

Sanborn, Hugh W., PhD, University of Iowa (1975), 1973, Adjunct Assistant Professor—psychology of religion, and religion and personality, 713-741-5850, Fax: 713-285-5486, E-mail: ucmgh@uh.edu

Stroup, John M., PhD, Yale University (1980), 1988, Harry and Hazel Chavanne Professor of Religious Studies—history of Christianity, especially the reformation and its European heritage, church-state relations, Protestant and Catholic political theology in relation to cultural criticism and modern ideologies, 713-527-8750 ext 2643, Fax: 713-285-5486, E-mail: stroup@rice.edu

Wyschogrod, Edith, PhD, Columbia (1970), 1992, J. Newton Rayzor Professor of Philosophy and Religious Thought—contemporary continental philosophy of religion, comparative philosophy, religion and literature, phenomenological and post-structuralist ethics, 713-527-8750 ext 2710, Fax: 713-285-5486, E-mail: stedith@rice. edu

The Richard Stockton College of New Jersey

Jim Leeds Rd
Pomona NJ 08240

Phone: 609-652-1776
Fax: 609-652-4550
URL: www.stockton.edu

TYPE OF INSTITUTION: Public
EXECUTIVE OFFICER: Vera King Farris, President
COORDINATOR: Anne D. Birdwhistell
UNDERGRADUATE ENROLLMENT: 6,000
GRADUATE ENROLLMENT: 400

University of Richmond

Dept of Religion
Richmond VA 23173

Phone: 804-289-8325
Fax: 804-287-6054
E-mail: sfisk@richmond.edu
URL: www.richmond.edu

TYPE OF INSTITUTION: Private
EXECUTIVE OFFICER: William E. Cooper, President
CHAIRPERSON: Frank E. Eakin, Jr.
UNDERGRADUATE ENROLLMENT: 3,200
DEGREES OFFERED: BA; Religion
UNDERGRADUATE MAJORS: 10
DEGREES CONFERRED: 7
DESCRIPTION OF UNDERGRADUATE PROGRAM: The academic study of religion is an integral part of the liberal arts curriculum at the University of Richmond. While a course in religious studies is not required for graduation, specially designed courses may meet field-of-study requirements in the general education curriculum. Majors are encouraged to pursue both breadth and depth in an atmosphere both nurturing and challenging.

FACULTY:

Bergren, Theodore A., PhD, University of Pennsylvania (1988), 1991, Associate Professor—New Testament, Christian origins, 804-289-8327, Fax: 804-287-6504, E-mail: tbergren@richmond.edu

Davis, G. Scott, PhD, Princeton University (1984), 1994, Lewis T. Booker Associate Professor of Religion and Ethics—ethics, 804-289-8331, Fax: 804-287-6504, E-mail: sdavis@richmond.edu

Eakin, Frank E., Jr., PhD, Duke University (1964), 1966, Weinstein-Rosenthal Professor of Jewish and Christian Studies—TaNaK, Judaism, Ancient Near East, 804-289-8326, Fax: 804-287-6504, E-mail: feakin@richmond.edu

Geaney, Jane M., PhD, University of Chicago (1996), 1997, Assistant Professor—comparative philosophy of religions, East Asian religions, 804-289-8330, Fax: 804-287-6504, E-mail: jgeaney@richmond.edu

James, Robison B., PhD, Duke University (1965), 1962, Camp Counsins Professor of Religion—philosophical and Christian theology, 804-289-8329, Fax: 804-287-6504, E-mail: rjames@richmond.edu

Shaw, Miranda E., PhD, Harvard University (1992), 1991, Associate Professor—history of religions, Buddhism, religions of India, gender and religion, 804-289-8692, Fax: 804-287-6504, E-mail: mshaw@richmond.edu

Ripon College

300 Seward St
Ripon WI 54971-0248

Phone: 920-748-8139
Fax: 920-748-7243
E-mail: smithb@acad.ripon.edu
URL: www.ripon.edu

TYPE OF INSTITUTION: Private, Non-Denominational
EXECUTIVE OFFICER: Paul B. Ranslow, President; David B. Seligman, Vice President and Dean of Faculty
CHAIRPERSON: Brian H. Smith, Dept of Religion
UNDERGRADUATE ENROLLMENT: 650

Rivier College

429 Main St, Nashua NH 03060

Roanoke College

221 College Lane
Salem VA 24153-3794

Phone: 540-375-2500
Fax: 540-375-2577
E-mail: @roanoke.edu

TYPE OF INSTITUTION: Private, Evangelical Lutheran Church in America
EXECUTIVE OFFICER: David Gring, President; Kenneth Garren, Dean
CHAIRPERSON: Robert Benne
UNDERGRADUATE ENROLLMENT: 1,700

Roanoke Bible College

PO Box 387, Elizabeth City NC 27907-0387

Roberts Wesleyan College

2301 Westside Drive
Rochester NY 14624

Phone: 716-594-6370
Fax: 716-594-6039
E-mail: ericksonm@roberts.edu
URL: www.roberts.edu

TYPE OF INSTITUTION: Private, Free Methodist
EXECUTIVE OFFICER: John Martin, Provost
CHAIRPERSON: David Basinger, PhD
UNDERGRADUATE ENROLLMENT: 1,071
GRADUATE ENROLLMENT: 338

DEGREES OFFERED: Religion/Philosophy, Contemporary Ministries

UNDERGRADUATE MAJORS: 68

DEGREES CONFERRED: 19

DESCRIPTION OF UNDERGRADUATE PROGRAM: Roberts Wesleyan College is a non-sectarian, coeducational college established within the Christian liberal arts tradition. All students are required to take six hours of biblical literature and three hours of philosophy. From a total of thirty majors offered by the college, two programs are available to students in this department: Religion/Philosophy (an interdepartmental major which prepares students for graduate study) and Contemporary Ministries (a multidisciplinary major).

FACULTY:

Basinger, David W., PhD, Nebraska (1975), 1979, Professor—philosophy, ethics, philosophy of religion, 716-594-6370, Fax: 716-594-6039, E-mail: basingerd@roberts.edu

Caton, Scott Brenon, PhD, University of Rochester (1998), 1990, Assistant Professor—ecclesiastical history, American intellectual and religious history, 716-594-6336, Fax: 716-594-6039, E-mail: catons@roberts.edu

Cullum, Douglas R., ThM, Duke University (1991), 1994, Assistant Professor—religion, theology, 716-594-6331, Fax: 716-594-6801, E-mail: cullumd@roberts.edu

Jackson, Douglas H., ThM, Dallas Theological Seminary (1973), 1998, Assistant Professor—biblical literature, Hebrew, 716-594-6498, Fax: 716-594-6039, E-mail: jacksondh@roberts.edu

Koehl, Andrew C., PhD, University of Notre Dame (1998), 1999, Assistant Professor—philosophy, ethics, 716-594-6503, Fax: 716-594-6039, E-mail: koehla@roberts.edu

LaCelle-Peterson, Kristina M., MPhil, Drew University (1992), 1998, Assistant Professor—biblical literature and interpretation, ethics, 716-594-6335, Fax: 716-594-6039, E-mail: lacellek@roberts.edu

ASSOCIATED FACULTY:

Davis, Casey W., PhD, Union Theological Seminary (1996), 1998, Assistant Professor—biblical studies, 716-594-6830, Fax: 716-594-6567, E-mail: davisc@roberts.edu

Martin, John A., PhD, University of North Texas (1991), Higher Education Administration, ThD, Dallas Theological Seminary (1980), 1996, Professor—Hebrew Scriptures, 716-594-6300, Fax: 716-594-6084, E-mail: martinj@roberts.edu

Vanderhoof, Wesley E., PhD, State University of New York, Buffalo (1985), 1968, Professor—biblical literature, religion, American religious history, 716-594-6220 Fax: 716-594-6371, E-mail: vanderhoofw@roberts.edu

---

University of Rochester

Dept of Religion and Classics
430 Rush Rhees Library, UR
Rochester NY 14627

Phone: 716-275-5378
Fax: 716-442-2749
E-mail: emal@uhura.cc.rochester.edu
URL: www.rochester.edu/college/rel/

TYPE OF INSTITUTION: Private, Non-Denominational

EXECUTIVE OFFICER: Thomas LeBlanc, Dean of the Faculty

CHAIRPERSON: Th. Emil Homerin

UNDERGRADUATE ENROLLMENT: 5,380

DEGREES OFFERED: BA

UNDERGRADUATE MAJORS: 92

DEGREES CONFERRED: 31

DESCRIPTION OF UNDERGRADUATE PROGRAM: In the Department of Religion and Classics students explore the great, classical civilization of West and East and the major religions that emerged from them. The Department offers programs of study in the history and philosophy of the world's major religions, in Greek, Latin, Hebrew, Arabic languages and literatures, Sanskrit, Yiddish, and in ancient Mediterranean and Asian civilizations. Through the study of important classical, biblical and religious writings, either in the original language or in translation, students critically examine the beliefs, ideas, values, rituals, and traditions that have shaped Western and Asian cultures and study the ways these have persisted and changed from ancient to contemporary times.

FACULTY:

Arnold, John, PhD, Arkansas (1997), 1997, Visiting Assistant Professor—Latin, late antiquity, 716-275-7215, E-mail: arnd@mail.rochester.edu

Beaumont, Catherine, Lecturer (part-time)—Arabic, 716-275-5224

Beaumont, Daniel E., PhD, Princeton (1991), 1993, Associate Professor—classical Arabic literature, 716-275-5224, E-mail: dano@troi.cc.rochester.edu

Braun, Wilhelm, PhD, Toronto, Professor Emeritus—Judaic Studies, Yiddish, 716-275-9360

Brennan, Joseph, SSL, Pontifical Biblical Institute, Rome (1957), 1986, Adjunct Visiting Professor—Hebrew Bible, 716-275-9371, E-mail: jbren83810@aol.com

Brooks, Douglas R., PhD, Harvard (1986), 1986, Professor—Asian religions, 716-275-9369, E-mail: dbrk@troi.cc.rochester.edu

Cadorette, Curt, STL, Regis College, Toronto (1985); PhD, University of St Michael's College, Toronto (1985), 1994, John Henry Newman Professorship in Roman Catholic Studies—Christian thought, 716-275-9368, E-mail: ccrt@troi.cc.rochester.edu

Fix, Tamar, Senior Lecturer—Hebrew, 716-275-9371, E-mail: tfix@mail.rochester.edu

Geier, Alfred, PhD, Johns Hopkins (1964), 1974, Associate Professor—classics, Greek literature and thought, mysticism, 716-275-9360

Goldberg, Yechiel, PhD (cand.), NYU, 1998, Visiting Instructor—Jewish mysticism & philosophy, 716-275-5378, E-mail: ysgo@troi.cc.rochester.edu

Green, William Scott, PhD, Brown (1974), 1974, Philip S. Bernstein Professor of Judaic Studies—history of Judaism, Hebrew Bible, theory of religion, Hebrew, 716-273-5001, Fax: 716-275-3480, E-mail: wmsg@db1.cc.rochester.edu

Homerin, Th. Emil, PhD, Chicago (1987), 1988, Associate Professor—Islamic studies, classical Arabic literature, mysticism, 716-275-4760, E-mail: theh@mail.rochester.edu

Merideth, Anne, PhD, Princeton (1999), 1995, Assistant Professor—New Testament, history and literature of early Christianity, 716-275-9367, E-mail: aemh@troi.cc.rochester.edu

Muller-Ortega, Paul, PhD, University of California, Santa Barbara (1985), 1997, Professor—Asian religions, 716-275-7780, E-mail: plml@troi.cc.rochester.edu

Resinski, Rebecca, PhD, UCLA (1998), 1998, Assistant Professor—Greek language, literature & mythology, 716-275-5112, E-mail: beci@troi.cc.rochester.edu

Wierenga, Edward, PhD, University of Massachusetts (1974), 1977, Professor—philosophy of religion, ethics, philosophical theology, 716-275-9370, E-mail: edwd@troi.cc.rochester.edu

Rockford College

Rockford IL 61108

Rockhurst College
1100 Rockhurst Rd, Kansas City MO 64110

Rocky Mountain College
1511 Poly Dr, Billings MT 59102

Rollins College

Dept of Philosophy and Religion
Box 2659
1000 Holt Ave
Winter Park FL 32789

Phone: 407-646-2139
Fax: 407-646-2517
E-mail: hoyt.edge@rollins.edu

TYPE OF INSTITUTION: Private, Non-Denominational

EXECUTIVE OFFICER: Rita Bornstein, President

CHAIRPERSON: Hoyt L. Edge

UNDERGRADUATE ENROLLMENT: 1,500

DEGREES OFFERED: BA with major or minor in Religious Studies, BA with major or minor in Philosophy

UNDERGRADUATE MAJORS: 21

DEGREES CONFERRED: 8

DESCRIPTION OF UNDERGRADUATE PROGRAM: A combined department in a liberal arts college, it offers courses in philosophy and religious studies. Philosophy majors and minors concentrate in particular philosophic modes in addition to more general studies; minors and majors in religious studies work in two or three religious traditions with study emphasizing sacred texts and other primary source materials. A capstone thesis or senior seminar is required for each major, an independent study for the minor.

FACULTY:

Cook, J. Thomas, PhD, Vanderbilt University (1981), 1982, Professor—philosophy of science, metaphysical issues such as human freedom, and normative and applied ethics, 407-646-2518, Fax: 407-646-2517, E-mail: thomas.cook@rollins.edu

Edge, Hoyt Littleton, PhD, Vanderbilt University (1970), 1970, Hugh F. and Jeanette G. McKean Chair and Professor of Philosophy—philosophy of psychology and parapsychology, American philosophy and philosophy of anthropology, 407-646-2178, Fax: 407-646-2517, E-mail: hoyt.edge@rollins.edu

Greenberg, Yudit Kornberg, PhD, Graduate Theological Union (1984), 1986, Professor—modern Jewish philosophy and intellectual history, medieval Jewish philosophy, Rabbinic thought and literature, 407-646-2176, Fax: 407-646-2517, E-mail: ygreen@rollins.edu

Koukal, David R., PhD, Duquesne University (1999), 1999, Visiting Assistant Professor—phenomenology (Husserl, Heidegger, Merleau-Ponty), theories of rhetoric and communication, social and political philosophy, 407-975-6456, Fax: 407-646-2517, E-mail: dkoukal@rollins.edu

McLaren, Margaret A., PhD, Northwestern University (1991), 1992, Assistant Professor—ethics, social and political philosophy, feminist theory, Continental philosophy, 407-646-1508, Fax: 407-646-2517, E-mail: mmclaren@rollins.edu (on leave 1999-2000)

Peters, Karl E., PhD, Columbia University (1971), 1973, Professor—history of Christian thought, contemporary religious thought, process philosophy, religion and science, 407-646-2168, Fax: 407-646-2517, E-mail: kpeters909@aol.com

Rubarth, Scott M., PhD, University of Toronto (1997), 1997, George D. and Harriet W. Cornell Scholar in Classical Studies—ancient philosophy, epistemology, Wittgenstein, classical literature and languages, 407-646-2177, Fax: 407-646-2517, E-mail: srubarth@rollins.edu

Wallace, Gregory L., PhD, Temple University (1999), 1999, Assistant Professor—New Testament interpretation and Christian origins, Hebrew Bible, African American studies, introduction to world religions, religion in America, sociology of religion, hermeneutics, 407-646-2139, Fax: 407-646-2517, E-mail: gwallace@rollins.edu

Wettstein, A. Arnold, PhD, McGill University (1968), 1968, Emeritus Professor—religion, contemporary religious thought, world religions, and Chinese thought and culture, 407-646-2579, Fax: 407-646-2517, E-mail: awettstein@rollins.edu

Rosary College

7900 W Division St, River Forest IL 60305

Rosemont College

Religious Studies Dept, Rosemont PA 19010

Rust College

150 Rust Ave, Holly Springs MS 38635

Rutgers the State University

Camden College of Arts and Sciences
Camden NJ 08102

Phone: 609-225-6237
Fax: 609-225-6541
E-mail: scharme@crab.rutgers.edu

TYPE OF INSTITUTION: Public
UNDERGRADUATE ENROLLMENT: 6

Rutgers-The State University of New Jersey

Dept of Religion
Faculty of Arts and Sciences
70 Lipman Dr, Loree 140, Douglass Campus
New Brunswick NJ 08903

Phone: 732-932-9641
Fax: 732-932-1271
URL: religion.rutgers.edu

TYPE OF INSTITUTION: Public, Non-Denominational

CHAIRPERSON: Alberto R. Green

DEGREES OFFERED: BA

UNDERGRADUATE MAJORS: 90

DEGREES CONFERRED: 61

DESCRIPTION OF UNDERGRADUATE PROGRAM: Rutgers University is composed of seven undergraduate colleges, a graduate school, and numerous professional schools and institutes on campuses in New Brunswick, Camden, and Newark. On the main campus in New Brunswick the Department of Religion forms part of the Faculty of Arts and Sciences and offers a full range of elective courses, honors work, and a major or minor available to students enrolled in all the colleges of the University. Graduate level religion courses are offered in conjunction with other departments of the University.

FACULTY:

Bowden, Henry W., PhD, Princeton University (1966), 1964, Professor—American religious history, history of religions, 732-932-3378, Fax: 732-932-1271

Chan, Chi-wah, PhD, University of California (1993), 1997, Adjunct (part-time)—Chinese studies and Indian philosophy

Green, Alberto R., PhD, University of Michigan (1973), 1979, Professor—Ancient Near Eastern religions, Old Testament, history of religions, 732-932-1516, Fax: 732-932-1271

Haq, Syed Nomanul, PhD, University of London (1990), 1996, Assistant Professor—Islamic theology, Islamic philosophy, history of religions, 732-932-3289, Fax: 732-932-1271

Johnson, James T., PhD, Princeton University (1968), 1969, Professor—ethics, religious thought, religion and society, 732-932-9637, Fax: 732-932-1271

Jones, James W., PhD, Brown University (1970), 1971, Professor—religion and psychology, religion and science, 732-932-9623, Fax: 732-932-1271

Myladil, Thomas J., PhD, Fordham University (1994), 1995, Adjunct (part-time)—historical theology, world religions, Hinduism, Asian religions, 732-932-9641, Fax: 732-932-1271

Obayashi, Hiroshi, PhD, University of Pennsylvania (1967), 1967, Professor—religious thought, history of religions, religion and society, 732-932-9638, Fax: 732-932-1271

Pavlin, James D., PhD, New York University (1998), 1998, Adjunct (part-time)—Islamic history and theology, Arabic religious literature

Smith, Mahlon H., MSL, Pontifical Institute of Medieval Studies (1974), 1969, Associate Professor—New Testament, history of religious thought, 732-932-3287, Fax: 732-932-1271

Tripolitis, Antonia, PhD, University of Pennsylvania (1971), 1987, Associate Professor—history of Greek and Latin literature, hellenistic religions, hellenistic literature/languages, 732-932-3288, Fax: 732-932-1271

Yu, Chun-fang, PhD, Columbia University (1972), 1972, Professor—history of religions, Chinese Buddhism, East Asian religions, 732-932-3291, Fax: 732-932-1271

Zamani, Amir N., PhD, Columbia (1990), 1995, Adjunct (part-time)—Sufism, Islam

College of the Sacred Heart

Santurce PR 00914

Sacred Heart University

5151 Park Ave
Fairfield CT 06432

Phone: 203-371-7730
Fax: 203-371-7807
E-mail: griggr@sacredheart.edu
URL: www.sacredheart.edu

TYPE OF INSTITUTION: Private, Roman Catholic
EXECUTIVE OFFICER: Anthony Cernera, President
CHAIRPERSON: Edward Bordeau
UNDERGRADUATE ENROLLMENT: 20
GRADUATE ENROLLMENT: 25

Sacred Heart Major Seminary

2701 Chicago Blvd
Detroit MI 48206

Phone: 313-883-8500
Fax: 313-868-6440

TYPE OF INSTITUTION: Private, Roman Catholic
EXECUTIVE OFFICER: Allen Vigneron, Rector/President
UNDERGRADUATE ENROLLMENT: 211
GRADUATE ENROLLMENT: 96

Sacred Heart School of Theology

7335 S Hwy 100
PO Box 429
Hales Corners WI 53130-0429

Phone: 414-425-8300
Fax: 414-529-6999
E-mail: shst@msn.com

TYPE OF INSTITUTION: Denominational: Roman Catholic
EXECUTIVE OFFICE: James D. Brackin, SCJ, President
CHAIRPERSON: Thomas L. Knoebel
GRADUATE ENROLLMENT: 125

St Ambrose University

518 W Locust St
Davenport IA 52803

Phone: 319-333-6442
Fax: 319-333-6243
E-mail: cwinter@saunix.sau.edu
URL: www.sau.edu

TYPE OF INSTITUTION: Catholic
EXECUTIVE OFFICER: Edward Rogalski, President
CHAIRPERSON: Fr. Ed Dunn, Undergraduate Theology
DIRECTOR: Corinne Winter, Master of Pastoral Studies

UNDERGRADUATE ENROLLMENT: 3

Saint Andrew's College

1121 College Drive
Saskatoon SK S7N 0W3
Canada

Phone: 306-966-8970
Fax: 306-966-8981
URL: www.stu.saskatoon.sk.ca

TYPE OF INSTITUTION: Denominational: United Church of Canada
EXECUTIVE OFFICERS: Christopher Lind, President
GRADUATE ENROLLMENT: 30

St Andrews Presbyterian College

1700 Dogwood Mile
Laurinburg NC 28352

Phone: 910-277-5258
Fax: 910-277-5020
E-mail: mbringle@tartan.sapc.edu

TYPE OF INSTITUTION: Private, Presbyterian
EXECUTIVE OFFICER: Lawrence E. Schulz, Vice President for Academic Affairs
CHAIRPERSON: Carl F. Walters
UNDERGRADUATE ENROLLMENT: 650

St Anselm College

100 St Anselm Drive
Manchester NH 03102

Phone: 603-641-7052
Fax: 603-641-7116
E-mail: dsweetla@anselm.edu

TYPE OF INSTITUTION: Denominational: Roman Catholic
EXECUTIVE OFFICER: Jonathan P. DeFelice, OSB, President
CHAIRPERSON: Dennis M. Sweetland
UNDERGRADUATE ENROLLMENT: 2,000

Saint Augustine's Seminary of Toronto

2661 Kingston Road
Scarborough ON M1M 1M3
Canada

Phone: 416-261-7207
Fax: 416-261-2529
URL: www.staugustines.on.ca

TYPE OF INSTITUTION: Denominational: Roman Catholic
EXECUTIVE OFFICER: John A. Boissonneau, Rector
GRADUATE ENROLLMENT: 84

Saint Augustine's College

1315 Oakwood Ave, Raleigh NC 27610

College of St Benedict

St Joseph MN 56374

Phone: 320-363-5302
E-mail: vsmiles@csbsju.edu
URL: www.csbsju.edu/

TYPE OF INSTITUTION: Private, Roman Catholic Benedictine

EXECUTIVE OFFICER: Mary Lyons, President

CHAIRPERSON: Vincent Smiles

UNDERGRADUATE ENROLLMENT: 1,936

DEGREES OFFERED: BA

UNDERGRADUATE MAJORS: 18 (plus 8 at St John's University)

DEGREES CONFERRED: 4 (plus 2 at St John's University)

DESCRIPTION OF UNDERGRADUATE PROGRAM: In a coordinate relationship with St John's University, the department offers undergraduate majors in 4 concentrations. Theological studies requires 36 credits distributed over the following areas: scripture, liturgy, doctrinal theology, moral theology, historical theology and Judaic studies or world religions. Theology/secondary education requires 32 theology credits plus a minor in secondary education that includes student teaching. Religious education requires 32 theology credits plus courses in education and an internship. Pastoral ministry requires 32 theology credits plus sources in psychology and social work and an internship. The department also cooperates with the Music department to offer a degree in liturgical music.

FACULTY:

Backous, Timothy, STD, Alphonsiana, Rome (1989), 1989, St John's University Chaplain and Assistant Professor—moral theology, 320-363-2791, E-mail: tbackous@csbsju.edu

Bobertz, Charles, PhD, Yale University (1988), 1993, Assistant Professor—New Testament and Patristics, 320-363-3220, E-mail: cbobertz@csbsju.edu

Buchanan, Daniel, PhD, University of Chicago (1998), Assistant Professor—church history, 320-363-3181, E-mail: dbuchanan@csbsju.edu

Cahoy, William, PhD, Yale University (1989), 1999, 1990, Dean of St John's School of Theology and Associate Professor—systematic theology, 320-363-3182, E-mail: bcahoy@csbsju.edu

Connell, Martin, PhD, University of Notre Dame (1995), Assistant Professor—liturgy, 320-363-2135, E-mail: mconnell@csbsju.edu

Cotter, David, STD, Gregorian, Rome (1989), 1995, Assistant Professor—Old Testament, 320-363-2589, E-mail: dcotter@csbsju.edu

Culhane, Alberic, MA, Catholic University (1963), 1957, Associate Professor—scripture, 320-363-2245, E-mail: aculhane@csbsju.edu

Cytron, Barry, PhD, Iowa State (1982), 1996, Jay Phillips Chair in Jewish Studies, 320-363-3104, E-mail: bcytron@csbsju.edu

Durken, Daniel, MA, Catholic University (1963), 1955, Professor—scripture, 320-363-3875, E-mail: ddurken@csbsju.edu

Evans, Bernard, PhD, Catholic University of America (1986), 1981, Associate Professor—moral theology, 320-363-2106, E-mail: bfevans@csbsju.edu

Finn, Daniel, PhD, University of Chicago (1977), 1977, Clemens Professor of Economics and Theology, 320-363-3048, E-mail: dfinn@csbsju.edu

Hollas, Eric, PhD, Yale University (1985), 1977, Assistant Professor and Director of Hill Monastic Microfilm Library—church history, 320-363-3515, E-mail: ehollas@csbsju.edu

Kasling, Kim, AMusD, University of Michigan (1969), 1977, Professor—music, 320-363-2862, E-mail: kkasling@csbsju.edu

Kasprick, Roger, MA, Catholic University (1973), 1960, Assistant Professor—systematic theology, 320-363-2109, E-mail: rkasprick@csbsju.edu

Kaster, Jeffrey, MA, St John's (1984), 1987, Lecturer—pastoral theology, 320-363-2110, E-mail: jkaster@csbsju.edu

Kraft, Katherine, DMin, Pacific School of Religion (1982), 1990, Assistant Professor—systematic theology, 320-363-5980, E-mail: kkraft@csbsju.edu

Launderville, Dale, PhD, Catholic University of America (1987), 1987, Associate Professor—Old Testament

Merkle, John, PhD, Catholic University of Louvain (1982), 1977, Professor—systematic theology, 320-363-5925, E-mail: jmerkle@csbsju.edu

Patella, Michael, SSD, Ecole Biblique (1995), 1995, Assistant Professor—New Testament, 320-363-2108, E-mail: mpatella@csbsju.edu

Reuter, Mary, PhD, Duquesne (1982), 1981, Associate Professor—spirituality, 320-363-5126, E-mail: mreuter@csbsju.edu

Rolfson, Helen, DrScRel, University of Strasbourg (1972), 1981, Associate Professor—spirituality, 320-363-2105, E-mail: hrolfson@csbsju.edu

Ruff, Anthony, ThD, University of Graz, Austria (1998), Assistant Professor—liturgy and liturgical music, 320-363-3233, E-mail: aruff@csbsju.edu

Smiles, Vincent, PhD, Fordham (1989), 1992, Assistant Professor—New Testament, 320-363-5302, E-mail: vsmiles@csbsju.edu

Stewart, Columba, DPhil, University of Oxford (1989), 1983, Associate Professor—monastic studies, 320-363-2112, E-mail: cstewart@csbsju.edu

Theimer, Axel, DM, University of Minnesota (1984), 1969, Professor—music, 320-363-3374, E-mail: atheimer@csbsju.edu

Wiley, Tatha, PhD, Boston College (1994), Assistant Professor—systematic theology, 320-363-2109, E-mail: twiley@csbsju.edu

Wolfe, Regina Wentzel, PhD, University of London, King's College (1993), 1992, Assistant Professor—moral theology, 320-363-2110, E-mail: rwolfe@csbsju.edu

Wood, Susan, PhD, Marquette University (1986), 1992, Associate Professor—systematic theology, 320-363-2104, E-mail: swood@csbsju.edu

---

St Bernard's Institute

1100 S Goodman St
Rochester NY 14620-2545

Phone: 716-271-3657
Fax: 716-271-2045
URL: www.sbi.edu

TYPE OF INSTITUTION: Private, Roman Catholic
EXECUTIVE OFFICER: Patricia Schoeller, President
UNDERGRADUATE ENROLLMENT: 150

St Bonaventure University

Dept of Theology
St Bonaventure NY 14778-2349

Phone: 716-375-2226
Fax: 716-375-7665
E-mail: whelan@sbu.edu
URL: www.sbu.edu

TYPE OF INSTITUTION: Private
EXECUTIVE OFFICER: Edward Eckert, Vice President for Academic Affairs
CHAIRPERSON: Winifred Whelan, OSF
UNDERGRADUATE ENROLLMENT: 2,500
GRADUATE ENROLLMENT: 500

The College of St Catherine

2004 Randolph Avenue
Mail # 4222
St Paul MN 55105

Phone: 651-690-6000
Fax: 651-690-6024
E-mail: thwest@stkate.edu
URL: www.stkate.edu

TYPE OF INSTITUTION: Private, Roman Catholic
EXECUTIVE OFFICER: Sr. Andrea Lea, IHM, President
CHAIRPERSON: Thomas H. West
COORDINATOR: Shawn Madigan, CSJ
UNDERGRADUATE ENROLLMENT: 1,800
GRADUATE ENROLLMENT: 250

St Charles Seminary

209 Flagg Pl, Staten Island NY 10304

St Charles Borromeo Seminary

1000 E Wynnewood Rd, Overbrook PA 19096-3099

Saint Cloud State University

720 4th Ave S, AS-209, Saint Cloud MN 56301

SS Cyril and Methodius Seminary

3535 Indian Trail
Orchard Lake MI 48324

Phone: 248-683-0311
Fax: 248-738-6735
E—mail: deansoff@sscms.edu
URL: www.sscms.edu.deansoff

TYPE OF INSTITUTION: Private, Roman Catholic
EXECUTIVE OFFICER: Francis B. Koper, Rector

GRADUATE ENROLLMENT: 99

St Edwards University
Austin TX 78704

College of St Elizabeth
Dept of Philosophy and Religious Studies, Convent Station NJ 07961

College of Saint Elizabeth

2 Convent Rd
Morristown NJ 07960

Phone: 973-290-4337
Fax: 973-290-4312
E-mail: flanagan@liza.st-elizabeth.edu

TYPE OF INSTITUTION: Private
EXECUTIVE OFFICER: Francis Raftery, SC, President
CHAIRPERSON: Kathleen Flanagan, SC
UNDERGRADUATE ENROLLMENT: 1,403
GRADUATE ENROLLMENT: 388
GRADUATE PROGRAM
Graduate Advisor: Kathleen Flanagan, SC, PhD
Graduate Degrees Offered: MA
Degrees Conferred: 1
Graduate Students in Residence: 0
Not in Residence: 29
Average Number of New Students Enrolled: 10
Women Students: 25
Minority Students: 1
Foreign Students: 0
Minimum GRE Score Requisite to Admission: No
Minimum GPA Score Requisite to Admission: Yes; 3.0 on 4.0 scale
Foreign Language Proficiency Evaluated: No
Attrition Among Students: 3%
DESCRIPTION OF GRADUATE PROGRAM AND RESEARCH FACILITES: The MA in the theology program is designed primarily as a part-time program mainly for lay students within the Roman Catholic tradition. The program is geared towards those who seek deeper understanding of the Christian faith and/or seek to serve the community in parish or other church-related ministry. The program strives to wed together rigorous academic study with pastoral reflection. Thirty-six credit total with 12 credits core with 24 credits elective.
ACADEMIC PLAN, ADMISSION REQUIREMENTS, FINANCIAL AID: Applicants for admission to a master's degree program must meet at least two minimal requirements: Possess a bachelor's degree from a regionally accredited college or university or have evidence of equivalency if a degree was awarded at a foreign institution of higher education. Demonstrate potential for graduate work, ordinarily by having maintained a "B" average during undergraduate study or previous graduate study.

FACULTY:

Ciorra, Anthony, PhD, Fordham University (1990), 1991, Associate Professor—Bible, spirituality, liturgical theology

Flanagan, M. Kathleen, SC, PhD, Union Theological Seminary, NY (1979), 1987, Professor—American religious history, American Catholic history, Roman Catholic theology, the Mystery of Christ

Incardona, James, PhD, Loyola University Chicago (1999), Assistant Professor—Christian ethics, systematic theology

Joyce, Ellen L., SC, PhD, Fordham University (1981), 1988, Professor—ecclesiology, spirituality, ethics

Santamaria, Anthony, PhD, University of Toronto (1999), Assistant Professor—philosophy, ethics, metaphysics, ancient and medieval philosophy

ADJUNCT FACULTY:

Fulton, David, JCD, Gregorian University Rome, 1996, STD University of St Thomas Aquinas, Rome 1988

Parr, Charles J., BA, St Bernard College; MA, Immaculate Conception Seminary; EdS, Seton Hall University; MA, PhD, Catholic University of America

Swartz, Alice, RSM, BA (English Literature), Georgian Court College; MA Biblical Studies, Providence College; MA Jewish-Christian Studies, Seton Hall University; PhD Liturgical Studies, Drew University

---

College of St Francis

Dept of Philosophy and Religious Studies, Joliet IL 60435

St Francis College

2701 Spring St, Fort Wayne IN 46808

St Francis College

180 Remsen Street
Brooklyn NY 11201-4398

Phone: 718-522-2300
Fax: 718-522-1274

TYPE OF INSTITUTION: Private, Franciscan heritage
EXECUTIVE OFFICER: Frank Macchiarola, President
CHAIRPERSON: Kusumita Priscilla Pedersen
UNDERGRADUATE ENROLLMENT: 2,000

St Francis College

Department of Philosophical and Religious Studies
PO Box 600
Loretto PA 15940-0600

Phone: 814-472-3396
Fax: 814-472-3044
E-mail: mmckale@sfcpa.edu
URL: www.sfcpa.edu/

TYPE OF INSTITUTION: Private, Catholic-Franciscan
EXECUTIVE OFFICER: Rev. Christian Oravec, TOR, President

CHAIRPERSON: Michael McKale
COORDINATOR: Michael McKale
UNDERGRADUATE ENROLLMENT: 1,600
GRADUATE ENROLLMENT: 500

Saint Francis Seminary

3257 S Lake Dr
St Francis WI 53235

Phone: 414-747-6400
Fax: 414-747-6442
E-mail: dean@sfs.edu
URL: www.sfs.edu

TYPE OF INSTITUTION: Private, Roman Catholic
EXECUTIVE OFFICERS: Andrew L. Nelson, Rector
COORDINATOR: David A. Stosur
GRADUATE ENROLLMENT: 105

St Francis Xavier University

PO Box 5000
Antigonish NS B2G 2W5
Canada

Phone: 902-863-3300
Fax: 902-867-2448
E-mail: sriley@stfx.ca
URL: www.stfx.ca/

TYPE OF INSTITUTION: Public, Roman Catholic heritage
EXECUTIVE OFFICERS: Sean Riley, President; Ronald W. Johnson, Academic Vice President
CHAIRPERSON: Margaret Y. MacDonald
UNDERGRADUATE ENROLLMENT: 3,300
GRADUATE ENROLLMENT: 650

St Hermans Theological Seminary

414 Mission Rd, Suite 1, Kodiak AK 99615

Saint Hyacinth College and Seminary

66 School St, Granby MA 01033

Saint Jerome's University

Waterloo ON N2L 3G3
Canada

Phone: 519-884-8111, ext 266
Fax: 519-884-5759
E-mail: cdvanin@watarts.uwaterloo.ca

TYPE OF INSTITUTION: Public, Roman Catholic
EXECUTIVE OFFICER: Douglas Letson, President
CHAIRPERSON: Cristina Vanin
UNDERGRADUATE ENROLLMENT: 800

Saint John's College

1160 Camino Cruz Blanca, Santa Fe NM 87501

St John's Seminary

127 Lake St, Brighton MA 02135

St John's Seminary

5012 Seminary Road
Camarillo CA 93012-2598

Phone: 805-482-2755
Fax: 805-482-3470
E-mail: registrar-sjs@sjs-sc.org

TYPE OF INSTITUTION: Denominational: Roman Catholic
EXECUTIVE OFFICER: Jeremiah J. McCarthy, Rector/President
GRADUATE ENROLLMENT: 86

St John's Seminary College

5118 Seminary Rd
Camarillo CA 93012

Phone: 805-482-2755
Fax: 805-987-5097

TYPE OF INSTITUTION: Denominational: Catholic
EXECUTIVE OFFICER: Edward Wm. Clark, President/Rector
CHAIRPERSON: Tracey Sharp
UNDERGRADUATE ENROLLMENT: 90

St John's University

PO Box 7288
Collegeville MN 56321

Phone: 320-363-2100
Fax: 320-363-3145
E-mail: vsmiles@csbsju.edu
URL: www.csbsju.edu/sot

TYPE OF INSTITUTION: Private, Roman Catholic Benedictine
EXECUTIVE OFFICER: Dietrich Reinhart, President
CHAIRPERSONS: Vincent Smiles (Undergraduate); William J. Cahoy (Graduate)
UNDERGRADUATE ENROLLMENT: 1,704
GRADUATE ENROLLMENT: 109
DEGREES OFFERED: BA
UNDERGRADUATE MAJORS: 8 (plus 18 at College of St Benedict)
DEGREES CONFERRED: 2 (plus 4 at College of St Benedict)
DESCRIPTION OF UNDERGRADUATE PROGRAM: In a coordinate relationship with the College of St Benedict, the department offers undergraduate majors in 4 concentrations. Theological studies requires 36 credits distributed over the following areas: scripture, liturgy, doctrinal theology, moral theology, historical theology and Judaic studies or world religions. Theology/secondary education requires 32 theology credits plus a minor in secondary edu-

cation that includes student teaching. Religious education requires 32 theology credits plus courses in education and an internship. Pastoral ministry requires 32 theology credits plus courses in psychology and social work and an internship. The department also cooperates with the Music department to offer a degree in liturgical music.

GRADUATE PROGRAM

Member of the Council on Graduate Studies in Religion

Graduate Advisor: William Cahoy

Graduate Degrees Offered: MA; MDiv

Degrees Conferred: 21

Graduate Students in Residence: 80%

Not in Residence: 20%

Average No. of New Students Enrolled: 34

Women Students: 39

Minority Students: 1

Foreign Students: 17

Minimum GRE Score Requisite to Admission: Yes; 400

Minimum GPA Score Requisite to Admission: Yes; 3.0

Foreign Language Proficiency Evaluated: No

Financial Aid to First Year Students: 98.5%

Financial Aid to Other Students: 98%

Attrition Among Students: 2%

Graduates Placed: 95%

DESCRIPTION OF GRADUATE PROGRAM AND RESEARCH FACILITIES: Master of Arts degrees in Theology (30 credits), Liturgical Studies (30 credits), Pastoral Ministry (36 credits), Liturgical Music (36 credits), and a Master of Divinity degree (78 credits) are offered. Coursework for the MA usually requires two years of full-time study. However, with sufficient theological background, coursework for the MA degrees can be completed in one academic year and two summers. The MDiv (78 credits) is a three-year pastoral degree. Prerequisites for MA, MDiv: credits each in philosophy, theology, and humanities/social sciences or equivalent. Prerequisite courses are available on campus and can be integrated into the overall program. Special degrees in liturgy include the MA in Liturgical Studies and the MA in Liturgical Music. Students in Liturgical Studies select a minimum of 24 credits from liturgy courses. Liturgical Music students investigate theological and liturgical foundations and develop strong leadership skills in music. The MA in Pastoral Ministry (48 credits) and the MDiv (78 credits) are pastoral degrees. Each is designed to combine the study of theological principles with an examination of pastoral issues and concerns. Internships or practica include the following areas: religious education, rural ministry, liturgy, parish ministry. The Jerusalem Studies Program is an opportunity for students to travel and study in the Holy Land. Credits earned through the Jerusalem Studies Program are applied to the degree program. The program is available in semester and summer formats. The Alcuin Library at Saint John's has holdings of more than 350,000 volumes and 1,000 periodicals. The Hill Monastics Manuscript Library contains microfilm copies of over 74,000 manuscripts containing some 23,000,000 pages. The presence of major ecumenical initiatives as the Institute for Ecumenical and Cultural Research, the House of Prayer of the Episcopal Diocese of Minnesota, and the Jay Phillips Center for Jewish-Christian Learning broadens theological conversations and opportunities. Admission Requirements: completed application, official transcripts for all college and graduate work, three letters of recommendation, and results from either the Miller Analogies Test or the Graduate Record Exam.

FACULTY:

Backous, Timothy, STD, Alphonsiana, Rome (1989), 1989, Assistant Professor—moral theology, 320-363-2791, E-mail: tbackous@csbsju.edu

Bobertz, Charles, PhD, Yale University (1988), 1993, Associate Professor—New Testament and Patristics, 320-363-3220, E-mail: cbobertz@csbsju.edu

Bouley, Allan, STD, San Anselmo, Rome (1973), 1969, Professor—liturgical studies, 320-363-2103, E-mail: abouley@csbsju.edu

Buchanan, Daniel, PhD, University of Chicago (1998), Assistant Professor—church history, 320-363-3181, E-mail: dbuchanan@csbsju.edu

Cahoy, William, PhD, Yale University (1989), 1990, Dean of School of Theology and Associate Professor—systematic theology, 320-363-3182, E-mail: bcahoy@csbsju.edu

Connell, Martin, PhD, University of Notre Dame (1995), Assistant Professor—liturgy, 320-363-2135, E-mail: mconnell@csbsju.edu

Cotter, David, STD, Gregorian, Rome (1989), 1995, Assistant Professor—Old Testament, 320-363-2589, E-mail: dcotter@csbsju.edu

Culhane, Alberic, MA, Catholic University (1963), 1957, Associate Professor—scripture, 320-363-2245, E-mail: aculhane@csbsju.edu

Cytron, Barry, PhD, Iowa State (1982), 1996, Jay Phillips Chair in Jewish Studies, 320-363-3104, E-mail: bcytron@csbsju.edu

Durken, Daniel, MA, Catholic University (1963), 1955, Professor—scripture, 320-363-3875, E-mail: ddurken@csbsju.edu

Evans, Bernard, PhD, Catholic University of America (1986), 1981, Associate Professor—moral theology, 320-363-2106, E-mail: bfevans@csbsju.edu

Finn, Daniel, PhD, University of Chicago (1977), 1977, Clemens Professor of Economics and Theology, 320-363-3048, E-mail: dfinn@csbsju.edu

Hollas, Eric, PhD, Yale University (1985), 1977, Assistant Professor and Director of Hill Monastic Microfilm Library—church history, 320-363-3515, E-mail: ehollas@csbsju.edu

Kasling, Kim, AMusD, University of Michigan (1969), 1977, Professor—music, 320-363-2862, E-mail: kkasling@csbsju.edu

Kasprick, Roger, MA, Catholic University (1973), 1960, Assistant Professor—systematic theology, 320-363-2109, E-mail: rkasprick@csbsju.edu

Kaster, Jeffrey, MA, St John's (1984), 1987, Lecturer—pastoral theology, 320-363-2110, E-mail: jkaster@csbsju.edu

Kraft, Katherine, DMin, Pacific School of Religion (1982), 1990, Assistant Professor—systematic theology, 320-363-5980, E-mail: kkraft@csbsju.edu

Launderville, Dale, PhD, Catholic University of America (1986), 1981, Associate Professor—scripture, 320-363-3389, E-mail: dlaundervill@csbsju.edu

Merkle, John, PhD, Catholic University of Louvain (1982), 1977, Professor—systematic theology, 320-363-5925, E-mail: jmerkle@csbsju.edu

Naughton, Michael, MS, Kansas State University (1976), 1972, Assistant Professor—pastoral theology, 320-363-2239, E-mail: mnaughton@csbsju.edu

Patella, Michael, SSD, Ecole Biblique (1995), 1995, Assistant Professor—New Testament, 320-363-2108, E-mail: mpatella@csbsju.edu

Reuter, Mary, PhD, Duquesne (1982), 1981, Associate Professor—spirituality, 320-363-5126, E-mail: mreuter@csbsju.edu

Rolfson, Helen, DrScRel, University of Strasbourg (1972), 1981, Associate Professor—spirituality, 320-363-2105, E-mail: hrolfson@csbsju.edu

Ruff, Anthony, ThD, University of Graz, Austria (1998), Assistant Professor—liturgy and liturgical music, 320-363-3233, E-mail: aruff@csbsju.edu

Seasoltz, R. Kevin, JCD, Catholic University of America (1962), 1972, Professor—liturgical studies and canon law, 320-363-3127, E-mail: kseasoltz@csbsju.edu

Smiles, Vincent, PhD, Fordham (1989), 1992, Associate Professor—New Testament, 320-363-5302, E-mail: vsmiles@csbsju.edu

Steiner, Luke, SSL, Pontifical Biblical Institute, Rome (1960), 1960, Associate Professor—New Testament, 320-363-3559, E-mail: lsteiner@csbsju.edu

Stewart, Columba, DPhil, University of Oxford (1989), 1983, Associate Professor—monastic studies, 320-363-2112, E-mail: cstewart@csbsju.edu

Theimer, Axel, DM, University of Minnesota (1984), 1969, Professor—music, 320-363-3374, E-mail: atheimer@csbsju.edu

Wiley, Tatha, PhD, Boston College (1994), Assistant Professor—systematic theology, 320-363-2109, E-mail: twiley@csbsju.edu

Wolfe, Regina Wentzel, PhD, University of London, King's College (1993), 1992, Assistant Professor—moral theology, 320-363-2110, E-mail: rwolfe@csbsju.edu

Wood, Susan, PhD, Marquette University (1986), 1992, Associate Professor—systematic theology, 320-363-2104, E-mail: swood@csbsju.edu

---

St John's University

Dept of Theology and Religious Studies   **Phone: 718-990-6467**
8000 Utopia Parkway   **Fax: 718-990-1907**
Jamaica NY 11439   **E-mail: theology@stjohns.edu**

TYPE OF INSTITUTION: Private, Roman Catholic

EXECUTIVE OFFICERS: Brian O'Connell, CM, Dean; Louis H. Primavera, Associate Dean (Graduate)

CHAIRPERSON: Jean-Pierre Ruiz

UNDERGRADUATE ENROLLMENT: 12,000

GRADUATE ENROLLMENT: 5,000

DEGREES OFFERED: BA, BA/MA

UNDERGRADUATE MAJORS: 11

DEGREES CONFERRED: 9

DESCRIPTION OF UNDERGRADUATE PROGRAM: As part of their core curriculum requirement, all undergraduates must take at least 3 courses in theology, choosing from a selection of courses in the areas of biblical studies, systematic theology, and religious ethics, respectively. In addition, the department offers an undergraduate major in theology (made up of 12 specified courses chosen under the guidance of a faculty adviser). Programs and courses are designed to systematically present and explore the meaning and relevance of Christian belief in the light of Scripture, traditional Church teaching, and the specific goals set forth by Vatican Council II, and to cultivate sympathetic appreciation of all significant human religious manifestations.

GRADUATE PROGRAM

Graduate Advisor: Jean-Pierre Ruiz

Graduate Degrees Offered: MA

Degrees Conferred: 10 MA

Graduate Students in Residence: 54 MA

Not in Residence: 22 MA

Average No. of New Students Enrolled: 22 MA

Women Students: 26 MA

Minority Students: 10 MA

Foreign Students: 11 MA

Minimum GRE Score Requisite to Admission: No

Minimum GPA Score Requisite to Admission: Yes; 3.0 on 4.0 scale

Foreign Language Proficiency Evaluated: No

Financial Aid to First Year Students: 10% MA

Financial Aid to Other Students: 10% MA

Attrition Among Students: 5% MA

DESCRIPTION OF GRADUATE PROGRAM AND RESEARCH FACILITIES: In keeping with the objectives of the Second Vatican Council, the Graduate Program of the Department of Theology and Religious Studies seeks to examine the richness of the Catholic faith and its theological heritage in the light of modern human experience. This experience includes the values of other sciences, other religions and other cultures. The program provides an environment of academic excellence flexible enough to fit the needs of those interested in pursuing further research degrees, professional ministry, or parish service, as well as those interested in this area for personal enrichment. In addition to Master of Arts, Master of Divinity, and Certificate programs, the Department of Theology and Religious Studies also offers an intensive, accelerated, combined program leading to both the BA and MA degrees in five years of full-time study.

ACADEMIC PLAN, ADMISSION REQUIREMENTS, FINANCIAL AID: The applicant for matriculation in the Department of Theology and Religious Studies must have a Bachelor's Degree which normally includes twenty-four undergraduate credits in theology, philosophy, and/or related subjects and an overall "B" average on the baccalaureate level. MA students may choose to specialize in one of six areas of theology: Biblical Studies, Historical Studies, Systematic Theology, Moral Theology, Interfaith Studies, Pastoral Theology. Students may select either a thesis or a non-thesis program in each of these areas, with the exception of the Catechetical Ministry concentration. Scholarship aid and tuition remissions are available for qualified students.

FACULTY:

Albano, Peter J., CM, PhD, Claremont Graduate School (1976), 1968, Assistant Professor—philosophy of religion, theology and culture, psychology and education

Bulman, Raymond F., PhD, Columbia University (1973), 1963, Professor—systematic theology, foundational theology

Connolly-Weinert, Francis D., PhD, Fordham University (1979), 1980, Associate Professor—New Testament literature and theology, Qumran literature

Devine, Richard J., CM, STD, University of Fribourg (1963), 1966, Associate Professor—moral theology, medical ethics

Devoy, Loretta M., OP, PhD, Fordham University (1987), 1987, Associate Professor—history of Christianity (19th-20th centuries), spirituality

Ettlinger, Gerard H., SJ, DPhil, Oxford University (1972), 1989, The John A. Flynn Chair in Theology—patristics, early Christian and classical culture, Greek

Heaney-Hunter, Joann, PhD, Fordham University (1988), 1987, Associate Professor—history of Christianity, marriage

Kirk, Pamela J., DTheol, Ludwig-Maximilians University, Munich (1985), 1990, Associate Professor—systematic theology, women's studies, Latin American theology

Martone, Marilyn A., PhD, Fordham University (1994), 1994, Assistant Professor—moral theology, medical ethics, feminist ethics

McKenna, John H., CM, STD, University of Trier (1971), 1972, Professor—sacramental theology, liturgy

Primeaux, Patrick, SM, PhD, St Michael's College, University of Toronto (1979), 1992, Assistant Professor—values in business, church management

Rahim, Habibeh, PhD, Harvard University (1989), 1997, Assistant Professor—Islamic studies, world religions, religion and literature, religion and art

Ruiz, Jean-Pierre M., STD, Pontifical Gregorian University (1989), 1991, Assistant Professor—biblical studies, Hispanic/Latino theology

Surlis, Paul J., STD, St Patrick's College, Maynooth (1963), 1975, Associate Professor—Christian social ethics, theologies of liberation

Upton, Julia A., RSM, PhD, Fordham University (1981), 1980, Professor—liturgy, sacramental theology

Warren, Michael, PhD, Catholic University of America (1974), 1975, Professor—catechetics, youth ministry, church and culture

White, Leland J., PhD, Duke University (1974), 1982, Professor—theology and culture, systematic theology, ministry and the law

Wifall, Walter R., Jr., PhD, The Johns Hopkins University (1965), 1970, Professor—Old Testament literature and theology, Hebrew

---

St Johns Fisher College

Dept of Religious Studies, Rochester NY 14618

Saint John Vianney College Seminary

2900 SW 87th Ave, Miami FL 33165

Saint Joseph College

1678 Asylum Ave
West Hartford CT 06117

Phone: 860-232-4571, ext 2299
Fax: 860-233-5695
E-mail: jthompson@sjc.edu

TYPE OF INSTITUTION: Private, Roman Catholic
CHAIRPERSON: J. Milburn Thompson
UNDERGRADUATE ENROLLMENT: 20

Saint Joseph's College

Highway 231
Rensselaer IN 47978

Phone: 219-866-6000
Fax: 219-866-6300
E-mail: saintjoe.edu
URL: www.saintjoe.edu/~dept64/

TYPE OF INSTITUTION: Private, Roman Catholic
EXECUTIVE OFFICER: Albert Shannon, President

CHAIRPERSONS: Timothy McFarland (Undergraduate); James Challancin (Graduate)
UNDERGRADUATE ENROLLMENT: 950
GRADUATE ENROLLMENT: 28

St Josephs College of Maine

278 Whites Bridge Rd
Standish ME 04084-5263

Phone: 207-893-7951
E-mail: msunderm@sjcme.edu

TYPE OF INSTITUTION: Private, Roman Catholic
EXECUTIVE OFFICER: Daniel Sheridan, Vice President for Academic Affairs
CHAIRPERSON: Marilyn Sunderman
UNDERGRADUATE ENROLLMENT: 1,000

St Josephs College

222 Clinton Ave, Brooklyn NY 11205

College of Saint Joseph

Clement Rd, Rutland VT 05701

Saint Josephs College, Suffolk Campus

155 Roe Blvd, Patchogue NY 11772

Saint Joseph Seminary College

St Benedict LA 70457

St Joseph's Seminary

Dunwoodie, Yonkers NY 10704

St Joseph's University

Department of Theology
5600 City Avenue
Philadelphia PA 19131

Phone: 610-660-1865
Fax: 610-660-2160
E-mail: paspan@sju.edu

TYPE OF INSTITUTION: Private
EXECUTIVE OFFICER: Judith Chapman, Dean
CHAIRPERSON: Paul F. Aspan
UNDERGRADUATE ENROLLMENT: 3,250
GRADUATE ENROLLMENT: 2,250
DEGREES OFFERED: BA

UNDERGRADUATE MAJORS: 13

DEGREES CONFERRED: 7

DESCRIPTION OF UNDERGRADUATE PROGRAM: As a Catholic university in the Jesuit tradition, Saint Joseph's regards the religious dimension of human life as an integral part of a truly liberal education. Students complete a minimum of three courses in the area of theology as part of the general education requirement. Attention is given to the thought of the Christian tradition in the organization of the theology program. Departmental offerings also feature several courses which study other religious traditions. All courses in the department are taught as academic disciplines fully respecting the personal religious options of each student. Individuals with a keen interest in religious studies are urged to participate in the Theology Club, which sponsors lectures and discussions on current theological topics. Theology majors who distinguish themselves academically are inducted into the University's chapter of Theta Alpha Kappa, the National Honor Society for Religious Studies. Theology majors may take advantage of a flexible curriculum which allows them a generous number of elective credits to apply to a double major or a minor in another field. Graduates of the theolgy department are found in numerous career fields including law, business, medicine, ministry, education, and social services.

FACULTY:

Aspan, Paul F., PhD, Vanderbilt (1990), 1987, Assistant Professor—New Testament studies, introduction to Bible

Carpenter, David W., PhD, University of Chicago (1987), 1986, Assistant Professor—history of religion, comparative studies

Clark, Peter A., PhD, Loyola University of Chicago (1996), Associate Professor—medical ethics

Feske, Millicent C., PhD, Emory University (1992), 1993, Assistant Professor—social ethics

Finnegan, Gerald, PhD, Union Theological Seminary (1978), 1980, Assistant Professor—systematic theology, modern Catholicism

Genovesi, Vincent J., PhD, Emory University (1973), 1973, Professor—Christian ethics, medical ethics, Christian marriage

Krahmer, Shawn M., PhD, (1995), 1995, Assistant Professor—historical theology

Pfeil, Margaret R., PhD, University of Notre Dame (1999), 1999, Assistant Professor—social ethics

Smith, Mark S., PhD, Yale University (1985), 1993, Associate Professor—Hebrew scriptures

Tripole, Martin R., STD, Institut Catholique de Paris (1972), 1972, Associate Professor—biblical Christology, church

---

St Lawrence University

Canton NY 13617

Phone: 315-229-5130
Fax: 315-229-5628
E-mail: mgre@music.stlawu.edu
URL: www.stlawu.edu

TYPE OF INSTITUTION: Private

EXECUTIVE OFFICER: Thomas B. Coburn, Academic Dean & Vice President of the University

CHAIRPERSON: Michael R. Greenwald

UNDERGRADUATE ENROLLMENT: 2,000

Saint Leo College

Dept of Religion-MC 2127
PO Box 6665
Saint Leo FL 33574-6665

Phone: 352-588-8288
Fax: 352-588-8300
E-mail: las@saintleo.edu

TYPE OF INSTITUTION: Private, Catholic
EXECUTIVE OFFICER: Robert Imperato, Dean of Liberal Arts and Sciences
CHAIRPERSON: Robert Imperato
UNDERGRADUATE ENROLLMENT: 6,000

Saint Louis University

3800 Lindell Blvd
PO Box 56907
St Louis MO 63156-0907

Phone: 314-977-2878
Fax: 314-977-2947
E-mail: theology@slu.edu
URL: www.slu.edu/colleges/as/theology

TYPE OF INSTITUTION: Private, Jesuit
EXECUTIVE OFFICERS: Donald Brennan, Dean of Graduate Studies; Shirley Dowdy, Dean of
    Arts and Sciences
CHAIRPERSON: John J. Mueller
COORDINATOR: Kenneth B. Steinhauser
UNDERGRADUATE ENROLLMENT: 53
GRADUATE ENROLLMENT: 62

Saint Louis Christian College

1360 Grandview Dr, Florissant MO 63033

Saint Louis Rabbinical College

7400 Olive Rd, Saint Louis MO 63130

Saint Martin's College

Dept of Religious Studies
5300 Pacific Ave SE
Lacey WA 98503

Phone: 360-491-4700
Fax: 360-459-4124
E-mail: dsuter@stmartin.edu

TYPE OF INSTITUTION: Private, Roman Catholic
EXECUTIVE OFFICER: David Suter, Dean of Humanities
CHAIRPERSON: Kilian J. Malvey, OSB
UNDERGRADUATE ENROLLMENT: 975

Saint Martin's College

700 College St SE, Olympia WA 98503

Saint Mary's College

Moraga CA 94575

Saint Mary's College

Dept of Religious Studies
Notre Dame IN 46556

Phone: 219-284-4534
Fax: 219-284-4716
E-mail: incandel@saintmarys.edu
URL: www.saintma-
rys.edu/~incandel/RLST.html

TYPE OF INSTITUTION: Private, Roman Catholic (women's)
EXECUTIVE OFFICER: Marilou Eldred, President
CHAIRPERSON: Joseph M. Incandela
UNDERGRADUATE ENROLLMENT: 1,500

Saint Mary College

Dept of Theology
4100 South 4th Street
Leavenworth KS 66048-5082

Phone: 913-682-5151 ext 4332
Fax: 913-758-6140
E-mail: woodk@hub.smcks.edu
URL: www.smcks.edu

TYPE OF INSTITUTION: Private, Roman Catholic, sponsored by Sisters of Charity of
Leavenworth
EXECUTIVE OFFICER: Rev. Richard J. Mucowski, OFM
CHAIRPERSON: Sr. Kathleen Wood, SCL
UNDERGRADUATE ENROLLMENT: 8
DEGREES OFFERED: BA Theology, BA Pastoral Ministry
UNDERGRADUATE MAJORS: 8
DEGREES CONFERRED: 3
DESCRIPTION OF UNDERGRADUATE PROGRAM: Saint Mary College is a small Midwestern
Liberal Arts College, our Mission Statement commits the college community to "seek to pre-
pare graduates to live value-centered lives of learning, service, and character rich according
to the best resources within each person." The Theology Department contributes to this mission through the variety of courses offered for General Education and by supporting the spiritual environment of the institution. The program comes out of a Catholic heritage, open to
and respectful of other religious traditions with a focus on helping students come to a deeper
knowledge and faith. Two degrees are offered in the department: a 30 hour BA in Theology
which provides a background in the key areas of Theology and additional hours in Philosophy, History and a Language; a 32 hour BA in Pastoral Ministry. The Ministry degree has
been recently instituted and integral to its completion is personal/spiritual development and
supervised experience in a parish or church-related setting.
FACULTY:
McReynolds, Sally Ann, ND, PhD, Catholic University of America (1988), 1992, Assistant Professor—systematic and moral theology, 913-758-6317, Fax: 913-758-6140, E-mail:
samcr@hub.smcks.edu

Minges, Mary Beth, SCL, MA, Saint Michael College, VT (1994), 1999, Instructor in Theology—systematic theology, pastoral ministry, 913-682-5151 ext 6492, Fax: 913-758-6140

Steele, Diane, SCL, MA, Notre Dame (1993), PhD (cand.) Notre Dame, on leave for study—systematic theology, Christian anthropology, 219-277-5833, E-mail: diane.m.steel.25@nd.edu

Wood, Kathleen, SCL, MA, Boston College (1982), 1991, Chair, Associate Professor—scripture, pastoral ministry, church history, 913-758-4332, Fax: 913-758-6140, E-mail: woodk@hub.smcks.edu

Saint Mary's College of Maryland

Dept of Philosophy and Religious Studies
St Marys City MD 20686

Phone: 301-862-0337
Fax: 301-862-0436

TYPE OF INSTITUTION: Public, Non-Denominational
EXECUTIVE OFFICER: Mel Endy, Provost
CHAIRPERSON: Alan Paskow
COORDINATOR: Katharina Von Kellenbach (Religious Studies)
UNDERGRADUATE ENROLLMENT: 1,400

Saint Mary's College

3535 Indian Trail
Orchard Lake MI 48324

Phone: 248-682-1885
Fax: 248-683-0402

TYPE OF INSTITUTION: Private, Roman Catholic
EXECUTIVE OFFICER: Thaddeus Radzilowski, President
CHAIRPERSON: Dennis Castillo
UNDERGRADUATE ENROLLMENT: 330

College of St Mary

Omaha NE 68124

St Mary's Seminary and University

5400 Roland Ave
Baltimore MD 21210-1994

Phone: 410-864-4000
Fax: 410-864-4205
URL: stmarys.edu

TYPE OF INSTITUTION: Private, Roman Catholic
EXECUTIVE OFFICER: Robert Leavitt, SS, President/Rector

St Mary Seminary

28700 Euclid Ave, Wickliffe OH 44092-2527

Saint Mary's University of Minnesota

Theology Department
700 Terrace Heights #46
Winona MN 55987-1399

Phone: 507-457-1797
Fax: 507-457-1633
E-mail: rsmith@smumn.edu
URL: www.smumn.edu/

TYPE OF INSTITUTION: Private, Roman Catholic

EXECUTIVE OFFICER: Louis B. DeThomasis, FSC, President

CHAIRPERSON: Robert Smith, FSC

UNDERGRADUATE ENROLLMENT: 1,300

GRADUATE ENROLLMENT: 2,800

DEGREES OFFERED: BA in Theology or Pastoral and Youth Ministry

UNDERGRADUATE MAJORS: 20

DEGREES CONFERRED: 6

DESCRIPTION OF UNDERGRADUATE PROGRAM: The Theology Department brings about awareness and appreciation of the Catholic heritage and a fertile contact between that heritage and contemporary thought. With links to Saint Mary's Press, a major publisher in Catholic religious education, and Immaculate Heart of Mary Seminary, the Department is in a unique position to explore and understand critical aspects in theology and pastoral ministry. It also helps staff the university's Institute in Pastoral Ministries as well as the liberal studies curriculum. The two major programs in the Department prepare students for advanced theological study and for pastoral ministries, especially youth ministry, in the Roman Catholic church. All majors must complete the Theological Foundations and additional courses prescribed for either the Theology Major or the Pastoral and Youth Ministries Major. The minor program promotes fundamental awareness of the Catholic vision of life and is merited by students who complete eighteen credits in theology.

GRADUATE PROGRAM

Graduate Advisor: Gregory Sobolewski

Graduate Degrees Offered: MA in Pastoral Ministries

Degrees Conferred: 18 MA

Not in Residence: 75 MA

Average No. of New Students Enrolled: 25 MA

Women Students: 50 MA

Minimum GRE Score Requisite to Admission: No

Minimum GPA Score Requisite to Admission: Yes; 2.75 of 4.0

Foreign Language Proficiency Evaluated: No

Financial Aid to Other Students: 15% MA

Attrition Among Students: 3% MA

DESCRIPTION OF GRADUATE PROGRAM AND RESEARCH FACILITIES: The Institute in Pastoral Ministries responds to the educational needs of persons engaged in the pastoral ministries of the Roman Catholic church. It offers affordable, nontraditional academic programs that meet the needs of active ministers. The Institute offers a Master of Arts in Pastoral Ministries and a Certificate in Pastoral Ministries that are completed ordinarily in three summers. Each summer requires a two-week residence on the Winona campus that is preceded by preparatory reading and prewriting and is followed by completion of research requirements. A highlight of the program is the Integrated Pastoral Research project that integrates theology and Catholic teaching with the pastoral situation and imagination of each student. The certificate program requires participation in the two-week residency and completion of preparatory reading; certificate students are not required to do research or the Integrated Pastoral Research project.

ACADEMIC PLAN, ADMISSION REQUIREMENTS, AND FINANCIAL AID: Admission: 1) An earned bachelor's degree with a GPA of 2.75 or better from an accredited institution; persons with less than a 2.75 GPA may be admitted provisionally. 2) Two letters of recommendation: one from a pastor, administrator, or supervisor; and one from a colleague. 3) A two-page double-spaced typed essay stating one's ministerial goals and aspirations, including consideration of one's motivation for enrolling in the Institute. Financial Aid: Scholarships are not currently available but standard governmental aid and loans are available.

FACULTY:

Becker, William M., STD, Pontifical Gregorian University (1994), 1994, Assistant Professor—fundamental theology, 507-457-7373, Fax: 507-457-8601, E-mail: wbecker@smumn.edu

Schneider, Diane M., PhD, University of Toronto (1991), 1995, Assistant Professor—pastoral theology and spirituality, 507-457-1424, Fax: 507-457-1633, E-mail: dschneid@smumn.edu

Smith, Robert J., FSC, PhD, Marquette University (1992), 1989, Associate Professor—sexual ethics and moral theology, 507-457-1797, Fax: 507-457-1633, E-mail: rsmith@smumn.edu

Sobolewski, Gregory L., PhD, Marquette University (1993), 1991, Associate Professor—historical theology, 507-457-1767, Fax: 507-457-1633, E-mail: gsobolew@smumn.edu

Saint Mary's University

One Camino Santa Maria
San Antonio TX 78228-8585

Phone: 210-436-3310
Fax: 210-431-6884
E-mail: theojohn@stmarytx.edu
URL: www.stmarytx.edu/acad/theo/index.htm

TYPE OF INSTITUTION: Private, Roman Catholic

EXECUTIVE OFFICER: Rev. John Moder, SM, President

CHAIRPERSON: John A. Leies, SM

UNDERGRADUATE ENROLLMENT: 2,600

GRADUATE ENROLLMENT: 1,400

DEGREES OFFERED: BA Theology; B of Applied Theology (BAT)

UNDERGRADUATE MAJORS: 8 BA; 7 BAT

DEGREES CONFERRED: 7

DESCRIPTION OF UNDERGRADUATE PROGRAM: The undergraduate program includes the BA and the Bachelor of Applied Theology degree. From the perspective of the Roman Catholic Tradition the BA proposes to explore how religious meaning is characteristically preserved in scripture, is thematized by theology and ritual, provides the basic categories for pursuing answers to ultimate questions and draws members of each generation into ethical and religious commitment. The BAT is designed for mature students who have met degree requirements and have completed the equivalent of approximately 30 semester hours of ministerial, vocational, occupational, or technical specialization. Permanent Diaconate programs, Diocesan Religious Education certification, etc. qualify.

GRADUATE PROGRAM

Member of the Council on Graduate Studies in Religion

Graduate Advisor: Geraldine Telepak

Graduate Degrees Offered: MA

Degrees Conferred: 10 MA

Graduate Students in Residence: 4 MA

Not in Residence: 46 MA

Average No. of New Students Enrolled: 10 MA

Women Students: 20 MA

Minority Students: 18 MA

Foreign Students: 1 MA

Minimum GRE Score Requisite to Admission: Yes, GPA x GRE = 1200

Minimum GPA Score Requisite to Admission: Yes, 3.0 on 4.0 scale

Foreign Language Proficiency Evaluated: Yes

Financial Aid to First Year Students: 100% MA

Financial Aid to Other Students: 100% MA

Attrition Among Students: 15% MA

Graduates Placed: 100% MA

DESCRIPTION OF GRADUATE PROGRAM AND RESEARCH FACILITIES: The MA in Theology, intended for preparing persons for or already engaged in church ministry, aims at promoting critical theological study and reflection. It requires 36 semester hours or 30 semester hours with a thesis. The Master of Arts in Pastoral Ministry is a 39-hour non-thesis program. It is intended for persons preparing for or already engaged in various church ministries and aims at integrating critical theological study and sound administrative practice within the Roman Catholic tradition. It requires 39 semester hours including a practicum which provides for on-sight experience in parish, Catholic school, diocesan office and other administrative areas. The Academic Library has holdings of almost 200,000 volumes and over 1,000 current periodicals. Students also have access to holdings of five other private and four public colleges and university libraries in San Antonio.

ACADEMIC PLAN, ADMISSION REQUIREMENTS, FINANCIAL AID: The University operates on academic and summer sessions. Undergraduate theology majors are required to take 30 semester hours in theology and courses in philosophy and sociology or religion. Financial aid, college work study and some scholarships are available.

FACULTY:

Bolin, Thomas M., PhD, Marquette University, 1995, Assistant Professor—Hebrew Bible

Doersching, Lawrence, SM, DMin, Eden Theological Seminary, 1993, Lecturer—introductory theology

Langlinais, J. Willis, STD, Fribourg (1954), 1963, Professor—moral theology

Leies, John A., STD, Fribourg (1954), 1963, Professor—moral theology

Miller, Charles H., STD, San Anselmo, Rome (1973), 1979, Professor—Bible, archaeology, hermeneutics

Milne, Mary K., MA, St Mary's (1973), 1974, Lecturer (part-time)—Bible, archaeology

Mongrain, Kevin, PhD, Yale University, 1999, Assistant Professor—systematic theology

Montague, George T., STD, Fribourg (1960), 1961, Professor—Bible

Neville, Richard, MA, St Mary's (1990), Lecturer (part-time)—systematic theology

O'Connor, Robert B., PhD, University of Texas, Austin, 1970, Associate Professor—theology

Sauer, James B., PhD, St Paul University, 1992, Lecturer—systematic theology

Telepak, Geraldine, DMin, Austin Presbyterian Theological Seminary, 1992, Associate Professor—theology/pastoral ministry

Saint Mary's University

Dept of Religious Studies
Halifax, Nova Scotia B3H 3C3
Canada

Phone: 902-420-5823
Fax: 902-420-5181
E-mail: paul.bowlby@stmarys.ca
URL: www.stmarys.ca

TYPE OF INSTITUTION: Public
EXECUTIVE OFFICER: Kenneth Ozmon, President
CHAIRPERSON: Paul Bowlby
UNDERGRADUATE ENROLLMENT: 8000
GRADUATE ENROLLMENT: 100

University of St Mary of the Lake

1000 East Maple Avenue
Mundelein IL 60060

Phone: 847-566-6401
Fax: 847-566-7330
URL: www.vocations.org

TYPE OF INSTITUTION: Denominational: Roman Catholic
EXECUTIVE OFFICER: John Canary, Rector-President
GRADUATE ENROLLMENT: 180

Saint Mary-of-the-Woods College

St Mary-of-the-Woods IN 47876

Phone: 812-535-5151

TYPE OF INSTITUTION: Private, Roman Catholic
EXECUTIVE OFFICER: Joan Lescinski, CSJ, President
CHAIRPERSONS: Mary L. Milano and L. Bernard LaMontagne
COORDINATOR: Ruth Eileen Dwyer
UNDERGRADUATE ENROLLMENT: 1,196
GRADUATE ENROLLMENT: 82

St Meinrad School of Theology

One Hill Drive
St Meinrad IN 47577

Phone: 812-357-6611
Fax: 812-357-6964
E-mail: apply@saintmeinrad.edu
URL: www.saintmeinrad.edu

TYPE OF INSTITUTION: Private, Roman Catholic
EXECUTIVE OFFICER: Mark O'Keefe, OSB, President-Rector
CHAIRPERSON: Nathaniel Reeves, OSB, Academic Dean
GRADUATE ENROLLMENT: 112
GRADUATE PROGRAM
Graduate Advisor: Nathaniel Reeves, OSB, Academic Dean
Graduate Degrees Offered: MA; Other: MTS

Degrees Conferred: 21 MA; 6 Other: MTS

Graduate Students in Residence: 38 MA; 1 Other: MTS

Not in Residence: 5 MA; 19 Other

Women Students: 4 MA; 14 Other

Minority Students: 1 MA; 0 Other

Foreign Students: 5 MA; 0 Other

Minimum GRE Score Requisite to Admission: No

Minimum GPA Score Requisite to Admission: Yes; 2.0 on 4.0 scale

Foreign Language Proficiency Evaluated: No

DESCRIPTION OF GRADUATE PROGRAM AND RESEARCH FACILITIES: The MDiv program is primarily for students preparing for ministry as priests. It consists of eight semesters and four January interterms of study on a full-time basis, distributed into 88 credits in required courses, 27 credits in elective courses, and 16 practicum units. The MTS program (48 credits) offers courses in a general theological curriculum which investigates the sources and resources of the Christian tradition. Required areas of theological investigation include courses in systematic studies, biblical and historical studies, and pastoral studies. The MA program (48 credits) is designed for those who wish to establish a foundation in Catholic thought and life, including its philosophical basis.

ACADEMIC PLAN, ADMISSION REQUIREMENTS, FINANCIAL AID: The academic year is made up of four terms: fall semester, January interterm, spring semester, and a six week summer session with two consecutive three week sections. Applicants must have a bachelor's degree and possess competence in the skills of reading, speaking, and writing English. Information on scholarships and financial aid, including grants, loans, and employment opportunities is available from the Director of Financial Aid.

FACULTY:

Buckel, John, PhD, University of Louvain (1988), 1989, Associate Professor—scripture

Carr, Ephrem, OSB, STD, Pontifical Athenaeum of Sant' Anselmo (1978), 1999, Visiting Associate Professor—church history and patristics

Davis, Cyprian, OSB, DrSciHist, University of Louvain (1977), 1963, Professor—church history

DeBona, Guerric, OSB, PhD, Indiana University (1996), 1999, Assistant Professor—homiletics

Denz, David, PhD, University of Notre Dame (1981), 1991, Associate Professor—philosophy

Dietlein, Damian, OSB, SSL, Pontifical Biblical Institute, Rome (1961), 1968, Associate Professor—scripture

DuVall, Justin, OSB, AMLS, University of Michigan (1979), 1998, Adjunct Instructor—pastoral studies

Ginter, Mark, PhD, Marquette University (1997), 1997, Assistant Professor—moral theology

Hagan, Harry, OSB, SSD, Pontifical Biblical Institute, Rome (1986), 1979, Associate Professor—scripture

Hensell, Eugene, OSB, PhD, St Louis University (1975), 1979 Associate Professor—scripture

Jefford, Clayton, PhD, Claremont Graduate School (1988), 1989, Associate Professor—scripture

Kelly, Columa, OSB, MusSacD, Pontifical Institute of Sacred Music (1963), 1998, Visiting Professor—church music

Kilcourse, George, PhD, Fordham University (1974), 1999, Visiting Professor

Knott, J. Ronald, MDiv, Saint Meinrad School of Theology (1970), 1997, Visiting Instructor—homiletics

LaMothe, Ryan, PhD, Vanderbilt University (1994), 1996, Assistant Professor—pastoral care and counseling

LeBeau, Dorothy, PhD, The Catholic University of America (1998), 1998, Assistant Professor—spirituality

Mansini, Guy, OSB, STD, Gregorian University, Rome (1984), 1984, Associate Professor—systematic theology

Neufelder, Jerome, MDiv, Saint Meinrad School of Theology (1970), 1985, Assistant Professor—spirituality

O'Keefe, Mark, OSB, STD, Catholic University of America (1987), 1987, Associate Professor—moral theology

Pelzel, Morris, PhD, Catholic University of America (1994), 1994, Assistant Professor—systematic theology

Reeves, Nathaniel, OSB, JCL, Gregorian University, Rome (1980), 1984, Instructor—canon law

Richstatter, Thomas, OFM, STD, Institut Catholique de Paris (1976), 1984, Professor—sacramental/liturigical theology

Ring, D. Gill, MA, Purdue University (1970), 1991, Assistant Professor—philosophy

Robinson, Denis, OSB, MDiv, Saint Meinrad School of Theology (1993), 1997, Visiting Instructor—systematic theology

Smith, Clare, RSM, MS, University of Pittsburgh (1981), 1997, Adjunct Instructor—French and Latin

Stasiak, Kurt, OSB, STD, Sant' Anselmo, Rome (1993), 1986, Associate Professor—sacramental/liturgical theology

Stern, Richard, EdD, Northern Illinois University (1990), 1990, Associate Professor—homiletics

Thomas, John, MDiv, Saint Meinrad School of Theology (1993), 1997, Adjunct Instructor—pastoral studies

Walters, Thomas, PhD, Wayne State University (1980), 1983, Professor—religious education

Warner, Shirley Ann, OSU, MTS, Saint Meinrad School of Theology (1993), 1997, Instructor—pastoral studies

Weigman, Joseph, MA, Bowling Green State University (1998), 1999, Visiting Instructor—pastoral studies

White, Cajetan, OSB, MDiv, Saint Meinrad School of Theology (1973), 1984, Adjunct Instructor—homiletics in Spanish

White, Joseph, PhD, University of Notre Dame (1980), 1999, Visiting Assistant Professor—church history

---

Saint Michael's College

Winooski Park
Colchester VT 05439

Phone: 802-654-2362
Fax: 802-654-2664
E-mail: emahoney@smcvt.edu

TYPE OF INSTITUTION: Private, Roman Catholic
EXECUTIVE OFFICER: Janet Watson Sheeran, Provost/Vice President for Academic Affairs
CHAIRPERSON: Richard N. Berube, SSE (Undergraduate)
COORDINATOR: Edward J. Mahoney (Graduate Theology/Pastoral Ministry)
UNDERGRADUATE ENROLLMENT: 1,700

GRADUATE ENROLLMENT: 750

University of St Michael's College

Faculty of Theology   **Phone: 416-926-7140**
81 St Mary St   **Fax: 416-926-7294**
Toronto, Ontario M5S 1J4   **URL: www.utoronto.ca/stmikes**
Canada
TYPE OF INSTITUTION: Public, Roman Catholic

EXECUTIVE OFFICER: Brian F. Hogan, CSB, Dean of Theology

CHAIRPERSON: Brian F. Hogan, CSB

GRADUATE ENROLLMENT: 232

GRADUATE PROGRAM

Member of the Council on Graduate Studies in Religion

Graduate Advisor: T. Allan Smith

Graduate Degrees Offered: MA; PhD; ThD; ThM; DMin

Degrees Conferred: 6 MA; 5 PhD; 1 ThM

Graduate Students in Residence: 8 MA; 11 PhD/ThD; 1 ThM; 3 DMin

Not in Residence: 13 MA; 21 PhD/ThD; 9 ThM; 4 DMin

Average No. of New Students Enrolled: 3 MA; 5 PhD/ThD; 2 ThM; 3 DMin

Women Students: 7 MA; 26 PhD/ThD; 4 DMin

Minority Students: 2 PhD/ThD; 4 Other

Foreign Students: 1 MA; 22 PhD/ThD; 4 ThM

Minimum GRE Score Requisite to Admission: No

Minimum GPA Score Requisite to Admission: Yes, 3.7 on 4.0 scale

Foreign Language Proficiency Evaluated: Yes

Financial Aid to First Year Students: 50% MA; 75% PhD

Financial Aid to Other Students: 50% MA; 75% PhD

Attrition Among Students: 10% MA; 10% PhD

Graduates Placed: 80% PhD

DESCRIPTION OF GRADUATE PROGRAM AND RESEARCH FACILITIES: The University of St Michael's College is a member of the Toronto School of Theology. Access to the seven libraries of the TST colleges as well as the collection of the University of Toronto, one of the premier collections in North America. As well, St Michael's hosts the collection of the Pontifical Institute of Medieaval Studies, a renowned resource for medieval studies.

ACADEMIC PLAN, ADMISSION REQUIREMENTS, FINANCIAL AID: 1) a statement of approximately 100 words indicating the applicant's intentions and interests; 2) two letters of academic reference; 3) for applicants not graduating from a university where English is the main language of instruction, a TOEFL score of not less than 600 and a TWE score of not less than 5.0. Master of Theology admission requirements: 1) a degree in Arts or its equivalent from an accredited college or university; 2) a Master of Divinity with at least second-class standing (B+) from an accredited theological institution; 3) reading knowledge of one modern (French or German) or one ancient (Greek, Hebrew, Latin) language. General program requirements: either 6 semestered courses, the completion of a master's thesis, and reading competence in one ancient and one modern research language; or 8 semestered courses, the completion of a major paper, and reading competence in one ancient and one modern research language. Master of Arts in Theology (MA) admission requirements: BA from an accredited college or university with at least a second-class standing (B+). General program requirements: 14 semestered courses (taken over two years); the preparation of a master's thesis; reading competence in one ancient and one modern research language. Doctor of Philosophy/Doctor of Theology (PhD/ThD) admission requirements: 1) BA from an accredited college or university; 2) first theological degree (MDiv, MA, STB) from an ATS accredited institution with a first class (A) standing; 3) submission of a thesis-length paper if a thesis was not required by the master's degree; 4) reading knowledge of one modern (French or German) and one ancient (Greek, Hebrew, Latin) language. General program requirements: 12 courses (over two years); comprehensive evaluation; reading knowledge of two modern (normally French and German) and one ancient (Greek, Hebrew, Latin) language; 4) the preparation and successful defense of a doctoral dissertation.

FACULTY:

Anderson, Anne, DMin, University of Toronto/Regis College (1990), 1999, Director of Jewish Studies Program including Israel Intersession Program—pastoral theology and ministry in health care, 416-926-1300 ext 3341, Fax: 416-926-7294, E-mail: aanders@epas.utoronto.ca

Bowman, Lorna M. A., EdD, Columbia (1984), 1988, Associate Professor—religious education, 416-926-7140, Fax: 416-926-7294, E-mail: lbowman@chass.utoronto.ca

Brunning, Jacqueline, PhD, University of Toronto (1981), 1979, Adjunct Professor—philosophy, 416-926-7140, Fax: 416-926-7276

Cormie, Lee F., PhD, University of Chicago (1977), 1979, Associate Professor—Christian ethics, systematic theology and social sciences, 416-926-7140, Fax: 416-926-7294, E-mail: lcormie@chass.utoronto.ca

Donovan, Daniel L., DTheol, Münster (1971), 1971, Professor—systematic theology, 416-926-7140, Fax: 416-926-7276

D'Souza, Mario O., PhD, University of Toronto (1988), 1999, Assistant Professor—religious education, 416-926-1300 ext 3608, Fax: 416-926-7294, E-mail: mdsouza@chass.utoronto.ca

Dunn, Stephen G., STD, Alphonsianum (1971), 1970, Director, Elliott Allen Institute for Theology and Ecology and Associate Professor—Christian ethics, 416-926-7140, Fax: 416-926-7294, E-mail: sdunn@chass.utoronto.ca

Fedwick, Paul, PhD, University of St Michael's College (1974), 1982, Associate Professor—church history, 416-926-7140, Fax: 416-926-7294

Fritz, Maureena, PhD, University of Ottawa (1971), 1972, Professor Emerita—religious education and Jewish studies, E-mail: fritz@hujivms.huji.ac.il

Hogan, Brian F., PhD, University of Toronto (1986), 1987, Dean and Associate Professor—church history, 416-926-7265, Fax: 416-926-7294, E-mail: bhogan@chass.utoronto.ca

Irwin, William H., SSD, Pontifical Biblical Institute (1974), 1965, Professor Emeritus—Old Testament, 416-926-7140, Fax: 416-926-7294, E-mail: irwinw@chass.utoronto.ca

Kloppenborg, John S., PhD, University of St Michael's College (1984), 1988, Associate Professor—New Testament, 416-926-7140, Fax: 416-926-7294, E-mail: kloppen@chass.utoronto.ca

Leonard, Ellen M., PhD, University of St Michael's College (1978), 1977, Professor Emerita—systematic theology, 416-926-7140, Fax: 416-926-7294, E-mail: leonard@chass.utoronto.ca

Meagher, John C., PhD, London (1961); PhD, Princeton (1962); PhD, McMaster (1975); 1968, Professor—historical theology, New Testament, 416-926-7140, Fax: 416-926-7276, E-mail: jmeagher@chass.utoronto.ca

O'Gara, Margaret, PhD, University of St Michael's College (1980), 1976, Associate Professor—systematic theology, 416-926-7140, Fax: 416-926-7294

Sheehan, Mary Ellen, STD, Louvain (1975), 1978, Associate Professor—systematic and pastoral theology, 416-926-7140, Fax: 416-926-7294

Smith, T. Allan, DTheol, Erlangen (1988), Associate Professor—church history, theology, 416-926-1300 ext 3411, Fax: 416-926-7291, E-mail: allan.smith@utoronto.ca

Vertin, Michael, PhD, University of Toronto (1973), 1981, Adjunct Professor—systematic theology, philosophy, 416-926-1300, Fax: 416-926-7294, E-mail: mvertin@chass.utoronto.ca

Walsh, J. Leo, STD, Lateran (1965), 1977, Associate Professor—Christian ethics, 416-926-7140, Fax: 416-926-7294

Whalen, David M., DMin, University of Toronto; University of St Michael's College (1992), 1987, Director of Basic Degree Programs, Theological Field Education, Summer School Program, 416-926-7140, Fax: 416-926-7294, E-mail: dwhalen@chass.utoronto.ca

---

St Norbert College

100 Grant Street
De Pere WI 54115

Phone: 920-403-3956
Fax: 920-403-4086
E-mail: eberhj@mail.snc.edu

TYPE OF INSTITUTION: Private, Roman Catholic

EXECUTIVE OFFICER: Thomas J. Trebon, Academic Dean, Vice President

CHAIRPERSON: Howard J. Ebert

UNDERGRADUATE ENROLLMENT: 2,000

GRADUATE ENROLLMENT: 60

St Olaf College

1520 St Olaf Avenue
Northfield MN 55057

Phone: 507-646-3080
Fax: 507-646-3549
E-mail: religion-dept@stolaf.edu
URL: www.stolaf.edu/depts/religion

TYPE OF INSTITUTION: Private, ELCA

EXECUTIVE OFFICER: Mark Edwards, President; James Pence, Dean of the College

CHAIRPERSON: John Barbour

UNDERGRADUATE ENROLLMENT: 2,850

DEGREES OFFERED: BA

UNDERGRADUATE MAJORS: 53

DEGREES CONFERRED: 31

DESCRIPTION OF UNDERGRADUATE PROGRAM: Program Description: St Olaf is a liberal arts college and the Department of Religion gives opportunities for the study of religion within that context. All students do biblical and theological studies as part of their general education program, and a wide variety of additional courses in historical studies, ethics, history of religions and religion and literature are offered. The religion major involves work in both Christianity and other religious traditions. Students are exposed to major approaches to studying religion by taking courses in the areas of sacred texts, religion in history and culture, and religious thought. They are also expected to do more intensive, integrative work through advanced courses and seminars.

FACULTY:

Barbour, John D., PhD, University of Chicago (1981), 1982, Professor—religion and literature, ethics, 507-646-3083. E-mail: barbourj@stolaf.edu

Beckman, Patricia Zimmerman, PhD, University of Chicago (2000), 1999, Assistant Professor—history of Christianity, 507-646-3340, E-mail: beckman@stolaf.edu

Booth, David, PhD, University of Chicago (1984), 1985, Associate Professor—religious thought, 507-646-3575, E-mail: booth@stolaf.edu

Granquist, Mark, PhD, University of Chicago (1992), 1992, Assistant Professor—history of Christianity, 507-646-3894, E-mail: granquis@stolaf.edu

Hanson, James, PhD, Princeton Seminary (1997), 1992, Assistant Professor—new testament, 507-646-3340, E-mail: hansonj@stolaf.edu

Lagerquist, L. DeAne, PhD, University of Chicago (1986), 1988, Associate Professor—history of Christianity, 507-646-3175, E-mail: lagerqui@stolaf.edu

Lindley, Sussan H., PhD, Duke University (1974), 1976, Professor—history of Christianity, 507-646-3094, E-mail: lindley@stolaf.edu

Lund, Eric, PhD, Yale University (1979), 1979, Professor—history of Christianity, 507-646-3090, E-mail: lund@stolaf.edu

Malotky, Daniel, PhD, University of Chicago (1999), 1998, Assistant Professor—theology, ethics, 507-646-3344, E-mail: malotky@stolaf.edu

Marshall, Bruce D., PhD, Yale University (1985), 1985, Professor—theology 507-646-3895, E-mail: marshalb@stolaf.edu

Odell, Margaret, PhD, University of Pittsburgh (1988), 1994, Assistant Professor—Hebrew Bible, 507-646-3085, E-mail: odell@stolaf.edu

Poehlmann, William R., PhD, Harvard University (1974), 1973, Associate Professor—New Testament, 507-646-3087, E-mail: poehlman@stolaf.edu

Rader, Rosemary, PhD, Stanford University, 1995, Visiting Associate Professor (part time)—history of Christianity, 507-646-3086, E-mail: raderr@stolaf.edu

Rambachan, Anantanand, PhD, University of Leeds (1984), 1985, Professor—world religions, Hinduism, 507-646-3081, E-mail: rambacha@stolaf.edu

Reed, Barbara E., PhD, University of Iowa (1982), 1982, Associate Professor—world religions, Buddhism, 507-646-3086, E-mail: reed@stolaf.edu

Santurri, Edmund N., PhD, Yale University (1984), 1980, Professor—theology, ethics, 507-646-3084, E-mail: santurri@stolaf.edu

Schuurman, Douglas, PhD, University of Chicago (1988), 1986, Associate Professor—ethics, theology, 507-646-3091, E-mail: schuurma@stolaf.edu

Stansell, Gary, DrTheol, Heidelberg University (1981), 1973, Professor—Hebrew Bible, 507-646-3082, E-mail: stansell@stolaf.edu

Wilson, Charles A., PhD, University of Chicago (1986), 1973, Professor—theology, 507-646-3089, E-mail: wilson@stolaf.edu

---

St Patrick's Seminary

320 Middlefield Rd, Menlo Park CA 94025

Saint Paul's College

115 College Drive
Lawrenceville VA 23868

Phone: 804-848-3964
804-848-3111, ext 222
Fax: 804-848-2867

TYPE OF INSTITUTION: Private, Episcopal
EXECUTIVE OFFICER: Thomas M. Law, President
UNDERGRADUATE ENROLLMENT: 607

Saint Paul's College

University of Waterloo, Waterloo, Ontario N2L 3G5 Canada

St Paul School of Theology

5123 Truman Rd, Kansas City MO 64127

Saint Paul Seminary

2260 Summit Ave, St Paul MN 55105

Saint Paul University

223 Main Street
Ottawa, Ontario K1S 1C4
Canada

Phone: 613-236-1393
Fax: 613-782-3033
E-mail: info@ustpaul.ca

TYPE OF INSTITUTION: Public
EXECUTIVE OFFICER: Dale M. Schlitt, OMI, Rector; Achiel Peelman OMI, Vice-Rector, Academic
COORDINATOR: Colette Mangin (BA Christian Studies Program)
UNDERGRADUATE ENROLLMENT: 375
GRADUATE ENROLLMENT: 400

Saint Peter's College

Jersey City NJ 07306

Saint Peter's Seminary

1040 Waterloo St N, London, Ontario N6A 3Y1 Canada

The Saint Petersburg Theological Seminary

6550 Mango Ave S
St Petersburg FL 33707

Phone: 813-345-7022
Fax: 813-345-7022

TYPE OF INSTITUTION: Non-Denominational
EXECUTIVE OFFICER: Wellington W. Whittlesey, President of the Seminary
CHAIRPERSON: James Cook
COORDINATOR: George Pierce
UNDERGRADUATE ENROLLMENT: 50
GRADUATE ENROLLMENT: 50

College of St Rose

Albany NY 12203

College of St Scholastica

Dept of Religious Studies, Duluth MN 55811

St Stephen's College

Univ of Alberta Campus
8810-112 St
Edmonton AB T6G 2J6 Canada

Phone: 403-439-7311
Fax: 403-433-8875
E-mail: westerma@gpu.srv.ualberta.ca
URL: www.ualberta.ca/st.stephens/

TYPE OF INSTITUTION: Denominational: United Church of Canada
EXECUTIVE OFFICER: Christopher Levan, President
UNDERGRADUATE ENROLLMENT: 400
GRADUATE ENROLLMENT: 250

Saint Thomas University

16400 NW 32nd Ave, Miami FL 33054

University of St Thomas

Mail #AQU300
2115 Summit Ave
St Paul MN 55105-1096

Phone: 612-962-5300
Fax: 612-962-5322
E-mail: ljdimond@stthomas.edu
URL: www.stthomas.edu/www/
theo_http/index.html

TYPE OF INSTITUTION: Private, Roman Catholic
EXECUTIVE OFFICER: Rev. Dennis J. Dease, President
CHAIRPERSON: Catherine A. Cory
UNDERGRADUATE ENROLLMENT: 5,304
GRADUATE ENROLLMENT: 5,486
DEGREES OFFERED: BA
UNDERGRADUATE MAJORS: 87
DEGREES CONFERRED: 19

DESCRIPTION OF UNDERGRADUATE PROGRAM: Within the context of a liberal arts tradition, we strive to assist students to become theologically reflective about their experience and their culture. This is done from within the Catholic tradition and in an ecumenical conversation with other theological traditions.

FACULTY:

Batten, Alicia J., PhD (cand.), University of St Michael's College, 1998—New Testament, E-mail: ajbatten@stthomas.edu

Boyle, John F., PhD, University of Toronto (1989), 1990—history of Christianity, E-mail: jfboyle@stthomas.edu

Brady, Bernard V., PhD, University of Chicago (1988), 1989—ethics, E-mail: bvbrady@stthomas.edu

Briel, Don, PhD, University of Strasbourg (1980), 1981—systematic theology, E-mail: djbriel@stthomas.edu

Burr, Elizabeth G., PhD, Harvard University, 1996—historical theology, E-mail: cgburr@stthomas.edu

Cavanaugh, William T., PhD, Duke University (1996), 1995—systematic theology, E-mail: wtcavanaugh@stthomas.edu

Cory, Catherine, PhD, University of Notre Dame (1993), 1991—New Testament, E-mail: cacory@stthomas.edu

Cytron, Barry D., PhD, Iowa State (1982), 1988—Jewish studies, E-mail: bdcytron@stthomas.edu

Hallman, Joseph, PhD, Fordham University (1970), 1981—systematic theology, E-mail: jmhallman@stthomas.edu

Harrington, Jay, OP, PhD/STD, Catholic University of Louvain (1998), 1997—New Testament, E-mail: jmharrington@stthomas.edu

Hart, David Bentley, PhD, University of Virginia, 1997—historical theology, E-mail: dbhart@stthomas.edu

Hollerich, Michael J., PhD, University of Chicago (1986), 1993—history of Christianity, E-mail: mjhollerich@stthomas.edu

Hughes, Seán F., PhD (cand.) Trinity College, Cambridge, UK—historical, E-mail: sfhughes@stthomas.edu

Joncas, Jan Michael, SLD, Pontificio Istituto Liturgico Ateneo S. Anselmo (1991), 1991—liturgics, E-mail: jmjoncas@stthomas.edu

Jordon, Sherry, PhD, Yale University (1995), 1993—historical theology, E-mail: sejordon@stthomas.edu

Kennedy, Arthur, PhD, Boston University (1978), 1974—systematic theology, E-mail: alkennedy@stthomas.edu

King-Lenzmeier, Anne, PhD, Fordham University (1987), 1985—systematic theology, E-mail: ahkinglenzme@stthomas.edu

Landry, David T., PhD, Vanderbilt University (1992), 1991—New Testament, E-mail: dtlandry@stthomas.edu

Michalak, Joseph T., MA, University of St Thomas, 1996—moral theology, E-mail: jtmichalak@stthomas.edu

Naughton, Michael, PhD, Marquette University (1991), 1991—ethics, E-mail: mjnaughton@stthomas.edu

Nelson-Pallmeyer, Jack A., MDiv, Union Theological Seminary, 1977—justice and peace studies, E-mail: janelsonpal@stthomas.edu

Nichols, Terence, PhD, Marquette University (1988), 1988—systematic theology, E-mail: tlnichols@stthomas.edu

Patton, Corrine L., PhD, Yale University (1991), 1996—Old Testament/Hebrew Bible, E-mail: clpatton@stthomas.edu

Penchansky, David, PhD, Vanderbilt University (1988), 1989—Old Testament, E-mail: d9penchansky@stthomas.edu

Posey, Thaddeus J., OFMCap, PhD, St Louis University (1993), 1993—historical theology, E-mail: tjposey@stthomas.edu

Smith, David, STD/SSL, Angelicum University (1970), Pontifical Biblical Commission (1975), 1970—New Testament, E-mail: dwsmith@stthomas.edu

Snyder, Kenneth D., PhD, Catholic University of America (1996), 1997—history of Christianity, E-mail: kdsnyder@stthomas.edu

Spencer, Marguerite L., MA, JD, University of Minnesota Law School (1995), 1997—systematic theology, E-mail: mlspencer@stthomas.edu

Stevenson, William, PhD, Boston College (1997), 1997—systematics, E-mail: wbstevenson@stthomas.edu

Thompson, Christopher J., PhD, Marquette University (1994), 1992—moral theology, E-mail: cjthompson@stthomas.edu

Windley-Daoust, Susan M., PhD, Vanderbilt University (1998), 1996—systematic theology, E-mail: smwindley@stthomas.edu

Wojda, Paul, PhD, University of Notre Dame, (1993), 1992—moral theology, E-mail: pjwojda@stthomas.edu

Yee, Gale A., PhD, University of St Michael's College (1985), 1984—Old Testament studies, E-mail: gayee@stthomas.edu

---

University of St Thomas

3800 Montrose Blvd
Houston TX 77006-4696

Phone: 713-522-7911
800-460-8878
Fax: 713-525-2125
E-mail: admissions@stthom.edu
URL: www.stthom.edu

TYPE OF INSTITUTION: Private, Roman Catholic
EXECUTIVE OFFICER: J. Michael Miller, CSB, President
CHAIRPERSON: Daniel Callam, CSB
UNDERGRADUATE ENROLLMENT: 1,597
GRADUATE ENROLLMENT: 1,099

University of St Thomas School of Theology at St Mary's Seminary

9845 Memorial Drive
Houston TX 77024-3498

Phone: 713-686-4345
Fax: 713-683-8673
E-mail: brusatti@stthom.edu

TYPE OF INSTITUTION: Private, Roman Catholic
EXECUTIVE OFFICER: Louis T. Brusatti, CM, Dean

UNDERGRADUATE ENROLLMENT: 75
GRADUATE ENROLLMENT: 115

St Thomas University

Dept of Religious Studies
Fredericton, New Brunswick E3B 5G3
Canada

Phone: 506-452-0640
Fax: 506-450-9615
E-mail: lbatt@stthomasu.ca

TYPE OF INSTITUTION: Public, Roman Catholic
EXECUTIVE OFFICER: Daniel O'Brien, President
CHAIRPERSON: Michael George
UNDERGRADUATE ENROLLMENT: 2,020

St Thomas Aquinas College

Sparkill NY 10976

St Tikhon's Orthodox Theological Seminary

St Tikhon's RoadPO Box 130, South Canaan PA 18459

St Vincent College

Latrobe PA 15650

Saint Vincent Seminary

300 Fraser Purchase Rd
Latrobe PA 15650-2690

Phone: 412-537-4592
Fax: 412-532-5052

TYPE OF INSTITUTION: Private, Roman Catholic
EXECUTIVE OFFICER: Thomas Acklin, OSB, President-Rector
GRADUATE ENROLLMENT: 94

St Vincent de Paul Regional Seminary

10701 S Military Trail
Boynton Beach FL 33436

Phone: 561-732-4424
Fax: 561-737-2205

TYPE OF INSTITUTION: Private, Roman Catholic
EXECUTIVE OFFICER: Pablo Navarro, Rector/President
GRADUATE ENROLLMENT: 96

St Vladimir's Orthodox Theological Seminary

575 Scarsdale Rd, Crestwood NY 10707

Saint Xavier University

3700 W 103rd St
Chicago IL 60655

Phone: 773-298-3445
Fax: 773-779-9061
E-mail: martin@sxu.edu

TYPE OF INSTITUTION: Private, Roman Catholic
EXECUTIVE OFFICER: Larry Frank, Dean of the School of Arts and Sciences
CHAIRPERSON: Troy W. Martin
COORDINATOR: Avis Clendenen, Director of the Pastoral Ministry Institute
UNDERGRADUATE ENROLLMENT: 2,800
GRADUATE ENROLLMENT: 1,400

Salem College

PO Box 10548
Winston-Salem NC 27108-0548

Phone: 910-721-2708

TYPE OF INSTITUTION: Denominational: Moravian
EXECUTIVE OFFICER: Julianne Still Thrift, President
CHAIRPERSON: Tasha Rushing
UNDERGRADUATE ENROLLMENT: 650
GRADUATE ENROLLMENT: 108

Salem College

Salem WV 26426

Salve Regina University

100 Ochre Point Avenue
Newport RI 02840

Phone: 401-847-6650
Fax: 401-847-0372
E-mail: greeleyj@salve.edu
URL: www.salve.edu

TYPE OF INSTITUTION: Denominational: Roman Catholic
EXECUTIVE OFFICER: Barbara Kathe, Academic Vice-President
CHAIRPERSON: John Greeley
UNDERGRADUATE ENROLLMENT: 1,600
GRADUATE ENROLLMENT: 400

Samford University

Department of Religion and Philosophy
Box 2251, 800 Lakeshore Dr
Birmingham AL 35229

Phone: 205-870-2925
Fax: 205-870-2535
E-mail: dlsansom@samford.edu
URL: www.samford.edu

TYPE OF INSTITUTION: Private, Southern Baptist

EXECUTIVE OFFICER: Thomas E. Corts, President
CHAIRPERSON: Dennis L. Sansom
UNDERGRADUATE ENROLLMENT: 4,600
GRADUATE ENROLLMENT: 1,550

University of San Diego

Dept of Theology and Religious Studies
5998 Alcala Park
San Diego CA 92110-2492
TYPE OF INSTITUTION: Private, Catholic
EXECUTIVE OFFICER: Patrick Drinan, Dean, College of Arts and Sciences
CHAIRPERSON: Gary Macy
COORDINATOR: Ronald A. Pachence

Phone: 619-260-4525
Fax: 619-260-2260

San Diego State University

Dept of Religious Studies
5500 Campanile Drive
San Diego CA 92182

Phone: 619-594-5185
Fax: 619-594-1004
E-mail: erother@mail.sdsu.edu
URL: www.rohan.sdsu.edu/dept/
relstweb/relst.html

TYPE OF INSTITUTION: Public
EXECUTIVE OFFICER: Stephen L. Weber, President
CHAIRPERSON: Linda D. Holler
UNDERGRADUATE ENROLLMENT: 24,000
DEGREES OFFERED: AB in Religious Studies
UNDERGRADUATE MAJORS: 41
DEGREES CONFERRED: 14
DESCRIPTION OF UNDERGRADUATE PROGRAM: The Department offers both a major and minor in religious studies with the AB degree in liberal arts and sciences. Majors are expected to do upper division work in three areas: Western Religious Traditions, Eastern Religious Traditions, Religion and Culture. Minors are expected to focus their work within one of these areas. The Department also participates with other departments in offering an individualized MA in Interdisciplinary Studies which may emphasize religious studies.
FACULTY:
Anderson, Allan W., PhD, Columbia University (1962), 1970, Professor Emeritus—religion and spirituality, philosophy and psychology of religion
Boni, Pat, PhD, Temple University (1982), 1989, Lecturer (part-time)—Judaism, world religions
Downing, Christine R., PhD, Drew University (1966), 1974, Professor Emeritus—religion and psychology, religion and literature
Friedman, Maurice S., PhD, University of Chicago (1950), 1973, Professor Emeritus—modern Jewish thought, religion and literature, philosophy of religion
Gefter, Irving, PhD, Brandeis University (1976), 1969, Assistant Professor Emeritus—Hebrew scriptures, Talmudic Judaism

Gillman, John L., PhD, University of Louvain (1980), 1988, Lecturer (part-time)—Early Christianity, world religions

Holler, Linda D., PhD, Vanderbilt University (1981), 1981, Associate Professor—religious ethics, religion and science, phenomenological philosophy, E-mail: lholler@mail.sdsu.edu

Johnson, Willard L., PhD, University of Wisconsin (1972), 1977, Professor—Shamanism, native religions, Hinduism and Buddhism, religious experience, E-mail: wjohnson@mail.sdsu.edu

Jordan, G. Ray, Jr., PhD, University of Southern California (1957), 1966, Professor Emeritus (teaches spring semesters)—psychology and phenomenology of religion, Oriental religions, world religions

Kelly, Mary L., PhD, Vanderbilt University (1993), 1994, Lecturer (part-time)—feminist ethics, world religions, women's studies

Khalil, Issa J., PhD, University of Chicago (1972), 1969, Associate Professor Emeritus—patristics, New Testament, history of Christian thought

Kohn, Risa Levitt, PhD, University of California, San Diego(1997), 1997, Assistant Professor—Judaism, Hebrew Scriptures, E-mail: rkohn@mail.sdsu.edu

Moore, Rebecca E., PhD, Marquette University (1996), 1999, Assistant Professor—Christianity, new religious movements, Jewish-Christian relations, E-mail: remoore@mail.sdsu.edu

Mueller, Howard R., PhD, University of London (1977), 1981, Lecturer (part-time)—philosophy of religion, Oriental and existential philosophy

Shavit, Samy Swead, PhD, University of California, Los Angeles (1993), 1995, Lecturer (part-time)—Islamic studies

Sparks, Irving Alan, PhD, Claremont Graduate University (1970), 1974, Professor Emeritus—New Testament, Hellenistic religions, E-mail: irving.sparks@sdsu.edu

Thomas, Jesse J., PhD, Northwestern University (1967), 1979, Lecturer (part-time)—religion and society, prehistoric religions, psychology

Trout, Polly, PhD, Boston University (1998), 1998, Lecturer (part-time)—world religions, American religious history

---

University of San Francisco

Dept of Theology and Religious Studies
2130 Fulton St
San Francisco CA 94117-1080

Phone: 415-422-6601
Fax: 415-422-2346
E-mail: graduate@usfca.edu
URL: www.usfca.edu

TYPE OF INSTITUTION: Private, Roman Catholic, Jesuit
EXECUTIVE OFFICER: John P. Schlegel, SJ, President
CHAIRPERSON: Paul Bernadicou, SJ
UNDERGRADUATE ENROLLMENT: 4,903
GRADUATE ENROLLMENT: 3,233

San Francisco State University

1600 Holloway Ave, San Francisco CA 94132

San Francisco Theological Seminary

2 Kensington Road
San Anselmo CA 94960

Phone: 415-258-6500
Fax: 415-258-1608
E-mail: sftsinfo@sfts.edu
URL: www.sfts.edu

TYPE OF INSTITUTION: Private, PC (USA)
EXECUTIVE OFFICER: Donald W. McCullough, President
GRADUATE ENROLLMENT: 700

San Jose Christian College

PO Box 1090
790 S 12th St
San Jose CA 95112

Phone: 408-293-9058
Fax: 408-293-7352
E-mail: sjcc1939@800.com

TYPE OF INSTITUTION: Non-Denominational
EXECUTIVE OFFICER: Mike Bowman, Vice President of Academic Affairs
CHAIRPERSON: Jon H. McFarland
UNDERGRADUATE ENROLLMENT: 350

San Jose State University

Comparative Religious Studies Program
One Washington Square
San Jose CA 95192-0097

Phone: 408-924-4313
Fax: 408-924-4372
E-mail: rkeady@email.sjsu.edu
URL: www.sjsu.edu/depts/religious_stud-ies/religious_studies.html

TYPE OF INSTITUTION: Public
EXECUTIVE OFFICER: Robert Caret, President
COORDINATOR: Richard E. Keady
UNDERGRADUATE ENROLLMENT: 30
DEGREES OFFERED: BA
UNDERGRADUATE MAJORS: 30
DEGREES CONFERRED: 10

DESCRIPTION OF UNDERGRADUATE PROGRAM: Most modern nations, including the U.S., guarantee freedom of religious belief and practice as a human birthright. However, the knowledge and understanding of religions that leads citizens to embrace religious pluralism and tolerance, which we call religious literacy, must be learned. Members of the Comparative Religious Studies Program's faculty are committed to guiding students in the kinds of learning needed for this task. In other words, it is our goal to provide students with the key elements of religious literacy: knowledge of the basic data in the study of religions, respect and tolerance for diverse religious perspectives, and critical thinking skills that can be applied to explanations of religion from insiders (believers, participants, etc.) as well as outsiders (anthropologists, historians, etc.). The program presents scholarly interpretations of the world's religious traditions. It aims to be as global as possible in covering the great diversity of religions and as inclusive as possible in covering the various methodological approaches to the study of religion.

FACULTY:

Jochim, Christian, PhD, University of Southern California (1980), 1985, Professor—religions of Asia, theories in the study of religion, Chinese studies, 408-924-1365, Fax: 408 924-4372, E-mail: jochim@sjsu.edu

Keady, Richard E., PhD, Claremont Graduate School (1975), 1972, Professor—modern religious thought, theology, ethical and social issues, 408-924-4312, Fax: 408-924-4372, E-mail: rkeady@email.sjsu.edu

Kramer, Kenneth P., PhD, Temple University (1971), 1989, Professor—religion and literature, comparative religions, religious experience, 408-924-4314, Fax: 408-924-4372, E-mail: kramer@email.sjsu.edu

Phan, Chánh Công, PhD, University of Chicago (1986), 1990, Assistant Professor—religions of Asia, comparative philosophy, Vietnamese studies, 408-924-4577, Fax: 408-924-4372, E-mail: ccphan@email.sjsu.edu

Rycenga, Jennifer, PhD, Graduate Theological Union (1992), 1995, Associate Professor—religion in America, religion and gender/sexuality, music and spirituality, 408-924-1367, Fax: 408-924-4372, E-mail: rycenjen@email.sjsu.edu

Zussman, Mira, PhD, University of California, Berkeley (1982), 1989, Professor—Islam, Judaism, anthropology of religion, Middle Eastern studies, 408-924-1364, Fax: 408-924-4372, E-mail: mzussman@email.sjsu.edu

---

Santa Clara University

Religious Studies Dept
500 El Camino Real
Santa Clara CA 95053-0335

Phone: 408-554-4547
Fax: 408-554-2387
URL: www-relg-studies.scu.edu

TYPE OF INSTITUTION: Private, Roman Catholic Jesuit

EXECUTIVE OFFICER: Peter Facione, Dean

CHAIRPERSON: Denise L. Carmody

UNDERGRADUATE ENROLLMENT: 4,332

GRADUATE ENROLLMENT: 3,375

DEGREES OFFERED: BA in Religious Studies

UNDERGRADUATE MAJORS: 19

DEGREES CONFERRED: 6

DESCRIPTION OF UNDERGRADUATE PROGRAM: Santa Clara, the oldest university in California, was founded in the Jesuit and Catholic tradition. The University, therefore, regards that academic discipline which is explicitly concerned with a critical understanding of the religious question as a central moment in the student's liberal education. In this context, the Religious Studies Department fulfills a twofold function: to offer courses as part of the University's core curriculum and to offer a major area of study for those who wish to concentrate in the study of religion. The Department offers a wide range of courses, with a special emphasis on the Catholic tradition. This emphasis, however, is not exclusive, and the Department is ecumenical in its faculty and in its approach to the study of religion.

GRADUATE PROGRAM

Member of the Council on Graduate Studies in Religion

Graduate Director: Ana Maria Pineda, RSM

Graduate Degrees Offered: MA

Degrees Conferred: 18 MA

Graduate Students in Residence: 5 MA

Not in Residence: 125 MA

Average No. of New Students Enrolled: 32 MA

Women Students: 69 MA

Minority Students: 18 MA

Foreign Students: 14 MA

Minimum GRE Score Requisite to Admission: No

Minimum GPA Score Requisite to Admission: No

Foreign Language Proficiency Evaluated: Yes

Financial Aid to First Year Students: 85% MA

Financial Aid to Other Students: 75% MA

Attrition Among Students: 5% MA

Graduates Placed: 95% MA

DESCRIPTION OF GRADUATE PROGRAM: The Religious Studies Department of Santa Clara University initiated its graduate program in Pastoral Ministries in the fall of 1983. It offers the following degrees: Master of Arts in Catechetics, Master of Arts in Pastoral Liturgy, Master of Arts in Spirituality, and Master of Arts in Liturgical Music. The program offers a well-defined educational schema with six required theology courses as foundational to each area of specialization. Although the curriculum has other specific requirements, it is flexible and sensitive to the needs and goals of individual students offering opportunity for some personal curriculum design and development. For the MA degree: 50 units with thesis; or 54 units with elective; comprehensive examinations. A pastoral thesis is optional.

ADMISSION REQUIREMENTS AND FINANCIAL AID: Santa Clara University operates on the quarter system (3 quarters a year, with a 6-week summer school session for undergraduates, and two 3-week summer sessions for the graduate program). The Admissions Committee for the Graduate Program in Pastoral Ministries reviews each applicant's transcripts, work experience, letter of intent, and personal recommendations. A personal interview with the Director of the program is requested whenever possible. A 25% tuition remission is offered to any applicant involved in a church ministry. Some additional scholarship funds are available.

FACULTY:

Baker, Cynthia M., PhD, Duke University (1997), Assistant Professor—Jewish studies, 408-551-7153, Fax: 408-554-2387, E-mail: cbaker@scu.edu

Bell, Catherine M., PhD, University of Chicago (1983), 1985, Bernard J. Hanley Professor—history of religions, Chinese and Asian religions, women and religion, 408-554-4035, Fax: 408-554-2387, E-mail: cbell@scu.edu

Brancatelli, Robert, PhD (cand.), Catholic University of America, 1998, Lecturer—theology & spirituality of marriage, catechetics, 408-554-4758, E-mail: rbrancatelli@scu.edu

Carmody, Denise L., PhD, Boston College (1970), 1994, Jesuit Community Professor—world religions, women and religion, Roman Catholicism, 408-554-7829, Fax: 408-554-2387, E-mail: dcarmodyl@scu.edu

Crowley, Paul G., SJ, PhD, Graduate Theological Union (1984), 1989, Director of Catholic Studies Program and Associate Professor—philosophic theology, hermeneutics, 408-554-4542, Fax: 408-554-2387, E-mail: pcrowley@scu.edu

Dorner, Rita Claire, OP, PhD, Catholic University (1987), 1983, Lecturer—liturgy, catechetics, Catholic theology, 408-554-4026, Fax: 408-554-2387, E-mail: rdorner@scu.edu

Fitzgerald, Paul, SJ, PhD, Sorbonne, France; STD, Institut Catholique de Paris (1997), 1997, Assistant Professor—sociology of religion, ecclesiology, social ethics, 408-554-4124, Fax: 408-554-2387, E-mail: pfitzgerald@scu.edu

Grassi, Joseph A., SSL, Angelicum; SSL, Pontifical Biblical Institute (1949), 1971, Professor—biblical studies, gospel criticism, 408-554-4167, Fax: 408-554-2387, E-mail: jgrassi@scu.edu

Jonte-Pace, Diane E., PhD, University of Chicago (1984), 1984, Associate Professor—psychology of religion, women and religion, 408-554-4751, Fax: 408-554-2387, E-mail: djonte-pace@scu.edu

McLean, Margaret R., PhD, Medical College of Wisconsin (1981), Graduate Theological Union (1997), 1989, Lecturer—Christian ethics, medical ethics, 408-554-7889, E-mail: mmclean@scu.edu

Murphy, Catherine M., PhD, University of Notre Dame (1999), 1998, Assistant Professor—New Testament, early Christian history, 408-554-1909, Fax: 408-554-2387, E-mail: cmurphy @scu.edu

Parrella, Frederick J., PhD, Fordham University (1974), 1977, Associate Professor—systematic theology, Christology, ecclesiology, theology of marriage, 408-554-4714, Fax: 408-554-2387, E-mail: fparrella@scu.edu

Perry, David L., PhD, University of Chicago Divinity School (19993), Lecturer—Christian ethics, social ethics, professional ethics, 408-554-7898, E-mail: dperry@scu.edu

Peters, Carmichael C., PhD, Graduate Theological Union (1996), 1996, Assistant Professor—philosophical theology, political theology, 408-554-4343, Fax: 408-554-2387, E-mail: cpeters@scu.edu

Pinault, David, PhD, University of Pennsylvania (1986), 1997, Associate Professor—Islamic and Arabic studies, 408-554-6987, Fax: 408-554-2387, E-mail: dpinault@scu.edu

Pineda, Ana Maria, RSM, STD, Universidad Pontificia de Salamanca (1992), 1997, Associate Professor and Director of Pastoral Ministries Graduate Program 1999, 408-554-6958, Fax: 408-554-2387, E-mail: ampineda@scu.edu

Pleins, John David, PhD, University of Michigan (1986), 1987, Associate Professor—Hebrew Bible, Old Testament, archaeology, 408-554-4763, Fax: 408-554-2387, E-mail: dpleins@scu.edu

Riley, Philip Boo, PhD, McMaster University (1980), 1978, Associate Professor—method in theology, systematic theology, philosophy of religion, Lonergan studies, 408-554-4455, Fax: 408-554-2387, E-mail: priley@scu.edu

Sharkey, Gregory, SJ, DPhil, Oxford University (1995), Assistant Professor (1998-99)—Asian religions, 408-554-4715, E-mail: gsharkey@scu.edu

Smith, Francis R., SJ, STD, Pontifical Gregorian University (1976), 1974, Associate Professor—Catholic systematic theology, Christology, liberation theology, 408-554-4044, Fax: 408-554-2387, E-mail: fsmith@scu.edu

Spohn, William C., PhD, University of Chicago Divinity School (1978), 1992, Presidential Professor of Ethics and the Common Good—philosophy, Christian ethics, theological ethics, 408-554-2390, Fax: 408-554-2387, E-mail: wspohn@scu.edu

Tassone, Salvatore A., SJ, STD, Pontifical Gregorian University (1968), 1968, Lecturer—biblical studies, New Testament, 408-554-4595, Fax: 408-554-2387, E-mail: stassone@scu.edu

Wright, Tennant C., SJ, STL, Alma College (1963), 1968, Lecturer—religion and social questions, meditation, literature and religion-world religions, 408-554-4595, Fax: 408-554-2387, E-mail: twright@scu.edu

College of Santa Fe

Santa Fe NM 87501

Sara Schenirer Teachers Seminary

4622 14th Ave, Brooklyn NY 11219

Sarah Lawrence College

Bronxville NY 10708

University of Saskatchewan

Dept of Religious Studies
Rm 1019 Arts Bld, 9 Campus Dr
Saskatoon, Saskatchewan S7N 0W0 Canada

Phone: 306-966-6771
Fax: 306-966-4559
E-mail: kaye@admin.usask.ca

TYPE OF INSTITUTION: Public
CHAIRPERSON: Braj M Sinha, Head
UNDERGRADUATE ENROLLMENT: 16,328

Schreiner College

2100 Memorial Blvd
Kerrville TX 78028-5697

Phone: 830-896-5411
Fax: 830-896-3232
E-mail: www.schreiner.edu

TYPE OF INSTITUTION: Private, Presbyterian (USA)
EXECUTIVE OFFICER: J. Thompson Biggers, President
COORDINATOR: Loren M. Scribner
UNDERGRADUATE ENROLLMENT: 760
GRADUATE ENROLLMENT: 60

University of Scranton

Scranton PA 18510

Phone: 570-941-7736
Fax: 570-941-4309
E-mail: freinb1@uofs.edu
URL: academic.uofs.edu/depart-
ment/theology

TYPE OF INSTITUTION: Private, Roman Catholic
EXECUTIVE OFFICER: Joseph M. McShane, SJ, President
CHAIRPERSON: Brigid Curtin Frein
UNDERGRADUATE ENROLLMENT: 3,800
GRADUATE ENROLLMENT: 900
DEGREES OFFERED: BA

UNDERGRADUATE MAJORS: 15

DEGREES CONFERRED: 4

DESCRIPTION OF UNDERGRADUATE PROGRAM: The University of Scranton is a Catholic University in the Jesuit tradition. Within this framework, the Theology/Religious Studies Department endeavors to foster an understanding of the religious dimension of human life and to acquaint students with the wealth of the Christian theological tradition. All students at the University of Scranton are required to take a sequence of two introductory courses in Theology/Religious Studies. The undergraduate major requires 30 semester credits including one course in each of the following areas: Old Testament, New Testament, systematic, historical and moral theology. Also available are courses that focus on spirituality, history of religions and Jewish Studies.

GRADUATE PROGRAM

Graduate Advisor: Charles Pinches

Graduate Degrees Offered: MA

Degrees Conferred: 5

Graduate Students in Residence: 20

Not in Residence: 6

Average No. of New Students Enrolled: 5

Women Students: 12

Minority Students: 3

Foreign Students: 3

Minimum GRE Score Requisite to Admission: No

Minimum GPA Score Requisite to Admission: Yes; 2.75 on 4.0 scale

Foreign Language Proficiency Evaluated: No

Financial Aid to First Year Students: 100%

Financial Aid to Other Students: 100%

Attrition Among Students: 15%

Graduates Placed: 60%

DESCRIPTION OF GRADUATE PROGRAM AND RESEARCH FACILITIES: The Master of Arts program in theology is designed to provide rigorous, advanced study of theological topics, both historical and contemporary in nature. The program creates the context for serious discussion and study of these topics by both faculty and students. The University seeks to provide other resources that will encourage advanced theological study. The program requires completion of 30 graduate credits of which 15 credits are core requirements and 15 credits are electives. Students may pursue a specialty in either Eastern Christian Studies or Biblical Studies by taking 15 credits of electives in either area of concentration. Students choosing not to specialize may tailor elective courses to their own interests.

ACADEMIC PLAN, ADMISSION REQUIREMENTS, FINANCIAL AID: The master's program in theology may be pursued on either a full-time or part-time basis. Students are accepted to begin course work for the Fall and Spring semesters only. During the Fall and Spring semesters, courses meet once a week from 4:30 pm - 7:10 pm or from 7:20 pm - 10:00 pm Monday through Thursday. Applicants should submit: completed application form, $35 fee, three letters of recommendation, and official transcripts. All application materials should be submitted at least one month prior to the term in which one expects to begin graduate study. The tuition for the master's degree program in Theology is set at one-half of the regular graduate tuition. A limited number of graduate assistantships are awarded to full-time students each year. Graduate assistantships provide for tuition waiver and a stipend ranging from $4,200 to $7,200. Applications for graduate assistantships are available by calling the Graduate Office.

FACULTY:

Bader-Saye, Scott, PhD, Duke University (1997), 1997, Assistant Professor—moral theology, 570-941-7405, Fax: 570-941-4309, E-mail: badersayes2@uofs.edu

Begley, John J., STD, Gregorian University (1966), 1985, Associate Professor—systematics, 570-941-4290, Fax: 570-941-4309, E-mail: begleyj1@uofs.edu

Benestad, James Brian, PhD, Boston College (1979), 1976, Professor—moral theology, 570-941-7498, Fax: 570-941-4309, E-mail: benestadj1@uofs.edu

Casey, Stephen J., MA, Marquette University (1974), 1969, Associate Professor—moral theology, religion and society, 570-941-7590, Fax: 570-941-4309, E-mail: caseys1@uofs.edu

Foley, Mary Ann, PhD, Yale University (1991), 1991, Associate Professor—systematics, 570-941-4194, Fax: 570-941-4309, E-mail: foleym1@uofs.edu

Frein, Brigid Curtin, PhD, St Louis University (1989), 1988, Associate Professor/Chair—New Testament, 570-941-7736, Fax: 570-941-4309, E-mail: freinb1@uofs.edu

Johnson, Glen A. Poggi, MA, University of Virginia (1996), 1996, Adjunct Professor (part-time)—Early Christianity, 570-941-7957, Fax: 570-941-4309, E-mail: johnsong2@uofs.edu

Johnson, Maria Poggi, PhD, University of Virginia (1996), 1996, Assistant Professor—historical theology, 570-941-7957, Fax: 570-941-4309, E-mail: johnsonm1@uofs.edu

Katongole, Emmanuel, PhD, Louvain (1996), Visiting Assistant Professor—moral, systematic theology, Fax: 570-941-4309

Kopas, Jane, PhD, Graduate Theological Union (1976), 1978, Professor—systematics, 570-941-4227, Fax: 570-941-4309, E-mail: kopasj1@uofs.edu

Liberatore, Albert M., STL, Katholische Universitat Leuven (1990), 1990, Adjunct Professor (part-time)—systematics, 570-941-6309, Fax: 570-941-4309, E-mail: liberatorea1@uofs.edu

Mathews, Edward, PhD, Columbia University (1995), Adjunct Professor (part-time)—patristics, 570-941-6309, Fax: 570-941-4309, E-mail: egm381@uofs.edu

Mathews, Susan F., PhD, Catholic University (1987), 1988, Associate Professor—biblical studies, 570-941-6131, Fax: 570-941-4309, E-mail: sfm365@uofs.edu

Pinches, Charles R., PhD, University of Notre Dame (1984), 1990, Professor—moral theology, 570-941-4302, Fax: 570-941-4309, E-mail: pinchesc1@uofs.edu

Rousseau, Richard W., PhD, University of Ottawa (1969), 1978, Professor—historical theology, 570-941-7449, Fax: 570-941-4309, E-mail: rousseaur1@uofs.edu

Sable, Thomas F., PhD, Graduate Theological Union (1982), 1985, Associate Professor—Eastern Christian studies, 570-941-6141, Fax: 570-941-4309, E-mail: sable1@uofs.edu

Shapiro, Marc B., PhD, Harvard (1995), 1996, Assistant Professor—Jewish studies, 570-941-7956, Fax: 570-941-4309, E-mail: shapirom2@uofs.edu

Steele, E. Springs, PhD, University of Notre Dame (1981), 1979, Professor—spirituality, 570-941-7708, Fax: 570-941-4309, E-mail: steelee1@uofs.edu

Yevics, Philip, PhD, Drew University (1996), Adjunct Professor—Eastern Christian studies, 570-941-6309, Fax: 570-941-4309, E-mail: pey365@uofs.edu

Scripps College
Claremont CA 91711

Scripps/Claremont McKenna Colleges

Joint Program, 1030 Columbia, Claremont CA 91711

College of the Scriptures

PO Box 18027, Louisville KY 40218

Seabury-Western Theological Seminary

2122 Sheridan Rd
Evanston IL 60201

Phone: 847-328-9300
Fax: 847-328-9624
E-mail: swts@nwu.edu
URL: www.swts.nwu.edu

TYPE OF INSTITUTION: Private, Episcopalian
EXECUTIVE OFFICER: James B. Lemler, Dean President
GRADUATE ENROLLMENT: 173

Seattle University

Dept of Theology and Religious Studies
900 Broadway
Seattle WA 98122

Phone: 206-296-5320
Fax: 206-296-5997
E-mail: swen@seattleu.edu
URL: www.seattleu.edu/artsci/
departments/theology

TYPE OF INSTITUTION: Private, Catholic (Jesuit)
EXECUTIVE OFFICER: Stephen V. Sundborg, SJ, President
CHAIRPERSON: Jeanette Rodriguez
UNDERGRADUATE ENROLLMENT: 15

Seattle Bible College

2363 NW 80th St, Seattle WA 98117

Seattle Pacific University

School of Religion, 3307 Third Ave W, Seattle WA 98119

Selma University

1501 Lapsley St, Selma AL 36701

Seton Hall University

Graduate School of Theology, South Orange NJ 07079

Seton Hall University

Dept of Jewish Christian Studies
400 S Orange Ave
South Orange NJ 07079

Phone: 201-761-9463
Fax: 201-761-9596
E-mail: frizzela@shu.edu
URL: www.shu.edu/academics/arts_sci/gradu-ate/jewish/index.html

TYPE OF INSTITUTION: Private, Roman Catholic
EXECUTIVE OFFICER: Robert T. Sheeran, President
CHAIRPERSON: Rabbi Asher Finkel
UNDERGRADUATE ENROLLMENT: 3,800
GRADUATE ENROLLMENT: 4,600

Seton Hall University

Dept of Religious Studies
South Orange NJ 07079

Phone: 201-761-9480

TYPE OF INSTITUTION: Private, Roman Catholic
CHAIRPERSON: Gerald Pire
UNDERGRADUATE ENROLLMENT: 5,000

Seton Hill College

Greensburg PA 15601

Shasta Abbey, Headquarters of the Order of Buddhist Contemplatives

3724 Summit Drive
Mt Shasta CA 96067-9102

Phone: 530-926-4208
Fax: 530-926-0428
E-mail: shastaabbey@obcon.org
URL: www.obcon.org

TYPE OF INSTITUTION: Private, Buddhist monastery and seminary
EXECUTIVE OFFICER: Eko Little, MOBC, Abbot

Shasta Bible College

2980 Hartnell Ave
Redding CA 96002

Phone: 530-221-4275
Fax: 530-221-6929
E-mail: ggunn@shasta.edu
URL: www.shasta.edu

TYPE OF INSTITUTION: Private
EXECUTIVE OFFICER: David R. Nicholas, President
UNDERGRADUATE ENROLLMENT: 100
GRADUATE ENROLLMENT: 40

Shaw University

Dept of Religion and Philosophy
118 East South Street
Raleigh NC 27601

Phone: 919-546-8457
Fax: 919-546-8341
E-mail: wthursto@shawu.edu
URL: www.shawuniversity.edu

TYPE OF INSTITUTION: Private, Baptist
EXECUTIVE OFFICER: Talbert O. Shaw, President
CHAIRPERSON: William A. Thurston
UNDERGRADUATE ENROLLMENT: 2,500
DEGREES OFFERED: BA in Religion and Philosophy
UNDERGRADUATE MAJORS: 81
DEGREES CONFERRED: 15

Shaw University Divinity School

509 Hilltop Rd, Raleigh NC 27610

Sheldon Jackson College

801 Lincoln
Sitka AK 99835

Phone: 907-747-5295

TYPE OF INSTITUTION: Private, Presbyterian (USA)

Shenandoah University

Dept of Religion
1460 University Dr
Winchester VA 22601

Phone: 540-665-4561
Fax: 540-665-4644
E-mail: jcopenha@su.edu
URL: www.su.edu

TYPE OF INSTITUTION: Private, United Methodist
EXECUTIVE OFFICER: Joel Stegall, Vice-President of Academic Programs
CHAIRPERSON: John Copenhaver
UNDERGRADUATE ENROLLMENT: 1,400
GRADUATE ENROLLMENT: 850

Universite de Sherbrooke

2500 Blvd De l'Universite, Sherbrooke, Quebec J1K 2R1 Canada

Shiloh Bible College

3295 School St, Oakland CA 94602-3699

Shorter College

315 Shorter Ave
Rome GA 30165-4298

Phone: 706-233-7259
Fax: 706-236-1515
E-mail: ssheeley@shorter.edu
URL: www.shorter.edu

TYPE OF INSTITUTION: Private, Baptist
EXECUTIVE OFFICER: Harold E. Newman, Provost
CHAIRPERSON: Steven M. Sheeley
UNDERGRADUATE ENROLLMENT: 1,800
GRADUATE ENROLLMENT: 50

Sh'Or Yoshuv Rabbinical College

1526 Central Ave, Far Rockaway NY 11691

Siena College

515 Loudon Road
Loudonville NY 12211-1462

Phone: 518-783-2300
Fax: 518-783-2452
URL: www.siena.edu/relstudies

TYPE OF INSTITUTION: Private
EXECUTIVE OFFICER: Kevin Mackin, OFM, President
CHAIRPERSON: Mary Meany
UNDERGRADUATE ENROLLMENT: 2,500

Siena Heights University

1247 East Siena Heights Dr
Adrian MI 49221-1796

Phone: 517-264-7686
Fax: 517-264-7704
E-mail: sweeks@sienahts.edu
URL: www.sienahts.edu

TYPE OF INSTITUTION: Private, Catholic with Adrian Dominican Heritage
EXECUTIVE OFFICER: Sharon Weber, OP, Academic Dean
COORDINATOR: Susan Conley Weeks
UNDERGRADUATE ENROLLMENT: 1,400
GRADUATE ENROLLMENT: 300
DEGREES OFFERED: BA
UNDERGRADUATE MAJORS: 8-12
DEGREES CONFERRED: 3-5 annually
DESCRIPTION OF UNDERGRADUATE PROGRAM: Siena Heights is a private liberal arts university rooted in an Adrian Dominican expression of the Catholic tradition. The Siena Heights University Religious Studies Program includes 1) baccalaureat majors in religious studies or in ministry, 2) minors in ethics or in religious studies, 3) a (36 credit hour) certificate program for ministerial preparation and 4) service to the general education program.

FACULTY:

Foley, Nadine, PhD, Catholic University of America (1956), 1993, Professor of Religious Studies (part-time)—Hebrew scriptures, Christian scriptures, 517-266-3400, E-mail: adhistory@aol.com

Weeks, Susan Conley, DMin, Aquinas Institute (1980), 1984, Professor of Religious Studies—world religion, religion in public education, religion and film, 517-264-7686, E-mail: sweeks@sienahts.edu

Silver Lake College

2406 S Alverno Rd, Manitowoc WI 54220

Simmons Bible College

1811 Dumesnil, Louisville KY 40210

Simon Fraser University

Burnaby BC V5A 1S6 Canada　　　　　　　　**Phone: 604-291-4094**
Fax: 604-291-4989

TYPE OF INSTITUTION: Public
COORDINATOR: Mary Ann Stouck
UNDERGRADUATE ENROLLMENT: 15,000
GRADUATE ENROLLMENT: 3,000

Simon Greenleaf University

Graduate Schools of Theology　　　　　　　**Phone: 714-632-3434**
and Human Rights　　　　　　　　　　　　　　**Fax: 714-630-6109**
3855 East La Palma Ave　　　　　**E-mail: crjhazen@aol.com**
Anaheim CA 92807
TYPE OF INSTITUTION: Private, Non-Denominational
EXECUTIVE OFFICER: Dorsey Brause, Executive Vice-President
CHAIRPERSON: Craig James Hazen, Assistant Dean
GRADUATE ENROLLMENT: 70

Simpson College

701 North C Street　　　　　　　　　　**Phone: 515-961-1685**
Indianola IA 50125　　　　　　　　　　　　**Fax: 515-961-1498**
E-mail: betswort@storm.simpson.edu

TYPE OF INSTITUTION: Private, United Methodist
EXECUTIVE OFFICER: Stephen Jennings, President
CHAIRPERSON: Roger Betsworth
UNDERGRADUATE ENROLLMENT: 1,850

Simpson College

2211 College View Dr
Redding CA 96003-8606

Phone: 530-224-5600
Fax: 530-224-2051
URL: simpsonca.edu

TYPE OF INSTITUTION: Private, Christian and Missionary Alliance
EXECUTIVE OFFICER: Judi Fortune, Chief Academic Officer
CHAIRPERSON: David Strong
COORDINATOR: Richard Brown
UNDERGRADUATE ENROLLMENT: 163
GRADUATE ENROLLMENT: 100

University of Sioux Falls

Department of Religion and Philosophy
1101 West 22nd Street
Sioux Falls SD 57105

Phone: 605-331-6799
Fax: 605-331-6615
E-mail: richard.mayer@usiouxfalls.edu
URL: www.usiouxfalls.edu

TYPE OF INSTITUTION: Private, American Baptist Churches USA
EXECUTIVE OFFICER: Mark Benedetto, President
CHAIRPERSON: Richard Mayer
UNDERGRADUATE ENROLLMENT: 20

Skidmore College

Dept of Philosophy and Religion
815 No Broadway
Saratoga Springs NY 12866

Phone: 518-580-5400
Fax: 518-580-5259
E-mail: eweller@skidmore.edu

TYPE OF INSTITUTION: Private
EXECUTIVE OFFICER: David Porter, President
COORDINATOR: Eric Weller
UNDERGRADUATE ENROLLMENT: 2,100

Smith College

Northampton MA 01063

Phone: 413-585-3662
Fax: 413-585-3339
E-mail: dgunn@ernestine.smith.edu

TYPE OF INSTITUTION: Private
CHAIRPERSON: Karl P. Donfried
UNDERGRADUATE ENROLLMENT: 1,100
GRADUATE ENROLLMENT: 2

University of the South

Dept of Religion, Sewanee TN 37375

The School of Theology of the University of the South

335 Tennessee Ave
Sewanee TN 37383-0001

Phone: 931-598-1288
Fax: 931-598-1852
E-mail: theology@sewanee.edu
URL: www.sewanee.edu

TYPE OF INSTITUTION: Denominational: Episcopal Church

EXECUTIVE OFFICER: Guy Fitch Lytle, III, Dean

GRADUATE ENROLLMENT: 106

GRADUATE PROGRAM

Graduate Degrees Offered: STM and DMin in summer only; MDiv and MA in regular academic year (Sept-May)

Degrees Conferred: 1 MA; 8 DMin; 1 STM; 25 MDiv

Graduate Students in Residence: 2 MA; 75 Other

Graduate Students not in Residence: 17 Other

Average No. of New Students Enrolled: 51 Other

Women Students: 2 MA; 36 Other

Minority Students: 3 Other

Foreign Students: 1 Other

Minimum GRE Score Requisite to Admission: Yes, 400

Minimum GPA Score Requisite to Admission: No

Foreign Language Proficiency Evaluated: No

Financial Aid to First Year Students: 95% Other

Financial Aid to Other Students: 95% Other

Graduates Placed: 100% Other

DESCRIPTION OF GRADUATE PROGRAM AND RESEARCH FACILITIES: The MDiv program is a three-year professional degree for preparation for ordination. The MA is a two-year program for the academic study of theological disciplines in a church-related setting. The STM is a post-MDiv degree and as such is an academic research degree. The DMin is a post-MDiv degree aimed at gaining excellence in the practice of ministry. The first three are offered during Sept-May; and the latter two only in the summer session.

FACULTY:

Alexander, J. Neil, ThD, General Theological Seminary (1993), 1997, Professor—homiletics, 931-598-1392, Fax: 931-598-1852, E-mail: jalexand@sewanee.edu

Armentrout, Donald S., PhD, Vanderbilt University (1970), 1967, Associate Dean for Academic Affairs and Professor—church history and historical theology, dogmatic theology, 931-598-1373, Fax: 931-598-1852, E-mail: darmentr@sewanee.edu

Betz, Arnold G., PhD (cand.), Vanderbilt University (1997), 1996, Visiting Professor—Hebrew and old Testament (part-time), 931-598-1923, Fax: 931-598-1852, E-mail: abetz@sewanee.edu

Bosmyer, Peggy, MDiv, Virginia Theological Seminary (1974), 1994, Professor—contextual education and Director of Field Education, 931-598-1354, Fax: 931-598-1852, E-mail: pbosmyer@sewanee.edu

Bryan, Christopher, PhD, Exeter University (1983), 1983, Professor—New Testament, 931-598-1472, Fax: 931-598-1852, E-mail: cbryan@sewanee.edu

Burnett, Joe G., MDiv (1974), DMin, Perkins School of Theology (1985), 1999, Professor—pastoral theology, 931-598-3298, Fax: 931-598-1852, E-mail: jburnett@sewanee.edu

Campbell, Dennis G., MDiv, Memphis Theological Seminary (1990), DMin, University of the South (1999), 1994, Director of Ministry and Congregational Development, 931-598-1442, Fax: 931-598-1852, E-mail: dcampbel@sewanee.edu

Danaher, William J., Jr., PhD (cand.), Yale University (1994), 1999, Assistant Professor—theology and Christian ethics

Dunkly, James W., PhD, Vanderbilt University (1982), 1993, Lecturer (part-time)—New Testament, 931-598-1267, Fax: 931-598-1852, E-mail: jdunkly@sewanee.edu

Hughes, Robert D., III, PhD, University of St Michael's College, Toronto (1980), 1977, Professor—systematic theology, 931-598-1377, Fax: 931-598-1852, E-mail: rhughes@sewanee.edu

Lytle, Guy F., III, PhD, Princeton University (1976), 1991, Dean, Professor and Director—Anglican studies, pastoral theology, 931-598-1288, Fax: 931-598-1412, E-mail: glytle@sewanee.edu

Lytle, Maria R., BA, The Catholic University of America (1974), 1991, Instructor in Spanish language and liturgy (part-time), 931-598-1288, Fax: 931-598-1412, E-mail: mlytle@sewanee.edu

Monti, Joseph E., PhD, Vanderbilt University (1981), 1989, Associate Professor—Christian ethics and moral theology, 931-598-1379, Fax: 931-598-1852, E-mail: jmonti@sewanee.edu

Moore, David C., DMin, The University of the South (1987), 1996, Associate Dean—programs coordination, planning and management, theological reflection group leader, 931-598-1904, Fax: 931-598-1165, E-mail: dmoore@sewanee.edu

Smith, Richard A., DD, Newberry College (1975), 1986, Lecturer—Greek, theological reflection group leader, 931-598-1474, Fax: 931-598-1852, E-mail: rsmith@sewanee.edu

Wright, Rebecca A., PhD, Yale University (1989), 1990, Assistant Professor—Old Testament, 931-598-1575, Fax: 931-598-1852, E-mail: rwright@sewanee.edu

---

University of South Carolina

Dept of Religious Studies
Columbia SC 29208

Phone: 803-777-4100
Fax: 803-777-0213
E-mail: luchta@sc.edu
URL: www.cla.sc.edu/relg/index.htm

TYPE OF INSTITUTION: Public

EXECUTIVE OFFICER: John M. Palms, President

CHAIRPERSON: Carl D. Evans

UNDERGRADUATE ENROLLMENT: 16,000

GRADUATE ENROLLMENT: 10,000

DEGREES OFFERED: BA in Religious Studies

UNDERGRADUATE MAJORS: 36

DEGREES CONFERRED: 6

DESCRIPTION OF UNDERGRADUATE PROGRAM: The Department is an academic unit in the College of Liberal Arts. Its program is provided for students seeking a broad liberal arts education focused on the study of religion as an academic discipline and its relation to other fields of study. A program of interdisciplinary study is developed in close consultation between the departmental faculty and the individual student. A foundation for graduate study is provided.

GRADUATE PROGRAM

Member of the Council on Graduate Studies in Religion

Graduate Advisor: Anne M. Blackburn

Graduate Degrees Offered: MA

Degrees Conferred: 2 MA

Graduate Students in Residence: 20 MA

Not in Residence: 3 MA

Average No. of New Students Enrolled: 6 MA

Women Students: 13 MA

Minority Students: 1 MA

Foreign Students: 0 MA

Minimum GRE Score Requisite to Admission: No

Minimum GPA Score Requisite to Admission: No

Foreign Language Proficiency Evaluated: No

Financial Aid to First Year Students: 75% MA

Financial Aid to Other Students: 25% MA

Attrition Among Students: 10% MA

Graduates Placed: 50% MA

DESCRIPTION OF GRADUATE PROGRAM AND RESEARCH FACILITIES: The Master of Arts in Religious Studies degree is offered by the University of South Carolina in consortial arrangement with Columbia College and the Lutheran Theological Southern Seminary with the participation of Benedict College. Students may also take advantage of graduate programs in a number of other disciplines at USC, including history, philosophy, English, psychology, international studies and women's studies. The program offers four areas of concentration: Comparative Religion, Biblical and Near Eastern Studies, Theology and Religious Thought, and Religion and Culture.

ACADEMIC PLAN, ADMISSION REQUIREMENTS, FINANCIAL AID: MA applicants: Applicants must have a baccalaureate degree from an approved college or university and their grades must be indicative of graduate ability. Distinguished work in any discipline is acceptable. Candidates for admission must supply a transcript, a record of satisfactory scores on either the Miller Analogies Test or the general section of the Graduate Record Examination, two letters of recommendation, a personal statement of purpose, and a sample of their academic work. Recognizing that students interested in religious studies come from diverse backgrounds, the Department carefully considers each applicant on an individual basis. Graduate assistantships (up to $6000) with tuition reduction available to qualified applicants.

FACULTY:

Blackburn, Anne M., PhD, University of Chicago (1995), 1996, Assistant Professor—comparative religion and Buddhism, 803-777-2437, E-mail: blackburn@sc.edu

Cutsinger, James S., PhD, Harvard (1980), 1980, Associate Professor—theology and ethics, 803-777-2284, E-mail: cutsinger@sc.edu

Evans, Carl D., PhD, University of Chicago (1974), 1974, Associate Professor—Old Testament, ancient Near East, 803-777-4522, E-mail: evans-carl@sc.edu

French, Harold W., PhD, McMaster (1972), 1972, Professor Emeritus (part-time)—comparative religion, psychology of religion, 803-777-2178, E-mail: frenchh@sc.edu

Johnson, Alonzo, PhD, Union (1990), 1991, Associate Professor—contemporary religious thought, 803-777-9119, E-mail: ajohnson@sc.edu

Jones, Donald L., PhD, Duke (1966), 1967, Professor—New Testament, Christian origins, 803-777-2283, E-mail: jonesd@sc.edu

Lewis, Kevin, PhD, University of Chicago (1980), 1973, Associate Professor—religion, literature, and the arts, 803-777-2561, E-mail: kevin@sc.edu

Rao, K. L. Seshagiri, PhD, Harvard (1966), 1966, Adjunct Professor (part-time)—comparative religion, Hinduism, 803-777-0777, E-mail: srao@eh.sc.edu

South Carolina State College

Orangeburg SC 29117

University of South Dakota

Vermillion SD 57069

South Dakota State University

Brookings SD 57007

University of South Florida

Dept of Religious Studies CPR 304　　　　　**Phone: 813-974-2221**
4202 Fowler Ave　　　　　　　　　　　　　　**Fax: 813-974-1853**
Tampa FL 33620-5550　　　　**E-mail: morreall@luna.cas.usf.edu**

TYPE OF INSTITUTION: Public

EXECUTIVE OFFICERS: Betty Castor, President; David Stamps, Dean College Arts and Sciences

CHAIRPERSON: John Morreall

COORDINATOR: James F. Strange, Graduate Director

UNDERGRADUATE ENROLLMENT: 30,000

GRADUATE ENROLLMENT: 4,000

DEGREES OFFERED: BA, MA, ME

UNDERGRADUATE MAJORS: 46

DEGREES CONFERRED: 7

DESCRIPTION OF UNDERGRADUATE PROGRAM: The BA is a broad-based Humanities degree in Eastern and Western Religion. 36 credit hours are required for a major.

GRADUATE PROGRAM

Graduate Advisor: James F. Strange

Graduate Degrees Offered: MA

Degrees Conferred: 2 MA

Graduate Students in Residence: 40 MA

Average No. of New Students Enrolled: 10 MA

Women Students: 16 MA

Foreign Students: 2 MA

Minimum GRE Score Requisite to Admission: Yes; 1000

Minimum GPA Score Requisite to Admission: Yes; 3.0 on 4.0 scale

Foreign Language Proficiency Evaluated: No

Financial Aid to First Year Students: 10% MA

Financial Aid to Other Students: 10% MA

Attrition Among Students: 5% MA

Graduates Placed: 80% MA

DESCRIPTION OF GRADUATE PROGRAM AND RESEARCH FACILITIES: The Master of Arts in Religious Studies was implemented January of 1981. It requires 36 semester hours, including 6 hours for thesis; study of two religious traditions; a comprehensive examination and thesis. Courses of study are selected by the student in consultation with a faculty advisor. A language may be required for the study of particular religions.

ACADEMIC PLAN, ADMISSION REQUIREMENTS, FINANCIAL AID: South Florida operates on the semester system. Areas of study include contemporary religious thought; religion, ethics and society; comparative religion, biblical traditions. Admission allows for any undergraduate major, but a previous background in religion is expected. A variety of University financial aid is available, including teaching assistantships and out-of-state tuition waivers.

FACULTY:

DeChant, D., MA, University of South Florida (1986), Instructor—new religions, world religions

Fasching, D. J., PhD, Syracuse (1978), 1982, Professor—religion and culture, comparative religious ethics, religion and public policy, Judaism, Christianity, and the Holocaust, E-mail: fasching@luna.cas.usf.edu

Jorgensen, D. L., PhD, Ohio State (1979), 1991, Professor—American religion, new religions, religion and society, ethnography

Mandell, S. R., PhD, New York (1969), 1991, Professor—religion and the ancient world, E-mail: mandell@luna.cas.usf.edu

Mitchell, M. G., PhD, Emory (1980), 1981, Professor—Black church, religion and literature, liberation theology, E-mail: mmitchel@luna.cas.usf.edu

Morreall, J., PhD, Toronto (1975), Professor—philosophy of religion/ethics

Neusner, J., PhD, Columbia (1960), 1990, Graduate Research Professor—Judaic studies

Sonn, T., PhD, University of Chicago (1983), 1993, Professor—Islamic studies, E-mail: sonn@luna.cas.usf.edu

Strange, J. F., PhD, Drew (1970), 1972, Professor—biblical studies, biblical archaeology, ancient Near East, E-mail: strange@chuma.cas.usf.edu

---

South Florida Baptist Bible Institute

1813 SW 11th Ct   **Phone: 954-525-2470**
Ft Lauderdale FL 33312   **E-mail: jgplante@juno.com**
                                        URL: netministries.org/see/
                                        charmin.exe/cm01480

TYPE OF INSTITUTION: Private, Christian—Baptist

EXECUTIVE OFFICER: Jean-Guy Plante, President

South Florida Center for Theological Studies

Box 8348, Coral Gables FL 33124

Southeastern College of the Assemblies of God

1000 Longfellow Blvd, Lakeland FL 33801

Southeastern Baptist College

4229 Highway 15 N, Laurel MS 39440

Southeastern Baptist Theological Seminary

222 N Wingate St, Box 1889
Wake Forest NC 27587

Phone: 919-556-3101
Fax: 919-556-0998
E-mail: dean@sebts.edu
URL: www.sebts.edu

TYPE OF INSTITUTION: Private, Baptist
EXECUTIVE OFFICER: L. Russ Bush, Academic Vice President/Dean of the Faculty
UNDERGRADUATE ENROLLMENT: 300
GRADUATE ENROLLMENT: 1,600

Southeastern Bible College

3001 Hwy 280 E
Birmingham AL 35243

Phone: 205-970-9200
Fax: 205-970-9207
E-mail: info@sebc.edu
URL: www.sebc.edu

TYPE OF INSTITUTION: Private
EXECUTIVE OFFICER: John D. Talley III, President
UNDERGRADUATE ENROLLMENT: 180

University of Southern Alabama

Mobile AL 36608

Southern Arizona Bible College

Hwy 92, Hereford AZ 85615

The Southern Baptist Theological Seminary

2825 Lexington Road
Louisville KY 40280

Phone: 502-897-4011
Fax: 502-899-1781

TYPE OF INSTITUTION: Denominational: Southern Baptist

EXECUTIVE OFFICERS: R. Albert Mohler, Jr., President; Daniel L. Akin, Vice President of Academic Administration

GRADUATE ENROLLMENT: 1,502

The University of Southern California

School of Religion
328 Taper Hall of Humanities
Los Angeles CA 90089-0355

Phone: 213-740-0270
Fax: 213-740-7158
E-mail: wooton@usc.edu
URL: www.usc.edu/dept/LAS/religion

TYPE OF INSTITUTION: Private

CHAIRPERSON: John Crossley

UNDERGRADUATE ENROLLMENT: 15,215

GRADUATE ENROLLMENT: 9,815

DEGREES OFFERED: BA Religion, Minor Religion, Minor Bio-ethics

UNDERGRADUATE MAJORS: 28

DEGREES CONFERRED: 9

DESCRIPTION OF UNDERGRADUATE PROGRAM: The School of Religion at USC functions as a department of religious studies in the College of Letters, Arts and Sciences. The School offers courses in the major areas of religious studies: Bible and Near Eastern Religion; Ethics and Theology; Religion in World Societies; Religion in American Life; and Judaic Studies (in conjunction with Hebrew Union College-Jewish Institute of Religion, which adjoins the USC campus). Courses are designed to facilitate the appreciation and critical evaluation of all religious traditions in the light of past and present scholarship. An opportunity is also provided to focus on the social and ethical contributions and implications of our religious heritages. We therefore offer courses in Business Ethics, Medical Ethics, and Biblical and Near Eastern Archaeology through our Archaeological Research Center. A minor is offered in Bioethics. Major requirements: Seven upper division courses in at least three of the major areas listed above, with as many as four courses in any one area, plus a senior seminar. Minor requirements: Four upper division courses. A major is also offered with emphasis in Judaic Studies.

GRADUATE PROGRAM

Member of the Council on Graduate Studies in Religion

Graduate Advisor: William May

Graduate Degrees Offered: MA; PhD

Degrees Conferred: 5 MA; 3 PhD

Graduate Students in Residence: 3 MA; 13 PhD

Not in Residence: 2 MA; 33 PhD

Women Students: 4 MA; 20 PhD

Minority Students: 2 MA; 6 PhD

Minimum GRE Score Requisite to Admission: Yes, 1000

Minimum GPA Score Requisite to Admission: Yes, 3.0 on a scale of 4.0

Foreign Language Proficiency Evaluated: No

Financial Aid to Other Students: 0% MA; 28% PhD

DESCRIPTION OF GRADUATE PROGRAM AND RESEARCH FACULITIES: The School of Religion at USC has for the past 30 years offered an interdisciplinary program leading to an MA or PhD degree in Religion and Social Ethics. Because a number of our senior faculty have taken advantage of a retirement program offered by the University, the School will not be admitting new students to the Program in Religion and Social Ethics for fall 1999. The faculty is in process of redesigning the graduate program and defining new faculty positions. At the appropriate time, the new design and new faculty appointments will be announced.

ACADEMIC PLAN, ADMISSION REQUIREMENTS, FINANCIAL AID: The academic plan is dependent on the redesign of the graduate program currently underway, and will be announced when the new program is in place.

FACULTY:

Adler, Rachel, PhD, University of Southern California (1997), 1998, Assistant Professor—Jewish feminist theology and ethics, modern Jewish thought, Hebrew Bible, 213-740-8815, Fax: 213-740-7158, E-mail: rra@usc.edu

Briggs, Sheila, MA, Newham College, University of Cambridge (1978), 1984, Associate Professor—systematic and historical theology, feminist theology, Black theology, 213-740-0267, Fax: 213-740-7158, E-mail: sbriggs@usc.edu

Crossley, John P., Jr., ThD, San Francisco Theological Seminary (1962), 1970, Associate Professor—theological ethics, theology, professional ethics, 213-740-0275, Fax: 213-740-7158, E-mail: crossley@usc.edu

Hock, Ronald F., PhD, Yale University (1974), 1975, Professor—religions of Greco-Roman period, New Testament, social and intellectual history, 213-740-0279, Fax: 213-740-7158, E-mail: hock@usc.edu

May, William W., PhD, Drew University (1967), 1968, Associate Professor—social ethics, business ethics, medical ethics, 213-740-0278, Fax: 231-740-7158, E-mail: wmay@usc.edu

Miller, Donald E., PhD, University of Southern California (1975), 1975, Professor—sociology of religion, social ethics, 213-740-0278, Fax: 213-740-7158, E-mail: demiller@usc.edu

Rudisill, Alvin S., PhD, Drew University (1967), 1969, Associate Professor Emeritus—historical theology, medical ethics, church and society, 213-740-6808, Fax: 213-740-7158, E-mail: rudisill@usc.edu

Slingerman, Ted, Stanford University (1998), 1999, Assistant Professor—early Chinese thought, Asian religions, 213-740-8508, Fax: 213-740-9295, E-mail: slingerl@usc.edu

Zuckerman, Bruce E., PhD, Yale University (1980), 1980, Associate Professor—Old Testament, Semitic languages, 213-740-0271, Fax: 213-740-7158, E-mail: bzuckerman@usc.edu

---

Southern California Bible College and Seminary

2075 E Madison Ave
El Cajon CA 92019

Phone: 619-442-9841
Fax: 619-442-4510
E-mail: admissions@scbcs.edu

TYPE OF INSTITUTION: Private

EXECUTIVE OFFICER: Gary Coombs, President

UNDERGRADUATE ENROLLMENT: 85

GRADUATE ENROLLLMENT: 32

Southern Christian University

1200 Taylor Rd
Montgomery AL 36117-0240

Phone: 800-351-4040
Fax: 334-271-0002
E-mail: scuniversity@mindspring.com
URL: www.southernchristian.edu

TYPE OF INSTITUTION: Private, Non-Denominational
EXECUTIVE OFFICER: Rex Turner, Jr., President
CHAIRPERSON: James Crabtree
COORDINATOR: Mac Adkins
UNDERGRADUATE ENROLLMENT: 80
GRADUATE ENROLLMENT: 172

Southern Connecticut State College

New Haven CT 06515

Southern Illinois University

Carbondale IL 62901

Southern Methodist University

Dept of Religious Studies
PO Box 0202
Dallas TX 75275-0202

Phone: 214-768-2095
Fax: 214-768-3910
E-mail: reli@mail.smu.edu
URL: www.smu.edu/~dedman/relimenu.html

TYPE OF INSTITUTION: Private, United Methodist
CHAIRPERSON: Richard W. Cogley
UNDERGRADUATE ENROLLMENT: 5,600
GRADUATE ENROLLMENT: 4,400
DEGREES OFFERED: BA
UNDERGRADUATE MAJORS: 18
DEGREES CONFERRED: 11
DESCRIPTION OF UNDERGRADUATE PROGRAM: The Department of Religious Studies is situated in the Humanities Division of Dedman College, SMU's school of the Arts and Sciences. The BA degree is designed as a general liberal arts major, but also provides pre-professional training leading to graduate degrees in religious studies, theology, or other areas of the humanities. Departmental courses are offered in four areas: *philosophical* studies of religious ideas and values, *historical* studies of religious movements and institutions, *scientific* studies of religious beliefs and behavior, and *textual* studies of religious traditions and scriptures.
GRADUATE PROGRAM
Member of the Council on Graduate Studies in Religion
Graduate Advisor: William S. Babcock
Graduate Degrees Offered: MA; PhD

Degrees Conferred: 1 MA, 3 PhD

Graduate Students in Residence: 1 MA; 26 PhD/ThD

Not in Residence: 11 PhD/ThD

Average No. of New Students Enrolled: 6 PhD/ThD

Women Students: 10 PhD/ThD

Minority Students: 2 PhD/ThD

Foreign Students: 6 PhD/ThD

Minimum GRE Score Requisite to Admission: Yes; 1200 verbal and quantitative

Minimum GPA Score Requisite to Admission: Yes; 3.0 on 4.0 scale

Foreign Language Proficiency Evaluated: Yes

Financial Aid to First Year Students: 100% PhD

Financial Aid to Other Students: 100% PhD

Graduates Placed: 50% PhD

DESCRIPTION OF GRADUATE PROGRAM AND RESEARCH FACILITIES: Aside from concentrating on fields in which the SMU faculty and library resources are notably strong, the Graduate Program in Religious Studies places a high premium on directed independent study. Although a year-one core seminar is required in both degree programs, students demonstrate competence by successful completion of comprehensive examinations (in the PhD program, at the field as well as at the qualifying level) and by preparation and defense of an MA thesis and/or a PhD dissertation. PhD field specialization is possible in philosophy of religion, systematic theology, religious ethics, biblical studies (Hebrew Bible/Old Testament or New Testament), and history of the Christian tradition. The program draws support from the various Schools of SMU, including Perkins School of Theology, and from the University's five main libraries (2.8 million volumes; fully automated catalog), including Bridwell Library with its distinguished collections in religion and theology.

ACADEMIC PLAN, ADMISSION REQUIREMENTS, FINANCIAL AID: SMU operates on the semester system. Requirements for admission for both MA and PhD programs are: 1) BA, or equivalent, degree from an accredited institution; 2) cumulative GPA of 3.00 or above (on 4.00 scale); 3) satisfactory score on the General Test of the GRE (ordinarily combined score of 1200 or above on verbal and quantitative sections); 4) sufficient previous study in religion or related areas to prepare student to complete degree according to schedule. When English is not the applicant's native language, a TOEFL score of at least 550 (preferably 600) is also required. The deadline for completed applications is March 1. Tuition grants and stipends are available. The amount awarded will vary, but virtually every student receives financial aid in one or both of these forms. Grants and stipends are renewable each year (up to the deadline for the completion of the degree).

FACULTY:

Abraham, William J., DPhil, Oxford University (1977), 1985, Professor—philosophy of religion, 214-768-2040, Fax: 214-768-1042, E-mail: wabraham@mail.smu.edu

Aponte, Edwin David, PhD, Temple (1998), 1998, Assistant Professor—Hispanic Christianity and culture, 214-768-4808, Fax: 214-768-1042, E-mail: eaponte@mail.smu.edu

Babcock, William S., PhD, Yale (1971), 1967, Professor—history of Christianity, 214-768-2433, Fax: 214-768-1042, E-mail: wbabcock@mail.smu.edu

Barnard, G. William, PhD, University of Chicago (1994), 1994, Assistant Professor—social-scientific study of religion, mysticism, ways of being religious 214-768-2135, Fax: 214-768-3910, E-mail: bbarnard@mail.smu.edu

Bassler, Jouette M., PhD, Yale (1979), 1986, Professor—New Testament, 214-768-3553, Fax: 214-768-1042, E-mail: jbassler@mail.smu.edu

Cogley, Richard W., PhD, Princeton University (1983), 1987, Associate Professor—American religious history, history of Christianity, 214-768-2099, Fax: 214-768-3910, E-mail: rcogley@mail.smu.edu

Curran, Charles E., DST, Pontifical Gregorian University and Academic Alfonsina (1961), 1991, Professor—religious ethics, 214-768-4073, Fax: 214-768-4129, E-mail: ccurran@mail.smu.edu

Davis, Patricia, PhD, Princeton Theological Seminary (1991), 1991, Associate Professor—pastoral care, 214-768-2167, Fax: 214-768-1042, E-mail: pdavis@mail.smu.edu

Fewell, Danna N., PhD, Emory (1987), 1987, Assistant Professor—Old Testament, 214-768-2349, Fax: 214-768-1042, E-mail: dfewell@mail.smu.edu

Furnish, Victor Paul, PhD, Yale (1960), 1959, Professor—New Testament, 214-768-2390, Fax: 214-768-1042, E-mail: vfurnish@mail.smu.edu

Habito, Ruben L. F., MA DoctSt, University of Tokyo (1978), 1989, Professor—history of religions, 214-768-4334, Fax: 214-768-1042, E-mail: rhabito@mail.smu.edu

Holbert, John C., PhD, SMU (1975), 1979, Professor—Hebrew Bible, 214-768-3287, Fax: 214-768-1042, E-mail: jholbert@mail.smu.edu

Jones, Scott J., PhD, SMU (1992), 1997, Assistant Professor—Wesley studies, Methodist history, 214-768-4725, Fax: 214-768-1042, E-mail: sjjones@mail.smu.edu

Kirby, James E., PhD, Drew (1963), 1981, Professor—church history, 214-768-3322, Fax: 214-768-1042, E-mail: jkirby@mail.smu.edu

Kliever, Lonnie D., PhD, Duke (1963), 1975, Professor—philosophy of religion and religion and culture, 214-768-2102, Fax: 214-768-3910, E-mail: lkliever@mail.smu.edu

Lamoreaux, John C., PhD, Duke (1999), 1999, Assistant Professor—Islam, Eastern Orthodox Christianity, 214-768-1529, Fax: 214-768-3910, E-mail: jclam@mail.smu.edu

Lovin, Robin W., PhD, Harvard (1978), 1994, Professor—religious ethics, 214-768-2534, Fax: 214-768-2966, E-mail: rlovin@mail.smu.edu

May, William F., PhD, Yale (1962), 1985, Professor—ethics, 214-768-3467, Fax: 214-768-4129, E-mail: wmay@mail.smu.edu

Miles, Rebekkah, PhD, Chicago (1995), 1999, Associate Professor—ethics, 214-768-2082, Fax: 214-768-1042, E-mail: rlmiles@mail.smu.edu

Pedraja, Luis G., PhD, Virginia (1994), 1994, Assistant Professor—systematic theology, 214-768-2447, Fax: 214-768-1042, E-mail: lpedraja@mail.smu.edu

Rieger, Joerg M., PhD, Duke (1994), 1994, Assistant Professor—systematic theology, 214-768-2356, Fax: 214-768-1042, E-mail: jrieger@mail.smu.edu

Sylvest, Edward E., PhD, Southern Methodist University (1970), 1970, Associate Professor—history of Christianity, 214-768-3385, Fax: 214-768-1042, E-mail: esylvest@mail.smu.edu

Walker, Theodore, Jr., PhD, Notre Dame (1983), 1986, Associate Professor—religious ethics, 214-768-2446, Fax: 214-768-1042, E-mail: twalker@mail.smu.edu

Ward, James M., PhD, Union/Columbia (1955), 1960, Professor—Old Testament, 214-768-3801, Fax: 214-768-1042, E-mail: jmward@mail.smu.edu

Wood, Charles M., PhD, Yale (1972), 1976, Professor—systematic theology, philosophy of religion, 214-768-3608, Fax: 214-768-1042, E-mail: cwood@mail.smu.edu

Southern Missionary College

Collegedale TN 37315

University of Southern Mississippi

Philosophy and Religion Dept
Southern Station Box 5015
Hattiesburg MS 39406-5015

Phone: 601-266-4518
Fax: 601-266-5800
E-mail: fwood@usm.edu
URL: www.usm.edu

TYPE OF INSTITUTION: Public
EXECUTIVE OFFICER: Horace Fleming, President
CHAIRPERSON: Forest Wood, Jr.
UNDERGRADUATE ENROLLMENT: 19
GRADUATE ENROLLMENT: 9

Southern Nazarene University

6729 NW 39 Expressway
Bethany OK 73008-2694

Phone: 405-491-6368
Fax: 405-491-6658
E-mail: cauthron@snu.edu
URL: www.snu.edu

TYPE OF INSTITUTION: Private, Nazarene
EXECUTIVE OFFICER: Loren Gresham, President
CHAIRPERSON: Hal Cauthron
UNDERGRADUATE ENROLLMENT: 140
GRADUATE ENROLLMENT: 30

Southern Wesleyan University

PO Box 1020
Central SC 29630-1020

Phone: 864-639-2453
Fax: 864-639-0826

TYPE OF INSTITUTION: Private, The Wesleyan Church
EXECUTIVE OFFICER: David Spittal, President
CHAIRPERSON: James B. Bross
UNDERGRADUATE ENROLLMENT: 1,500
GRADUATE ENROLLMENT: 100

Southwest Baptist University

College of Christian Studies
1600 University Ave
Bolivar MO 65613

Phone: 417-326-1760

TYPE OF INSTITUTION: Denominational: Southern Baptist
EXECUTIVE OFFICER: Gordon Dutile, Associate Dean
UNDERGRADUATE ENROLLMENT: 3,000
GRADUATE ENROLLMENT: 575

Southwest Baptist Theological Seminary

Box 22000, Fort Worth TX 76122

Southwest Missouri State University

Dept of Religious Studies
901 S National
Springfield MO 65804

Phone: 417-836-5514
Fax: 417-836-4757
E-mail: jcm625f@mail.smsu.edu
URL: www.smsu.edu/

TYPE OF INSTITUTION: Public

EXECUTIVE OFFICER: Denny Pilant, Dean of the College of Humanities and Public Affairs

CHAIRPERSON: James C. Moyer

COORDINATORS: John Strong (Undergraduate); Stanley Burgess (Graduate)

UNDERGRADUATE ENROLLMENT: 1,500

GRADUATE ENROLLMENT: 30

DEGREES OFFERED: BA major, BA, BS, BSW, BS in Education minors

UNDERGRADUATE MAJORS: 43

DEGREES CONFERRED: 8

DESCRIPTION OF UNDERGRADUATE PROGRAM: Begun in 1969, the Religious Studies Department is one of the larger departments in the Midwest serving over 1,500 students each semester including about 40 majors, 75 minors, and 30 graduate students. It offers a broad diversity of courses in the academic study of religion. These courses are open to all students and meet General Education-Humanities requirements. The Department participates in the University Honors Program. The faculty includes thirteen full-time and eight part-time members with additional faculty in other departments teaching courses such as Sociology of Religion, Psychological Issues in Religion, etc.

GRADUATE PROGRAM

Member of the Council on Graduate Studies in Religion

Graduate Advisor: Stanley Burgess

Graduate Degrees Offered: MA

Degrees Conferred: 8 MA

Graduate Students in Residence: 25 MA

Not in Residence: 5 MA

Average No. of New Students Enrolled: 7 MA

Women Students: 8 MA

Foreign Students: 0 MA

Minimum GRE Score Requisite to Admission: No

Minimum GPA Score Requisite to Admission: Yes; 3.2 on 4.0 scale

Foreign Language Proficiency Evaluated: No

Financial Aid to First Year Students: 66% MA

Financial Aid to Other Students: 25% MA

Attrition Among Students: 25% MA

Graduates Placed: 100% MA

DESCRIPTION OF GRADUATE PROGRAM AND RESEARCH FACILITIES: The MA in Religious Studies requires the successful completion of a minimum of 32 graduate semester hours. These hours must be distributed with 18 hours in required courses dealing with History of Religions, Biblical Studies, History of Judaism and Christianity, and Religion, Self, and Society; three hours taken outside Religious Studies in a related Department; and 11 additional hours of electives chosen with the advice of the student's graduate committee. The student must submit a thesis or two reworked seminar papers, and pass a comprehensive examination (written and oral). Available for research is the University library and several other libraries, including theological libraries, in Springfield.

ACADEMIC PLAN, ADMISSION REQUIREMENTS, FINANCIAL AID: Admission to the MA in Religious Studies requires an undergraduate degree from an accredited college or university with a minimum overall GPA of 3.2 on a 4.0 scale, or 3.4 on the last 60 hours, or a minimum of 1000 on the combined verbal and analytical section of the GRE. Also required are 24 semester hours of Religious Studies (some semester hours can be in related disciplines) and 12 semester hours of one foreign language. Probationary admission, where warranted, is at the descretion of the Graduate Committee. Applicants should submit a completed application form plus original transcripts from all former institutions of higher learning. Students may apply to the University and the Department for financial aid. Up to eight graduate assistantships and one internship may be available.

FACULTY:

Berkwitz, Stephen C., PhD, University of California, Santa Barbara (1999), 1999, Assistant Professor—history of religions, Buddhism

Boyer, Mark G., MA, Indiana University (1981), 1989, Instructor (part-time)—New Testament

Burgess, Stanley M., PhD, University of Missouri, Columbia (1971), 1976, Professor—history of Christianity and Judaism, Eastern Christianity, women and religion, E-mail: smb209f@mail.smsu.edu

DeVries, LaMoine F., PhD, Southern Baptist Theological Seminary (1975), 1979, Professor—biblical studies, archaeology and the Bible, E-mail: lfd772f@mail.smsu.edu

Elkins, Kenneth R., ABD, University of Washington, Seattle (1999), 1989, Instructor (part-time)—religion in America, Holocaust

Embree, David E., MA, Southwest Missouri State University (1994), 1983, Lecturer—religion and society

Given, Mark D., PhD, University of North Carolina at Chapel Hill (1998), 1998, Assistant Professor—New Testament, Christian origins, Pauline studies, Luke-Acts studies, E-mail: mdg421f@mail.smsu.edu

Hedrick, Charles W., PhD, Claremont Graduate School (1977), 1980, Professor—New Testament, Christian origins, gnosticism, Nag Hammadi, E-mail: cwh156f@mail.smsu.edu

Hobbs, Lora, MS in Ed, University of Missouri, Columbia (1986), 1988, Lecturer—religion and society

Ingersoll, Julie, PhD, University of California, Santa Barbara (1997), 1999, Assistant Professor—sociology of religion, religion in America

Kellett, James R., DMin, Claremont School of Theology (1977), 1979, Instructor (part-time)—business ethics, New Testament

Llewellyn, John E., PhD, University of Chicago (1990), 1989, Assistant Professor—history of religions, South Asian religions, E-mail: jel807f@wpgate.smsu.edu

Luckert, Karl W., PhD, University of Chicago (1967), 1979, Professor Emeritus—history of religions, primitive and prehistoric religion, American Indian religions

Marler, William R., MDiv, Concordia Seminary (1983), 1990, Instructor (part-time)—religion in America

Matthews, Victor H., PhD, Brandeis University (1977), 1984, Professor—Old Testament, social world of ancient Israel, Mari studies, E-mail: vhm970f@mail.smsu.edu

McCutcheon, Russell, PhD, University of Toronto (1995), 1996, Associate Professor—modern religious thought, methodology, E-mail: rum628f@mail.smsu.edu

Michaels, J. Ramsey, ThD, Harvard University (1962), 1984, Professor Emeritus—New Testament and early Christianity, Jewish apocrypha

Moyer, James C., PhD, Brandeis University (1969), 1970, Professor—Old Testament, archaeology and history of Israel, E-mail: jcm625f@mail.smsu.edu

Pulley, Kathy J., PhD, Boston University (1989),1981, Associate Professor—religion and society, religion and public education, religious ethics, women and religion, E-mail: kjp093f@mail.smsu.edu

Pulley King, Micki A., MDiv, Harvard University (1988), 1989, Lecturer—religion and society

Sherwin, Rita, MAHL, Hebrew Union College-Jewish Institute of Religion (1992), 1994, Instructor (part-time)—Jewish studies

Smith, Leslie, MA, Southwest Missouri State University (1999), 1999, Instructor (part-time)—religion and society, E-mail: les497s@mail.smsu.edu

Strong, John T., PhD, Union Theological Seminary, Virginia (1993), 1992, Assistant Professor—biblical studies, E-mail: jos226f@mail.smsu.edu

tenZythoff, Gerrit J., PhD, University of Chicago (1967), 1969, Emeritus Professor—history of Christianity and Judaism, Islam

---

Southwestern College

100 College St
Winfield KS 67156

Phone: 316-221-8265
Fax: 316-221-8399
E-mail: srankin@jinx.sckans.edu
URL: www.sckans.edu

TYPE OF INSTITUTION: Private, United Methodist

EXECUTIVE OFFICER: W. Richard Merriman, Jr., President

CHAIRPERSON: Stephen W. Rankin

UNDERGRADUATE ENROLLMENT: 942

GRADUATE ENROLLMENT: 15

DEGREES OFFERED: BA (major in Philosophy and Religious Studies)

UNDERGRADUATE MAJORS: 12

DEGREES CONFERRED: 1

DESCRIPTION OF UNDERGRADUATE PROGRAM: Located in Winfield, Kansas, Southwestern College offers a challenging liberal arts curriculum that helps students apply what they learn through critical thinking, effective communication and problem solving. Philosophy and Religious Studies courses, classes, internships and activities are designed to produce inquisitive thinkers with hearts for service. In addition to the rigorous academic major, minors are offered in youth ministry, church music and Christian education. Southwestern's service learning programs encourage students to set the course for the rest of their lives with options emphasizing discipleship, leadership, volunteerism and diversity. Students are strongly encouraged to participate in numerous outreach and campus ministry opportunities. All of the Philosophy and Religious Studies faculty members teach in SC's integrative studies program, providing the department with a substantial role in the college's overall curriculum.

FACULTY:

Rankin, Stephen W., PhD, Northwestern University (1997), 1995, Assistant Professor of Religious Studies and Campus Minister—church history and theology, 316-221-8393, Fax: 316-221-8399, E-mail: srankin@jinx.sckans.edu

Sheppard, James A., PhD, The University of Sheffield, England (1999), 1997, Assistant Professor of Religion and Philosophy—philosophy and medieval studies, 316-221-8396, Fax: 316-221-8399, E-mail: sheppard@jinx.sckans.edu

Southwestern University

Georgetown TX 78626

Southwestern Adventist University

PO Box 567
Keene TX 76059

Phone: 817-645-3921
Fax: 817-556-4744
E-mail: willisl@swau.edu
URL: www.swau.edu

TYPE OF INSTITUTION: Private, Seventh-day Adventist
EXECUTIVE OFFICER: Marvin Anderson, President
CHAIRPERSON: Lloyd A. Willis
UNDERGRADUATE ENROLLMENT: 1,100
GRADUATE ENROLLMENT: 60

Southwestern Assemblies of God College

1200 Sycamore, Waxahachie TX 75765

Southwestern Christian College

Box J1, Terrell TX 75160

Southwestern College of Christian Ministry

PO Box 340, Bethany OK 73008

Southwestern Conservative Baptist Bible College

2625 E Cactus Rd, Phoenix AZ 85032

Southwestern School of Missions in India

2918 N Aris, Flagstaff AZ 86004

Spalding University

851 S Fourth St
Louisville KY 40203

Phone: 502-585-9911 ext 2315
Fax: 502-585-7158
E-mail: jmartos@spalding.edu
URL: www.spalding.edu

TYPE OF INSTITUTION: Private, Catholic

EXECUTIVE OFFICER: Joseph Martos, Director of the Russell Institute of Religion and Ministry

CHAIRPERSON: Joseph Martos

COORDINATORS: Adeline Fehribach (Undergraduate); Joseph Martos (Graduate)

UNDERGRADUATE ENROLLMENT: 950

GRADUATE ENROLLMENT: 450

DEGREES OFFERED: BA in Religious Studies

UNDERGRADUATE MAJORS: 5

DEGREES CONFERRED: 1

DESCRIPTION OF UNDERGRADUATE PROGRAM: The Russell Institute of Religion and Ministry functions as the religion department of Spalding University. In the area of religious studies, the department offers foundational courses (e.g., scripture, church history, Christian doctrine) and courses with a more specialized focus (e.g., feminism, ecumenism, health care). Majors take 33 semester hours in the department; minors take 21 semester hours. Majors and minors attend lower division courses with students who are taking religion courses in fulfillment of their general education requirement, but they also attend advanced courses with graduate students. Graduates are prepared to teach religion in a school setting, to minister in a parish setting, and to advance to graduate work in religious studies.

GRADUATE PROGRAM

Graduate Advisor: Joseph Martos

Graduate Degrees Offered: MA in Religious Studies

Degrees Conferred: 2 MA

Graduate Students in Residence: 0 MA

Not in Residence: 8 MA

Average No. of New Students Enrolled: 3 MA

Women Students: 3 MA

Minority Students: 1 MA

Minimum GRE Score Requisite to Admission: Yes; 1200

Minimum GPA Score Requisite to Admission: Yes; 2.5

Foreign Language Proficiency Evaluated: No

Financial Aid to First Year Students: 75%

Financial Aid to Other Students: 75%

Attrition Among Students: 15%

Graduates Placed: 100%

DESCRIPTION OF GRADUATE PROGRAM AND RESEARCH FACILITIES: The graduate program provides broad and thorough training in religion and theology in 36 semester hours of course work. The expertise acquired can be used as the academic foundation for a career in high school religion teaching, parish religious education, and other areas of Christian ministry. It can also provide a solid basis for advanced academic work at the doctoral level in theology or religion. Courses are designed to offer not only essential concepts but also knowledge about methodology in the study of religion and the practice of theology. Wherever possible, courses also facilitate the integration of theory and practice as well as the application of ideas and values to professional situations and everyday living. Elective courses in ministry are also available. For research, students have access to two nearby seminary libraries in addition to the resources of the university library.

ACADEMIC PLAN, ADMISSION REQUIREMENTS, FINANCIAL AID: Applicants must have 18 undergraduate hours in religious studies, or equivalent knowledge derived from non-credit education and professional experience. Two letters of reference, attesting to the applicant's academic ability and professional interests, are also required. Up to 12 graduate hours may be transferred from another institution. Spalding has a generous graduate scholarship program with particular attention given to minority applicants. Graduate assistantships are also available.

FACULTY:

Cato, Judy, PhD, University of Virginia (1990), 1990, Adjunct Assistant Professor—systematics, world religions, women's studies

Fehribach, Adeline, PhD, Vanderbilt University (1996), 1996, Assistant Professor—scripture

Hoyt-O'Connor, Paul, PhD, Boston College (1992), 1994, Assistant Professor—methodology, social ethics

Martos, Joseph, PhD, DePaul University (1973), 1992, Professor—history, systematics

Merkt, Joseph, STD, Catholic University of America (1982), 1991, Assistant Professor—ministry, morality, systematics

---

Spelman College

Box 1238, Atlanta GA 30314

Spertus College

618 S Michigan Ave
Chicago IL 60605

Phone: 312-922-9012
Fax: 312-922-6406
E-mail: college@spertus.edu
URL: www.spertus.edu

TYPE OF INSTITUTION: Private, Non-denominational

EXECUTIVE OFFICER: Howard A. Sulkin, President

CHAIRPERSONS: Byron L. Sherwin, Vice-President for Academic Affairs; Dean Bell, Associate Dean of Jewish Studies

GRADUATE ENROLLMENT: 300

GRADUATE PROGRAM

Graduate Advisors: Byron L. Sherwin, Dean Bell

Graduate Degrees Offered: MA; DJS; MS

Degrees Conferred: 5 MA; 110 MS

Graduate Students in Residence: 5 MA; 162 MS

Not in Residence: 138 MS; 26 DJS

Average No. of New Students Enrolled: 140

Women Students: 200

Minority Students: 96

Foreign Students: 15

Minimum GRE Score Requisite to Admission: No

Minimum GPA Score Requisite to Admission: Yes, 2.75-3.0 on 4.0 scale

Foreign Language Proficiency Evaluated: No

Financial Aid to First Year Students: 60% MA; 25% DJS; 10% MS

Financial Aid to Other Students: 65% MA; 30% DJS; 15% MS

Attrition Among Students: 10%

DESCRIPTION OF GRADUATE PROGRAM AND RESEARCH FACILITIES: We offer 6 masters programs and the Doctor of Jewish Studies. Five of these masters programs are in Jewish Studies with a variety of admissions requirements. We also offer a master of science in human services administration. Our library contains about 100,000 volumes and periodicals, mostly in Jewish Studies. We also have an extensive museum of Judaica.

ACADEMIC PLAN, ADMISSION REQUIREMENTS, FINANCIAL AID: Curriculum and admissions requirements differ for each degree offered. We participate in federal loan programs, and also have a scholarship endowment.

FACULTY:

Bell, Dean, PhD, University of California, Berkeley—medieval Jewish history

Dulin, Rachel, PhD, Northwestern University—Hebrew language, ancient Israel

Grossfeld, Bernard, PhD, Johns Hopkins University—Targum, Bible

Lefkovitz, Elliot, PhD, University of Michigan—Jewish education, modern Jewish history

Mirelman, Victor, PhD, Columbia University—Jewish thought, Jewish history, Latin American Jewry

Sherwin, Byron L., PhD, University of Chicago—Jewish philosophy, mysticism and religion

Stampfer, Nathaniel, PhD, Northwestern University—Jewish education, liturgy, Yiddish, Jewish history

---

Spring Arbor College

106 Main St, Spring Arbor MI 49283

Spring Hill College

**4000 Dauphin St
Mobile AL 36608-1791**

**Phone: 334-380-3094
Fax: 334-460-2190
E-mail: grad@shc.edu
URL: www.shc.edu**

TYPE OF INSTITUTION: Private, Catholic Jesuit

EXECUTIVE OFFICER: Noreen Carrocci, Academic Vice President

CHAIRPERSON: Christopher J. Viscardi, SJ

UNDERGRADUATE ENROLLMENT: 1,000

GRADUATE ENROLLMENT: 300

Springfield College
263 Alden St, Springfield MA 01109

Stanford University

Dept of Religious Studies
Stanford CA 94305-2165

Phone: 650-723-3322
Fax: 650-725-1476
E-mail: toy@leland.stanford.edu
URL: www.stanford.edu/dept/relstud/

TYPE OF INSTITUTION: Private
EXECUTIVE OFFICER: Malcolm Beasley, Dean
CHAIRPERSON: Arnold Eisen
UNDERGRADUATE ENROLLMENT: 6,577
GRADUATE ENROLLMENT: 7,467
DEGREES OFFERED: AB, AB-Honors, AB Philosophy and Religion
UNDERGRADUATE MAJORS: 13
DEGREES CONFERRED: 15
DESCRIPTION OF UNDERGRADUATE PROGRAM: The faculty offers general undergraduate courses and more specialized classes and seminars in the traditions of Buddhism, Christianity, Hinduism, Islam, Judaism and Chinese and Japanese religions, as well as philosophy of religion, hermeneutics, ethics, etc. The major is designed to give the student a knowledge of at least two traditions, several different approaches to the study of religion, and appreciation of the diversity and depth of the problems religions seek to solve. Undergraduate majors must complete 60 quarter units, of which 40 must be advanced. An Honors major may be elected, as well as a joint major in Philosophy and Religious Studies.
GRADUATE PROGRAM
Member of the Council on Graduate Studies in Religion
Graduate Advisor: Hester Gelber
Graduate Degrees Offered: MA; PhD
Degrees Conferred: 5 MA; 4 PhD
Graduate Students in Residence: 8 MA; 20 PhD
Not in Residence: 8 PhD
Average No. of New Students Enrolled: 5 MA; 4 PhD
Women Students: 1 MA; 14 PhD
Foreign Students: 1 MA; 1 PhD
Minimum GRE Score Requisite to Admission: No
Minimum GPA Score Requisite to Admission: No
Foreign Language Proficiency Evaluated: No
Financial Aid to First Year Students: 100% PhD
DESCRIPTION OF GRADUATE PROGRAM AND RESEARCH FACILITIES: The graduate program emphasizes the fields of modern Western religious thought, Judaic studies, and East Asian religions (especially Buddhism), and offers opportunities for advanced work in philosophy of religion, theory of religion, comparative religion, and religious ethics. The Department offers both the MA and PhD degrees, as well as a joint doctoral degree in Humanities. The MA program typically requires one year. The PhD requires a minimum of three years of

full-time coursework in residence. Before undertaking the dissertation, the student takes a set of written and oral Qualifying Examinations on a) the chosen field, b) the area of specialization within the field, and c) the discipline of religious studies. Before submitting the dissertation, the student defends it before the faculty in the University Oral Examination. Stanford libraries give abundant support to research in the ancient, medieval and modern periods in the various religious traditions. Students in Judaic Studies have the special resources of the Salo Baron collection, and students with interests in Asian, Islamic and modern religion have the unique advantages of the Hoover Institution Library. Libraries at the University of California at Berkeley and the Graduate Theological Union offer exchange service. For detailed information, write the Chairman or Graduate Director of the Department.

ACADEMIC PLAN, ADMISSION REQUIREMENTS, FINANCIAL AID: The Department admits on average four students for PhD study a year and about five MA candidates. PhD candidates are fully funded for the first four years (or three if they have an MA in Religious Studies). Additional funding may be available for teaching assistantships. Admission requirements include an accredited baccalaureate degree in a field related to the student's planned area of research, GRE aptitude scores, three recommendations, transcripts, statement of purpose in intended field and a sample of scholarly work. Deadlines: admission and financial aid, January 5.

FACULTY:

Bielefeldt, Carl W., PhD, University of California, Berkeley (1980), 1980, Professor—East Asian religions, Japanese Buddhism

Busto, Rudy V., PhD, University of California, Berkeley (1990), 1990, Assistant Professor—religion and ethnic studies

Eisen, Arnold M., PhD, Hebrew University, Jerusalem (1978), 1986, Professor—modern Jewish thought, sociology of religion

Faure, Bernard R., Doctorat d'Etat ès Lettres et Sciences Humaines, Université de Paris-VII, France (1985), 1987, Professor—Chinese and Japanese Buddhism

Gelber, Hester G., PhD, University of Wisconsin (1974), 1982, Associate Professor—medieval religious thought, philosophy of religion

Gregg, Robert C., PhD, University of Pennsylvania (1974), 1987, Professor—history of early Christianity

Harvey, Van A., PhD, Yale University (1957), 1977, Professor Emeritus—European religious thought since the Enlightenment, philosophy of religion

Nivison, David S., PhD, Harvard University (1953), 1958, Professor Emeritus—classical Chinese religious thought and philosophy

Sheehan, Thomas, PhD, Fordham University (1971), 1999, Professor—philosophy of religion, European religious thought since the Enlightenment, continental philosophy

Sockness, Brent, PhD, University of Chicago (1996), 1996, Assistant Professor—modern Western religious thought since the Enlightenment, ethics

Yearley, Lee H., PhD, University of Chicago (1969), 1968, Evans-Wentz Professor—comparative ethics, Christian thought, classical Chinese thought

---

Stephen F. Austin State College
Nacogdoches TX 75961

Stephens College

Religion and Philosophy Dept
Columbia MO 65201

Phone: 573-876-7147
E-mail: whitehill@wc.stephens.edu
URL: www.stephens.edu

TYPE OF INSTITUTION: Private
EXECUTIVE OFFICER: Marcia Kierscht President
CHAIRPERSON: James Whitehill
UNDERGRADUATE ENROLLMENT: 12

Sterling College

Sterling KS 67579

Phone: 316-278-4274
Fax: 316-278-2775
E-mail: mgraham@acc.stercolks.edu

TYPE OF INSTITUTION: Private, Presbyterian USA
EXECUTIVE OFFICER: Bob Campbell, Interim President
CHAIRPERSON: J. Michele Graham
UNDERGRADUATE ENROLLMENT: 475

Stetson University

421 N Woodland Blvd
Unit 8354
Deland FL 32720

Phone: 904-822-8930
Fax: 904-822-8936
E-mail: mreddish@stetson.edu
URL: www.stetson.edu/department/religion

TYPE OF INSTITUTION: Private, Non-Denominational
EXECUTIVE OFFICER: H. Douglas Lee, President
CHAIRPERSON: Mitchell G. Reddish
UNDERGRADUATE ENROLLMENT: 1,900
GRADUATE ENROLLMENT: 1,000

Stillman College

PO Box 1430
Tuscaloosa AL 35403

Phone: 205-366-8828
Fax: 205-366-8996
E-mail: jones_f@acad.stillman.edu

TYPE OF INSTITUTION: Denominational: Presbyterian USA
EXECUTIVE OFFICER: Cordell Wynn, President
CHAIRPERSON: Neil N. Jones
UNDERGRADUATE ENROLLMENT: 900

Stonehill College

320 Washington St
North Easton MA 02357-1135

Phone: 508-565-1081
Fax: 508-565-1444
URL: www.stonehill.edu

TYPE OF INSTITUTION: Denominational: Roman Catholic
EXECUTIVE OFFICER: Bartley MacPhaidin, CSC, President
CHAIRPERSON: Gregory J. Shaw
UNDERGRADUATE ENROLLMENT: 2,000

Suffolk University

Philosophy Dept
8 Ashburton Place
Boston MA 02108

Phone: 617-573-8399
Fax: 617-723-7255
E-mail: skeefe@acad.suffolk.edu

TYPE OF INSTITUTION: Private
EXECUTIVE OFFICER: Michael Ronayne, Dean
CHAIRPERSON: Kenneth Greenberg, Chairperson of Philosophy Dept.
COORDINATOR: Donna Giancola, Director Religious Studies Program
UNDERGRADUATE ENROLLMENT: 3,383
GRADUATE ENROLLMENT: 1,542
DEGREES OFFERED: The Religious Studies Program is an interdisciplinary minor program housed within the Philosophy Department. Students earn a BA or BS degree with a minor in Religious Studies.
UNDERGRADUATE MAJORS: There are 5 minors currently enrolled in this program.
DEGREES CONFERRED: The Philosophy Department expects 5 Religious Studies minors to receive BA or BS degrees.
DESCRIPTION OF UNDERGRADUATE PROGRAM: The Religious Studies Program at Suffolk University is an interdisciplinary program designed to give students the opportunity to explore the nature and meanings of world religions. Religious thought and dogma, in both western and non-western cultures, from ancient civilizations to modern times, will be presented as a vehicle for expanding the various ways in which religious ideas and practices can be understood. The Religious Studies minor contains courses taught in a number of departments in the College of Liberal Arts and Sciences, as well as interdisciplinary field work and directed studies. Courses constituting the minor in Religious Studies are devoted to exploring the intellectual, socio-cultural and aesthetic aspects of religious beliefs and practices. The Religious Studies Program offers a minor from an interdisciplinary list of courses and covers a wide range of perspectives: from History of Christianity, Bible as Literature, and Religion in American Society, to Oriental Philosophy, African-American Religion, Women in Spirituality, and Philosophy of Religion. Requirements for a minor are satisfied by successfully completing 18 semester hours of course work in Religious Studies. One course must be either Phenomenology of Religion, Philosophy of Religion, or Humanities and Religious Tradition.
FACULTY:
This program was started in the Fall of 1994. All the professors may be reached by calling (617) 573-8000.
Boone, Gloria, PhD, Ohio University, Professor—communication and journalism
Burke, Mary, PhD, University of Connecticut, Assistant Professor—government

Feldman, Eileen, MA, Northeastern University, Boston, Lecturer—English

Giancola, Donna, PhD, Boston University, Director of Religious Studies Program and Associate Professor—philosophy

Goldstein, Audrey, Diploma, School of the Museum of Fine Arts, Associate Professor—art and design

Marchant, Frederick, PhD, University of Chicago, Professor—English

McCarthy, Joseph, PhD, Boston College, Professor—education and human services

Outwater, Dennis, PhD, University of Chicago, Professor—philosophy

Smythe, Lanier, PhD, University of North Carolina, Chairperson and Professor—humanities and modern languages

Snow, Beatrice, PhD, University of New Hampshire, Chairperson and Professor—biology

---

Summit Christian College

1025 W Rudisill Blvd, Fort Wayne IN 46807

Swarthmore College

Department of Religion
500 College Ave
Swarthmore PA 19081

Phone: 610-328-8045
Fax: 610-328-7687
E-mail: emcelrol@swarthmore.edu
URL: www.swarthmore.edu/
humanities/religion

TYPE OF INSTITUTION: Private

CHAIRPERSON: Mark I. Wallace

DEGREES OFFERED: BA Major in Course, BA Major or Minor in Honors

UNDERGRADUATE MAJORS: 42

DEGREES CONFERRED: 20

DESCRIPTION OF UNDERGRADUATE PROGRAM: We apply several methodologies to the study of the religious traditions of the West and the religious traditions of Africa and Asia—historical investigation, textual criticism, philosophical analysis, socio-cultural interpretation—in the interests of a holistic understanding of religion, and we strive for an empathetic and responsible treatment of the issues encountered in our subject matter and raised by our students.

FACULTY:

Chireau, Yvonne P., PhD, Princeton (1994), 1994, Assistant Professor—African-American religion, American religion, folk religions, 610-328-8041, Fax: 610-328-7687, E-mail: ychirea1@swarthmore.edu

Deutsch, Nathaniel, PhD, University of Chicago (1995), 1995, Assistant Professor—biblical studies, early Judaism, early Christiantiy and Gnosticism, 610-328-8467, Fax: 610-328-7687, E-mail: ndeutsc1@swarthmore.edu

Frost, J. William, PhD, Wisconsin (1968), 1973, Professor and Director of Friends Historical Library—American religious history, Quakerism, peace studies, 610-328-8496, Fax: 610-328-7687, E-mail: jfrost1@swarthmore.edu

Hopkins, Steven, PhD, Harvard University (1994), 1993, Assistant Professor—comparative religion and religions of South Asia, 610-328-8054, Fax: 610-328-7687, E-mail: shopkin1@swarthmore.edu

Khan, Ruqayya Y., PhD, University of Pennsylvania (1997), 1998, Visiting Assistant Professor—Islam, 610-328-8035, Fax: 610-328-7687, E-mail: rkhan1@swarthmore.edu

Ross, Ellen M., PhD, University of Chicago (1987), 1991, Associate Professor—medieval religious life and thought, women's studies, 610-328-8691, Fax: 610-328-7687, E-mail: eross1@swarthmore.edu

Swearer, Donald K., PhD, Princeton (1967), 1970, Professor—Buddhism, history of religion, Asian religions, 610-328-8035, Fax: 610-328-7687, E-mail: dsweare1@swarthmore.edu

Wallace, Mark I., PhD, University of Chicago (1986), 1989, Associate Professor—philosophy of religion, critical theory, religion and ecology, 610-328-7829, Fax: 610-328-7687, E-mail: mwallac1@swarthmore.edu

Swedenborg School of Religion

PO Box E, 48 Sargent St, Newton MA 02158

Sweet Briar College

Dept of Religion, Sweet Briar VA 24595

Sweetwater Bible College

14240 N 43rd Ave, Glendale AZ 85306

Syracuse University

Dept of Religion
Rm 501 Hall of Languages
Syracuse NY 13244-1170

Phone: 315-443-3861
Fax: 315-443-3958
E-mail: cbwillia@mailbox.syr.edu
URL: syllabus.syr.edu/rel/homepage
/main.htm

TYPE OF INSTITUTION: Private

EXECUTIVE OFFICER: Robert G. Jensen, Dean of the College of Arts and Sciences

CHAIRPERSON: James B. Wiggins

UNDERGRADUATE ENROLLMENT: 10,000

GRADUATE ENROLLMENT: 4,800

DEGREES OFFERED: BA

UNDERGRADUATE MAJORS: 19

DEGREES CONFERRED: 3

DESCRIPTION OF UNDERGRADUATE PROGRAM: The Department of Religion offers widely varied courses which explore the manifestations of religion in various cultural contexts and examine the belief systems and the individual and cultic practices found in the several major religious traditions. The history and sacred writings of Christianity, Judaism, Hinduism, and Buddhism are studied with emphasis on the relationship of religious thought to related concerns in psychology, literature, the arts, philosophy, mythology, and the social sciences.

GRADUATE PROGRAM

Member of the Council on Graduate Studies in Religion

Graduate Advisor: Philip P. Arnold

Graduate Degrees Offered: MA; PhD; MPhil

Degrees Conferred: 2 MA; 4 PhD; 3 MPhil

Graduate Students in Residence: 7 MA; 32 PhD

Not in Residence: 0 MA; 7 PhD

Average No. of New Students Enrolled: 4 MA; 3 PhD

Women Students: 2 MA; 14 PhD

Minority Students: 1 MA; 3 PhD

Foreign Students: 1 MA; 8 PhD

Minimum GRE Score Requisite to Admission: No

Minimum GPA Score Requisite to Admission: No

Foreign Language Proficiency Evaluated: Yes; GSFLT Score: 490 German; 510 French; or, a departmentally set exam, evaluated by faculty members

Financial Aid to First Year Students: 100% MA; 50% PhD

Financial Aid to Other Students: 66% MA; 28% PhD

Attrition Among Students: 0% MA; 0% PhD

Graduates Placed: 0% MA; 50% PhD

DESCRIPTION OF GRADUATE PROGRAM: Syracuse University's interdisciplinary program in religion emphasizes studies of the intersection of religions and cultures. The program focuses on contemporary problems of interpretation, although the sources studied may be ancient or modern. Students are encouraged to investigate both religious dimensions of secular culture and traditional religions as cultural phenomena. Major areas of study include: Judaism; Christianity; North American Religions; Religions of South Asia; East Asian Religions; Greco-Roman Religions; Philosophy of Religion; Theology and Hermeneutics; Depth Psychology; Religious Ethics; Religion and Literature; Mythology; and Biblical Criticism and Interpretation. Course seminars, visiting professorships, guest lecturers, and topical colloquia provide opportunity for faculty and students to articulate and broaden their own areas of specialization and competence within the broad contours of the program of religion.

ACADEMIC PLAN, ADMISSION REQUIREMENTS, FINANCIAL AID: Financial aid plans available: Competitive University Fellowships (tuition + $11,384); Graduate Assistantships (tuition + $9,112); and scholarships (tuition). For further information, contact the Director of Graduate Studies.

FACULTY:

Arnold, Philip P., PhD, University of Chicago (1992), 1996, Associate Professor—history of religions, Native American traditions, American religions, material culture, ritual landscapes, 315-443-5718/3861, E-mail: pparnold@mailbox.syr.edu

Braiterman, Zachary J., PhD, Stanford University (1995), Assistant Professor—works in the field of modern Jewish thought and culture, specializing in the 20th century, modern and contemporary religious thought, medieval Jewish philosophy, biblical and rabbinic sources, art history, 315-443-5719/3861, E-mail: zbraiter@mailbox.syr.edu

Frieden, Ken, PhD, Yale University (1984), 1993, Professor and B. G. Ruldolph Chair—Hebrew, Yiddish, European, and American Judaic literature, 315-443-1894, E-mail: kfrieden@mailbox.syr.edu

Gold, Ann Grodzins, PhD, University of Chicago (1984), 1993, Professor—teaching and research on religion in South Asia, 315-443-5717/3861, E-mail: aggold@mailbox.syr.edu

Hamner, M. Gail, PhD, Duke University (1997), 1998, Assistant Professor—specializes in religion and culture with teaching interests in religion and film, pragmatism, critical theory, women's studies, and popular culture, 315-443-5716/3861, E-mail: mghamner@mailbox.syr.edu

Miller, David M., PhD, Drew University (1963), 1967, Watson-Ledden Professor—religion, teaching and research work are at the intersections of theology, comparative mythology, literary theory and depth psychology, 315-443-5722/3861, E-mail: dlmiller@mailbox.syr.edu

Miller, Patricia Cox, PhD, University of Chicago (1979), 1977, Professor—religious traditions in classical and Greco-Roman antiquity, 315-443-5714/3861, E-mail: plmiller@mailbox.syr.edu

Pilgrim, Richard B., PhD, University of Chicago (1970), 1970, Associate Professor and Assistant Dean—religion and art in Japan, Mahayana Buddhist thought and practice, 315-443-5726/3861, E-mail: rbpilgri@cas.syr.edu

Wallwork, Ernest E., PhD, Harvard University (1971), 1983, Professor—religious ethics, bioethics, psychology and sociology of religion and morals, 315-443-5720/3861, E-mail: eewallwo@mailbox.syr.edu

Watts, James W., PhD, Yale University (1990), 1999, Associate Professor—Hebrew Bible and ancient near Eastern religious traditions, ancient near Eastern legal systems, rhetoric in the ancient near East, New Testament

Wiggins, James B., PhD, Drew University (1963), 1963, Department Chair and Eliphalet Remington Professor of Religion—Western religion and culture, comparative religion study, hermeneutics, 315-443-2241/3861, E-mail: jbwiggin@mailbox.syr.edu

Winquist, Charles E., PhD, University of Chicago (1970), 1986, Thomas J. Watson Professor of Religion—research and teaching in philosophical theology, critical theory and hermeneutics, 315-443-5715/3861, E-mail: cewinqui@mailbox.syr.edu

S

Tabernacle Baptist Bible College and Theological Seminary

717 N Whitehurst Landing Rd
Virginia Beach VA 23464

Phone: 757-420-1960
Fax: 757-424-3014
E-mail: lb7143@aol.com

TYPE OF INSTITUTION: Private, Baptist
EXECUTIVE OFFICER: Thomas M. Strouse, Dean
UNDERGRADUATE ENROLLMENT: 70
GRADUATE ENROLLMENT: 30

Tabor College

400 S Jefferson
Hillsboro KS 67063-1799

Phone: 316-947-3121
Fax: 316-947-2607
E-mail: (person)@tcnet.tabor.edu
URL: www.tabor.edu

TYPE OF INSTITUTION: Denominational: Mennonite Brethren
EXECUTIVE OFFICERS: Larry Nikkel, President
CHAIRPERSON: Douglas B. Miller
UNDERGRADUATE ENROLLMENT: 500

Talbot School of Theology

Biola University
13800 Biola Avenue
La Mirada CA 90639

Phone: 562-903-4816
Fax: 562-903-4759
E-mail: admissions@biola.edu
URL: www.talbot.edu

TYPE OF INSTITUTION: Private, Non-Denominational
EXECUTIVE OFFICER: Dennis H. Dirks, Dean
UNDERGRADUATE ENROLLMENT: 2,395
GRADUATE ENROLLMENT: 1,229

Talladega College

627 W Battle St, Talladega AL 35160

Talmudic College of Florida

4014 Chase Ave, Miami Beach FL 33140

Talmudical Academy of New Jersey

PO Box 7, Adelphia NJ 07110

Talmudical Institute of Upstate New York

769 Park Ave, Rochester NY 14607

Talmudical Yeshiva of Philadelphia

6063 Drexel Rd
Philadelphia PA 19131

Phone: 215-477-1000
Fax: 215-477-5065
E-mail: typp@juno.com

TYPE OF INSTITUTION: Private, Jewish
EXECUTIVE OFFICER: Erwin Weinberg, President
UNDERGRADUATE ENROLLMENT: 112

Rabbinical College Talshe

28400 Euclid Ave, Wickliffe OH 44092

The University of Tampa

Tampa FL 33606

Rabbinical College of Tash

144 Wilson St, Brooklyn NY 11219

Taylor University

Upland IN 46989

Telshe Yeshiva-Chicago

3535 W Foster Ave, Chicago IL 60625

Temple University

Department of Religion CS11
Philadelphia PA 19122

Phone: 215-204-7707
Fax: 215-204-2535

TYPE OF INSTITUTION: Public
CHAIRPERSON: John C. Rains
UNDERGRADUATE ENROLLMENT: 30,000
GRADUATE ENROLLMENT: 6,800

Temple Baptist College

11965 Kenn Rd, Cincinnati OH 45240

University of Tennessee, Chattanooga

Philosophy and Religion Department
615 McCallie Avenue
Chattanooga TN 37403

Phone: 423-755-4334
Fax: 423-755-4153
E-mail: herbert-burhenn@utc.edu
URL: www.utc.edu

TYPE OF INSTITUTION: Public

EXECUTIVE OFFICER: Bill Stacy, Chancellor

CHAIRPERSON: Herbert Burhenn

UNDERGRADUATE ENROLLMENT: 7,323

GRADUATE ENROLLMENT: 1,359

DEGREES OFFERED: BA

UNDERGRADUATE MAJORS: 39

DEGREES CONFERRED: 8

DESCRIPTION OF UNDERGRADUATE PROGRAM: The Department of Philosophy and Religion offers a 30-hour undergraduate major with separate concentrations in Philosophy, Religious Studies, and Philosophy and Religion.

FACULTY:

Burhenn, Herbert W. L., PhD, Yale (1970), 1970, Professor—philosophy of religion, primitive religions, 423-755-4336, E-mail: herbert-burhenn@utc.edu

Cory, Matthew, PhD, State University of New York, Binghamton (1999), 1999, Assistant Professor—philosophy, 423-755-4334

Eskildsen, Stephen, PhD, British Columbia (1994), 1998, Assistant Professor—Asian religions, Taoism, 423-755-4655, E-mail: stephen-eskildsen@utc.edu

Frodeman, Robert L., PhD, Pennsylvania State (1988), 1997, Assistant Professor—environmental ethics; 19th and 20th C. Continental philosophy, philosophy of the earth sciences. 423-755-4472, E-mail: robert-frodeman@utc.edu

Hibbs, H. Darren, PhD, University of Arkansas (1999), 1999, Assistant Professor—philosophy, 423-755-4334

Klinefelter, Donald S., PhD, Chicago (1967), 1969, UC Foundation Professor—ethics, philosophy of religion, 423-755-4338, E-mail: donald-klinefelter@utc.edu

Lippy, Charles H., PhD, Princeton (1972), 1994, LeRoy A. Martin Distinguished Professor of Religious Studies—American religion, 423-755-4340, E-mail: charles-lippy@utc.edu

Phillips, John F., PhD, Wisconsin (1980), 1980, Professor—Greek philosophy, Hellenistic religions, 423-755-4347, E-mail: john-phillips@utc.edu

Resnick, Irven M., PhD, Virginia (1983), 1990, Professor and Chair of Excellence in Judaic Studies—Judaic studies, history of Christian thought, 423-755-4446, E-mail: irven-resnick@utc.edu

Switala, Kristin, PhD, Vanderbilt (1993), 1993, UC Foundation Associate Professor—continental philosophy, aesthetics, 423-755-4318, E-mail: kristin-switala@utc.edu

University of Tennessee, Knoxville

Dept of Religious Studies
501 McClung Tower
Knoxville TN 37996-0450

Phone: 865-974-2466
Fax: 865-974-0965
E-mail: creynol2@utk.edu
URL: web.utk.edu/~religion/

TYPE OF INSTITUTION: Public

CHAIRPERSON: Charles H. Reynolds

UNDERGRADUATE ENROLLMENT: 19,693

GRADUATE ENROLLMENT: 5,919

DEGREES OFFERED: BA

UNDERGRADUATE MAJORS: 48

DEGREES CONFERRED: 12

DESCRIPTION OF UNDERGRADUATE PROGRAM: The curriculum provides opportunities to explore diverse modes of religious experience and expression. Integral to both the humanities and social sciences divisions of the College of Arts and Sciences, religious studies courses utilize various methods of inquiring (textual, comparative, historical, empirical, analytic, ethical, theological, etc.) in an effort to interpret and understand the major religious traditions of human history and the present era. Introductory courses provide acquaintance with several traditions and opportunity to reflect on the nature and function of religion in human culture. The undergraduate major is designed with sufficient flexibility for a baccalaureate program responsive to student interests and inclusive of work in the various disciplines of the humanities and social sciences essential to a comprehensive undergraduate education. Opportunity is also provided for the development of special competence in a selected tradition or area of study. Faculty and students also participate in interdisciplinary programs such as American Studies, Asian Studies, African-American Studies, Mediterranean Studies, Medieval Studies, Comparative Literature, and Medical Ethics.

GRADUATE PROGRAM

Graduate Advisor: Rosalind Hackett, Department of Religious Studies

Graduate Degrees Offered: MA in Philosophy with a track in Religious Studies

DESCRIPTION OF GRADUATE PROGRAM AND RESEARCH FACILITIES: The Master of Arts degree requires at least thirty hours of approved graduate credit. Six hours may be earned by writing a Master of Arts thesis, and up to six hours may be approved from courses not taught in Religious Studies. This is generally expected to be a two year full-time program of study. The Department currently offers eight graduate teaching assistantships, each with a full tuition waver.

FACULTY:

Dungan, David L., ThD, Harvard (1967), 1967, Professor—Hellenistic religions, early Christianity, 423-974-2466, Fax: 423-974-0965, E-mail: dungan@utk.edu

Fitzgerald, James L., PhD, Chicago (1980), 1978, Associate Professor—religious and philosophical traditions of India, 423-974-6982, Fax: 423-974-0965, E-mail: jftzgrld@utkux1.utk.edu

Gwynne, Rosalind W., PhD, Washington (1982), 1981, Associate Professor—Islamic theology and literature, Arabic, 423-974-6988, Fax: 423-974-0965, E-mail: warda@utkux.utk.edu

Hackett, Rosalind I. J., PhD, Aberdeen (1986) 1986, Professor—African religions, new religious movements, sociology and anthropology of religion, 423-974-6980, Fax: 423-974-0965, E-mail: rhackett@utk.edu

Heffernan, Thomas J. A., PhD, Cambridge (1977), 1975, Adjunct Professor—Bible as literature, medieval literature and culture, 423-974-6968, Fax: 423-974-0965, E-mail: theffern@utkvx.utk.edu

Hodges, John O., PhD, Chicago (1980), 1982, Associate Professor—African-American religion, religion and literature, 423-974-6983, Fax: 423-974-0965, E-mail: jo-hodges@utkvx.utk.edu

Hulsether, Mark D., PhD, Minnesota (1992), 1993, Associate Professor—religion in America, 423-974-2182, Fax: 423-974-0965, E-mail: mhulseth@utk.utk.edu

Humphreys, W. Lee, ThD, Union, New York (1970), 1970, Professor—ancient Near Eastern religions and cultures, Mediterranean studies, Hebrew, ancient Israelite and early Jewish religious traditions, 423-974-6688, Fax: 423-974-0965

Levering, Miriam L., PhD, Harvard (1978), 1982, Associate Professor—religions and philosophies of China and Japan, 423-974-6979, Fax: 423-974-0965 or 423-637-1537, E-mail: mleverin@utk.edu

Linge, David E., PhD, Vanderbilt (1968), 1968, Professor—philosophy of religion, Western religious thought and institutions, religion and ecology, 423-974-6981, Fax: 423-974-0965, E-mail: dlinge@utk.edu

Lusby, F. Stanley, MDiv, Colgate Rochester (1946), Professor Emeritus—history of religions, Buddhism and Asian cultures, contemporary religious thought: East and West, 423-974-2466, Fax: 423-974-0965, E-mail: tvns24a@prodigy.com

Norman, Ralph V., Jr., PhD, Yale (1961), 1966, Professor—philosophical theology, Western philosophical and religious thought, process thought, theology and culture, theology and literature, 423-974-2757, Fax: 423-974-0965, E-mail: jnorman@utk.edu

Reynolds, Charles H., PhD, Harvard (1968), 1969, Professor and Head—religious and philosophical ethics, 423-974-4360, Fax: 423-974-0965, E-mail: creynol2@utk.edu

Schmidt, Gilya G., PhD, Pittsburgh (1991), 1993, Professor—Judaic religion, 423-974-6985, Fax: 423-974-0965, E-mail: gschmidt@utk.edu

Tober, Linda M., PhD, Vanderbilt (1982), 1979, Adjunct Assistant Professor—problems of theodicy, phenomenology of the history of religions, myth, symbol and ritual, 423-974-6768, Fax: 423-974-8542, E-mail: ltober@utk.edu

---

Tennessee Bible College

PO Box 865
Cookeville TN 38503

Phone: 931-526-2616
Fax: 931-372-7258

TYPE OF INSTITUTION: Private
EXECUTIVE OFFICER: Malcolm L. Hill, President

Tennessee Temple University

1815 Union Ave, Chattanooga TN 37404

Tennessee Wesleyan College

PO Box 40
Athens TN 37303

Phone: 423-745-7504
Fax: 423-744-9968

TYPE OF INSTITUTION: Private, United Methodist

EXECUTIVE OFFICER: B. James Dawson, President
CHAIRPERSON: Sam Roberts
UNDERGRADUATE ENROLLMENT: 630

Texas College

2404 N Grand Ave, Tyler TX 75712-4500

University of Texas at Austin

Religious Studies Program
Waggener Hall, Room 212
Austin TX 78712-1181

Phone: 512-232-1438
Fax: 512-232-1439
E-mail: johannaj@mail.utexas.edu

TYPE OF INSTITUTION: Public
EXECUTIVE OFFICER: Sheldon Eckland-Olson, Dean of Liberal Arts
COORDINATOR: L. Michael White

University of Texas at El Paso

El Paso TX 79902

Texas Baptist Institute and Seminary

PO Box 570, Henderson TX 75652

Texas Christian University

Dept of Religion
TCU Box 298100
Fort Worth TX 76129

Phone: 817-257-7440
Fax: 817-257-7495
E-mail: d.schmidt@tcu.edu

TYPE OF INSTITUTION: Denominational: Christian Church (Disciples of Christ)
EXECUTIVE OFFICER: Michael R. Ferrari, Chancellor
CHAIRPERSON: Daryl D. Schmidt
UNDERGRADUATE ENROLLMENT: 6,254
GRADUATE ENROLLMENT: 1,141
DEGREES OFFERED: BA
UNDERGRADUATE MAJORS: 52
DEGREES CONFERRED: 9
DESCRIPTION OF UNDERGRADUATE PROGRAM: The academic study of religion is available
as a major on the BA degree and as a minor on the BA or BS degree. A major in Religion re-
quires 27 semester hours, with at least three in each of the areas of biblical studies, contem-
porary developments, history of Christianity, and history of religions; six hours in
methodological and constructive studies; and six hours in issues, topics, and interdisciplinary studies. An interdisciplinary program with a double major in Religion and other fields is
possible even in cases where different degrees are involved (e.g., BA and BS).

FACULTY:

Atwood, D. James, PhD, Vanderbilt University (1978), 1983, Instructor and Assistant to the Dean of Admissions—church history, 817-257-6446, E-mail: j.atwood@tcu.edu

Camp, Claudia V., PhD, Duke University (1982), 1980, Professor—Old Testament, hermeneutics, 817-257-6449, E-mail: c.camp@tcu.edu

Flowers, Ronald B., PhD, University of Iowa (1967), 1966, John F. Weatherly Professor—American religion, sects and cults, church and state, 817-257-7440, E-mail: r.flowers@tcu.edu

Fort, Andrew O., PhD, University of Pennsylvania (1982), 1982, Professor—Asian religions, 817-257-6448, E-mail: a.fort@tcu.edu

Grant, C. David, PhD, Harvard University (1981), 1981, Associate Professor—modern religious thought, Christian theology, 817-257-6447, E-mail: d.grant@tcu.edu

Gunn, David M., PhD, University of Newcastle upon Tyne, England (1975), 1993, A. A. Bradford Professor—Old Testament, 817-257-7441, E-mail: d.gunn@tcu.edu

Havea, Jione, PhD (cand.), Southern Methodist University, 1999, Lecturer—biblical studies, 817-257-6453, E-mail: j.havea@tcu.edu

Jaynes, Jan, PhD, Baylor University (1996), 1999, Lecturer—biblical studies, 817-257-6443, E-mail: j.jaynes@tcu.edu

Lahutsky, Nadia M., PhD, Vanderbilt University (1984), 1981, Associate Professor— history of the Christian tradition, women in religion, 817-257-6451, E-mail: n.lahutsky@tcu.edu

Lawrence, Kenneth T., PhD, Boston University (1971), 1972, Associate Professor— religion and arts, religion and learning process, 817-257-6444, E-mail: k.lawrence@tcu.edu

Middleton, Darren J. N., PhD, University of Glasgow (1996), 1998, Assistant Professor—Christianity and literature, 817-257-6445, E-mail: d.middleton2@tcu.edu

Schmidt, Daryl D., PhD, Graduate Theological Union (1979), 1979, Professor—Greek, New Testament, 817-257-6453, E-mail: d.schmidt@tcu.edu

Sodiq, Yushau, PhD, Temple University (1991), 1992, Associate Professor—Islam, African religions, 817-257-6439, E-mail: y.sodiq@tcu.edu

---

Texas Lutheran University

1000 W Court Street
Seguin TX 78155

Phone: 830-372-8000
Fax: 830-372-8096
E-mail: nbeck@txlutheran.edu

TYPE OF INSTITUTION: Denominational: ELCA

EXECUTIVE OFFICER: John Mastersen, Provost

CHAIRPERSON: Norman A. Beck

UNDERGRADUATE ENROLLMENT: 1,500

DEGREES OFFERED: BA with a major in Theology (preprofessional concentration) and with a major in Theology (youth ministry concentrtion)

UNDERGRADUATE MAJORS: 30

DEGREES CONFERRED: 9

DESCRIPTION OF UNDERGRADUATE PROGRAM: In support of the general education goals of Texas Lutheran University, the theological faculty works with other disciplines and with the Campus Ministry Program to assist students in developing and enhancing their understanding in the following areas: a) the nature of faith, religious language, and theology as an academic discipline, b) biblical literature, its developmental processes and literary genres, and the critical approach to its interpretation, c) other religions and one's own religion in other cultures.

FACULTY:

Beck, Norman A., PhD, Princeton Theological Seminary (1967), 1975, Professor—theology and classical languages, 830-372-6066, Fax: 830-372-8096, E-mail: nbeck@txlutheran.edu

Dryer, Richard, MAHL, Hebrew Union College-Jewish Institute of Religion (1970), 1993, Instructor—theology, Judaism, part-time, 830-372-8000, Fax: 830-372-8096

Gilbertson, Mark O., PhD, University of Southern California (1973), 1973, Professor—philosophy, 830-372-6068, Fax: 830-372-8096, E-mail: mgilbertson@txlutheran.edu

Koenig, Darryl, MDiv, Luther Theological Seminary (1975), 1995, Instructor—youth ministry (part-time), 830-372-6566, Fax: 830-372-8096

Ruge-Jones, Philip, PhD, Lutheran School of Theology at Chicago (1999), 1999, Assistant Professor—systematic theology, 830-372-6067, Fax: 830-373-8096, E-mail: pruge-jones@txlutheran.edu

Schneider, Carolyn, PhD, Princeton Theological Seminary (1999), 1999, Assistant Professor—historical theology, 830-372-8080, Fax: 830-372-8096, E-mail: cschneider@txlutheran.edu

Tallier, Lee, MA, Pacific Lutheran Theological Seminary (1999), 1999, Instructor (part-time)—theology, 830-372-8000, Fax: 830-372-8096

Texas Wesleyan University

Dept of Religion and Philosophy, Fort Worth TX 76105

Theological School of the Protestant Reformed Churches

4949 Ivanrest Ave SW
Grandville MI 49418

Phone: 616-531-1490
Fax: 616-531-3033
E-mail: decker@prca.org

TYPE OF INSTITUTION: Private, Protestant Reformed
EXECUTIVE OFFICER: Robert Decker, Rector
GRADUATE ENROLLMENT: 7

College of Theology and Urban Studies

200 Plymouth St, San Francisco CA 94112

Thiel College

75 College Avenue
Greenville PA 16125

Phone: 724-589-2106
Fax: 724-589-2021
E-mail: cthompso@thiel.edu

TYPE OF INSTITUTION: Private, Evangelical Lutheran Church in America
EXECUTIVE OFFICER: Robert Olson, Vice President for Academic Affairs
CHAIRPERSON: Curtis L. Thompson
UNDERGRADUATE ENROLLMENT: 1,030

Thomas Aquinas College

10000 N Ojai Rd
Santa Paula CA 93060

Phone: 805-525-4417
Fax: 805-525-9342
E-mail: admissions@thomasaquinas.edu
URL: thomasaquinas.edu

TYPE OF INSTITUTION: Private, Roman Catholic
EXECUTIVE OFFICER: Thomas E. Dillon, President
UNDERGRADUATE ENROLLMENT: 268

Thomas More College

Crestview Hills KY 41017

Toccoa Falls College

Toccoa Falls GA 30598

University of Toledo

Toledo OH 43606

Torah Remimah Talmudical Seminary

555 Ocean Pkwy, Brooklyn NY 11218

University of Toronto

Dept and Centre for the
Study of Religion
123 St George St
Toronto, Ontario M5S 2E8 Canada

Phone: 416-978-2395
Fax: 416-978-1610
E-mail: religion.undergrad@utoronto.ca
religion.grad@utoronto.ca

TYPE OF INSTITUTION: Public
CHAIRPERSON: Joseph Goering
COORDINATOR: James DiCenso
UNDERGRADUATE ENROLLMENT: 1,250
GRADUATE ENROLLMENT: 88

Toronto School of Theology

47 Queen's Park Cresent E
Toronto, Ontario M5S 2C3
Canada

Phone: 416-978-4039
Fax: 416-978-7821
E-mail: registrar.tst@utoronto.ca

TYPE OF INSTITUTION: Multi-Denominational: Ecumenical Cluster of 7 Schools
EXECUTIVE OFFICER: David Neelands, Director

GRADUATE ENROLLMENT: 1,015

Tougaloo College
Tougaloo MS 39174

Towson State College
Towson MD 21204

Transylvania University

300 N Broadway
Lexington KY 40508

Phone: 606-233-8300
Fax: 606-233-8797
E-mail: pjones@transy.edu
URL: www.transy.edu

TYPE OF INSTITUTION: Private, Disciples of Christ
EXECUTIVE OFFICER: Charles L. Shearer, President
COORDINATOR: Paul H. Jones
UNDERGRADUATE ENROLLMENT: 1,075
DEGREES OFFERED: BA
UNDERGRADUATE MAJORS: 5
DEGREES CONFERRED: 6
DESCRIPTION OF UNDERGRADUATE PROGRAM: The religion program offers one of the twenty-five majors in the liberal arts curriculum at Transylvania. In addition to a major or a minor in religious studies, students may choose religion courses to meet distribution requirements in the Humanities and in the Non-Western areas. Understanding the role of religion in structuring societies and in defining human values is a main concern in the religion program at Transylvania.
FACULTY:

Jones, Paul Henry, PhD, Vanderbilt University (1988), 1985, Professor—Bible, theology, church history, liturgics, 606-233-8113, Fax: 606-233-8797, E-mail: pjones@transy.edu

Points, G. Phillip, PhD, University of Chicago (1974), 1964, Professor—religion and culture, world religions, ethics, philosophy of religion, 606-233-8235, Fax: 606-233-8797, E-mail: gpoints@transy.edu

Transylvania Bible School

927 Freeport Rd
Freeport PA 16229

Phone: 724-295-2464
Fax: 724-295-2464

TYPE OF INSTITUTION: Private, Independent
EXECUTIVE OFFICER: Henry Clay Shilling, President

Trenton State College
Trenton NJ 08650

Trevecca Nazarene College

333 Murfreesboro Road, Nashville TN 37203

Trinity College

300 Summit St
Hartford CT 06106

Phone: 860-297-2472
Fax: 860-297-5358
E-mail: ronald.kiener@trincoll.edu
URL: www.trincoll.edu/academics/depart-
ments/relg

TYPE OF INSTITUTION: Private, Non-Denominational
EXECUTIVE OFFICER: Raymond Baker, Dean of the Faculty
CHAIRPERSON: Ronald C. Kiener
UNDERGRADUATE ENROLLMENT: 1,800

Trinity College

Washington DC 20017

Trinity College

2065 Half Day Road, Deerfield IL 60015

Trinity College

Colchester Ave, Burlington VT 05401

Trinity College

Faculty of Divinity
6 Hoskin Ave
Toronto, Ontario M5S 1H8 Canada

Phone: 416-978-2164
Fax: 416-978-4949
E-mail: divinity@trinity.utoronto.ca
URL: www.trinity.utoronto.ca

TYPE OF INSTITUTION: Denominational: Anglican
EXECUTIVE OFFICER: Donald Wiebe, Dean of Divinity
CHAIRPERSONS: Brian Ruttan (Basic Degree); Marsha Hewitt (Advanced Degree)
UNDERGRADUATE ENROLLMENT: 60
GRADUATE ENROLLMENT: 20

Trinity School of Biblical Studies

7255 S Trl Military, Lake Worth FL 33463

Trinity University

Department of Religion
715 Stadium Drive, TU#95
San Antonio TX 78212-7200

Phone: 210-999-8426
Fax: 210-999-7305
**URL: www.trinity.edu/departments/public_re-
lations/Academic/religion.htm**

TYPE OF INSTITUTION: Private

EXECUTIVE OFFICER: Gary Kates, Dean of Humanities and Arts

CHAIRPERSON: C. Mackenzie Brown

UNDERGRADUATE ENROLLMENT: 2,247

GRADUATE ENROLLMENT: 220

DEGREES OFFERED: BA

UNDERGRADUATE MAJORS: 22

DEGREES CONFERRED: 13

DESCRIPTION OF UNDERGRADUATE PROGRAM: The Religion Department at Trinity offers a major and a minor, as well as courses for the Common Curriculum and electives. The major in religion requires 30 hours, and includes a distributional requirement with at least one course in each of three areas: religious traditions of Asia; Jewish and Christian traditions; and contemporary developments and ethical issues. The Religion program at Trinity aims to develop, through consideration of diverse religious traditions, intellectual insight into and awareness of different ways of thinking critically about religion. Through the study of religion the Department strives to assist students in developing informed and creative ways of enriching their own understanding of the world and of fulfilling their responsibilities as educated persons to the larger society in which they live.

FACULTY:

Brackenridge, R. Douglas, PhD, University of Glasgow (1962), 1962, Professor—history of Christianity, religion in America, biblical studies, 210-999-8460, E-mail: dbracken@trinity.edu

Brown, C. Mackenzie, PhD, Harvard University (1973), 1973, Professor—Asian religions (India), religion and science, 210-999-8429, E-mail: mbrown@trinity.edu

Garcia, Francisco O., PhD, Princeton University (1967), 1966, Professor—Old Testament literature, history and religion, Judaism, Islam, 210-999-8427, E-mail: fgarcia@trinity.edu

Nadeau, Randall L., PhD, University of British Columbia (1990), 1990, Associate Professor—Asian religions (China, Japan), 210-999-8433, E-mail: rnadeau@trinity.edu

Ross, Mary Ellen, PhD, University of Chicago (1983), 1982, Associate Professor—religious ethics, religion and the social sciences, 210-999-8461, E-mail: mross@trinity.edu

Starkey, Peggy, PhD, Union Theological Seminary (1978), 1999, Instructor, Term Appointment (1999-00)—world religions, 210-999-8428, E-mail: mstarkey@trinity.edu

Walker, William O., Jr., PhD, Duke University (1962), 1962, Professor—New Testament literature, history, and religion, early Christianity, 210-999-8105, E-mail: wwalker@trinity.edu

Trinity Baptist College

800 Hammond Blvd
Jacksonville FL 32221

Phone: 904-596-2400
Fax: 904-695-9357
E-mail: trinity@tbc.edu
URL: www.tbc.edu

TYPE OF INSTITUTION: Private, Independent Baptist
EXECUTIVE OFFICER: Charles T. Schoemaker, Executive Vice-President
UNDERGRADUATE ENROLLMENT: 327

Trinity Bible College

50 6th Ave S
Ellendale ND 58436

Phone: 701-349-5770
Fax: 701-349-5443

TYPE OF INSTITUTION: Private, Assembly of God
EXECUTIVE OFFICER: Howard Young, President
CHAIRPERSON: John Katter
UNDERGRADUATE ENROLLMENT: 351

Trinity Christian College

Theology Dept, 6601 W College Dr, Palos Heights IL 60463

Trinity Episcopal School for Ministry

311 11th St
Ambridge PA 15003

Phone: 724-266-3838
Fax: 724-266-4617
E-mail: tesm@tesm.edu
URL: www.episopalian.org

TYPE OF INSTITUTION: Private, Episcopal
EXECUTIVE OFFICER: Peter C. Moore, Dean and President
CHAIRPERSON: Stephen F. Noll
COORDINATOR: Barbara Hopkins
GRADUATE ENROLLMENT: 125

Trinity Graduate School

Trinity International University
3855 E Lapalma Ave
Anaheim CA 92807

Phone: 714-632-3434
Fax: 714-630-6109
E-mail: beckwith@tiu.edu
URL: www.tiu.edu

TYPE OF INSTITUTION: Private, Evangelical Free Church of America
EXECUTIVE OFFICER: Shannon Verleur, CEO
CHAIRPERSON: Francis J. Beckwith
GRADUATE ENROLLMENT: 50

Trinity International University

2065 Half Day Rd
Deerfield IL 60015

Phone: 847-945-8800
Fax: 847-317-8090
E-mail: tedsadm@trin.edu (Graduate)
URL: www.tiu.edu

TYPE OF INSTITUTION: Denominational: Evangelical Free Church of America
EXECUTIVE OFFICERS: Gregory L. Waybright, President; Barry Beitzel, Provost; Jeanette
    Hsieh, Dean, College of Arts and Sciences; W. Bingham Hunter, Dean, Divinity School
UNDERGRADUATE ENROLLMENT: 945
GRADUATE ENROLLMENT: 1,534

Trinity Life Bible College

5225 Hillsdale At Madison
Sacramento CA 95842

Phone: 916-348-4689
Fax: 916-334-2315
E-mail: trinitylifebiblecollege@trinitylife.org
URL: www.tlbc.edu

TYPE OF INSTITUTION: Private, Assembly of God
EXECUTIVE OFFICER: Ronald W. Harden, President
UNDERGRADUATE ENROLLMENT: 170

Trinity Lutheran Seminary

2199 East Main Street
Columbus OH 43209-2334

Phone: 614-235-4136
Fax: 614-238-0263

TYPE OF INSTITUTION: Denominational: Evangelical Lutheran
EXECUTIVE OFFICER: Dennis A. Anderson, President
GRADUATE ENROLLMENT: 256

Trinity Western University

7600 Glover Rd
Langley, British Columbia V2Y 1Y1 Canada

Phone: 604-888-7511
Fax: 604-888-5336

TYPE OF INSTITUTION: Private, Evangelical Free, Mennonite, Baptist
EXECUTIVE OFFICER: R. Neil Snider, President
CHAIRPERSON: Craig C. Broyles; Craig A. Evans, Director Graduate Program
UNDERGRADUATE ENROLLMENT: 1,800
GRADUATE ENROLLMENT: 250

Tri-State Baptist College

6001 Goodman Rd, Walls MS 38680

Troy State University
Troy AL 36081

Truman State University

Division of Social Science
100 E Normal
Kirksville MO 63501

Phone: 660-785-4636
Fax: 660-785-4181
E-mail: socsci@truman.edu
URL: www.truman.edu

TYPE OF INSTITUTION: Public

EXECUTIVE OFFICER: James J. Lyons, Head, Division of Social Science

CHAIRPERSON: James J. Lyons

COORDINATOR: David Murphy

UNDERGRADUATE ENROLLMENT: 5,800

GRADUATE ENROLLMENT: 250

DEGREES OFFERED: BA

UNDERGRADUATE MAJORS: 48

DEGREES CONFERRED: 13

DESCRIPTION OF UNDERGRADUATE PROGRAM: The Department offers a combination of Philosophy and Religion courses with some history included.

FACULTY:

Alexander, Natalie, PhD, Northwestern University (1989), Associate Professor—20th century continental, feminism, history of philosophy

Appold, Mark, ThD, Tübingen University (1975), Adjunct Associate Professor—Old and New Testaments, Christian thought

Ashcraft, William, PhD, University of Virginia (1995), Assistant Professor—American religious history

Blair, Kathryn, PhD, University of Missouri, Columbia (1971), Professor—ethics, feminism

Burton, Patricia, PhD, University of Texas, Austin (1988), Associate Professor—ancient and medieval philosophy, logic

Gruber, David, PhD, Vanderbilt University (1987), Associate Professor—social and political philosophy, contemporary and continental philosophy

Hsieh, Ding-hwa, PhD, University of California, Los Angeles (1993), Assistant Professor—Buddhism, Chinese religions and culture

Mohler, Chad, PhD, Princeton (1999), Assistant Professor—epistemology, logic

Murphy, David, PhD, University of Chicago (1988), Associate Professor—contemporary theology, religious ethics

Pflueger, Lloyd, PhD, University of California, Santa Barbara (1990), Associate Professor—Asian religion, Indian philosophy, classical Sanskrit

Pollard, Stephen, PhD, University of Texas, Austin (1983), Associate Professor—logic, philosophy of mathematics

Tufts University
Medford MA 02155

Tulane University

University Chapel
1229 Broadway
New Orleans LA 70118

Phone: 504-866-8793
Fax: 504-866-8793

TYPE OF INSTITUTION: Private, Non-Denominational
EXECUTIVE OFFICER: Val Ambrose McInnes, OP
CHAIRPERSON: Frank T. Birtel

The University of Tulsa

Dept of Philosophy and Religion
600 S College Ave
Tulsa OK 74104-3189

Phone: 918-631-2279
Fax: 918-631-2057
E-mail: sharon-haltom@utulsa.edu
URL: www.utulsa.edu

TYPE OF INSTITUTION: Private, historical affiliation with the Presbyterian Church

EXECUTIVE OFFICER: Robert Lawless, President

CHAIRPERSON: Jane Ackerman

UNDERGRADUATE ENROLLMENT: 2,550

DEGREES OFFERED: BA

UNDERGRADUATE MAJORS: 6

DESCRIPTION OF UNDERGRADUATE PROGRAM: The Department of Philosophy and Religion offers students programs in two separate disciplines, philosophy and religious studies. The study of philosophy develops critical thinking, the ability to see implications and alternatives, and the human imagination. In addition, our courses introduce a person to those great thinkers and ideas that have influenced our past and present culture. A BA degree is offered for students completing a major in philosophy. Religion courses permit students to deepen their understanding of humanity's personal and cultural experience of religion. Our offerings include introductory courses of interest to the general student and courses in the following curriculum areas: the Bible and literature; ethics and society; and philosophy and religion. The BA degree is offered for students completing a self-designed major in religion.

FACULTY:

Ackerman, Jane E., PhD, University of Kentucky (1982), 1990, Associate Professor—religious studies, 918-631-2290, Fax: 918-631-2057, E-mail: jane-ackerman@utulsa.edu

Bowlin, John R., PhD, Princeton University (1993), 1990, Associate Professor—religion, 918-631-2410, Fax: 918-631-2057, E-mail: john-bowlin@utulsa.edu

Capaldi, Nicholas, PhD, Columbia University (1965), 1991, McFarlin Professor—philosophy, 918-631-2962, Fax: 918-631-2057, E-mail: nicholas-capaldi@utulsa.edu

Hittinger, Russell, PhD, St Louis University (1986), 1996, Warren Professor—Catholic studies, 918-631-3081, Fax: 918-631-2057, E-mail: russell-hittinger@utulsa.edu

Howland, Jacob A., PhD, Pennsylvania State University (1987), 1988, Associate Professor—philosophy, 918-631-2799, Fax: 918-631-2057, E-mail: jacob-howland@utulsa.edu

Knight, Henry, DMin, Emory University (1975), 1991, University Chaplain and Associate Professor—religion, 918-631-2546, Fax: 918-631-2066, E-mail: henry-knight@utulsa.edu

Lind, Richard W., PhD, University of Southern California (1971), 1971, Associate Professor—philosophy, 918-631-2963, Fax: 918-631-2057, E-mail: richard-lind@utulsa.edu

Tusculum College

Greenville TN 37743

Tyndale Seminary

25 Ballyconnor Court
North York ON M2M 4B3
Canada

Phone: 416-226-6380
Fax: 416-226-9464
E-mail: seminary@tyndale-canada.edu
URL: www.tyndale-canada.edu

TYPE OF INSTITUTION: Private, Inter/Multi-Denominational
EXECUTIVE OFFICERS: Brian C. Stiller, President; Jeffrey P. Greenman, Academic Dean
GRADUATE ENROLLMENT: TBC

Unification Theological Seminary

10 Dock Road
Barrytown NY 12507

Phone: 914-752-3100
Fax: 914-758-2156
E-mail: utspres@epix.net
URL: www.uts.edu

TYPE OF INSTITUTION: Private, Unification
EXECUTIVE OFFICER: Theodore T. Shimmyo, President
GRADUATE ENROLLMENT: 175

Union College

310 College St
Barbourville KY 40906-1499

Phone: 606-546-4151
E-mail: unionky.edu

TYPE OF INSTITUTION: Denominational: United Methodist
EXECUTIVE OFFICER: Vernon G. Miles, Vice President for Academic Affairs
CHAIRPERSON: Russell Sisson
UNDERGRADUATE ENROLLMENT: 600
GRADUATE ENROLLMENT: 400

Union College

Lincoln NE 68506

Union College

Schenectady NY 12308

Union University

Jackson TN 38305

Union Baptist Theological Seminary

1300 Milton St, New Orleans LA 70122

The Union Institute

440 E McMillan St
Cincinnati OH 45206-1947

Phone: 800-486-3116
Fax: 513-861-0779
E-mail: tui.edu
URL: tui.edu

TYPE OF INSTITUTION: Private
EXECUTIVE OFFICER: Mervyn Cadwallader, President
COORDINATOR: Alvin Hall, Dean, Graduate School of Interdisciplinary Arts and Sciences

UNDERGRADUATE ENROLLMENT: 782
GRADUATE ENROLLMENT: 1,237

Union Theological Seminary in New York City

3041 Broadway
New York NY 10027

Phone: 212-662-7100
Fax: 212-280-1416
URL: www.uts.columbia.edu

TYPE OF INSTITUTION: Non-Denominational
EXECUTIVE OFFICER: Joseph C. Hough, Jr., President
CHAIRPERSON: Rosemary S. Keller, Academic Dean
GRADUATE ENROLLMENT: 299 (MDiv, MA, STM, PhD); 131 (MA, STM, PhD)
GRADUATE PROGRAM
Member of the Council on Graduate Studies in Religion
Graduate Advisor: Rosemary S. Keller, Academic Dean
Graduate Degrees Offered: MA; PhD; STM
Degrees Conferred: 18 MA; 8 PhD; 6 STM
Graduate Students in Residence: 28 MA; 21 PhD; 10 STM
Not in Residence: 0 MA; 72 PhD; 0 STM
Average No. of New Students Enrolled: 14 MA; 10 PhD; 7 STM
Women Students: 11 MA; 52 PhD; 5 STM
Minority Students: 2 MA; 27 PhD; 4 STM
Foreign Students: 0 MA; 12 PhD; 6 STM
Minimum GRE Score Requisite to Admission: No
Minimum GPA Score Requisite to Admission: No
Foreign Language Proficiency Evaluated: No
Financial Aid to First Year Students: 95% MA; 90% PhD; 95% STM
Financial Aid to Other Students: 95% MA; 90% PhD
Attrition Among Students: 14% MA; 3% PhD; 0% STM
Graduates Placed: 50%
DESCRIPTION OF GRADUATE PROGRAM AND RESEARCH FACILITIES: The PhD program
offered at Union Seminary is organized into two areas of concentration: *Studies in Forma-
tive Texts, Histories and Traditions* includes Old Testament, New Testament and Christian
Origins, Early, Reformation, and Modern Christianity; *Studies in Constructive Theologies,
Praxis and Ethics* includes Systematic Theology, Christian Ethics, Ecumenical Studies
Preaching and Worship Studies, Psychiatry & Religion, and Religion & Education. Union also
cooperates with the Graduate School of Arts & Sciences of Columbia University in jointly offering the degree of PhD in Religion. Applicants to Union's PhD program must have a thorough grounding in the major theological disciplines, usually acquired through an MDiv
program at Union or some other accredited institution. The STM program is for those who
have a post-baccalaureate theological degree and desire a year of further study in some particular area of Christian studies. The MA is a two-year program in graduate theological education for the student not seeking ordination. The Seminary also offers the degree of Master
of Divinity. The Seminary Library has more than a million items, including a number of special collections, and is part of computer-assisted networks which make available the major
collections in theology and religious studies in libraries across the nation. In the immediate
neighborhood of the Seminary, Morningside Heights, some ten million volumes are available

to students because of Union's proximity to Columbia University, Barnard College, Teachers College, the Manhattan School of Music, and The Jewish Theological Seminary.

ACADEMIC PLAN, ADMISSION REQUIREMENTS, FINANCIAL AID: The academic year is divided into two semesters. During the first two academic years of doctoral candidacy, or the equivalent if studies are pursued part-time, the candidate is considered to be in residence. While in residence the candidate must complete 40 points of academic work and in the following semester, complete four field examinations which are planned by the student in consultation with the faculty of the field of specialization. Proficiency in reading the languages needed for one's field of study (French, German, Spanish) must be demonstrated by examinations taken in the first semester of residency, and in any case no later than the end of the first year. Following the successful completion of the 40 points of course work and the language and field examinations, the MPhil degree is awarded to the candidate. The candidate then writes a dissertation on a subject approved by the faculty and defends it *viva voce* before a committee of the faculty. The STM degree requires 24 points of course work and an extended paper written for a seminar; the program is normally complete in one academic year. Applications for admission to the STM or PhD programs must be submitted by January 6. Applications for the PhD program must be accompanied by complete transcripts of the applicants academic studies to date, including college, GRE scores (aptitude only), letters of recommendation, a 20-page academic essay that is a sample of the applicant's work, and a 500-word statement on the applicant's reasons for undertaking doctoral studies. Candidates for the PhD may apply for financial aid; some scholarships and some tutorships are available, but it is not possible to finance one's studies entirely through the Seminary's aid program. Financial aid is normally not available to STM students except for a few fellowships for foreign students.

FACULTY:

Boys, Mary C., EdD, Columbia University (1978), 1994, Skinner & McAlpin Professor—practical theology, 212-280-1367, Fax: 212-280-1539; E-mail: mboys@uts.columbia.edu

Carr, David, PhD, Claremont Graduate School (1988), 1999, Professor—Old Testament, 212-280-1382, Fax: 212-280-1539

Chung, Hyun Kyun, PhD, Union Theological Seminary (1989), 1996, Associate Professor—ecumenical studies, 212-280-1365, Fax: 212-280-1539

Cone, James Hal, PhD, Northwestern University (1965), 1969, Charles A. Briggs Distinguished Professor—systematic theology, 212-280-1369, Fax: 212-280-1539, E-mail: jcone@uts.columbia.edu

Cooper, Alan Mitchell, PhD, Yale University (1976), 1998, Professor—Bible, 212-280-1565, Fax: 212-280-1539, E-mail: amcooper@ix.netcom.com

Díaz-Stevens, Ana María, PhD, Fordham University (1983), 1993, Professor—church and society, 212-280-1362; Fax: 212-280-1539, E-mail: dstevens@uts.columbia.edu

Harris, Michael Wesley, PhD, Harvard University (1982), 1998, Professor—church history, 212-280-1394, Fax: 212-280-1539, E-mail: mwharris@uts.columbia.edu

Hough, Joseph C., Jr., PhD, Yale University (1965), 1999, President of the Faculty and William E. Dodge Professor—social ethics, 212-280-1401, Fax: 212-280-1440, E-mail: jhough@uts.columbia.edu

Kahl, Brigitte, ThD, Humboldt-University of Berlin (1983), 1997, Professor—New Testament, 212-280-1388, Fax: 212-280-1539, E-mail: brigitte@uts.columbia.edu

Keller, Rosemary Skinner, PhD, University of Illinois (1977), 1996, Academic Dean and Professor—church history, 212-280-1550, Fax: 212-280-1539, E-mail: rkeller@uts.columbia.edu

Lotz, David Walter, ThD, Union Theological Seminary (1971), 1968, Washburn Professor—church history, 212-280-1377, Fax: 212-280-1539

Lundblad, Barbara, MDiv, Yale Divinity School (1979), 1997, Associate Professor—preaching, 212-280-1549, Fax: 212-289-1539, E-mail: lundblad@uts.columbia.edu

McGuckin, John Anthony, PhD, Durham University (1980), 1997, Professor—early church history, 212-280-1391, Fax: 212-280-1539, E-mail: jmcguckn@uts.columbia.edu

Morse, Christopher L., PhD, Union Theological Seminary (1976), 1974, Dietrich Bonhoeffer Professor—theology, ethics, 212-280-1368, Fax: 212-280-1539, E-mail: cmorse@uts.columbia.edu

Rasmussen, Larry L., PhD, Union Theological Seminary (1970), 1986, Reinhold Niebuhr Professor—social ethics, 212-280-1364, Fax: 212-280-1539, E-mail: lrasmusn@uts.columbia.edu

Styers, Randall G., PhD, Duke University (1997), 1997, Assistant Professor—philosophy of religion, 212-280-1397, Fax: 212-280-1539, E-mail: rstyers@uts.columbia.edu

Talvacchia, Kathleen, EdD, Columbia University (1992), 1994, Assistant Professor—ministry and theology, 212-280-1392, Fax: 212-280-1539, E-mail: ktalv@uts.columbia.edu

Townes, Emilie M., PhD, Garret-Evangelical Theological Seminary/Northwestern University (1989), 1999, Professor—Christian ethics, 212-280-1378, Fax: 212-280-1539, E-mail: emtownes@uts.columbia.edu

Ulanov, Ann Belford, PhD, Union Theological Seminary (1967), 1966, Christiane Brooks Johnson Memorial Professor—psychiatry and religion, 212-280-1380, Fax: 212-280-1539

Walton, Janet Roland, EdD, Columbia Universty (1979), 1980, Professor—worship, 212-280-1381, Fax: 212-280-1539, E-mail: jwalton@uts.columbia.edu

Weidmann, Frederick W., PhD, Yale University (1993), 1995, Assistant Professor—New Testament, 212-280-1310, Fax: 212-280-1539, E-mail: fweidman@uts.columbia.edu

Williams, Delores S., PhD, Union Theological Seminary (1991), 1991, Paul Tillich Professor—theology and culture, 212-280-1363, Fax: 212-280-1539, E-mail: dwillms@uts.columbia.edu

Wimbush, Vincent L., PhD, Harvard University (1983), 1990, Professor—New Testament and Christian origins, 212-280-1390, Fax: 212-280-1539, E-mail: vwimbush@uts.columbia.edu

Wright, Edwina Maria, MDiv, McCormick Theological Seminary (1985), 1998, Assistant Professor—Old Testament, 212-280-1370, Fax: 212-280-1539, E-mail: ew165@columbia.edu

---

Union Theological Seminary and Presbyterian School of Christian Education

3401 Brook Rd
Richmond VA 23227

Phone: 804-355-0671
Fax: 804-355-3919
E-mail: jcarroll@utsva.edu
URL: www.utsva.edu

TYPE OF INSTITUTION: Private, Presbyterian Church (USA)

EXECUTIVE OFFICER: Louis B. Weeks, President

CHAIRPERSONS: John T. Carroll (Theology); James A. Brashler (Education)

COORDINATORS: Dawn DeVries (Graduate Studies)

GRADUATE ENROLLMENT: 80

DEGREES CONFERRED: 16

DESCRIPTION OF PROFESSIONAL DEGREE PROGRAM: Union-PSCE is related to the Presbyterian Church (USA) and the Reformed tradition; it has an ecumenical student body and ethos; its focus is the MDiv and the MA, and prepares men and women for teaching and preaching vocations in the church.

GRADUATE PROGRAM

Member of the Council on Graduate Studies in Religion

Graduate Advisors: Dawn DeVries

Graduate Degrees Offered: PhD; ThM, EdD

Degrees Conferred: 8 PhD; 7 ThM; 1 EdD

Graduate Students in Residence: 20 PhD/EdD; 6 ThM

Not in Residence: 53 PhD/EdD; 1 ThM

Average No. of New Students Enrolled: 9 PhD/EdD; 5 ThM

Women Students: 30 PhD/EdD; 1 ThM

Minority Students: 8 PhD/EdD; 0 ThM

Foreign Students: 16 PhD/EdD; 3 ThM

Minimum GRE Score Requisite to Admission: No

Minimum GPA Score Requisite to Admission: No

Foreign Language Proficiency Evaluated: Yes

Financial Aid to First Year Students: 100% PhD; 100% EdD

Financial Aid to Other Students: 78% PhD; 73% EdD

Attrition Among Students: 2.7% PhD/EdD

Graduates Placed: 75% PhD; 100% EdD

DESCRIPTION OF GRADUATE PROGRAM AND RESEARCH FACILITIES: The ThM program is designed to be an additional year of academic preparation for Christian leadership in pastoral and educational ministries. The EdD program prepares persons for teaching and administrative positions in universities and seminaries in the field of Christian education. The basic requisite for admission to the program is a master's degree in Christian education or a related field and two years' professional experience following the master's degree. The PhD program develops scholarly leadership for the church, for the communities to which it ministers, and for teaching in colleges and seminaries. Programs are offered in biblical studies, history, theology, ethics, and practical theology. Two years of full-time residence are required, leading to doctoral exams. Languages: a basic competence in two languages of scholarship is required before a dissertation proposal can be approved. All PhD requirements must ordinarily be completed within five years of beginning the program. The new Morton library has substantial holdings and the latest facilities available for researchers.

ACADEMIC PLAN, ADMISSION REQUIREMENTS, FINANCIAL AID: The academic calendar: Fall term (12 weeks), January term (3 weeks), Spring term (12 weeks), and May term (3 weeks). Admission: MDiv or its equivalent required for ThM and PhD. For the EdD, the basic requisite for admission to the program is an MA in Christian education or a related field and two years' professional experience following the master's degree. GRE General Test required for EdD and PhD; TOEFL for foreign students; other requirements are listed in catalog. Financial aid and fellowships available for ThM, PhD and EdD.

FACULTY:

Arnold, William V., PhD, Southern Baptist Theological Seminary (1970), 1976, Professor—pastoral counseling, 804-278-4286, Fax: 804-355-3919

Benedetto, Robert, MLS, University of Hawaii (1982), 1994, Associate Professor—associate librarian, 804-278-4313, Fax: 804-278-4375

Brashler, James A., PhD, Claremont Graduate School (1977), 1995, Professor—biblical studies, 804-254-8047, Fax: 804-254-8047

Brisson, E. Carson, PhD, Southern Baptist Theological Seminary (1987), 1991, Associate Professor—biblical languages, 804-278-4340, Fax: 804-355-3919

Brown, Charles E., PhD, Princeton Theological Seminary (1982), 1987, Professor—pastoral counseling, 804-278-4288, Fax: 804-355-3919

Brown, William P., PhD, Emory University (1991), 1991, Professor—Old Testament, 804-278-4263, Fax: 804-355-3919

Byars, Ronald P., PhD, Michigan State University (1979), 1999, Professor—preaching and worship, 804-278-4277, Fax: 804-355-3919

Carroll, John T., PhD, Princeton Theological Seminary (1986), 1992, Professor—New Testament, 804-278-4242, Fax: 804-355-3919

Cascante, Fernando A., EdD, Presbyterian School of Christian Education (1992), 1999, Assistant Professor—Christian education, 804-355-0671, Fax: 804-254-8060

DeVries, Dawn, PhD, University of Chicago (1994), 1995, Professor—theology, 804-278-4283, Fax: 804-355-3919

Fowlkes, Mary Anne, PhD, Georgia State University (1979), 1987, Professor—early childhood education, 804-254-8026, Fax: 804-254-8060

Gench, Frances Taylor, PhD, Union Theological Seminary in Virginia (1988), 1999, Professor—New Testament, 804-278-4276, Fax: 804-355-3919

Gerrish, Brian A., PhD, Columbia University (1958), 1996, Distinguished Service Professor—theology, 804-278-4219, Fax: 804-355-3919

Hawley, Gwen A., PhD, University of North Carolina, Chapel Hill (1984), 1981, Professor—faith development/group processes, 804-254-8066, Fax: 804-254-8060

Hess, Kurtis C., DMin, McCormick Theological Seminary (1975), 1985, Professor—field education and placement, 804-278-4236, Fax: 804-355-3919

Kingsbury, Jack D., DrTheol, University of Basel (1967), 1977, Professor—New Testament, 804-278-4284, Fax: 804-355-3919

Legg, Pamela Mitchell, EdD, Presbyterian School of Christian Education (1986), 1994, Professor—educational theory/design, 804-254-8071, Fax: 804-254-8060

McBride, S. Dean, PhD, Harvard University (1969), 1984, Professor—Old Testament, 804-278-4282, Fax: 804-355-3919

Ottati, Douglas F., PhD, University of Chicago (1980), 1977, Professor—theology, 804-278-4290, Fax: 804-355-3919

Simmons, Henry C., PhD, University of Ottawa (1970), 1985, Professor—religion and aging 804-254-8045, Fax: 804-254-8060

Skreslet, Stanley H., PhD, Yale University (1987), 1997, Associate Professor—Christian missions, 804-278-4261, Fax: 804-355-3919

Stein, Craig C., PhD, Emory University (1995), 1995, Assistant Professor—theology, 804-278-4285, Fax: 804-355-3919

Swezey, Charles M., PhD, Vanderbilt University (1978), 1974, Professor—Christian ethics, 804-278-4287, Fax: 804-355-3919

Towner, W. Sibley, PhD, Yale University (1965), 1975, Professor—Old Testament, 804-278-4262, Fax: 804-355-3919

Trotti, John B., PhD, Yale University (1964), 1968, Professor—librarian, 804-278-4311, Fax: 804-278-4375

Valeri, Mark R., PhD, Princeton University (1985), 1996, Professor—church history, 804-278-4264, Fax: 804-355-3919

Vann, Jane R., PhD, Union Theological Seminary, New York City (1995), 1995, Associate Professor—Christian education, 804-278-4291, Fax: 804-355-3919

Walaskay, Paul W., PhD, Duke University (1973), 1983, Professor—biblical studies, 804-254-8068, Fax: 804-254-8060

Weaver, Rebecca H., PhD, Southern Methodist University (1984), 1983, Professor—church history, 804-278-4289, Fax: 804-355-3919

Weeks, Louis B., PhD, Duke University (1970), 1994, President and Professor—historical theology, 804-278-4200, Fax: 804-355-3919

Zink-Sawyer, Beverly Ann, PhD, Vanderbilt University (1997), 1995, Associate Professor—preaching and worship, 804-278-4307, Fax: 804-355-3919

United Bible College and Seminary
1231 Emeralda Dr, Box 15284, Orlando FL 32858

United Bible Institute of United Theological Seminary
4805 N Saginaw St, Flint MI 48505

United Talmudical Academy
82 Lee Ave, Brooklyn NY 11211

United Theological Seminary of the Twin Cities

3000 Fifth St NW
New Brighton MN 55112

Phone: 651-633-4311
Fax: 651-633-4315
E-mail: general@unitedseminary-mn.org
URL: www.unitedseminary-mn.org

TYPE OF INSTITUTION: Private, Multi-Denominational
EXECUTIVE OFFICER: H. Wilson Yates, President
COORDINATOR: Richard W. Weis
GRADUATE ENROLLMENT: 235

United Theological Seminary

1810 Harvard Blvd
Dayton OH 45406

Phone: 937-278-5817
Fax: 937-278-1218
E-mail: utscom@dnaco.net
URL: www.united.edu/

TYPE OF INSTITUTION: Denominational: United Methodist
EXECUTIVE OFFICER: TBA
GRADUATE ENROLLMENT: 498

DESCRIPTION OF GRADUATE PROGRAM AND RESEARCH FACILITIES: United Theological Seminary is a graduate professional school of the United Methodist Church. Its purpose is to educate persons for Christian ministry that is both local and global. The library's special strengths include biblical studies, theology, ecumenics, Christian education, pastoral care and counseling, denominational history (Evangelical United Brethren), missiology, and Judaic studies. The school is a member of the On-line Computer Library Center.

ACADEMIC PLAN, ADMISSION REQUIREMENTS, FINANCIAL AID: United Theological Seminary operates on a semester system with two fourteen-week semesters during the regular academic year, a January term, and a six-week summer school conducted in cooperation with the University of Dayton. Application for master's-level study must include a bachelor's degree with at least a 3.0 grade-point average and three letters of recommendation, and a statement of purpose. Financial aid is provided on a need basis and students applying for financial aid are expected to submit a form to the FAFSA. Deadline is March 15.

FACULTY:

Bohler, Carolyn J., PhD, School of Theology at Claremont (1982), 1982, Professor—pastoral theology and counseling

Boomershine, Thomas E., PhD, Union Theological Seminary, New York (1974), 1979, Professor—New Testament

Dalton, Russell G., EdD, Union Theological Seminary, Presbyterian School of Christian Education (1998), 1998, Assistant Professor—Christianity and communication

Dixon, Valerie Elverton, PhD, Temple University (1998), 1998, Assistant Professor—Christian ethics

Dozeman, Thomas, PhD, Columbia University (1985), 1988, Professor—Old Testament

Farmer, Kathleen A., PhD, Southern Methodist University (1978), 1978, Professor—Old Testament

Hertig, Paul, PhD, Fuller Theological Seminary School of World Mission (1995), 1998, Associate Professor—world Christianity

Hertig, Young Lee, PhD, Fuller Theological Seminary (1991), 1998, Associate Professor—world Christianity

Inbody, Tyron L., PhD, University of Chicago (1973), 1976, Professor—theology

Kim, Ai Ra, PhD, Drew University (1991), 1998, Associate Professor—church and society

McCabe, Kendall K., PhD, University of St Andrews, Scotland (1980), 1980, 1999 Academic Dean and Professor—homiletics, worship

Park, Andrew Sung, PhD, Graduate Theological Union (1986), 1992, Professor—theology

Roberson, J. T., PhD, Fordham University (1993), 1992, Dean and 1998, Associate Professor of Church Leadership—doctoral studies

Rogers, Donald B., PhD, Princeton Theological Seminary (1967), 1969, Professor—Christian education

Roslof, Edward E., PhD, University of North Carolina, Chapel Hill (1994), 1995, Associate Professor—church history

Thomas, Norman E., PhD, Boston University (1968), 1983, Professor—world Christianity

Welborn, Laurence L., PhD, Vanderbilt University (1993), 1991, Associate Professor—New Testament

Zaragoza, Edward C., PhD, The Graduate School, Drew University (1990), 1998, Assistant Professor and Dean of Masters Studies—church history

Upsala College

East Orange NJ 07019

Upsala College

Wirths Campus, Rd 3, Box 138-A, Sussex NJ 07461

Urbana College

Urbana OH 43078

Ursinus College

Collegeville PA 19426

Ursuline College

2550 Lander Rd
Pepper Pike OH 44124

Phone: 440-449-4200
Fax: 440-646-8318

TYPE OF INSTITUTION: Private, Roman Catholic
EXECUTIVE OFFICER: S. Diana Stano, OSU, President
CHAIRPERSON: Dolores L. Christie
UNDERGRADUATE ENROLLMENT: 970
GRADUATE ENROLLMENT: 180

University of Utah

Salt Lake City UT 84112

Valdosta State College

Valdosta GA 31601

Valley Forge Christian College

1401 Charlestown Road
Phoenixville PA 19460

Phone: 610-935-0450

TYPE OF INSTITUTION: Denominational: Assemblies of God
EXECUTIVE OFFICER: Philip McLeod, Vice President for Academic Affairs
CHAIRPERSON: Malcolm R. Brubaker
UNDERGRADUATE ENROLLMENT: 525

Valparaiso University

Dept of Theology
Valparaiso IN 46383

Phone: 219-464-6001
Fax: 219-464-5511
E-mail: david.truemper@valpo.edu
URL: www.valpo.edu

TYPE OF INSTITUTION: Private, Lutheran
EXECUTIVE OFFICER: Albert R. Trost, Dean
CHAIRPERSON: David G. Truemper
UNDERGRADUATE ENROLLMENT: 2,905
GRADUATE ENROLLMENT: 275
DEGREES OFFERED: BA
UNDERGRADUATE MAJORS: 43
DEGREES CONFERRED: 9

DESCRIPTION OF UNDERGRADUATE PROGRAM: The Department of Theology, as a part of the University's College of Arts and Sciences, provides the instruction for the University's general requirement of 6 hours in theology within the context of the liberal arts. Courses are offered in a wide variety of areas, including biblical and historical studies, constructive theology, ethics, church and ministry, theology and culture, and history of religions. The Department of Theology offers a 27-hour major in theology and a 42-hour major in diaconal ministry. In addition the Department of Theology coordinates programs in pre-seminary studies, including instruction in the biblical languages.

FACULTY:

Albers, James W., ThD, Concordia Seminary, St Louis (1972), 1965, Professor—church history, American church history

Baepler, Richard P., PhD, Chicago (1964), 1954, Professor—early church history (retired)

Bass, Dorothy C., PhD, Brown University (1980), 1990, Adjunct Professor—church history

Brockopp, Daniel, STM, Lutheran School of Theology (1966), 1964, Associate Professor—worship and liturgy (retired)

Cho, Wai-Tung, PhD, Princeton Theological Seminary (1996), 1997, Lilly Fellow, Lecturer—systematic theology

DeMaris, Richard E., PhD, Columbia University (1990), 1988, Associate Professor—biblical studies and archaeology

Green, Bettye, Deaconess, Valparaiso University (1991), 1994, Instructor (part-time)—deaconess education

Harre, Alan F., PhD, Wayne State (1976), 1988, Professor and President of the University—Christian education

Jones, Gregory A., MDiv, Chicago (1980), 1993, Instructor (part-time)—theology

Kauppi, Lynn A., PhD, Lutheran School of Theology at Chicago (1998), 1998, Adjunct Assistant Professor—New Testament, theology

Keller, Walter E., PhD, Cambridge (1968), 1959, Professor—biblical theology (retired)

Kispert, Robert C., PhD, University of Chicago (1997), 1996—pastoral care, theology

Knapp, Stephen A., ThM, Chicago (1987); MDiv, Concordia Theological Seminary, Springfield (1976), 1994, Adjunct Assistant Professor—Old Testament theology

Krodel, Gottfried G., ThD, Friedrich Alexander University, Erlangen (1955), 1965, Professor—Reformation history and theology (retired)

Leeb, Carolyn S., ThM, PhD, Lutheran School of Theology at Chicago (1995), (1998), 1997, Assistant Professor—biblical studies, theology

Ludwig, Theodore M., ThD, Concordia Seminary, St Louis (1963), PhD, Chicago (1975), 1968, Surjits Patheja Chair in World Religion and Ethics, 1998, Professor—history of religions, East Asian religions

Megill-Cobbler, Thelma, PhD, Princeton Theological Seminary (1992), 1997, Assistant Professor—systematic theology

Moore, James F., PhD, Chicago (1982), 1980, Professor—philosophical theology

Niedner, Frederick A., ThD, Christ Seminary-Seminex (1979), 1973, Professor—biblical theology

Pahl, Jon, PhD, Chicago (1990), 1988, Associate Professor—history of Christianity, religion in America

Rast, Walter E., PhD, Chicago (1966), 1961, Senior Research Professor—biblical theology and archaeology

Senne, Edgar P., MA, Chicago (1969), 1962, Associate Professor—history of religions (retired)

Truemper, David G., PhD, Lutheran School of Theology at Chicago (1974), 1967, Professor—systematic theology

VanDoorn-Harder, Nelly, PhD, Free University of Amsterdam, Amsterdam, Holland (1993), 1999, Assistant Professor—Islamic Studies, history of religions

Wangerin, Walter M., Jr., MA, Miami University (1968), 1991, Emil and Elfrieda Jochum University Professor—theology and literature

Weber, David K., MDiv, Concordia Theological Seminary, Fort Wayne (1982), 1997, Visiting Instructor—ethics, theology

Williams, E. Louise, BA, Valparaiso (1967), 1975, Assistant Professor (part-time)—deaconess work

Wolkow, Rabbi Leo R., MEd, Boston University (1957), 1996, Adjunct Assistant Professor (part time)—Judaism

---

Vancouver School of Theology

6000 Iona Drive
Vancouver BC V6T 1L4 Canada

Phone: 604-822-9031
Fax: 604-822-9212
E-mail: budphil@interchg.ubc.ca

TYPE OF INSTITUTION: Private, ACC, UCC, PCC, UML

EXECUTIVE OFFICER: W. J. Phillips, Principal
GRADUATE ENROLLMENT: 125

Vanderbilt University

Graduate Dept of Religion
218 Divinity
Nashville TN 37240

Phone: 615-343-3977
Fax: 615-343-9957
E-mail: cathy.j.griswold@vanderbilt.edu

TYPE OF INSTITUTION: Private
EXECUTIVE OFFICER: H. Jackson Forstman, Acting Dean
CHAIRPERSON: Douglas A. Knight
UNDERGRADUATE ENROLLMENT: 5,800
GRADUATE ENROLLMENT: 4,290
DEGREES OFFERED: BA, BS
UNDERGRADUATE MAJORS: 12
DEGREES CONFERRED: 0
GRADUATE PROGRAM
Member of the Council on Graduate Studies in Religion
Graduate Advisor: Douglas A. Knight, Chair
Graduate Degrees Offered: MA; PhD
Degrees Conferred: 7 MA; 20 PhD; 9 MA En Passant
Graduate Students in Residence: 16 MA; 105 PhD
Not in Residence: 14 MA; 57 PhD
Average No. of New Students Enrolled: 5 MA; 15 PhD
Women Students: 17 MA; 81 PhD
Minority Students: 6 MA; 25 PhD
Foreign Students: 1 MA; 29 PhD
Minimum GRE Score Requisite to Admission: No
Minimum GPA Score Requisite to Admission: Yes; 3.0 on 4.0 scale
Foreign Language Proficiency Evaluated: Yes; GSFLT Score: 550 German; 550 French; 550 Spanish
Financial Aid to First Year Students: 95% MA; 95% PhD
Financial Aid to Other Students: 95% MA; 95% PhD
Attrition Among Students: 25% PhD
Graduates Placed: 70% PhD
DESCRIPTION OF GRADUATE PROGRAM AND RESEARCH FACILITIES: The Graduate Department of Religion offers programs leading to the MA and PhD degrees. Degree programs are available in Hebrew Bible, New Testament, Historical Studies, History and Critical Theories of Religion, Ethical Studies, Religion and Personality, Theological Studies, and Homiletics (PhD minor only). The study of religion employs a variety of methods—historical, literary, social-scientific, constructive, and more. The MA program is designed to enable students to explore personal interests or vocational options, to acquire a background for secondary school teaching, and/or to attain a foundation for doctoral studies. The PhD program is designed for students seeking competence as scholars and teachers in the major disciplines of religious studies and theology.

ACADEMIC PLAN, ADMISSION REQUIREMENTS, FINANCIAL AID: Applicants to the MA program should have a Bachelor's degree with at least a B average, from an accredited college; applicants to the PhD program will usually have additional post-baccalaureate work in an MA, MDiv, or MTS program. The MA program requires a reading knowledge of one foreign language, 24 semester hours of course work, and a thesis. The PhD program requires a reading knowledge of at least two foreign languages (depending on the program) and and 72 semester hours of graduate work for credit. The candidate must complete a minimum of 24 semester hours in formal course work at Vanderbilt. For the PhD program, the Graduate School permits up to one year's "transfer credit" for previous post-baccalaureate work of graduate quality. Following the qualifying examinations, a candidate for the degree writes a dissertation which makes an original contribution to scholarship.

Most graduate students receive financial assistance in the form of tuition support. Several PhD Departmental Fellowships (full tuition plus stipend) are also awarded annually. In addition, applicants are also eligible for University Graduate Fellowships, Harold S. Vanderbilt Fellowships, and Dean's Fellowships (for outstanding African-American scholars), awarded by the Graduate School on a competitive basis. Teaching and research assistantships are also available. The application deadline is January 15; later applications will be considered if places are still available.

FACULTY:

Anderson, Victor, PhD, Princeton (1992), 1992, Assistant Professor—Christian ethics, 615-343-3973, E-mail: victor.anderson@vanderbilt.edu

Arai, Paula K. R., PhD, Harvard (1993), 1994, Assistant Professor—history of religions, 615-322-6340, E-mail: paula.k.arai@vanderbilt.edu

Baldwin, Lewis V., PhD, Northwestern (1980), 1984, Associate Professor—church history, 615-322-6358

Bond, L. Susan, PhD, Vanderbilt University (1996), 1995, Assistant Professor—homiletics and liturgics, 615-343-3972, E-mail: susan.bond@vanderbilt.edu

Burns, J. Patout, PhD, Yale (1974), 1999, Professor—Catholic studies, 615-322-3543, E-mail: j.patout.burns@vanderbilt.edu

Buttrick, David G., MDiv, Union Theological Seminary, New York (1951), Professor—homiletics and liturgics, 615-343-3978, E-mail: david.g.buttrick@vanderbilt.edu

Conklin, Beth Ann, PhD, California, San Francisco (1980), 1991, Associate Professor—anthropology, 615-322-3306

DeHart, Paul, PhD, University of Chicago (1997), 1997, Assistant Professor—theology, 615-343-7516, E-mail: paul.j.dehart@vanderbilt.edu

Dobbs-Weinstein, Idit, PhD, Toronto (1987), 1987, Associate Professor—philosophy, 615-343-8671, E-mail: dobbswi@ctrvax.vanderbilt.edu

Franke, William P., PhD, Stanford (1991), 1991, Associate Professor—religious studies, comparative literature, and Italian, 615-322-6902, E-mail: william.p.franke@vanderbilt.edu

Gay, Volney P., PhD, Chicago (1976), 1979, Professor—religion and personality, 615-322-2462, E-mail: volney.p.gay@vanderbilt.edu

Geller, Jay, PhD, Duke (1985), 1994, Lecturer—modern Judaism and philosophy of religion, 615-343-2462, E-mail: gellerj@ctrvax.vanderbilt.edu

Goodman, Lenn E., DPhil, Oxford (1968), 1994, Professor—philosophy and religious studies, 615-343-3158, E-mail: lgoodman@ctrvax.vanderbilt.edu

Gregor, Thomas A., PhD, Columbia (1969), 1975, Professor—anthropology, 615-322-7523, E-mail: gregorta@ctrvax.vanderbilt.edu

Haas, Peter J., Brown (1980), 1980, Associate Professor—Jewish literature and thought, 615-322-6339, E-mail: peter.j.haas@vanderbilt.edu

Harrod, Howard L., PhD, Yale (1965), 1968, Professor—social ethics, sociology of religion, 615-343-3991, E-mail: howard.harrod@vanderbilt.edu

Hodgson, Peter C., PhD, Yale (1963), 1965, Professor—theology, 615-343-3988, E-mail: peter.c.hodgson@vanderbilt.edu

Hummel, Leonard M., PhD, Boston University (1999), 1999, Assistant Professor—pastoral counseling and pastoral theology, 615-343-3975, E-mail: leonard.m.hummel@vanderbilt.edu

Johnson, Dale A., ThD, Union Theological Seminary, New York (1967), 1969, Professor—church history, history of Christian thought, 615-343-3982, E-mail: dale.a.johnson@vanderbilt.edu

Knight, Douglas A., DrTheol, Göttingen (1973), 1973, Professor—Hebrew Bible, 615-343-5008, E-mail: douglas.a.knight@vanderbilt.edu

Levine, Amy-Jill, PhD, Duke (1984), 1994, Professor—New Testament, 615-343-3967, E-mail: amy-jill.levine@vanderbilt.edu

McFague, Sallie, PhD, Yale (1964), 1970, Professor—theology, 615-343-3983, E-mail: sallie.mcfague@vanderbilt.edu

Meeks, M. Douglas, PhD, Duke in cooperation with Tuebingen University (1971), 1998, Professor—theology, 615-343-3989, E-mail: m.douglas.meeks@vanderbilt.edu

Miller-McLemore, Bonnie, PhD, University of Chicago (1986), 1995, Associate Professor—pastoral theology and counseling, 615-343-3970, E-mail: bonnie.miller-mclemore@vanderbilt.edu

Monaghan, John D., PhD, Pennsylvania (1987), 1988, Associate Professor—anthropology, 615-322-7525

Patte, Daniel M., ThD, Chicago Theological Seminary (1971), 1971, Professor—New Testament, 615-322-6359, E-mail: daniel.m.patte@vanderbilt.edu

Sasson, Jack, PhD, Brandeis University (1966), 1999, Professor—Jewish Studies and Hebrew Bible, 615-343-3996, E-mail: jack.m.sasson@vanderbilt.edu

Segovia, Fernando F., PhD, Notre Dame (1978), 1984, Professor—New Testament, 615-343-3974, E-mail: fernando.f.segovia@vanderbilt.edu

Sherkat, Darren E., PhD, Duke (1991), 1991, Associate Professor—sociology, 615-322-7515, E-mail: sherkade@ctrvax.vanderbilt.edu

Weems, Renita J., PhD, Princeton Theological Seminary (1989), 1987, Associate Professor—Hebrew Bible, 615-343-7516, E-mail: renita.j.weems@vanderbilt.edu

Welch, Gay, PhD, Vanderbilt (1980), 1996, Assistant Professor—religious studies, 615-322-2457, E-mail: gay.h.welch@vanderbilt.edu

Zaner, Richard M., PhD, New School for Social Research (1961), 1981, Professor—medical ethics, 615-322-2252, E-mail: richard.zaner@mcmail.vanderbilt.edu

---

Vanguard University of Southern California

55 Fair Drive
Costa Mesa CA 92626

Phone: 714-556-3610
Fax: 714-957-9317
URL: www.vanguard.edu

TYPE OF INSTITUTION: Private, Assemblies of God
EXECUTIVE OFFICER: Murray W. Dempster, Vice President Academic Affairs
CHAIRPERSON: Donald Baldwin
UNDERGRADUATE ENROLLMENT: 1184

GRADUATE ENROLLMENT: 134

DEGREES OFFERED: BA in Religion

UNDERGRADUATE MAJORS: 149

DEGREES CONFERRED: 40

DESCRIPTION OF UNDERGRADUATE PROGRAM: The Division of Religion exists to provide each student with a theological foundation for a lifetime of Christian commitment, reflection and service. The contribution of religion to liberal arts in a Christian college is to help all students learn how to be responsible interpreters of scripture and of the Christian faith within their various disciplines. As responsible interpreters of scripture and of the Christian faith, our majors will be competent and gifted in the following areas: hermeneutics, historical theology, philosophical and ethical reflection, the nature and mission of the church, spirituality, and the leader's engagement with the issues of modern life and ministry.

GRADUATE PROGRAM

Graduate Degrees Offered: MA; MTS

Degrees Conferred: 7 MA; 1 MTS

Graduate Students in Residence: 12 MA

Not in Residence: 41 MA; 15 MTS

Average No. of New Students Enrolled: 13 MA; 8 MTS

Women Students: 13 MA; 8 MTS

Minority Students: 8 MA; 2 MTS

Foreign Students: 3 MA;

Minimum GRE Score Requisite to Admission: No

Minimum GPA Score Requisite to Admission: Yes; 3.0 MA, 2.5 MTS

Foreign Language Proficiency Evaluated: No

Financial Aid to First Year Students: 12 MA; 2 MTS

Financial Aid to Other Students: 22 MA; 2 MTS

Attrition Among Students: 13 MA; 4 MTS

DESCRIPTION OF GRADUATE PROGRAM AND RESEARCH FACILITIES: The fundamental purpose of the Graduate Program in Religion is to promote excellence in the study of scriptures, theological reflection and church leadership. To study scriptures, students are offered an opportunity to develop competence in the interpretation of biblical texts. To reflect theologically and ethically, students are offered an opportunity to examine the implications of biblical texts, the mission of the church and leadership responsibilities of those who serve the church. To explore church leadership, students are offered an opportunity to study the complexities of ministry and develop insights through theological studies and related social science disciplines. The Graduate Studies or Church Leadership concentration; and the Master of Theological Studies, a 48 unit professional graduate degree. Computer labs are available which include internet access.

ACADEMIC PLAN, ADMISSION REQUIREMENTS, FINANCIAL AID: Vanguard University of Southern California operates on the semester system plus a nine week/three course summer schedule. Graduate courses are offered principally at evenings, afternoons and weekends for the convenience of working students. Applicants for the MA degree should have a bachelor's degree, including at least 12 credit hours in Humanities and Social Science (each), and at least 24 credit hours in Religion. Applicants for the MTS degree should have a bachelor's degree. Documents required: two letters of recommendation and transcripts of all college work. Financial aid is primarily need based. Types of institutional aid include research/teaching assistantships. Dean's purse, ministerial discount, Smith Institute scholarship, and academic scholarships. Federal loans are also available.

FACULTY:

Baldwin, Donald E., PhD, University of Missouri (1978), 1977, Professor—philosophical theology, spiritual formation, 714-556-3610 ext 231

Benvenuti, Sheri, PhD (cand.), University of Southern California, 1996, Director of Graduate Studies, Assistant Professor—social ethics, 714-556-3610 ext 236

Camery-Hoggatt, Jerry A., PhD (1985), 1985, Boston University, Professor—New Testament, 714-556-3610 ext 237

Clark, David G., PhD, University of Notre Dame (1975), 1974, Professor—New Testament, 714-556-3610 ext 249

Dempster, Murray W., PhD, University of Southern California (1980), 1969, Professor and Academic Dean—social ethics, 714-556-3610 ext 212

Dogterom, William H., DMin (cand.), Assistant Professor—pastoral ministry

Heidebrecht, Nancy E., PhD, University of California (1993), 1984, Los Angeles, Associate Professor—Old Testament, archaeology, 714-556-3610 ext 230

Heuser, Roger D., PhD, New York University (1984), 1983, Dean of the Graduate School, Professor—leadership, organizational studies, 714-556-3610 ext 234

Macchia, Frank D., DTheology, Associate Professor—theology

Petersen, Douglas, PhD, Oxford Centre for Missions Studies (1995), 1988, Director of the Costa Rica Study Center, Associate Professor—inter-cultural ministries, 714-556-3610 ext 238

Shawchuck, Norman, PhD, Professor—church leadership studies

Williams, William C., PhD, New York University (1975), 1969, Professor—Old Testament, 714-556-3610 ext 239

Vassar College

Department of Religion
Box 738
Poughkeepsie NY 12604

Phone: 914-437-5520
Fax: 914-437-7287
E-mail: weborden@vaxsar.vassar.edu
URL: depts.vassar.edu/~religion/

TYPE OF INSTITUTION: Private, Non-Denominational

EXECUTIVE OFFICER: Frances Fergusson, President

CHAIRPERSON: Mark S. Cladis

UNDERGRADUATE ENROLLMENT: 2,250

DESCRIPTION OF UNDERGRADUATE PROGRAM: An integral part of the Liberal Arts curriculum, the academic study of religion at Vassar explores how people in different cultures have thought and acted in relation to the sacred. The Department offers a major in religion and, for students majoring in other fields, a correlate sequence in religion.

FACULTY:

Cladis, Mark S., PhD, Princeton University (1990), Associate Professor—religion and critical thought, religious ethics, 914-437-5518, E-mail: macladis@vaxsar.vassar.edu

Epstein, Marc M., PhD, Yale University (1992), Assistant Professor—religion and the arts, religion and popular culture in the Middle Ages, 914-437-5517, E-mail: maepstein@vaxsar.vassar.edu

Halpern-Amaru, Betsy, PhD, University of Massachusetts, Amherst (1983), Professor—post-biblical Judaism, early Christianity, medieval Jewish history, 914-437-5522, E-mail: amaru@vaxsar.vassar.edu

Jarow, Eric Huberman, PhD, Columbia University (1990), Assistant Professor—religion of Asia, psychology of religion, 914-437-5516, E-mail: erhuberman@vaxsar.vassar.edu

Leibovitch, Tova Weitzman, MA, Jewish Theological Seminary (1986), Lecturer—Hebrew language and literature, 914-437-5379, E-mail: toleibovitch@vaxsar.vassar.edu

LiDonnici, Lynn, PhD, University of Pennsylvania (1994), Assistant Professor—early Christianity and Greco-Roman religions, 914-437-7549, E-mail: lylidonnici@vaxsar.vassar.edu

Mamiya, Lawrence H., PhD, Columbia University (1975), Professor—sociology of religion, Africana studies, 914-437-5519, E-mail: mamiya@vaxsar.vassar.edu

Moore, Deborah Dash, PhD, Columbia University (1976), Professor—modern Judaism, American religions, 914-437-5521, E-mail: moored@vaxsar.vassar.edu

Park, Jin Y., PhD, State University of New York at Stony Brook (1998), Visiting Assistant Professor—Asian religion, 914-437-5517, E-mail: jipark@vaxsar.vassar.edu

---

Vennard College

Box 29, University Park IA 52595

University of Vermont

Religion Dept   **Phone: 802-656-3080**
481 Main Street   **URL: www.uvm.edu/~religion**
Burlington VT 05405

TYPE OF INSTITUTION: Public

EXECUTIVE OFFICERS: Judith Ramaley, President; Joan Smith, Dean of the College of Arts and Sciences

CHAIRPERSON: William E. Paden

UNDERGRADUATE ENROLLMENT: 7,200

GRADUATE ENROLLMENT: 1,400

DEGREES OFFERED: BA

UNDERGRADUATE MAJORS: 45

DEGREES CONFERRED: 15

DESCRIPTION OF UNDERGRADUATE PROGRAM: The department pursues the academic study of religion in the liberal arts context of the College of Arts and Sciences. Comparative, historical and theoretical perspectives are all intrinsic to the program and form components of the major and minor requirements.

FACULTY:

Chen, Weigang, PhD, Harvard (1999), 1999, Assistant Professor—religion in China, social theory, 802-656-3488

Clark, Anne L., PhD, Columbia University (1989), 1988, Associate Professor—history of Christianity, women and religion, 802-656-0231, Fax: 802-656-8429, E-mail: aclark@moose.uvm.edu

Martin, Luther H., PhD, Claremont Graduate School (1972), 1967, Professor—Hellenistic religions, religion in America, theory and method, 802-656-0657, Fax: 802-656-8429, E-mail: lmartin@uvm.vm

Paden, William E., PhD, Claremont Graduate School (1968), 1965, Professor—comparative religion, 802-656-0232, Fax: 802-656-8429, E-mail: wpaden@moose.uvm.edu

Rojas, Mary V., PhD (cand.), University of California, Santa Barbara, 1999, Lecturer—ethnic religious traditions of the US, 802-656-0230

Sugarman, Richard I., PhD, Boston University (1976), 1970, Associate Professor—Judaica, phenomenology of religion, 802-656-4383, Fax: 802-656-8429

Trainor, Kevin M., PhD, Columbia University (1990), 1990, Associate Professor—Buddhism, religious ritual, 802-656-3488, Fax: 802-656-8429, E-mail: ktrainor@moose.uvm.edu

Uddin, Sufia, PhD (in progress), University of Pennsylvania, 1999, Assistant Professor—Islam, 802-656-0227

Victoria College

University of Toronto, Toronto, Ontario M5S 1K7 Canada

University of Victoria

Centre for Studies in Religion and Society
Sedgewick Bldg B102, PO Box 1700
Victoria BC V8W 2Y2 Canada

Phone: 250-721-6325
Fax: 250-721-6234
E-mail: csrs@uvic.ca
URL: web.uvic.ca/csrs

TYPE OF INSTITUTION: Public, Non-Denominational

EXECUTIVE OFFICER: Harold Coward, Director

ACADEMIC PLAN, ADMISSION REQUIREMENTS, FINANCIAL AID: Offers scholarships to graduate students researching issues of religion and society at the University of Victoria, ie. The Ian H. Stewart Graduate Student Fellowships (2 annually), The Winifred E. Lonsdale Fellowship (1 annually—with Department of History). Offers non-stipendiary visiting research fellowships.

FACULTY:

Coward, Harold G., PhD, McMaster University (1973), 1992, Professor—Hinduism, religion and society, Indian philosophy, Jung and Eastern thought, 250-721-6325, Fax: 250-721-6234, E-mail: csrs@uvic.ca

Villanova University

Dept of Theology and Religious Studies
800 Lancaster Ave
Villanova PA 19085

Phone: 610-519-4730
Fax: 610-519-6697
E-mail: achappell@ucis.vill.edu
URL: www.vill.edu

TYPE OF INSTITUTION: Private, Roman Catholic

EXECUTIVE OFFICER: Edmund J. Dobbin, OSA, President

CHAIRPERSON: Arthur B. Chappell, OSA

COORDINATOR: Paul Danove

University of Virginia

Dept of Religious Studies
B-10 Cocke Hall
Charlottesville VA 22903

Phone: 804-924-3741
Fax: 804-924-1467
URL: www.virginia.edu/~relig

TYPE OF INSTITUTION: Public

CHAIRPERSON: Harry Gamble

COORDINATORS: Heather Warren, Undergraduate; Larry Bouchard, Graduate

UNDERGRADUATE ENROLLMENT: 10,000

GRADUATE ENROLLMENT: 7,000

DEGREES OFFERED: BA in Religious Studies

UNDERGRADUATE MAJORS: 180

DEGREES CONFERRED: 65

DESCRIPTION OF UNDERGRADUATE PROGRAM: Undergraduate course offerings include survey and advanced work in the major religious traditions of the world, both Eastern and Western, as well as in selected aspects of religious thought. Various perspectives and methods are brought to bear on the materials—historical, sociological, philosophical, literary, and psychological. Thus the study of religion within the Department is broad in subject matter and interdisciplinary in approach. The program for undergraduate majors entails 30 semester hours of work.

GRADUATE PROGRAM

Member of the Council on Graduate Studies in Religion

Graduate Advisor: Larry Bouchard

Graduate Degrees Offered: MA; PhD

Degrees Conferred: 16 MA; 10 PhD

Graduate Students in Residence: 35 MA; 83 PhD

Not in Residence: 14 MA; 33 PhD

Average No. of New Students Enrolled: 8 MA; 16 PhD

Women Students: 23 MA; 36 PhD

Minority Students: 2 MA; 6 PhD

Foreign Students: 4 MA; 4 PhD

Minimum GRE Score Requisite to Admission: No

Minimum GPA Score Requisite to Admission: No

Foreign Language Proficiency Evaluated: Yes; GSFLT Score: 600 German; 600 French

Financial Aid to First Year Students: 50% PhD

Financial Aid to Other Students: 60% PhD

Attrition Among Students: 1% MA; 1% PhD

Graduates Placed: 85% PhD

DESCRIPTION OF GRADUATE PROGRAM AND RESEARCH FACILITIES: The Department offers MA-PhD programs in Philosophical Theology; Christianity and Judaism in Antiquity; Religious Ethics; Religion and Literature; European and American Religious History; and History of Religions. Reading competence in both French and German is normally required of doctoral students. Other or additional language requirements, however, are set by individual programs.

ACADEMIC PLAN, ADMISSION REQUIREMENTS, FINANCIAL AID: Students with less than an overall grade-point average of B in their college work are not considered admissible to the MA program. Students with a grade-point average of less than A- are not ordinarily considered admissible to the doctoral program. The Graduate Record Examination is a standard requirement of the Graduate School. A limited amount of fellowship aid is available to highly qualified students. The Department regularly employs approximately 20 graduate students as Teaching Assistants. A substantial amount of financial aid is also available through "work-study" arrangements and student loans.

FACULTY:

Bouchard, Larry, PhD, University of Chicago (1984), 1984, Associate Professor—religion and literature, 824-924-6710, E-mail: ldb4k@virginia.edu

Childress, James F., PhD, Yale University (1968), 1978, Edwin B. Kyle Professor of Religious Studies—religious ethics, 804-924-6724, E-mail: jfc7c@virginia.edu

Ferreira, M. Jamie, PhD, Princeton University (1977), 1980, Professor—philosophy of religion, 824-924-6712, E-mail: mjf5e@virginia.edu

Fogarty, Gerald P., PhD, Yale University (1969), 1975, William R. Kenan, Jr. Professor—history of American and modern European Catholicism, 804-924-6707, E-mail: gpf@virginia.edu

Freeman, R. Edward, PhD, Washington University, St Louis (1978), 1988, Professor—business ethics, 804-924-0935

Gamble, Harry Y., PhD, Yale University (1970), 1970, Professor—New Testament studies, early Christian history, 804-924-6714, E-mail: hyg@virginia.edu

Germano, David F., PhD, University of Wisconsin, Madison (1992), 1992, Associate Professor—Buddhist studies, Asian religions, 804-924-6728, E-mail: dfg9w@faraday.clas.virginia.edu

Gilkey, Langdon, PhD, Columbia University (1954), 1990, Visiting Scholar—theology

Groner, Paul, PhD, Yale University (1980), 1980, Professor—Buddhist studies, 804-924-6715, E-mail: psg3w@darwin.clas.virginia.edu

Hoehler-Fatton, Cynthia, PhD, University of Virginia (1993), 1997, Assistant Professor—African religions, history of religions, 804-924-6314, E-mail: chh3a@virginia.edu

Hopkins, P. Jeffrey, PhD, University of Wisconsin, Madison (1973), 1973, Professor—Northern Buddhism, Tibetan language, 804-924-6716, E-mail: pjh9q@virginia.edu

Hunter, James D., PhD, Rutgers University (1981), 1983, Professor—sociology of religion

Kovacs, Judith L., PhD, Columbia University-Union Theological Seminary (1978), 1984, Assistant Professor—New Testament studies, E-mail: jlk4n@virginia.edu

Lang, Karen C., PhD, University of Washington (1983), 1982, Associate Professor—Buddhist studies, 804-924-0846, E-mail: kcl@fermi.clas.virginia.edu

Mathewes, Charles, PhD, University of Chicago (1997), 1997, Assistant Professor—religious studies, 804-924-6708, E-mail: ctm9d@virginia.edu

Menn, Esther M., PhD, University of Chicago Divinity School (1995), 1995, Assistant Professor—Hebrew Bible/Old Testament studies, 804-924-6722, E-mail: emm2k@virginia.edu

Midelfort, Erik, PhD, Yale University (1970), 1970, Professor—early modern Europe

Milbank, John, PhD, University of Birmingham (1986), 1999, Frances Ball Professor of Philosophical Theology—theology, ethics, and culture, 804-924-6723

Monius, Anne, PhD, University of Harvard (1997), 1997, Assistant Professor—religious studies, 804-982-2283, E-mail: amas@virginia.edu

Noble, Thomas F. X., PhD, Michigan State (1974), 1980, Professor—medieval history

Ochs, Peter, PhD, Yale University (1980), 1997, Professor—Bronfman Professorship of Modern Jewish thought, 804-924-6718, E-mail: pwo3v@virginia.edu

Ochs, Vanessa, PhD, Drew University (1999), 1998, Lecturer—anthropology of religion, Judaica, women and religion, 804-924-6722, E-mail: vlo4n@virginia.edu

Ray, Benjamin C., PhD, University of Chicago (1971), 1978, Professor—history of religions, African religion, 804-924-6720, E-mail: bcr@virginia.edu

Rogers, Eugene F., PhD, Yale University (1992), 1993, Associate Professor—theological studies, 804-924-6721, E-mail: er8m@virginia.edu

Sachedina, Abdulaziz A., PhD, University of Toronto (1976), 1976, Professor—Islamic studies, 804-924-6725, E-mail: aas@virginia.edu

Thompson, Augustine, PhD, Berkeley (1988), 1999, Associate Professor—history of Christianity

Thompson, Kenneth W., PhD, University of Chicago (1950), 1977, Professor—social ethics, international affairs

Warren, Heather A., PhD, Johns Hopkins University (1991), 1991, Associate Professor—religious history, 804-924-6719, E-mail: haw6w@virginia.edu

Wilken, Robert L., PhD, University of Chicago (1963), 1985, William R. Kenan, Jr., Professor of the History of Christianity—early Christian history, 804-924-6709, E-mail: rlw2w@virginia.edu

Wilson, William M., PhD, University of Virginia (1980), 1987, Lecturer—theological studies

---

Virginia Seminary and College

2058 Garfield Ave, Lynchburg VA 24501

Virginia Commonwealth University

915 W Franklin
Richmond VA 23284-2025

Phone: 804-828-1224
Fax: 804-828-8714
E-mail: cedwards@cabell.vcu.edu

TYPE OF INSTITUTION: Public
EXECUTIVE OFFICER: Eugene Trani, President
COORDINATOR: Cliff Edwards
UNDERGRADUATE ENROLLMENT: 16,000
GRADUATE ENROLLMENT: 5,000

Virginia Intermont College

Bristol VA 24201

Virginia Polytechnic Institute and State University

Religious Studies Program
Blacksburg VA 24061-0135

Phone: 540-231-6112
Fax: 540-231-7013
E-mail: malbon@vtvm1.cc.vt.edu
URL: www.cis.vt.edu/rel/religion.html

TYPE OF INSTITUTION: Public
COORDINATOR: Elizabeth Struthers Malbon

Virginia Union University

1601 W Leigh St, Richmond VA 23220

Virginia Wesleyan College

Religious Studies
1584 Wesleyan Dr
Norfolk VA 23502

Phone: 757-455-3406
Fax: 757-461-5025
E-mail: cwansink@vwc.edu
URL: www.vwc.edu/academic_life/
programs/religion/index.htm

TYPE OF INSTITUTION: Private, United Methodist

EXECUTIVE OFFICER: William Greer, President

COORDINATOR: Craig S. Wansink

UNDERGRADUATE ENROLLMENT: 1,125

DEGREES OFFERED: BA with departmental Religious Studies major

UNDERGRADUATE MAJORS: 16

DEGREES CONFERRED: 4

DESCRIPTION OF UNDERGRADUATE PROGRAM: Religious Studies courses are primarily constituent parts of a liberal arts curriculum but secondarily also act as the focus in the preparation of students who are Religious Studies majors, Divisional Majors with emphasis in Religious Studies, or simply Religious Service students. Departmental majors are required to schedule a 30 credit hour core of upper level courses. Other major programs are planned on an individual basis. Certain Religious Studies courses are also available through the Adult Studies program.

FACULTY:

Cookson, Catherine, PhD, Indiana University (1997), 1998, Assistant Professor—religion and law, Christian ethics, religion and social issues, 757-455-3128, E-mail: ccookson@vwc.edu

Patton, Darrell D., DMin, San Francisco Theological Seminary (1984), 1985, Assistant Professor (part-time)—practical theology

Shealy, William R., PhD, Drew University (1966), 1968, Professor—religion and culture, history of Christian thought, comparative religion and ethics, 757-455-3225, E-mail: wshealy@vwc.edu

Vial, Theodore M., PhD, University of Chicago (1994), 1997, Assistant Professor—history of Christian thought, theoretical approaches to religion, religion and culture, 757-455-3225, E-mail: tvial@vwc.edu

Wansink, Craig S., PhD, Yale University (1993), 1993, Associate Professor—biblical studies, biblical languages, history of early church, comparative religion, 757-455-3406, E-mail: cwansink@vwc.edu

Vision Christian University

940 Montecito Way, PO Box 356, Ramona CA 92065

Viterbo College

815 S Ninth St, LaCrosse WI 54601

Voorhees College

1411 Voorhees Rd
Denmark SC 29042

Phone: 803-703-7075
Fax: 803-793-3068
E-mail: retzlaff@voorhees.edu
URL: ec.voorhees.edu/wcb

TYPE OF INSTITUTION: Private, Episcopal
EXECUTIVE OFFICER: Leonard E. Dawson, President
CHAIRPERSON: K. Gavid Godwin
COORDINATOR: George Retzlaff
UNDERGRADUATE ENROLLMENT: 956

Wabash College

Crawfordsville IN 47933

Phone: 765-361-6262
Fax: 765-361-6051
E-mail: placherw@wabash.edu
URL: www.wabash.edu

TYPE OF INSTITUTION: Private, Non-Denominational
EXECUTIVE OFFICER: Mauri Ditzler, Academic Dean
CHAIRPERSON: William C. Placher
UNDERGRADUATE ENROLLMENT: 800
DEGREES OFFERED: AB
UNDERGRADUATE MAJORS: 40
DEGREES CONFERRED: 19

DESCRIPTION OF UNDERGRADUATE PROGRAM: The department offers work in both Christianity and Asian religions. Its long tradition of excellence was augmented two years ago when Wabash became the site of the Wabash Center for Teaching and Learning in Theology and Religion, a national program devoted to excellence in teaching and funded by the Lilly Endowment.

FACULTY:

Blix, David S., PhD, University of Chicago (1988), 1996, Visiting Assistant Professor—Asian religions, Christian theology, 765-361-6075, E-mail: blixd@wabash.edu

Peebles, Hall, PhD, Yale University (1959), 1958, Evans Professor Emeritus—Hebrew Bible, Chinese religions, ethics, 765-361-6333, E-mail: peeblesh@wabash.edu

Placher, William C., PhD, Yale University (1975), 1974, Professor—Christian theology, philosophy of religion, 765-361-6262, E-mail: placherw@wabash.edu

Royalty, Robert M., PhD, Yale University (1995), 1999, Assistant Professor—New Testament, Hebrew Bible, 765-361-6046, E-mail: royaltyr@wabash.edu

Smith, J. Warren, PhD, Yale University (1999), 1999, Visiting Assistant Professor—historical theology, 765-361-6264, E-mail: smithw@wabash.edu

Webb, Stephen H., PhD, University of Chicago (1989), 1989, Associate Professor—theology, philosophy of religion, religion and literature, 765-361-6264, E-mail: webbs@wabash.edu

Williams, Raymond B., PhD, University of Chicago (1966), 1965, Lafollette Distinguished Professor and Director of the Wabash Center—New Tesatment, religions of India, religion and higher education, 765-361-6336, Fax: 765-361-6051, E-mail: williamr@wabash.edu

Wadhams Hall Seminary College

6866 State Highway 37
Ogdenburg NY 13669

Phone: 315-393-4231
Fax: 315-393-4249
E-mail: whsc@gisco.net
URL: www.wadhams.edu

TYPE OF INSTITUTION: Private, Roman Catholic
EXECUTIVE OFFICER: Robert H. Aucoin, STL, President
CHAIRPERSON: Guy F. Roddy, FIC
UNDERGRADUATE ENROLLMENT: 24

Wagner College

Staten Island NY 10301

Wake Forest University

Box 7545
Winston-Salem NC 27109

Phone: 336-758-5461
Fax: 336-758-4462
E-mail: pricel@wfu.edu
URL: wfu./edu/academic-departments/
religion/

TYPE OF INSTITUTION: Private

EXECUTIVE OFFICER: Thomas K. Hearn, President; Paul D. Escott, Dean of College

CHAIRPERSON: Charles A. Kimball

COORDINATOR: Kenneth G. Hoglund, MA Program in Religion

UNDERGRADUATE ENROLLMENT: 3,700

GRADUATE ENROLLMENT: 3,000

DEGREES OFFERED: BA Religion, MA Religion, MA Pastoral Care

UNDERGRADUATE MAJORS: 52

DEGREES CONFERRED: 18

DESCRIPTION OF UNDERGRADUATE PROGRAM: Wake Forest is a private, liberal arts institution distinguished by a small enrollment and expansive resources. The Department of Religion is committed to excellence in the academic study of religion. The teaching and research focus on the Christian tradition, while also engaging the world's other religious traditions. The undergraduate program serves the curricular requirements of the university and leads to a major and a minor in religion. The religion major and minor are designed both for students interested in a broad liberal arts education and for students preparing for graduate study or professional ministry.

GRADUATE PROGRAM

Graduate Advisor: Dr. Kenneth Hoglund

Graduate Degrees Offered: MA

Degrees Conferred: 7 MA

Graduate Students in Residence: 21 MA

Not in Residence: 3 MA

Average No. of New Students Enrolled: 8 MA

Women Students: 14 MA

Minority Students: 1 MA

Foreign Students: 0 MA

Minimum GRE Score Requisite to Admission: No

Minimum GPA Score Requisite to Admission: No

Foreign Language Proficiency Evaluated: No

Financial Aid to First Year Students: 95%

Financial Aid to Other Students: 95% MA

Attrition Among Students: 6% MA

DESCRIPTION OF GRADUATE PROGRAM AND RESEARCH FACILITIES: The Master of Arts in Religion provides a rigorous academic program in several disciplines of religious study.

The degree serves either as a terminal degree or as preparation for doctoral study. A special feature of the program is the opportunity to engage in archaeological research on site in Israel. Wake Forest is an active participant in the Sepphoris Regional Project. Coursework is offered in Hebrew and Christian scripture, theology, history of Christianity comparative religion, Eastern religions, Near Eastern languages and archaeology. Individual instruction is also available in the form of graduate reading courses in a number of specialized areas tailored to the needs and abilities of the student. The Master of Arts in Pastoral Counseling is offered in cooperation with the School of Pastoral Care at the North Carolina Baptist Hospital in Winston Salem. A professional theological degree is a prerequisite for this program.

ACADEMIC PLAN, ADMISSION REQUIREMENTS, FINANCIAL AID: The graduate program in religion admits 6-8 students per year to pursue a two-year course of study. Applicants should have a combined score of 1,000 on the verbal and quantitative sections of the GRE. In accord with University requirements for the Master of Arts degree, the program in religion requires thirty hours of course work demonstrated competence in a modern research language, and a thesis. The thesis must demonstrate the student's competence in framing a question for research and in sustaining an extended argument to support the thesis statements. Wake Forest University provides scholarships amounting to half tuition or full tuition and a small number of fellowships.

FACULTY:

Boyd, Stephen B., PhD, Harvard (1983), 1985, Professor—history of Christianity and historical theology, 336-758-5458, Fax: 336-758-4462, E-mail: boyd@wfu.edu

Collins, John E., PhD, Princeton (1969), 1970, Professor—eastern religions, science and religion, 336-758-5463, Fax: 336-758-4462, E-mail: collins@wfu.edu

Ford, James L., PhD, Princeton (1998), 1998, Assistant Professor—East Asian religions, Buddhism, 336-758-4191, Fax: 336-758-4462, E-mail: fordj@wfu.edu

Foskett, Mary F., PhD, Emory, (1997), 1997, Assistant Professor—New Testament, Christian origins, 336-758-5653, Fax: 336-758-4462, E-mail: foskettm@wfu.edu

Hoglund, Kenneth G., PhD, Duke (1989),1990, Associate Professor—Hebrew Scriptures, Near Eastern languages, archaeology, 336-758-5120, Fax: 336-758-4462, E-mail: hoglund@wfu.edu

Horton, Fred L., PhD, Duke, (1970), 1970, Professor—New Testament, Near Eastern languages, archaeology, 336-758-5460-Fax: 336-758-4462, E-mail: horton@wfu.edu

Ilesanmi, Simeon O., PhD, Southern Methodist (1993), 1993, Associate Professor—ethics, African studies, 336-758-5459, Fax: 336-758-4462, E-mail: ilesanmi@wfu.edu

Kimball, Charles A., ThD, Harvard (987), 1996, Professor and Chair—world religions, Islam, 336-758-5465, Fax: 336-758-4462, E-mail: kimball@wfu.edu

Pleasants, Phyllis R., PhD, The Southern Baptist Theological Seminary (1991), 1998, Visiting Associate Professor—church history, Christian tradition, 336-758-5462, Fax: 336-758-4462, E-mail: pleasanp@wfu.edu

---

Walla Walla College

204 S College Ave
College Place WA 99324

Phone: 509-527-2194
Fax: 509-527-2253
E-mail: burser@wwc.eduu

TYPE OF INSTITUTION: Private, Seventh-day Adventist
EXECUTIVE OFFICER: W. G. Nelson, President
CHAIRPERSON: Ernest Bursey
UNDERGRADUATE ENROLLMENT: 1,700

GRADUATE ENROLLMENT: 150-160

Walsh University

2020 Easton St NW
North Canton OH 44720

Phone: 330-490-7344
Fax: 330-499-8518
E-mail: frdon@alex.walsh.edu
URL: www.walsh.edu

TYPE OF INSTITUTION: Private, Roman Catholic

EXECUTIVE OFFICER: Kenneth N. Hamilton, Jr., President

CHAIRPERSON: Rev. Donald A. Miller, OFM

DEGREES OFFERED: BA

UNDERGRADUATE MAJORS: 2

DEGREES CONFERRED: 2

DESCRIPTION OF UNDERGRADUATE PROGRAM: The Department of Theology of Walsh University, offering a BA Theology and BA Pastoral Ministry, is a part of the Division of Humanities. It has as an overarching goal to expose students to the Catholic theological tradition and to the broader religious traditions out of which and within which that traditions flows. Due to the personal and academic background, interests and goals of students, the Department of Theology serves primarily as a core studies department.

FACULTY:

Harrington, Warren J., PhD, Fordham University (1980), 1975, Professor—systematic theology, 330-490-7053, Fax: 330-490-7165, E-mail: harrington@alex.walsh.edu

Miller, Donald A., OFM, PhD, Catholic University of America (1995), 1995, Assistant Professor—moral theology, 330-490-7344, Fax: 330-490-8518, E-mail: frdon@alex.walsh.edu

Torma, Joseph A., PhD, University of Ottawa (1973), 1983, Professor—ecclesiology, 330-490-7052, Fax: 330-490-7165, E-mail: torma@alex.walsh.edu

Warner Pacific College

2219 SE 68th, Portland OR 97215

Warner Southern College

5301 US Highway 27 S, Lake Wells FL 33853

Warren Wilson College

PO Box 9000
Asheville NC 28815-9000

Phone: 704-298-3325

TYPE OF INSTITUTION: Private, Presbyterian Church (USA)

EXECUTIVE OFFICER: Virginia McKinley, Vice President

CHAIRPERSON: John P. Casey

UNDERGRADUATE ENROLLMENT: 525

GRADUATE ENROLLMENT: 70

Wartburg College

222 Ninth Street NW
Waverly IA 50677-0903

Phone: 319-352-8346
Fax: 319-352-8213
E-mail: kleinhans@wartburg.edu
URL: www.wartburg.edu

TYPE OF INSTITUTION: Denominational: Evangelical Lutheran Church in America
EXECUTIVE OFFICER: Jack Ohle, President
CHAIRPERSON: Kathryn Kleinhans
UNDERGRADUATE ENROLLMENT: 1,541

Wartburg Theological Seminary

333 Wartburg Pl
PO Box 5004
Dubuque IA 52004-5004

Phone: 319-589-0200
Fax: 319-589-0333
URL: www.wartburgseminary.com

TYPE OF INSTITUTION: Private, ELCA
EXECUTIVE OFFICER: Duane H. Larson, President
GRADUATE ENROLLMENT: 160

Washburn University of Topeka

1700 College Ave, Topeka KS 66621

Washington College

300 Washington Ave
Chesterton MD 21620

Phone: 410-778-7860

TYPE OF INSTITUTION: Private, Non-Denominational
EXECUTIVE OFFICER: Joachim Scholz, Provost and Dean of the College
CHAIRPERSON: J. David Newell
UNDERGRADUATE ENROLLMENT: 900

Washington University

Religious Studies Program
Box 1050, One Brookings Dr
St Louis MO 63130

Phone: 314-935-4446
Fax: 314-935-7462
E-mail: akarmus@artsci.wustl.edu

TYPE OF INSTITUTION: Private, Non-Denominational
EXECUTIVE OFFICER: Mark Wrighton, Chancellor
COORDINATOR: Ahmet Karamustafa
UNDERGRADUATE ENROLLMENT: 5,000
GRADUATE ENROLLMENT: 5,000

University of Washington

Comparative Religion Program
Thomson Hall 425, Box 353650
Seattle WA 98195-3650

Phone: 206-543-4835
Fax: 206-685-0668
E-mail: jaffee@u.washington.edu
URL: jsis.artsci.washington.edu/
programs/relig

TYPE OF INSTITUTION: Public

COORDINATOR: Martin S. Jaffee

UNDERGRADUATE ENROLLMENT: 24,838

GRADUATE ENROLLMENT: 8,000

DEGREES OFFERED: BA

UNDERGRADUATE MAJORS: 60

DEGREES CONFERRED: 25

DESCRIPTION OF UNDERGRADUATE PROGRAM: The Comparative Religion Program is one of several interdisciplinary programs in the Jackson School of International Studies. Students completing the program requirements receive a Bachelor of Arts in Comparative Religion. The availability of a large number of courses in a broad range of religious traditions underscores the uniqueness of the Comparative Religion curriculum at the Jackson School. Course offerings introduce students to several approaches to the study of religion, e.g., historical, textual, anthropological, philosophical, psychological, and sociological. Drawing from programs within the Jackson School as well as from other University departments, the curriculum is highly international and trans-cultural in character.

GRADUATE PROGRAM

Member of the Council on Graduate Studies in Religion

Graduate Advisor: Martin S. Jaffee

Graduate Degrees Offered: MA

Degrees Conferred: 2 MA

Graduate Students in Residence: 13 MA

Not in Residence: 0 MA

Average No. of New Students Enrolled: 3-6 MA

Women Students: 2 MA

Minority Students: 0 MA

Minimum GRE Score Requisite to Admission: Yes; 1100 verbal and quantative

Minimum GPA Score Requisite to Admission: Yes; 3.0 on 4.0 scale

Foreign Language Proficiency Evaluated: Yes

Financial Aid to First Year Students: 20% MA

Financial Aid to Other Students: 40% MA

Attrition Among Students: 30% MA

Graduates Placed: 60% MA

DESCRIPTION OF GRADUATE PROGRAM AND RESEARCH FACILITIES: The Graduate program encourages students to study the primary sources of religious traditions from a broadly comparative perspective. Two field seminars in theoretical issues in the comparative study of religion prepare students to engage in advanced studies in the following major concentrations: Buddhism, Hinduism, Islam, Judaism, Christianity and Religion and Culture. Students normally declare one of these concentrations as a "major" and a second as "minor." Minors can also be selected from Greco-Roman religions and East Asian indigenous religions. These studies are supported by faculty in the Jackson School of International Studies and such departments and programs as History, Anthropology, Asian Languages and Literature, Near Eastern Languages and Cultures and Jewish Studies. Library resources are especially strong in South Asian, East Asian, Middle Eastern and European sources.

ACADEMIC PLAN, ADMISSION REQUIREMENTS, FINANCIAL AID: The MA requires a three-year competence in a primary source language (e.g., Arabic, Greek, Hebrew, Latin, Pali, Sanskrit) and a reading competence in a secondary scholarly language, normally French or German. Language preparation is not a requirement for admission, but students entering with at least one year of primary source language expect to complete their programs within 2 to 2 ½ years. Most successful recent applicants have prior experience in Religious Studies or related fields in the Humanities, although the Program does not hold this to be a requirement. Minimal financial aid is available from the Program in the form of four teaching assistantships per year (each for a single academic quarter only) and an annual Webb Fellowship (up to $2,000). Both are awarded on the basis of competition. Students normally finance their studies through some combination of savings, personal loans and part-time employment.

FACULTY:

Conlon, Frank F., PhD, Minnesota (1969), Professor—history, religions of India, E-mail: conlon@u.washington.edu

Cox, Collett D., PhD, Columbia (1983), Associate Professor—Asian languages and literature, Buddhism, study of religion, E-mail: collett@u.washington.edu

Ellingson, Ter, PhD, University of Wisconsin, Madison (1979), Associate Professor—ethnomusicology, anthropology, comparative religions and South Asian ritual, Buddhism, Shamanism, Tibet, Nepal, Sri Lanka, E-mail: ellingsn@u.washington.edu

Goldberg, Ellis, PhD, Berkeley (1983), Associate Professor—political science, Islam, religion and politics in the Middle East, E-mail: goldberg@u.washington.edu

Green, James W., PhD, University of Washington (1972), Senior Lecturer—anthropology, cross cultural, mental health, comparative aging, West Indies, Pakistan, Islam, E-mail: jwgreen@u.washington.edu

Harrell, Stevan C., PhD, Stanford (1974), Professor—anthropology and Jackson School of International Studies (China Program), Chinese folk religion, anthropology of religion, E-mail: stevehar@u.washington.edu

Jaffee, Martin S., PhD, Brown University (1980), Professor—Jackson School of International Studies (Comparative Religion and Jewish Studies), Rabbinic Judaism, study of religion, E-mail: jaffee@u.washington.edu

Kartsonis, Anna D., PhD, Institute of Fine Arts, New York (1982), Associate Professor—art history, Byzantine and medieval Christian art and religion, E-mail: kartsoni@u.washington.edu

Keyes, Charles F., PhD, Cornell (1967), Professor—anthropology, anthropology of religion, Buddhism, E-mail: keyes@u.washington.edu

Locke, Hubert G., MA, Michigan (1961), Professor—public affairs, social thought and ethics, E-mail: quillpen@u.washington.edu

McCracken, David, PhD, Chicago (1966), Professor—English, eighteenth-century English literature, E-mail: davidmcc@u.washington.edu

Noegel, Scott, PhD, Cornell (1995), Assistant Professor—Jackson School of International Studies (Jewish studies) and Department of Near Eastern Languages and Civilization, Hebrew Bible, Ancient Near Eastern languages and literature

O'Neil, Mary R., PhD, Stanford (1982), Associate Professor—history, Renaissance and Reformation, E-mail: oneilmr@u.washington.edu

Pauwels, Heidi, PhD, University of Washington (1994), Assistant Professor—Asian languages and literature, Hindu language and literature, E-mail: hpauwels@u.washington.edu

Stacey, Robert C., PhD, Yale (1983), Professor—history, medieval Christianity, medieval Judaism, E-mail: bstacey@u.washington.edu

Stark, Rodney, PhD, University of California, Berkeley (1971), Professor—sociology, sociology of religion and new religions

Vance, Eugene A., PhD, Cornell (1964), Professor—English and comparative literature, medieval French literature, literary theory, E-mail: vance@u.washington.edu

Walker, Joel, PhD, Princeton (1998), Assistant Professor—history; religion and society in the late Roman empire; late antiquity; Syriac Christian literature and history

Webb, Eugene, PhD, Columbia (1965), Professor—comparative literature and Jackson School of International Studies (Comparative Religion), philosophy of religion, modern Christian thought, religion and literature, E-mail: ewebb@u.washington.edu

Wheeler, Brannon, PhD, Chicago (1994), Assistant Professor—Near Eastern languages and civilization, Islam, comparative study of religion

Williams, Michael A., PhD, Harvard (1977), Professor—Jackson School of International Studies (Comparative Religion), early Christianity and religion in late antiquity, study of religion, E-mail: maw@u.washington.edu

Young, Glennys J., PhD, University of California, Berkeley (1989), Associate Professor—Jackson School of International Studies, imperial and Soviet Russia, E-mail: glennys@u.washington.edu

ASSOCIATE MEMBERS:

Allon, Mark W., PhD, Cambridge (1995), Research Associate—Asian L&L, British Library/UW, early Buddhist manuscripts, Buddhist studies

Bacharach, Jere L., PhD, Michigan (1967), Professor—Jackson School of International Studies, Islamic history

Coburn, Robert, PhD, Harvard (1958), Professor—philosophy, religion and philosophy

Iltis, Linda L., PhD, Wisconsin-Madison (1985), Affiliate Associate Professor—Jackson School of International Studies (Comparative Religion and South Asian Studies), Buddhism, Hinduism, anthropology of religion, ritual studies, women and religion

Rhodes, Lorna, PhD, Cornell (1973), Associate Professor—anthropology, medical anthropology and religion, religion in South Asia

Saloman, Richard G., PhD, Pennsylvania (1975), Associate Professor—Asian languages and literature, religion in India

Stacey, Robin C., PhD, Yale (1986), Associate Professor—history, medieval Christianity

Wellman, Jim, PhD, Chicago (1995), Lecturer—sociology of religion, American religion, Christian mysticism

EMERITUS:

Brandauer, Frederick P., PhD, Stanford 91973), Associate Professor—Asian languages and literature, Chinese religious literature

Mish'alani, James K., PhD, Brown (1961), Assistant Professor—philosophy, religion and ethics

Potter, Karl H., PhD, Harvard (1955), Professor—philosophy and Jackson School of International Studies, philosophies of India

---

Washington and Jefferson College

Washington PA 15301

Washington and Lee University

Lexington VA 24450

Phone: 540-463-8798
Fax: 540-463-8498
E-mail: lyle.k@wlu.edu
URL: www.wlu.edu

TYPE OF INSTITUTION: Private, Non-Denominational
EXECUTIVE OFFICER: John W. Elrod, President
CHAIRPERSON: Alexandra Brown
UNDERGRADUATE ENROLLMENT: 1,600
GRADUATE ENROLLMENT: 350
DEGREES OFFERED: BA
UNDERGRADUATE MAJORS: 8-10
DEGREES CONFERRED: 5

DESCRIPTION OF UNDERGRADUATE PROGRAM: Washington and Lee University offers an undergraduate liberal arts and sciences education and a separate program for a JD in law. The Religion Department includes Asian religion studies, Christian studies, Jewish studies, and comparative religious studies with strong emphases in Japanese, South Asian, and American religions and in religion and law. Course offerings include sociology and philosophy of religion. Graduates with degrees in religion enter a wide variety of vocations and graduate and professional degree programs.

FACULTY:

Beckley, Harlan R., PhD, Vanderbilt University (1978), 1974, Professor—Christian ethics, theology, 540-463-8784, E-mail: beckley.h@wlu.edu

Brown, Alexandra R., PhD, Columbia University, Union Theological Seminary (1990), 1987, Associate Professor—biblical studies, early Christianity, 540-463-8789, E-mail: brown.a@wlu.edu

Davis, Winston B., PhD, University of Chicago (1973), 1992, Professor—comparative study of religion and society, Japanese religion, 540-463-8787, E-mail: davis.w@wlu.edu

Lubin, Timothy, PhD, Columbia University (1994), 1997, Assistant Professor—South Asian religion, comparative study of religion, 540-463-8146, E-mail: lubin.t@wlu.edu

Marks, Richard G., PhD, University of California (1980), 1984, Professor—Jewish studies, comparative study of religion, Islam, 540-463-8788, E-mail: marks.r@wlu.edu

Sullivan, Winnifred F., PhD, University of Chicago (1993), 1994, Assistant Professor (part-time)—American religion and law, 540-463-8638, E-mail: sullivan.w@wlu.edu

Washington Bible College

6511 Princess Garden Pkwy
Lanham MD 20706

Phone: 301-552-1400
URL: www.dkari@bible.edu

TYPE OF INSTITUTION: Private, Non-Denominational
EXECUTIVE OFFICER: Homer Heater, Jr., President
COORDINATOR: Steve Layne
UNDERGRADUATE ENROLLMENT: 350
GRADUATE ENROLLMENT: 200

The Washington Montessori Institute

2119 S St NW, Washington DC 20008

Washington Theological Union

6896 Laurel Street NW
Washington, DC 20012

Phone: 202-726-8800
Fax: 202-726-1716
URL: www.wtu.edu

TYPE OF INSTITUTION: Private, Roman Catholic

EXECUTIVE OFFICER: Rev. Daniel McLellan, OFM, President; Rev. Anthony DeConciliis, CSC, Academic Vice-President and Dean

GRADUATE ENROLLMENT: 268

Graduate Degrees Offered: MA

Degrees Conferred: 10

Graduate Students in Residence: 3 MA

Not in Residence: 49 MA

Average number of New Students Enrolled: 14 MA

Women Students: 17 MA

Minority Students: 7 MA

Foreign Students: 6 MA

Minimum GRE Score Requisite to Admission: No

Minumum GPA Scpre Requisite to Admission: Yes; 2.5 on 4.0 scale

Foreign Language Proficiency Evaluated: Yes

Financial Aid to First-Year Students: 53% MA

Financial Aid to Other Students: 38% MA

DESCRIPTION OF GRADUATE PROGRAM AND RESEARCH FACILITIES: The Master of Arts in Theology program provides a well-rounded and thorough instruction to the science of theology. The curriculum consists of 36 credit hours of course work. The student chooses a concentration from one of the departments: Sacred Scripture, Systematic and Moral Theology, Ecclesiastical History, Word and Worship or Pastoral Studies and Church Law. Requirements: a thesis or two substantial research papers, two-part comprehensive exam (one in general theological knowledge and the second in the area of concentration), ability to read an academic foreign language. There is an excellent research library: 205,000 volumes and 470 periodicals with particular holdings in Franciscan Studies, Carmelite Studies and historical theology. In addition, there is direct access to the other schools of theology in the Washington, D.C. Area.

ACADEMIC PLAN, ADMISSION REQUIREMENTS, FINANCIAL AID: Ordinarily, the Master of Arts in Theology can be completed by a full-time student in two years. Requirements for admission include: Bachelor's degree from an accredited post-secondary school with a GPA of at least 2.5/4.0 and a minimum of 18 credits in religious studies and philosophy, application form, GRE scores, TOEFL (upon request), 1-2 page autobiography including reason for applying to the Union, two letters of recommendation, interview (telephone interview can be arranged in exceptional cases), $30 application fee. Financial assistance is available in the form of institutional scholarships based on demonstrated need and ministry goals, partners in ministry, and federal student loans.

FACULTY:

Blanchard, David S., PhD, University of Chicago (1982), Adjunct Faculty (part-time)—mission studies

Boadt, Lawrence, CSP, SSD, Pontifical Biblical Institute, Rome (1976), 1976, Professor Emeritus—sacred scripture

Buggert, Donald W., STD, Catholic University of America (1979), 1971, Professor—systematic theology, 202-541-5241, E—mail: buggert@wtu.edu

Burkhard, John, OFM Conv., Dr. es Sc.Rel., University of Strasbourg (1972), 1991, Associate Professor—systematic theology, 202-541-5250, E-mail: burkhard@wtu.edu

Cook, Joan, SC, PhD, Vanderbilt University (1989), 1997, Associate Professor—sacred scripture, 202-541-5232, E-mail: cook@wtu.edu

Coriden, James A., JCD, Gregorian University, Rome (1961), JD, Catholic University of America School of Law (1972), 1975, Professor—church law, 202-541-5243, E-mail: coriden@wtu.edu

DeConciliis, Anthony, CSC, PhD, Loyola College, Baltimore (1993), DMin, Andover Newton (1972), 1997, Academic Dean and Associate Professor—pastoral studies, 202-541-5220, E-mail: deconciliis@wtu.edu

Delio, Ilia, OSF, PhD, UMDNJ-Graduate School (1984), PhD, Fordham University (1996), 1997, Assistant Professor—ecclesiastical history, 202-541-5242, E-mail: delio@wtu.edu

Donders, Joseph, MAfr, PhD, Gregorian University, Rome (1961), Adjunct Faculty (part-time)—mission studies

Durbin, William, Duke University (1996), 1998, Assistant Professor—ecclesiastical history, 202-541-5248, E-mail: durbin@wtu.edu

Grigassy, Daniel, OFM, PhD, Catholic University of America (1985), 1991, Assistant Professor—word and worship, 202-541-5262, E-mail: grigassy@wtu.edu

Himes, Kenneth, OFM, PhD, Duke University (1981), 1980, Professor—moral theology, 202-541-5257, E-mail: himes@wtu.edu

Horn, Francis, OSA, JCD, Catholic University of America (1998), 1998, Assistant Professor—church law, 202-541-5250, E-mail: horn@wtu.edu

Koernke, Theresa F., IHM, PhD, University of Notre Dame (1983), 1993, Assistant Professor—systematic theology, word and worship, 202-541-5252, E-mail: koernke@wtu.edu

Long, Brid, SSL, STD, Gregorian University, Rome (1990), 1997, Associate Professor—pastoral studies, 202-541-5225, E-mail: long@wtu.edu

Maher, Mary V., SSND, PhD, Catholic University of America (1989), 1993, Assistant Professor—systematic theology, 202-541-5258, E-mail: maher@wtu.edu

Mindling, Joseph, OFM Cap., SSD, Pontifical Biblical Institute, Rome (1989), 1988, Assistant Professor—sacred scripture, 202-541-5254, E-mail: mindling@wtu.edu

Monti, Dominic, OFM, PhD, University of Chicago (1979), 1979, Associate Professor—ecclesiastical history, 202-541-5260, E-mail: monti@wtu.edu

Murphy, Roland, OCarm, STD, Catholic University of America (1948), Adjunct Faculty (part-time)—sacred scripture

O'Connor, David, ST, JCD, Catholic University of America (1958), 1973, Professor Emeritus—church law

O'Neil, Kevin, CSsR, STD, Academia Alphonsiana, Rome (1989), 1992, Assistant Professor—moral theology, 202-541-5263, E-mail: o'neil@wtu.edu

Scullion, James, OFM, PhD, Catholic University of America (1991), 1989, Assistant Professor—sacred scripture, 202-541-5256, E-mail: scullion@wtu.edu

Taggart, Bruce, OCam, PhD, Tufts University (1972), 1997, Assistant Professor—philosophy, 202-541-5241, E-mail: taggart@wtu.edu

Wallace, James A., CSsR, PhD, Northwestern University (1987), 1987, Professor—word and worship, 202-541-5261, E-mail: wallace@wtu.edu

Waznak, Robert, SS, PhD, Temple University (1974), 1980, Professor—word and worship, 202-541-5259, E-mail: waznak@wtu.edu

Welch, John, OCam, PhD, University of Notre Dame (1974), 1974, Professor—pastoral studies, 202-541-5240, E-mail: welch@wtu.edu

Wimmer, Joseph, OSA, STD, Gregorian University, Rome (1980), 1969, Associate Professor—sacred scripture, 202-541-5255, E-mail: wimmer@wtu.edu

---

University of Waterloo

Dept of Religious Studies
Waterloo, Ontario N2L 3G1
Canada

Phone: 519-885-0220 ext 257
Fax: 519-885-0014
E-mail: lemcginl@uwaterloo.ca
URL: arts.uwaterloo.ca/RELSTUD/index.htm

TYPE OF INSTITUTION: Public

EXECUTIVE OFFICER: R. R. Kerton, Dean of Arts

CHAIRPERSON: Thomas R. Yoder Neufeld

UNDERGRADUATE ENROLLMENT: 1,900

DEGREES OFFERED: Three-Year General, Four-Year General, Honours, Honours (Applied Studies Co-op), Religious Studies Joint Honours, Minor

UNDERGRADUATE MAJORS: 65

DEGREES CONFERRED: 15

DESCRIPTION OF UNDERGRADUATE PROGRAM: The Department of Religious Studies is by design and constitution a cooperative effort of five agencies: the Faculty of Arts, three affiliated church colleges and one federated university: Conrad Grebel College (Mennonite), Renison College (Anglican), St Paul's United College (United), and St Jerome's University (Roman Catholic). While the Department is located in the Faculty of Arts, the faculty represents a diversity of religious and cultural traditions. The Department of Religious Studies offers courses in world religions, psychology and sociology of religion, religion and art, with especially rich offerings in the Christian tradition (Scripture, theology, history, and ethics).

FACULTY:

Bird, Michael, PhD, University of Iowa (1975), 1969, Professor—religion and culture, religion and art, Renison College, 519-884-4404 ext 640, Fax: 519-884-5135, E-mail: msbird@uwaterloo.ca

Bryant, M. Darrol, PhD, University of St Michael's College (1976), 1973, Professor—history of Christian thought, interreligious dialogue, Renison College, 519-884-4404 ext 641, Fax: 519-884-5135, E-mail: mdbryant@uwaterloo.ca

Dawson, Lorne, PhD, McMaster University (1986), 1992, Associate Professor—theory and method, sociology/psychology of religion, UW Sociology, 519-888-4567 ext 5340, Fax: 519-746-7326, E-mail: ldawson@uwaterloo.ca

Fenn, Mavis, PhD, McMaster University (1994), 1998, Assistant Professor—Asian religion (specialization in Buddhism), death and dying, St Paul's College, 519-885-1460 ext 214, Fax: 519-885-6364, E-mail: mfenn@uwaterloo.ca

Frick, Peter, PhD, McMaster University (1989), 1989, Assistant Professor—New Testament, St Paul's College, 519-885-1460 ext 214, Fax: 519-885-6364, E-mail: pfrick@uwaterloo.ca

Gollnick, James, PhD, University of Toronto (1974), 1991, Associate Professor—psychology of religion, St Paul's College, 519-885-1460 ext 213, Fax: 519-885-6364, E-mail: jgollnic@uwaterloo.ca

Higgins, Michael W., PhD, York University (1979), 1982, Professor—Catholic studies, religion and literature, St Jerome's University, 519-884-8111 ext 253, Fax: 519-884-5759, E-mail: mwhiggin@uwaterloo.ca

Reimer, A. James, PhD, University of St Michael's College (1983), 1978, Professor—Christian theology, ethics, Conrad Grebel College, 519-885-0220 ext 234, Fax: 519-885-0014, E-mail: ajreimer@uwaterloo.ca

Sahas, Daniel J., PhD, Hartford Seminary Foundation (1969), 1969, Professor—Islam, Byzantine studies, UW Religious Studies, 519-888-4567 ext 3565, Fax: 519-746-3097, E-mail: dsahas@uwaterloo.ca

Seljak, David A., PhD, McGill University (1996), 1996, Assistant Professor—history of religion, religion and society, St Jerome's University, 519-884-8111 ext 232, Fax: 519-884-5759, E-mail: dseljak@uwaterloo.ca

Vanin, Cristina, PhD, Boston/Andover Newton Theological School (1997), 1991, Assistant Professor—theology and ethics, St Jerome's University, 519-884-8111 ext 266, Fax: 519-884-5759, E-mail: cdvaninb@uwaterloo.ca

Yoder Neufeld, Thomas R., ThD, Harvard University Divinity School (1989), 1983, Associate Professor—biblical studies, peace studies, Conrad Grebel College, 519-885-0220 ext 261, Fax: 519-885-0014, E-mail: tyoderne@uwaterloo.ca

Waterloo Lutheran Seminary

Wilfrid Laurier University
75 University Avenue W
Waterloo ON N2L 3C5Canada

Phone: 519-884-1970 ext 3234
Fax: 519-725-2434
URL: www.wlu.ca/~wwwsem/

TYPE OF INSTITUTION: Denominational: Eastern Synod, Evangelical Lutheran Church in Canada

EXECUTIVE OFFICER: Richard C. Crossman, Principal-Dean

GRADUATE ENROLLMENT: 130

Wayland Baptist University

WBU 344, 1900 W 7th, Plainview TX 79072

Wayne State University

5050 Cass, Detroit MI 48202

Waynesburg College

Waynesburg PA 15370

Phone: 724-852-3282
Fax: 724-627-6416

DEGREES OFFERED: BA

UNDERGRADUATE MAJORS: No religion major; a religion minor and a pre-ministerial program

DESCRIPTION OF UNDERGRADUATE PROGRAM: One full-time and two part-time instructors teach 5 courses to 100 students per semester. Six students are in the minor program; two in the pre-ministerial program.

FACULTY:

Kisner, Jeffrey A., PhD, Southern Baptist Theological Seminary (1989), 1989, Associate Professor—biblical studies, systematic theology, world religions, 724-852-3316, Fax: 724-627-6416, E-mail: jkisner@waynesburg.edu

Noftzger, Richard L., Jr., MDiv, Gordon-Conwell Theological Seminary (1980), 1996, Vice President for Institutional Planning, Research and Information Technologies and Instructor of Religion (part-time)—biblical studies, religion in America, church history, 724-852-3384, Fax: 724-627-6416, E-mail: noftzger@waynesburg.edu

---

Weber State College

3750 Harrison Bldg, Ogden UT 84403

Webster University

470 E Lockwood
St Louis MO 63119-3194

Phone: 314-968-7135
Fax: 314-963-6100
E-mail: heidemca@webster.edu
URL: www.webster.edu/

TYPE OF INSTITUTION: Private
EXECUTIVE OFFICER: Richard S. Meyers, President
CHAIRPERSON: Christopher P. Parr
UNDERGRADUATE ENROLLMENT: 11,500
GRADUATE ENROLLMENT: 2,500

Weimer College

PO Box 486
Weimer CA 95736

Phone: 530-637-4111, ext 7710
Fax: 530-637-4408
E-mail: college@weimar.edu
URL: www.weimar.org

TYPE OF INSTITUTION: Private, SDA

Wellesley College

106 Central Street
Wellesley MA 02481

Phone: 781-283-2609
Fax: 781-283-3648
E-mail: @wellesley.edu
URL: www.wellesley.edu

TYPE OF INSTITUTION: Private, Non-Denominational
EXECUTIVE OFFICER: Diana Chapman Walsh, President
CHAIRPERSON: Louise Marlow
UNDERGRADUATE ENROLLMENT: 2,500

Wells College

Aurora NY 13026

Phone: 315-364-3294

TYPE OF INSTITUTION: Private
CHAIRPERSON: Jenny Yates
UNDERGRADUATE ENROLLMENT: 400

Wesley College

120 N State St, Dover DE 19901

Wesley College

111 Wesley Circle, Florence MS 93073

Wesley Biblical Seminary

5980 Floral Dr
PO Box 9938
Jackson MS 39206-0938

Phone: 601-957-1314
Fax: 601-991-2100
URL: www.gowesley.com

TYPE OF INSTITUTION: Interdenominational: Wesleyan-Arminian
EXECUTIVE OFFICER: Donald Smith, President
GRADUATE ENROLLMENT: 100

Wesley Theological Seminary

4500 Massachusetts Ave NW
Washington DC 20016

Phone: 202-885-8600
Fax: 202-885-8605

TYPE OF INSTITUTION: Denominational: United Methodist
EXECUTIVE OFFICERS: Douglass Lewis, President; Bruce C. Birch, Dean
GRADUATE ENROLLMENT: 634

Wesleyan College

4760 Forsyth Road
Macon GA 31210

Phone: 912-757-5213
Fax: 912-757-5110
E-mail: kevin_schilbrack or jeff_prud-
homme@post.wesleyan-college.edu
URL: www.wesleyan-college.edu

TYPE OF INSTITUTION: Private, affiliated with the United Methodist Church
EXECUTIVE OFFICER: Nora Kizer Bell, President
UNDERGRADUATE ENROLLMENT: 586

Wesleyan University

Dept of Religion
171 Church Street
Middletown CT 06459-0029

Phone: 860-685-2820
Fax: 860-685-2821
URL: www.wesleyan.edu/religion/
home.html

TYPE OF INSTITUTION: Private
EXECUTIVE OFFICER: Douglas J. Bennet, President
CHAIRPERSON: Jeremy Zwelling
UNDERGRADUATE ENROLLMENT: 2,700
DEGREES OFFERED: BA
UNDERGRADUATE MAJORS: 45
DEGREES CONFERRED: 20
DESCRIPTION OF UNDERGRADUATE PROGRAM: The Department of Religion at Wesleyan
  has developed a curriculum adapted to the small university. It includes a wide range of
  courses to meet the diverse interests of a large percentage of the students in the University,
  but also enough depth in specific fields to challenge students who wish to concentrate in religious studies. The Department offers a cross-cultural, interdisciplinary and critical program
  that explores the variety of religious experiences and expressions. In addition to courses that
  demonstrate the power and limits of various critical theories in the study of religion, the Department provides opportunities to analyze: systems of belief and patterns of religious behavior; the history of religious traditions; the functions of religion in society; and various
  forms of religious expression such as myth, ritual, sacred story, scripture, liturgy, theological
  and philosophical reflection.
FACULTY:
Cameron, Ron, PhD, Harvard University, Professor—E-mail: rcameron@wesleyan.edu
Crites, Stephen D., (in Philosophy), PhD, Yale Univeristy, Professor—E-mail:
  scrites@wesleyan.edu
Klaaren, Eugene M., PhD, Harvard University, Associate Professor—E-mail: ek-
  laaren@wesleyan.edu
McAlister, Elizabeth A., PhD, Yale University, Assistant Professor—E-mail: emcalis-
  ter@wesleyan.edu
Smyers, Karen A., PhD, Princeton, Assistant Professor—E-mail: ksmyers@wesleyan.edu
Willis, Janice D., PhD, Columbia, Professor—E-mail: jwillis@wesleyan.edu
Zwelling, Jeremy, PhD, Brandeis, Associate Professor—E-mail: jzwelling@wesleyan.edu

West Coast Christian College

6901 N Maple Ave, Fresno CA 93710

University of West Florida

11000 University Pkwy
Pensacola FL 32514-5750

Phone: 850-474-2672
URL: www.uwf.edu

TYPE OF INSTITUTION: Public
CHAIRPERSON: L. W. (Toby) Howe

COORDINATOR: Barry R. Arnold
UNDERGRADUATE ENROLLMENT: 7,000
GRADUATE ENROLLMENT: 1,400

State University of West Georgia

Maple Street
Carrollton GA 30118

Phone: 770-836-6512
Fax: 770-830-2334
E-mail: bwantlan@westga.edu

TYPE OF INSTITUTION: Public
COORDINATOR: B. L. Wantland, Dept of Philosophy/English
UNDERGRADUATE ENROLLMENT: 8,000
GRADUATE ENROLLMENT:1,000

West Liberty State College

West Liberty WV 26074

West Texas State University

Canyon TX 79016

West Virginia University

Program for Religious Studies
PO 6324
Morgantown WV 26506-6324

Phone: 304-293-4995
Fax: 304-293-7329
E-mail: meitzen@wvnvm.wvnet.edu

TYPE OF INSTITUTION: Public
EXECUTIVE OFFICER: M. Duane Nellis, Dean, Eberly College of Arts and Science
CHAIRPERSON: Richard Montgomery
UNDERGRADUATE ENROLLMENT: 16,000

West Virginia Wesleyan College

59 College Ave
Buchhannon WV 26201

Phone: 304-473-8446
E-mail: holmes@wvwc.edu
URL: www.wvwc.edu/

TYPE OF INSTITUTION: Private, church related United Methodist
EXECUTIVE OFFICER: William R. Haden, President
CHAIRPERSON: Arthur B. Holmes
UNDERGRADUATE ENROLLMENT: 1,537

Western Baptist College

5000 Deer Park Dr SE, Salem OR 97301

Western Baptist Bible College

2119-25 Tracy Ave, Kansas City MO 64108

Western Carolina University

Philosophy and Religion
Cullowhee NC 28723

Phone: 704-227-7262
Fax: 704-227-7647
E-mail: jmclachla@wcu.edu

TYPE OF INSTITUTION: Public
EXECUTIVE OFFICER: John Bardo, Chancellor
COORDINATOR: James McLachlan

Western Conservative Baptist Seminary

5511 SE Hawthorne Blvd, Portland OR 97215

Western Evangelical Seminary

12753 SW 68th Avenue
Portland OR 97223

Phone: 503-554-6100
Fax: 503-598-4338
E-mail: tjohnson@georgefox.edu
URL: www.georgefox.edu/
academics/grad/wes/weshome.html

TYPE OF INSTITUTION: Private, Multi-Denominational
EXECUTIVE OFFICER: Tom Johnson, Dean
GRADUATE ENROLLMENT: 300

Western Illinois University

Dept of Philosophy and
Religious Studies
1 University Circle
Macomb IL 61455

Phone: 309-298-1057
Fax: 309-298-0285
E-mail: mario_morelli@ccmail.wiu.edu
URL: www.wiu.edu/users/miphil/

TYPE OF INSTITUTION: Public
EXECUTIVE OFFICER: Donald S. Spencer, President
CHAIRPERSON: Mario F. Morelli
UNDERGRADUATE ENROLLMENT: 11,000
GRADUATE ENROLLMENT: 1,200

Western Kentucky University

Dept of Philosophy and Religion, Bowling Green KY 42101

Western Maryland College

Dept of Philosophy and Religious Studies
Westminster MD 21157

Phone: 410-857-2460
Fax: 410-857-2729
E-mail: galles@wmdc.edu
URL: www.wmdc.edu

TYPE OF INSTITUTION: Private
EXECUTIVE OFFICER: Robert H. Chambers III, President
CHAIRPERSON: Gregory D. Alles
UNDERGRADUATE ENROLLMENT: 1,500

Western Michigan University

Dept of Comparative Religion
College of Arts and Sciences
Kalamazoo MI 49008

Phone: 616-387-4391
E-mail: e.thomas.lawson@wmich.edu

TYPE OF INSTITUTION: Public
EXECUTIVE OFFICER: Diether H. Haenicke, President
CHAIRPERSON: E. Thomas Lawson
UNDERGRADUATE ENROLLMENT: 20,187
GRADUATE ENROLLMENT: 6,350

University of Western Ontario

London, Ontario N6A 3K7 Canada

Western Theological Seminary

101 E 13th St
Holland MI 49423

Phone: 616-392-8555
Fax: 616-392-7717
E-mail: brownsonj@hope.edu
URL: www.westernsem.org

TYPE OF INSTITUTION: Denominational: Reformed Church in America
EXECUTIVE OFFICERS: Dennis N. Voskuil, President; James V. Brownson, Academic Dean
GRADUATE ENROLLMENT: 164

Western Washington State College

Bellingham WA 98225

Westminster College

501 Westminster Ave, Fulton MO 65251

Westminster College

Dept of Religion, History, Philosophy, and Classics	Phone: 724-946-7244
	Fax: 724-946-7256
319 South Market Street	E-mail: castroad@westminster.edu
New Wilmington PA 16172-0001	URL: www.westminster.edu

TYPE OF INSTITUTION: Private, related to the Presbyterian Church (USA) through the Synod of the Trinity

EXECUTIVE OFFICER: John Deegan, Jr., Vice President for Academic Affairs and Dean of College

CHAIRPERSON: A. Dwight Castro

COORDINATOR: Jeffrey J. Kripal

UNDERGRADUATE ENROLLMENT: 1,400

GRADUATE ENROLLMENT: 200

DEGREES OFFERED: BA, MEd

UNDERGRADUATE MAJORS: 21 (religion), 40 (history), 3 (philosophy), 2 (classics)

DEGREES CONFERRED: 16

DESCRIPTION OF UNDERGRADUATE PROGRAM: Westminster College is an independent, coeducational liberal arts college, related to the Presbyterian Church (U.S.A.). The Department of Religion, History, Philosophy and Classics brings together four of the central disciplines of the Humanities, each of which provides important insights into the nature of human experience. Although separate major programs are maintained in each of the component disciplines, the combination into a single department affords greater opportunities to explore the connections between the individual disciplines and to create exciting and relevant interdisciplinary courses, as well as to develop new interdisciplinary concentrations that draw on the varied expertise of the departmental faculty, many of whom have the academic training and background to teach courses in more than one of the component disciplines.

FACULTY:

Botzenhart-Viehe, Verena, PhD, University of California, Santa Barbara (1980), 1990, Associate Professor of History—U.S. foreign relations, twentieth-century Europe, Germany, E-mail: verenabv@westminster.edu

Castro, A. Dwight, PhD, Indiana University (1972), 1970, Professor of Classics—Greek and Roman history, Latin literature, New Testament Greek, E-mail: castroad@westminster.edu

Coble, Ann L., PhD, Saint Louis University (1999), 1999, Assistant Professor of Christian Education and Religion—Christian education, religion in America, E-mail: cobleal@westminster.edu

Kripal, Jeffrey J., PhD, University of Chicago (1993), 1993, Vira I. Heinz Associate Professor of Religion—history of religions, Asian studies, Roman Catholic studies, E-mail: kripaljj@westminster.edu

Martin, Russell E., PhD, Harvard University (1996), 1996, Assistant Professor of History—Russia and Russian Orthodoxy, E-mail: martinre@westminster.edu

Muth, Michael P., MA, Duke University (1994), 1997, Instructor of Philosophy—ancient and medieval philosophy, E-mail: muthmp@westminster.edu

Na, Kang-Yup, MDiv, Princeton Theological Seminary (1989), 1998, Instructor of Religion—biblical studies, E-mail: nak@westminster.edu

Rennie, Bryan S., PhD, University of Edinburgh, Scotland (1991), 1994, Assistant Professor of Religion and Philosophy—history and philosophy of religion, E-mail: brennie@westminster.edu

Sharkey, Eugene G., PhD, Rutgers University (1972), 1972, Professor of History—Latin America, military, U.S. intellectual, 20th Century America, E-mail: sharke@westminster.edu

Twining, David C., PhD, Case Western Reserve University (1988), 1990, Associate Professor of History—colonial, revolutionary and early national America, Tudor/Stuart England, E-mail: twinin@westminster.edu

---

Westminster Theological Seminary

1725 Bear Valley Pkwy, Escondido CA 92027

Westminster Theological Seminary

PO Box 27009
Philadelphia PA 19118

Phone: 800-373-0119
Fax: 215-887-5404
E-mail: admissions@wts.edu

TYPE OF INSTITUTION: Private
EXECUTIVE OFFICER: Samuel Logan, President
GRADUATE ENROLLMENT: 492

Westmont College

955 La Paz Road
Santa Barbara CA 93108

Phone: 805-565-6169
Fax: 805-565-7101
E-mail: lgundry@westmont.edu
URL: www.westmont.edu

TYPE OF INSTITUTION: Private

EXECUTIVE OFFICER: David Winter, President

CHAIRPERSON: Karen H. Jobes

UNDERGRADUATE ENROLLMENT: 1,200

DEGREES OFFERED: BA

UNDERGRADUATE MAJORS: 50

DEGREES CONFERRED: 20

DESCRIPTION OF UNDERGRADUATE PROGRAM: The Department of Religious Studies constitutes one of about twenty departments in a traditional program of the liberal arts. All four-year students have to take one course each in OT, NT, Theology, and Church History, Theological History, or Apologetics. Students who major in Religious Studies may emphasize Biblical Languages, Biblical Backgrounds/Archaeology, Theological/Historical Studies, Christian Mission, or Christian Mission with Urban Concentration. Courses are offered also in non-Christian World Religions. Though non-denominational, the department and its college are committed to American Evangelical Christianity plus open and honest dialogue with other traditions.

FACULTY:

Espinosa, Gaston, PhD (cand.), University of California, Santa Barbara (1998), 1996, Assistant Professor—history of Christianity, 805-565-7094, E-mail: espinosa@westmont.edu

Fisk, Bruce, PhD, Duke (1997), 1999, Assistant Professor—New Testament, 805-565-7369, E-mail: fisk@westmont.edu

Gundry, Robert H., PhD, University of Manchester (1961), 1962, Professor—New Testament, 805-565-6091, E-mail: gundry@westmont.edu

Jobes, Karen, PhD, Westminster Theological Seminary (1995), 1996, Assistant Professor—New Testament, 805-565-7269, E-mail: jobes@westmont.edu

Longman, Tremper, III, PhD, Yale University (1983), 1998, Professor—Old Testament, 805-565-6168, E-mail: longman@westmont.edu

Nelson, William, PhD, Harvard University (1991), 1986, Associate Professor—Old Testament, 805-565-6167, E-mail: nelson@westmont.edu

Whiteman, Curt, PhD, St Louis University (1982), 1976, Professor—historical theology, 805-565-7007, E-mail: whiteman@westmont.edu

Wilson, Jonathan R., PhD, Duke University (1989), 1989, Associate Professor—religious studies, 805-565-6199, E-mail: jwilson@westmont.edu

---

Weston Jesuit School of Theology

3 Phillips Place
Cambridge MA 02138

Phone: 617-492-1960
Fax: 617-492-5833
E-mail: admissionsinfo@wjst.edu
URL: www.wjst.edu

TYPE OF INSTITUTION: Private, Roman Catholic Jesuit

EXECUTIVE OFFICER: John R. Sachs, SJ, Academic Dean

GRADUATE ENROLLMENT: 254

GRADUATE PROGRAM

Graduate Degrees Offered: MA; MTS; MDiv; ThM; STL; STD

Degrees Conferred: 65 Other

Graduate Students in Residence: 170 Other

Not in Residence: 80 Other

Average No. of New Students Enrolled: 60 Other

Women Students: 50 Other

Minority Students: 5 Other

Foreign Students: 30 Other

Minimum GRE Score Requisite to Admission: No

Minimum GPA Score Requisite to Admission: No

Foreign Language Proficiency Evaluated: No

Financial Aid to First Year Students: 40% Other

Financial Aid to Other Students: 60% Other

Attrition Among Students: 2% Other

Graduates Placed: 100% Other

DESCRIPTION OF GRADUATE PROGRAM AND RESEARCH FACILITIES: Weston is one of nine schools in the Boston Theological Institute, among which are Harvard, Boston College, Andover Newton, and Boston University; there are more than 250 full-and part-time faculty offering more than 500 courses in which students may cross-register. The joint Weston-Episcopal Divinity School Library has 270,000 volumes and over 1,200 periodical titles.

ACADEMIC PLAN, ADMISSION REQUIREMENTS, FINANCIAL AID: MTS, 48 semester credits, 2 years; MDiv, 81 semester credits, 3 years; ThM, 24 semester credits, 1 year after MDiv or equivalent; STL, 33 semester credits, 2 years after MDiv or equivalent. Admissions requirements: 1) bachelor's degree gained with above-average grades from an accredited college; 2) at least one-third of the program in the liberal arts; 3) for those who do not possess a graduate degree, above-average scores on the Graduate Record Examination or the Miller Analogies Test. A limited amount of financial aid is available.

FACULTY:

Anatolios, Khaled, PhD, Boston College (1996), 1996, Assistant Professor—historical theology

Baldovin, John F., PhD, Yale (1982), 1999, Professor—historical-liturgial theology

Burke, Kevin F., STD, Weston Jesuit (1997), 1997, Assistant Professor—historical theology

Cardman, Francine J., PhD, Yale (1974), 1979, Associate Professor—historical theology

Clarke, Katherine M., PhD, Loyola Chicago (1981), 1992, Associate Professor—psychology and pastoral counseling

Clifford, Richard J., PhD, Harvard (1970), 1970, Professor—Old Testament

Farnham, Janice, PhD, Catholic University of America (1989), 1993, Assistant Professor—church history

Fink, Peter E., PhD, Emory (1976), 1975, Professor—sacramental-liturgical theology

Guider, Margaret, ThD, Harvard (1993), 1990, Faculty Director of Ministry Practica and Associate Professor—religion and society

Haight, Roger D., PhD, University of Chicago (1974), 1990, Professor—systematic theology

Harrington, Daniel J., PhD, Harvard (1970), 1972, Professor—New Testament

Kane, Thomas A., PhD, Ohio State (1981), 1983, Associate Professor—homiletics, liturgical practice

Keenan, James F., STD, Gregorian (1988), 1991, Professor—moral theology

Kselman, John S., PhD, Harvard University (1971), 1987, Associate Professor—Old Testament

Marrow, Stanley B., STD, Gregorian (1966), 1971, Professor—New Testament

Massaro, Thomas J., PhD, Emory (1997), 1997, Assistant Professor—moral theology

McDermott, Brian O., ThD, Nijmegen (1973), 1973, Associate Professor—systematic theology

O'Malley, John W., PhD, Harvard (1966), 1979, Professor—church history

Sachs, John R., ThD, University of Tübingen (1984), 1986, Dean and Associate Professor—systematic theology

Vacek, Edward V., PhD, Northwestern (1978), 1981, Associate Professor—moral theology

---

Wheaton College

Dept of Biblical and Theological, Archaeological, and World Religions
501 College Avenue
Wheaton IL 60187-5593

Phone: 630-752-5054
Fax: 630-752-5296
E-mail: btawr@wheaton.edu
URL: www.wheaton.edu/theology

TYPE OF INSTITUTION: Private

EXECUTIVE OFFICER: Stanton Jones, Provost and Dean of Graduate School

CHAIRPERSON: Andrew E. Hill

COORDINATORS: Gene Green (Undgrad), J. Julius Scott (Grad)

UNDERGRADUATE ENROLLMENT: 2,335

GRADUATE ENROLLMENT: 300

DEGREES OFFERED: BA

UNDERGRADUATE MAJORS: 180

DEGREES CONFERRED: 43

DESCRIPTION OF UNDERGRADUATE PROGRAM: Majors and minors in Biblical, Theological, Archaeological, and Religious Studies within a Christian Liberal Arts context. Emphasis on integration of learning with faith, and interaction with other disciplines of the college.

GRADUATE PROGRAM

Graduate Degrees Offered: MA

Degrees Conferred: 22 MA

DESCRIPTION OF GRADUATE DEPARTMENT: Majors in Biblical Studies, Church History and Theology and Religion in American Life. The graduate curriculum emphasis is on disciplinary and methodological concerns (rather than occupational or professional training), the development of an evangelical perspective, and interaction with the contemporary disciplines. The MA is used as preparation for further graduate study and Christian service.

FACULTY:

Bacote, Vincent, PhD (cand.), Drew, 1999, Instructor—theology

Bullock, C. Hassell, PhD, Hebrew Union College (1968), 1973, Professor—Old Testament, Judaica, 630-752-5271, E-mail: c.h.bullock@wheaton.edu

Burge, Gary, PhD, King's College, Aberdeen (1984), 1992, Professor—New Testament, 630-752-5932, E-mail: gary.burge@wheaton.edu

Callahan, James, PhD, Marquette University (1994), 1995, Assistant Professor—theology, E-mail: james.p.callahan@wheaton.edu

Elwell, Walter, PhD, Edinburgh (1970), 1975, Professor—New Testament, 630-752-5272

Ericson, Norman R., PhD, University of Chicago (1972), 1977, Professor—New Testament, 630-752-5273, E-mail: norman.r.ericson@wheaton.edu

Green, Gene, PhD, University of Aberdeen (1980), 1996, Associate Professor—New Testament, E-mail: gene.l.green@wheaton.edu

Hill, Andrew E., PhD, University of Michigan (1981), 1984, Professor—Old Testament, Near Eastern studies, Hebrew, 630-752-5274, E-mail: andrew.e.hill@wheaton.ed

Johnson, Alan F., ThD, Dallas Theological Seminary (1964), 1969, Professor—New Testament, Christian ethics, 630-752-5277, E-mail: alan.johnson@wheaton.edu

Lake, Donald M., PhD, University of Iowa (1967), 1970, Professor—systematic theology, world religions, 630-752-5278, E-mail: donald.m.lake@wheaton.edu

Lewis, James, PhD, University of Iowa (1976), 1994, Associate Professor—religious studies, 630-752-5056, E-mail: james.f.lewis@wheaton.edu

Long, Gary A., PhD, University of Chicago (1993), 1999, Visiting Assistant Professor— Old Testament, 630-752-5276

Long, Kathryn, PhD, Duke University (1993), 1993, Assistant Professor—church history

McRay, John, PhD, University of Chicago (1967), 1980, Professor—New Testament, archaeology, 630-752-5177, E-mail: john.mcray@wheaton.edu

Miguélez, Laura, PhD (cand.), Boston University, 1998, Assistant Professor—theology, E-mail: laura.c.miguelez@wheaton.edu

Monson, John, PhD, Harvard (1998), 1997, Assistant Professor—Archaeology, 630-752-5275, E-mail: john.m.monson@wheaton.edu

Noll, Mark, PhD, Vanderbilt (1975), 1978, Professor—religion in American life, church history, 630-752-5865

Okholm, Dennis, PhD, Princeton (1986), 1989, Associate Professor—systematic theology, Christian thought, medieval theology, 630-752-5055, E-mail: dennis.l.okholm@wheaton.edu

Phillips, Timothy, PhD, Vanderbilt (1986), 1987, Associate Professor—theology, 630-752-5279

Schultz, Richard, PhD, Yale (1989), 1995, Associate Professor—Old Testament, E-mail: richard.l.schultz@wheaton.edu

Scott, J. Julius, PhD, Manchester (1969), 1977, Professor—New Testament, 630-752-5280, E-mail: j.julius.scott@wheaton.edu

Webber, Robert E., ThD, Covenant Seminary (1968), 1968, Professor—theology and worship, 630-752-5281, e-mail: robert.e.webber@wheaton.edu

White, Manya, PhD (cand.), Hebrew Union, 1987, Visiting Instructor—Old Testament

Wolf, Herbert, PhD, Brandeis (1967), 1967, Professor—Old Testament, Hebrew, 630-752-5282, E-mail: hebert.m.wolf@wheaton.edu

---

Wheaton College

5 E Main St
Norton MA 02766

Phone: 508-285-8200
Fax: 508-285-2908
E-mail: jeffrey_timm@wheatonma.edu

TYPE OF INSTITUTION: Private, Non-Denominational
EXECUTIVE OFFICER: Dale Marshall, President
CHAIRPERSON: Jeffrey R. Timm
UNDERGRADUATE ENROLLMENT: 1,350

Wheeling Jesuit University

316 Washington Avenue
Wheeling WV 26003-6295

Phone: 304-243-2000
Fax: 304-243-2243
E-mail: hammond@wju.edu
URL: www.wju.edu

TYPE OF INSTITUTION: Private, Catholic
EXECUTIVE OFFICER: Debra Hull, Acting Chief Academic Officer/Dean
CHAIRPERSON: David M. Hammond
UNDERGRADUATE ENROLLMENT: 1,300
GRADUATE ENROLLMENT: 215

Whitman College

345 Boyer Ave
Walla Walla WA 99362

Phone: 509-527-5248
Fax: 509-527-5039
E-mail: whitman@whitman.edu
admission@whitman.edu
URL: www.whitman.edu/

TYPE OF INSTITUTION: Private, Non-Denominational

EXECUTIVE OFFICER: Patrick Keef, Dean of Faculty
CHAIRPERSON: Jonathan S. Walters
UNDERGRADUATE ENROLLMENT: 1,345

Whittier College

Dept of Religious Studies
13406 E Philadelphia St
Whittier CA 90608

Phone: 562-907-4200
Fax: 562-698-4067
E-mail: jprice@whittier.edu

TYPE OF INSTITUTION: Private, Non-Denominational
EXECUTIVE OFFICER: Katherine Haley Will, President
CHAIRPERSON: Joseph L. Price
UNDERGRADUATE ENROLLMENT: 1,300
DEGREES OFFERED: BA
UNDERGRADUATE MAJORS: 10
DEGREES CONFERRED: 4

DESCRIPTION OF UNDERGRADUATE PROGRAM: The religious studies program exemplifies the interconnectedness of knowledge as it explores questions about the nature of religion: Is religion a set of beliefs, a code of conduct, or a surge of ecstatic feeling? Does religion require membership in a church, synagogue, mosque, or temple? Or is religion a dynamic process of human transformation? Within a traditional liberal arts context that emphasizes the plurality of world cultures, the courses in religious studies explore the ways in which beliefs, practices, and symbols function in orienting the lives of peoples.

FACULTY:

Gottschall, Marilyn, PhD, University of Southern California (1998), 1995, Assistant Professor—women and religion, ethics, feminist theory, 562-907-4200, Fax: 562-907-4910

Price, Joseph L., PhD, Chicago (1982), 1982, Professor—theology, biblical literature, religion in America, 562-907-4910, E-mail: jprice@whittier.edu

Yocum, Glenn E., PhD, Pennsylvania (1976), 1973, Professor—religions of India, history of religions, 562-907-4200, Fax: 562-907-4910, E-mail: gyocum@whittier.edu

---

Whitworth College

Dept of Religion and Philosophy
Spokane WA 99251

Phone: 509-777-3275
Fax: 509-777-3274
E-mail: rmohrlang@whitworth.edu
URL: www.whitworth.edu/dept/relphil.htm

TYPE OF INSTITUTION: Private, church related, Presbyterian (PCUSA)
EXECUTIVE OFFICER: William Robinson, President
CHAIRPERSON: Roger Mohrlang
COORDINATOR: Gerald Sittser
UNDERGRADUATE ENROLLMENT: 1,600
GRADUATE ENROLLMENT: 400

Wichita State University

1845 Fairmount, Wichita KS 67208

Wilberforce University

Wilberforce OH 45384   **Phone: 937-376-2911**

DEGREES OFFERED: BA
UNDERGRADUATE MAJORS: 10
DEGREES CONFERRED: 2
FACULTY:

Scriven, Darryl, PhD, Purdue University (1999), 1998, Assistant Professor—philosophy and religion, social philosophy, philosophical theology, 937-376-2911 ext 668, Fax: 937-374-2398,
E-mail: dscriven@payne.wilberforce.edu

Wiley College

Marshall TX 75670

Sir Wilfred Grenfell College

Corner Brook, Newfoundland A2H 6H9   **Phone: 709-637-6279**
Canada   **E-mail: mnewton@swgc.mun.ca**
                                                  URL: www.swgc.mun.ca

TYPE OF INSTITUTION: Public
EXECUTIVE OFFICER: Adrian Fowler, Principal
COORDINATOR: Michael Newton
UNDERGRADUATE ENROLLMENT: 1,200

Wilfrid Laurier University

Dept of Religion and Culture   **Phone: 519-884-0710 ext 3330**
75 University Ave W   **Fax: 519-884-9387**
Waterloo, Ontario N2L 3C5 Canada   **URL: www.wlu.ca/~wwwrandc/**

TYPE OF INSTITUTION: Public
CHAIRPERSON: Kay Koppedrayer
UNDERGRADUATE ENROLLMENT: 7,500
GRADUATE ENROLLMENT: 900
DEGREES OFFERED: BA, MA
UNDERGRADUATE MAJORS: 45
DEGREES CONFERRED: 17

DESCRIPTION OF UNDERGRADUATE PROGRAM: The Department of Religion and Culture,
an integral part of the Faculty of Arts and Science of the University, offers a four-year Honors
program and a three-year Major in Religion and Culture. In addition it makes available general courses in religious studies as electives for students in other programs and participates

in the program of theological studies for students in Waterloo Lutheran Seminary. The Department offers courses in the areas of Ancient Near Eastern and Mediteranean religions (archaeology, literature, and history), Western religions (early to modern), and Asian, folk, and native religions. A variety of methodologies appropriate to the various specialities are employed.

GRADUATE PROGRAM

Member of the Council on Graduate Studies in Religion

Graduate Advisor: Michel Desjardins

Graduate Degrees Offered: MA

Degrees Conferred: 5 MA

Graduate Students in Residence: 25 MA

Not in Residence: 2 MA

Average No. of New Students Enrolled: 14 MA

Women Students: 11 MA

Minority Students: 1 MA

Foreign Students: 0 MA

Minimum GRE Score Requisite to Admission: No

Minimum GPA Score Requisite to Admission: Yes, B on a scale of A+ to F

Foreign Language Proficiency Evaluated: No

Financial Aid to First Year Students: 90% MA

Financial Aid to Other Students: 25% MA

Attrition Among Students: 10% MA

DESCRIPTION OF GRADUATE PROGRAM AND RESEARCH FACILITIES: The Master of Arts program has two basic options: the Regular Program and an interdisciplinary Humanities Option. The Regular Program and an interdisciplinary Humanities Option. The Regular MA program draws primarily on the resources of the faculty of the department, and also involves adjunct faculty from the University of Waterloo and Waterloo Lutheran Seminary. The areas of specialization are historical and textual studies of Western religions (Area I), and interdisciplinary approaches to religions in the contemporary world (Area II). Both areas attend to encounters between traditions and to the cultural context of religion. The interdisciplinary Humanities Option in addition includes adjunct faculty from Wilfrid Laurier's departments of Anthropology and Philosophy. In both programs, students may follow one of two streams to the MA: 1) Thesis stream: (6 one-term courses). The preparation of a thesis proposal and a thesis; oral defense of the thesis and 2) Eight-course stream: (8 one-term courses). The degree may be completed on a part-time basis. An archaeology laboratory is available to students with research interests in Near Eastern archaeology. Field studies courses are also available. The resources of the University Library are supplemented by the holdings of the University of Waterloo, the University of Guelph, and the inter-library loan service within Canada.

ACADEMIC PLAN, ADMISSION REQUIREMENTS, FINANCIAL AID: The Master's programs are based on an academic year consisting of three terms. Only term courses are offered, and continuous registration must be maintained. Admission to the regular Master's programs requires an Honours BA in Religion and Culture or its equivalent. Admission to the Humanities Option is on the basis of an honours degree or its equivalent from one of several fields, the most commonly accepted ones being anthropology, philosophy, or religious studies. An academic standing of "B" or better is required for admission to both programs. Qualifying courses are available to potential candidates who fall short of these qualifications. All applicants are considered for a WLU scholarship; students may also qualify for an Ontario Graduate Scholarship; and the Department offers a number of teaching and research assistantships.

FACULTY:

Desjardins, Michel, PhD, Toronto (1987), 1993, Associate Professor—Christian origins, Gnosticism, early Judaism and other religions of the Graeco-Roman world, 519-884-0710, ext 3323, E-mail: mdesjard@wlu.ca

Duncan, Carol B., MA, New York (1991), 1997, Lecturer—Religion and Society, African Diosporic religion and culture (especially the Caribbean), postcolonial thought, and religion, oral history, sociology of religion, 519-884-0710 ext. 3692, E-mail: cduncan@wlu.ca

Erb, Peter, PhD, Toronto (1976), 1974, Professor—late medieval spirituality and late medieval influences in Protestant spirituality, the radical Reformation and its North American heritage, Pietism, modern Roman Catholic thought, 519-884-0710, ext 3616, E-mail: perb@wlu.ca

Grimes, Ronald L., PhD, Columbia-Union (1970), 1974, Professor—ritual studies; popular culture in North America; religious autobiography; inter-religious conflict (especially among Hispanic-, Native-, and Anglo-American traditions); symbolic anthropology and religion, 519-884-0710, ext 3085, E-mail: rgrimes@wlu.ca

Koppedrayer, Kay, PhD, McMaster (1990), 1987, Associate Professor—Indology, especially South India, and Sanskrit and Tamil sources, focusing on social dynamics of religious movements, ritual expression, and caste relations, 519-884-0710, ext 3329, E-mail: kkoppedr@wlu.ca

Ross, Christopher F. J., PhD, Calgary (1973), 1988, Associate Professor—psychology of religion, relationship of religion to personal and social needs and conflicts, variations and stages of religious development, religious and secular approaches to personal and social change, 519-884-0710, ext 3679, E-mail: cross@wlu.ca

Shapiro, F., PhD, McMaster (1999), Assistant Professor—Jewish communities in North America and Israel, modern Jewish history, anthropology and sociology of religion, ethnic, religious, and national identity issues, pilgrimage, 519-884-0710 ext 3051

DEPARTMENT OF ANTHROPOLOGY, ARCHAEOLOGY, AND PHILOSOPHY ADJUNCT FACULTY:

Christie, T. Laird, PhD, Toronto (1969), 1974, Associate Professor—Native North American religious traditions, especially in relation to socio-cultural change, 519-884-0710, ext 3458, E-mail: lchristi@mach1.wlu.ca

Cristi, F. Renato, PhD, Toronto (1980), 1984, Professor—social and political theory, history of modern political thought, epistemology, Greek philosophy, Hegel, Marxism, 519-884-0710, ext 3346, E-mail: rcristi@mach1.wlo.ca

Daviau, P. M. Michèle, PhD, Toronto (1990), 1989, Associate Professor—Near Eastern studies, especially Syro-Palestinian archaeology and culture, ancient Mesopotamia and Egypt, Hebrew Bible, 519-884-0710, ext 6680, E-mail: mdaviau@mach1.wlu.ca

Groarke, Leo A., PhD, Western (1982), 1983, Professor—contemporary critiques of science and rationality, history of skepticism, epistemological bases of art, morality and religion, applied ethics, 519-884-0710, ext 3287, E-mail: lgroarke@mach1.wlu.ca

Guenther, Mathias G., PhD, Toronto (1973), 1971, Professor—religion in Africa, especially among the Kung, trance and altered states of consciousness, 519-884-0710, ext 3503, E-mail: mguenthe@mach1.wlu.ca

Jacobsen, Rockney, PhD, Alberta (1984), 1985, Associate Professor—philosophy of mind and language, Wittgenstein, twentieth century philosophy, seventeenth century philosophy, 519-884-0710, ext 3084, E-mail: rjacobse@mach1.wlu.ca

Litke, Robert F., PhD, Michigan (1974), 1974, Professor—philosophy and transpersonal psychology, world peace, conceptions of self and other, epistemology and altered states of consciousness, 519-884-0710, ext 3083, E-mail: blitke@mach1.wlu.ca

Lyons, Andrew P., DPhil, Oxford (1974), 1977, Associate Professor—history of social thought, anthropology of religion, the study of mass communications, 519-884-0710, ext 3660, E-mail: alyons@mach1.wlu.ca

Solomon, Graham, PhD, Western (1989), 1989, Associate Professor—history of science, history of ideas, philosophy of science, epistemology, 519-884-0710, ext 3686, E-mail: gsolomon@mach1.wlu.ca

Weir, Allison, PhD, York (1993), 1996, Assistant Professor—social and political thought, feminist theory, 19th and 20th century continental philosophy, 519-884-0710, ext 3113, E-mail: aweir@mach1.wlu.ca

WATERLOO LUTHERAN SEMINARY ADJUNCT FACULTY:

Arnal, Oscar L. Cole, PhD, Pittsburgh (1974), 1975, Professor—history of Modern Western Christianity, especially liberation movements; Roman Catholicism in France and Quebec; labour churches in prairie Canada, 519-884-0710, ext 3962, E-mail: ocole@mach1.wlu.ca

Crossman, Richard, PhD, Chicago (1976), 1970, Associate Professor—social ethics, especially in relation to politics, technology and economics, 519-884-0710, ext 3229, E-mail: rcrossma@mach1.wlu.ca

Hegadus, Tim, MA, Wilfrid Laurier (1991), Lecturer—early Christianity, New Testament to the fourth centruy, Christian relations to Graeco-Roman religions and Second Temple Judaism,early Christian biblical exegesis, Hellenistic mystery religions, Christian responses to pagan astrology, and Augustine, 519884-0710 ext 3530

Kelly, Robert A., PhD, Fuller Seminary (1981), 1984, Assistant Professor—Christian theology, systematic and historical (especially Luther s thought); Christian ethics, 519-884-0710, ext 3853, E-mail: rkelly@mach1.wlu.ca

Remus, Harold E., PhD, Pennsylvania (1981), 1974, WLU Professor Emeritus—Christian origins, including early Judaism and other religions of the Graeco-roman world; miracle and magic in that world, 519-884-0710, ext 3330, E-mail: hremus@mach1.wlu.ca

---

Willamette University

Dept of Religion, Salem OR 97301

College of William and Mary

Dept of Religion
PO Box 8795
Williamsburg VA 23187-8795

Phone: 757-221-2175
Fax: 757-221-2169
E-mail: mlraph@wm.edu
URL: www.wm.edu/religion

TYPE OF INSTITUTION: Public
EXECUTIVE OFFICER: Gillian T. Cell, Provost
CHAIRPERSON: Marc L. Raphael
UNDERGRADUATE ENROLLMENT: 5,500
DEGREES OFFERED: AB
UNDERGRADUATE MAJORS: 58
DEGREES CONFERRED: 25

DESCRIPTION OF UNDERGRADUATE PROGRAM: The College of William and Mary is primarily devoted to a liberal arts education, within which students are expected to do work in three areas: humanities, social sciences, and natural sciences. The Department of Religion is grouped with the humanities and offers a concentration and an honors program. The following areas of studies in religion are open to all students: Biblical Studies, Asian Religions, Ethics, Western Religious History and Thought, Studies in American Religion, Judaic Studies, and Islam.

FACULTY:

Como, Michael I., PhD, Stanford University (1999), 1999, Assistant Professor—East Asian religions, 757-221-2167, E-mail: micomo@wm.edu

Finn, Thomas M., ThD, Catholic University of America (1965), 1973, Chancellor Professor of Religion—Christian origins, patristics, medieval religion, and introduction to religion, 757-221-2170, E-mail: tmfinn@wm.edu

Galambush, Julie G., PhD, Emory University (1991), 1993, Assistant Professor—biblical studies, women studies, 757-221-2183, E-mail: jggala@wm.edu

Holmes, David L., PhD, Princeton University (1971), 1968, Professor—American religion, religious history, reformation, 757-221-2177, E-mail: dlholm@wm.edu

Livingston, James C., PhD, Columbia University (1965), 1968, Walter G. Mason Professor of Religion Emeritus—modern religious thought

Raphael, Marc L., PhD, UCLA (1972), 1989, Sophia and Nathan S. Gumenick Professor of Judaic Studies—Jewish studies, 757-221-2172, E-mail: mlraph@wm.edu

Sonn, Tamera, PhD, University of Chicago (1983), 1999, William R. Kenan, Jr. Professor of Humanities and Professor of Religion—Islam, 757-221-2181, E-mail: txsonn@wm.edu

Tiefel, Hans O., PhD, Yale University (1967), 1975, Professor—ethics, 757-221-2180, E-mail: hotief@wm.edu

Van Horn, Jack D., PhD, Columbia University (1972), 1970, Associate Professor—Asian religions, 757-221-2174, E-mail: jdvanx@wm.edu

Williams, John A., PhD, Princeton University (1958), 1988, William R. Kenan, Jr., Distinguished Professor of Humanities Emeritus—Islam

---

William Carey College

498 Tuscan Ave
Hattiesburg MS 39401

Phone: 601-582-6115
Fax: 601-582-6460
E-mail: vpchurch@wmcarey.edu
URL: www.wmcarey.edu

TYPE OF INSTITUTION: Private, Southern Baptist
EXECUTIVE OFFICER: Larry Kennedy, President, CEO
CHAIRPERSON: Daniel P. Caldwell
UNDERGRADUATE ENROLLMENT: 120

William Jewell College

500 College Hill
Liberty MO 64068

Phone: 816-781-7700
Fax: 816-415-5027
E-mail: chanceb@william.jewell.edu
URL: www.jewell.edu

TYPE OF INSTITUTION: Denominational: Missouri Baptist, American Baptist
EXECUTIVE OFFICER: Nina T. Pollard, Provost
CHAIRPERSON: Bradley Chance
UNDERGRADUATE ENROLLMENT: 1,200

William Penn College

201 Trueblood Ave, Oskaloosa IA 52577

William Tyndale College

35700 W Twelve Mile Rd, Farmington Hills MI 48331

Williams College

Dept of Religion
Stetson Hall
Williamstown MA 01267

Phone: 413-597-2990
Fax: 413-597-4088
E-mail: religion.dept@williams.edu
URL: www.williams.edu

TYPE OF INSTITUTION: Private
EXECUTIVE OFFICER: Harry C. Payne, President
CHAIRPERSON: William R. Darrow
UNDERGRADUATE ENROLLMENT: 2,150

Williams Baptist College

201 Fulbright Avenue
Walnut Ridge AR 72476

Phone: 870-886-6741
Fax: 870-886-3924
E-mail: admissions@wbclab.wbcoll.edu
URL: www.wbcoll.edu

TYPE OF INSTITUTION: Private, Baptist
EXECUTIVE OFFICER: Jerol Swaim, President; Ken Startup, Academic Dean
CHAIRPERSON: Kenneth Gore
UNDERGRADUATE ENROLLMENT: 704

Wilson College

Dept of Religion and Philosophy, Chambersburg PA 17201

University of Windsor

Windsor Ontario N9B 3P4
Canada

Phone: 519-253-4232
E-mail: mhmul@u.windsor.ca

TYPE OF INSTITUTION: Public
COORDINATOR: Maureen Muldoon

The Department of Religious Studies no longer exists. There is a program until the students who are currently enrolled complete their work.

Winebrenner Theological Seminary

701 E Melrose Ave
PO Box 478
Findlay OH 45840

Phone: 419-422-4824
or 1-800-992-4987
Fax: 419-422-3999
E-mail: wtseminary@aol.com
URL: www.winebrenner.edu

TYPE OF INSTITUTION: Denominational: Churches of God General Conference
EXECUTIVE OFFICER: David E. Draper, President
UNDERGRADUATE ENROLLMENT: 35
GRADUATE ENROLLMENT: 59

Wingate University

Wingate NC 28174-0157

Phone: 704-233-8085
Fax: 704-233-8285
E-mail: ebagley@wingate.edu
URL: www.wingate.edu;
www.wingate.edu/acad/religionphilo/
page1.htm

TYPE OF INSTITUTION: Private, Baptist
EXECUTIVE OFFICER: Jerry McGee, President
CHAIRPERSON: Edwin Bagley
UNDERGRADUATE ENROLLMENT: 1,400
GRADUATE ENROLLMENT: 200

University of Winnipeg

515 Portage Ave
Winnipeg, Manitoba R3B 2E9
Canada

Phone: 204-786-9107
Fax: 204-774-4134
E-mail: religious.studies@uwinnipeg.ca

TYPE OF INSTITUTION: Public
EXECUTIVE OFFICER: John Hofley, Dean
CHAIRPERSONS: Peggy Day (Undergraduate), Albert Welter (Graduate)
UNDERGRADUATE ENROLLMENT: 8,000
GRADUATE ENROLLMENT: 40 in Joint Masters Program

Winthrop University

701 Oakland Avenue
Rock Hill SC 29733

Phone: 803-323-2128
Fax: 803-323-2347
E-mail: danielw@winthrop.edu

TYPE OF INSTITUTION: Public
CHAIRPERSON: William Daniel
UNDERGRADUATE ENROLLMENT: 4,000
GRADUATE ENROLLMENT: 1,200

University of Wisconsin, Eau Claire

Park and Garfield
Eau Claire WI 54701

Phone: 715-836-2545
E-maiL brummejj@uwec.edu
URL: www.uwec.edu

TYPE OF INSTITUTION: Public
EXECUTIVE OFFICER: Donald Mash, Chancellor
CHAIRPERSON: James Brummer
UNDERGRADUATE ENROLLMENT: 80

University of Wisconsin, Madison

Religious Studies Program
1240 Van Hise Hall, 1220 Linden Drive
Madison WI 53706

Phone: 608-262-0524
Fax: 608-265-3538
E-mail: rsp@facstaff.wisc.edu
URL: polyglot.lss.wisc.edu/resp/relstud.htm

TYPE OF INSTITUTION: Public
EXECUTIVE OFFICER: David Ward, Chancellor
COORDINATOR: Charles L. Cohen

University of Wisconsin, Milwaukee

Comparative Study of Religion
PO Box 413
Milwaukee WI 53201

Phone: 414-229-4361
Fax: 414-229-2435
E-mail: jdh2@csd.uwm.edu

TYPE OF INSTITUTION: Public
EXECUTIVE OFFICER: Nancy Zimpher, Chancellor
COORDINATOR: J. David Hoeveler, Jr.
UNDERGRADUATE ENROLLMENT: 1,200
DEGREES OFFERED: BA
UNDERGRADUATE MAJORS: 17
DEGREES CONFERRED: 2

DESCRIPTION OF UNDERGRADUATE PROGRAM: The Comparative Study of Religion Program was established in 1982 as a new BA degree program in the College of Letters and Science at the University of Wisconsin, Milwaukee. This institution is the urban-focused university in the state system, drawing the vast majority of its students from the metropolitan Milwaukee area.

FACULTY:

Baldassaro, Lawrence A., PhD, Indiana University (1972), 1981, Professor—Dante, medieval Italian literature

Baron, F. Xavier, PhD, University of Iowa (1969), 1981, Associate Professor—Arthurian literature

Bellegarde-Smith, Patrick D., PhD, American University (1977), 1990, Associate Professor—Afro-Carribean, African religions

Bendiner, Kenneth, PhD, Columbia University (1979), 1985, Professor—19th and 20th century religious painting

Bharadwaj, Lakshimi, PhD, University of Wisconsin, Madison (1969), 1990, Associate Professor—sociology of religion

Fischer, J. Denny, PhD, University of Illinois (1958), 1981, Associate Professor—literary aspects of the English Bible, Old and New Testament

Gray, Joseph Patrick, PhD, University of Colorado, Boulder (1976), 1981, Professor—anthropology of religion, symbolic anthropology

Hamdani, Abbas H., PhD, University of London (1950), 1981, Professor—medieval Islam, modern Middle East, cultural and social history of Islam

Hansen, Anne R., PhD, Harvard University (1999), 1999, Assistant Professor—Buddhist studies, history and development of Theravada Buddhism, South East Asian religions

Hawi, Sami S., PhD, State University of New York, Buffalo (1971), 1981, Associate Professor—Islamic theology, philosophy, mysticism, medieval Christian philosophy

Hayes, Jeffrey, PhD, University of Maryland (1982), 1989, Professor—American and modern art

Hoeveler, J. David, Jr., PhD, University of Illinois, Urbana-Champaign (1971), 1981, Professor—American religious history

Hoey, Lawrence Robert, PhD, University of Chicago (1981), 1981, Associate Professor—medieval architecture, early Christian and Byzantine art

Mazor, Yair, PhD, University of Tel Aviv (1983), 1994, Professor—modern Hebrew literature, comparative literature, biblical literature

Mondadori, Fabrizio, PhD, Harvard (1972), 1989, Professor—metaphysics, philosophy of language, continental philosophy

Monti, Richard C., PhD, Harvard (1973), 1981, Professor—Latin literature, Greek literature

Mulroy, David D., PhD, Stanford University (1971), 1981, Associate Professor—classical mythology

Neevel, Walter G., Jr., PhD, Harvard University (1974), 1981, Associate Professor—Asian religions, Hindu and Buddhist religion and philosophy, theory and methods

Shey, H. James, PhD, University of Iowa (1968), 1981, Associate Professor—classical mythology, Egyptian mythology

Skalitzky, Rachel I., PhD, Fordham University (1968), 1981, Associate Professor—medieval religious studies, feminist religious studies, patristics

Stark, Bruce R., PhD, Columbia University (1979), 1981, Associate Professor—Old Norse mythology, mythic heroes and heroines

Stone, Andrea, PhD, University of Texas (1983), 1985, Professor—Pre-Columbian iconography

Swanson, Roy Arthur, PhD, University of Illinois, Urbana-Champaign (1954), 1981, Professor—comparative mythology, New Testament, history of Christianity

Wainwright, William J., PhD, University of Michigan (1961), 1981, Professor—philosophy of religion

Waldbaum, Jane C., PhD, Harvard University (1968), 1981, Professor—ancient Greek art and archaeology, ancient Egyptian and Near Eastern art and archaeology, ancient Roman art and archaeology

Washabaugh, William, PhD, Wayne State University (1974), 1981, Professor—cross-cultural perspectives on religion, West Indian religions

Wiesner-Hanks, Merry E., PhD, University of Wisconsin, Madison (1979), 1985, Professor—history of Christianity

Wind, Barry, PhD, New York University (1972), 1981, Professor—Renaissance and Baroque art

---

University of Wisconsin, Oshkosh

Dept of Religious Studies	**Phone: 920-424-4406**
800 Algoma Blvd	**Fax: 920-424-0882**
Oshkosh WI 54901	**E-mail: URBROCK@uwosh.edu**
	URL: www.uwosh.edu/departments/religious

TYPE OF INSTITUTION: Public

EXECUTIVE OFFICER: John E. Kerrigan, Chancellor

COORDINATOR: William J. Urbrock

UNDERGRADUATE ENROLLMENT: 9,100

DEGREES OFFERED: BA/BS major in Study of Religion

UNDERGRADUATE MAJORS: 22

DEGREES CONFERRED: 3

DESCRIPTION OF UNDERGRADUATE PROGRAM: Inaugurated in 1968, the Department has achieved recognition as a strong representative of the Humanities Division within the College of Letters and Science. The Department has built a reputation for outstanding scholarship and teaching and boasts two members on the Honors Faculty of the university. The Department offers general education courses in the Humanities and non-Western culture and a certified teaching Major and Minor. The undergraduate Major in the Study of Religion was authorized by the University of Wisconsin Board of Regents in 1982.

FACULTY:

Beane, Wendell Charles, PhD, University of Chicago (1971), 1979, Professor—history of religions, myth and mysticism, religion and healing, 920-424-7072, E-mail: beane@uwosh.edu

Corley, Kathleen E., PhD, The Claremont Graduate School (1992), 1992, Associate Professor—biblical studies, women in antiquity, history of Christianity, 920-424-7383, E-mail: corley@uwosh.edu

Linenthal, Edward Tabor, PhD, University of California, Santa Barbara (1979), 1979, Professor—war and American memory, contemporary American religion, 920-424-4407, E-mail: etl@uwosh.edu

Lishka, Dennis, PhD, University of Wisconsin, Madison (1976), 1985, Assistant Professor—Buddhism, Japanese religions, world religions, 920-424-7071, E-mail: lishka@uwosh.edu

Taylor, Bron R., PhD, University of Southern California (1988), 1989, Professor—social ethics, environmental ethics, religion and politics, 920-424-7183, E-mail: taylor@uwosh.edu

Urbrock, William J., PhD, Harvard University (1975), 1972, Professor—Hebrew Bible, ancient Near Eastern religion, 920-424-7307, E-mail: urbrock@uwosh.edu

University of Wisconsin, Stevens Point

Department of Philosophy
Stevens Point WI 54481

Phone: 715-346-3340
Fax: 715-346-4215
E-mail: dfadner@uwsp.edu
URL: www.uwsp.edu/acad/phil

TYPE OF INSTITUTION: Public
EXECUTIVE OFFICER: Thomas F. George, Chancellor
CHAIRPERSON: Donald E. Fadner, Chair of Philosophy Department
COORDINATOR: Alice Keefe
UNDERGRADUATE ENROLLMENT: 8,165
GRADUATE ENROLLMENT: 352

University of Wisconsin, Whitewater

Dept of Philosophy and Religious Studies, Whitewater WI 53190

Wisconsin Lutheran College

8830 W Bluemound Rd, Milwaukee WI 53226

Wisconsin Lutheran Seminary

11831N Seminary Drive 65W
Mequon WI 53092

Phone: 414-242-8100
Fax: 414-242-8110
E-mail: president@wls.wels.net
URL: www.wls.wels.net

TYPE OF INSTITUTION: Denominational: Wisconsin Evangelical Lutheran Synod
EXECUTIVE OFFICER: David J. Valleskey, President
GRADUATE ENROLLMENT: 146

Wittenberg University

PO Box 720
Springfield OH 45501

Phone: 937-327-7400
Fax: 937-327-6340
URL: www.wittenberg.edu

TYPE OF INSTITUTION: Private, Lutheran (ELCA)
EXECUTIVE OFFICER: Baird Tipson, President
CHAIRPERSON: Paul T. Nelson
UNDERGRADUATE ENROLLMENT: 2,100
DEGREES OFFERED: BA
UNDERGRADUATE MAJORS: 6
DEGREES CONFERRED: 2
DESCRIPTION OF UNDERGRADUATE PROGRAM: A general education requirement of one
course in religious or philosophical inquiry reflects Wittenberg's belief that the study of relig-

ion is integral to the liberal arts. Departmental majors and minors are required to pursue historical studies in Western and non-Western traditions; explore various methods of textual interpretation; undertake critical approaches to the study of religious phenomena; and engage in cultural and ethical analyses of religious practices, ideas, values, and institutions. Courses in Indian and Islamic traditions, American religious history, and philosophy and sociology of religion offered by other departments are crosslisted. For more information on our curriculum and faculty, please consult our Website: http://www.wittenberg.edu/

FACULTY:

Copeland, Warren R., PhD, University of Chicago (1977), 1977, Professor—social ethics, 937-327-7402

Kaiser, Barbara E., PhD, University of Chicago (1983), 1980, Associate Professor—biblical studies, 937-327-7405

Millen, Rochelle L., PhD, McMaster University (1984), 1988, Associate Professor—Judaic studies, 937-327-7404

Nelson, Paul T., PhD, Yale University (1984), 1985, Professor—religious ethics, bioethics, Christian thought, 937-327-7403, E-mail: pnelson@wittenberg.edu

Swanger, Eugene R., PhD, University of Iowa (1971), 1967, Professor—comparative history of religions, Chinese and Japanese religious traditions, phenomenology, 937-327-7401

Tipson, Baird, PhD, Yale University (1972), 1995, Professor—American religious history, 937-327-7916

Wofford College

429 N Church Street
Spartanburg SC 29303-3663

Phone: 864-597-4560
Fax: 864-597-4019
E-mail: bullardjm@wofford.edu
URL: www.wofford.edu/religion

TYPE OF INSTITUTION: Private, United Methodist

EXECUTIVE OFFICER: Joab M. Lesesne, President

CHAIRPERSON: John M. Bullard

UNDERGRADUATE ENROLLMENT: 1,140

DEGREES OFFERED: BA Major; Interdepartmental Concentration

UNDERGRADUATE MAJORS: 20

DEGREES CONFERRED: 8

DESCRIPTION OF UNDERGRADUATE PROGRAM: Since its opening in 1854, Wofford College has emphasized critical study of the Bible and of religion as indispensable to classical liberal education. As a Phi Beta Kappa college, Wofford regularly sends her graduates to leading seminaries and university graduate schools. The curriculum in religion is divided into five categories: Introductory General Education courses, Biblical Interpretation (historical background, literature, theology), Christian Doctrine and Ethics, Religious Traditions (including Asian religions and the American religious tradition), and Advanced Studies (interdisciplinary seminars and independent research). Religion majors are obliged to select courses from each category. The writing of essays and use of computers are emphasized in all religion courses.

FACULTY:

Barrett, Charles D., PhD, Drew (1968), 1966, Peter B. Hendrix Professor—Christian thought, Reformation studies, contemporary theology, 864-597-4561, E-mail: barrettcd@wofford.edu

Bullard, John M., PhD, Yale (1962), 1961, Albert C. Outler Professor—Bible (especially Old Testament), Hinduism, Buddhism, Judaism, Islam, Palestinian archaeology, biblical theology, 864-597-4560, E-mail: bullardjm@wofford.edu

McGehee, Larry T., PhD, Yale (1969), 1982, Professor—church history, religion in America, 864-597-4195, E-mail: mcgeheelt@wofford.edu

Mount, William W., PhD, Yale (1969), 1977, Professor—Bible (especially New Testament), Christian origins, Greek, 864-597-4562, E-mail: mountww@wofford.edu

---

The College of Wooster

College Ave
Wooster OH 44691

Phone: 216-263-2000
URL: www.wooster.edu

TYPE OF INSTITUTION: Private, Presbyterian
EXECUTIVE OFFICER: H. Stanton Hales, President
CHAIRPERSON: Charles Kammer
UNDERGRADUATE ENROLLMENT: 1,650

Worcester Polytech Institute

100 Institute Road
Worcester MA 01609

Phone: 508-831-5000
URL: www.wpi.edu

TYPE OF INSTITUTION: Private
EXECUTIVE OFFICER: Edward A. Parrish, President
UNDERGRADUATE ENROLLMENT: 2,500
GRADUATE ENROLLMENT: 500

World Institute of Religious Education

87 Road 3950, Farmington NM 87401-7979

Wright State University

Dept of Religion
3640 Colonel Glenn Hwy
Dayton OH 45435

Phone: 937-775-2274
Fax: 937-775-2707
E-mail: charles.taylor@wright.edu
URL: www.wright.edu

TYPE OF INSTITUTION: Public
EXECUTIVE OFFICER: Kim Goldenberg, President
CHAIRPERSON: Charles S. Taylor
UNDERGRADUATE ENROLLMENT: 16,000
DEGREES OFFERED: BA
UNDERGRADUATE MAJORS: 32
DEGREES CONFERRED: 6

DESCRIPTION OF UNDERGRADUATE PROGRAM: Wright State University's Department of Religion is devoted to a comprehensive and non-sectarian inquiry into religion as one of the significant areas of human life and thought. Our curriculum is arranged so that students are exposed to a balanced representation of human religious activity: Eastern, Western, and American (including African-American) religions; religious thought; biblical studies; ethics and philosophy of religion. The Department also participates in a Masters of Humanities Program sponsored by the College of Liberal Arts. This interdisciplinary program is designed for students wishing to pursue a broadly based graduate study of a given historical period, cultural region, artistic theme, or other humanistic focus, but allows concentration in Religious Study. Admission to the graduate program is handled through other administrative units but information may be obtained by writing the chairperson.

FACULTY:

Barr, David L., PhD, Florida State University (1974), 1975, Professor—New Testament studies, public education religion studies

Chamberlain, M. Ava, PhD, Columbia University (1990), 1995, Assistant Professor—American religious history

Dvorak, Katharine L., PhD, University of Chicago (1985), 1998, Assistant Professor—religion and American society

Griffin, Paul R., PhD, Emory University (1983), 1988, Professor—African-American religious history, history of Christian thought

Reece, Robert D., PhD, Yale (1969), 1969, Professor and Chair of Department of Community Health (WSU School of Medicine)—ethics

Taylor, Charles S., PhD, Boston College (1974), 1977, Professor—modern German philosophy, ancient Greek philosophy, aesthetics

Verman, Mark, PhD, Harvard University (1984), 1999, Associate Professor—medieval Jewish history and literature, post-biblical Hebrew literature, medieval studies, Near Eastern studies

Wycliffe College

5 Hoskin Avenue
Toronto, Ontario M5S 1H7 Canada

Phone: 416-946-3535
Fax: 416-946-3545
E-mail: registrar.wycliffe@utoronto.ca

TYPE OF INSTITUTION: Private, Anglican Church of Canada
EXECUTIVE OFFICER: George Sumner, Principal

University of Wyoming

Religious Studies Program
Hoyt Hall
Laramie WY 82071-3353

Phone: 307-766-2616
Fax: 307-766-3189
E-mail: pflesher@uwyo.edu
URL: religion-web.uwyo.edu

TYPE OF INSTITUTION: Public
CHAIRPERSON: Paul V. M. Flesher
UNDERGRADUATE ENROLLMENT: 15

Xavier University of Louisiana

7325 Palmetto St
New Orleans LA 70125

Phone: 504-485-5457
Fax: 504-485-7947
URL: www.xula.edu/

TYPE OF INSTITUTION: Private, historically Black and Catholic
EXECUTIVE OFFICER: Norman C. Francis, President
CHAIRPERSON: Gerald M. Boodoo

Xavier University

Theology Dept
3800 Victory Pkwy
Cincinnati OH 45207-4442

Phone: 513-745-3026
Fax: 513-745-3215
E-mail: bhill@xavier.xv.edu

TYPE OF INSTITUTION: Private, Roman Catholic
EXECUTIVE OFFICER: Rev. James Hoff, SJ, President
CHAIRPERSON: Brennan R. Hill
UNDERGRADUATE ENROLLMENT: 3,000
GRADUATE ENROLLMENT: 80

Yale University

PO Box 208287
Yale Station
New Haven CT 06520

Phone: 203-432-0828
Fax: 203-432-7844
URL: www.yale.edu/religiousstudies/

TYPE OF INSTITUTION: Private

CHAIRPERSON: Carlos M. N. Eire

UNDERGRADUATE ENROLLMENT: 5,100

GRADUATE ENROLLMENT: 2,500

DEGREES OFFERED: BA, PhD (MA and MPhil)

UNDERGRADUATE MAJORS: 19

DEGREES CONFERRED: 11

DESCRIPTION OF UNDERGRADUATE PROGRAM: The Yale Department of Religious Studies offers courses which, broadly speaking, consider the historical factors and contemporary issues of religious phenomena in human life. The Department aims to help the student understand religious works of literature, historical developments of religious tradition and practice, modes of religious thought, and varieties of world views in and among religions. To this study are brought the insights of several disciplines. The various methods of inquiry (textual and historical, behavioral and institutional, philosophical and theological) are used to provide breadth and comprehensiveness to the undergraduate study of religion. Each major is expected to demonstrate a degree of expertise in at least two religious traditions (Buddhism, Hinduism, Judaism, Christianity, Islam) or program areas (i.e., behavioral and institutional, philosophical and theological, ethics, religion and culture), and is also expected to develop familiarity with more than one method of study.

GRADUATE PROGRAM

Member of the Council on Graduate Studies in Religion

Graduate Advisor: James E. Dittes

Graduate Degrees Offered: MA, PhD

Degrees Conferred: 15 PhD

Graduate Students in Residence: 68 PhD

Not in Residence: 22 PhD

Average No. of New Students Enrolled: 10 PhD

Women Students: 32 PhD

Minority Students: 4 PhD

Foreign Students: 4 PhD

Minimum GRE Score Requisite to Admission: No

Minimum GPA Score Requisite to Admission: No

Foreign Language Proficiency Evaluated: GSFLT Score: German; French; Dept Proficiency Exam

Financial Aid to First Year Students: 100% PhD

Financial Aid to Other Students: 95% PhD

Graduates Placed: 100% PhD

DESCRIPTION OF GRADUATE PROGRAM AND RESEARCH FACILITIES: The Yale doctoral program in religious studies is designed to train persons with superior academic ability for research and teaching in ten fields of specialization: American Religious History, Ancient Christianity, Buddhism, Ethics, Hebrew Bible/Old Testament, Islam, Judaic Studies, New Testament, Philosophy, and Theology. Students may combine these fields with each other or with other fields of study, especially in Near Eastern Languages and Literatures, Philosophy, Sociology, Anthropology, Psychology, History and area studies. For example, excellent resources are available for such programs as these: biblical religions and antiquity, Bible and ethics, hermeneutics and the study of religion. Students and applicants are invited after careful investigation of available resources to propose still other programs of study for which they have clear goals and good preparation.

ACADEMIC PLAN, ADMISSION REQIREMENTS, FINANCIAL AID: The Department admits only for the Doctor of Philosophy degree. The Master of Arts degree and/or Master of Philosophy degree can be earned en route to the PhD. Normally, students should expect to complete their PhD program in six years. The MDiv, MAR, and STM degrees are awarded by the Divinity School at Yale, not the Department of Religious Studies. The Divinity School does not award a doctoral degree. Each student's program—courses, examinations, dissertation—is developed individually. The first two years of residence are normally devoted to course work. The purpose of this period is to provide a comprehensive background for teaching and research in a field. There are no specific course requirements, however, and course work is usually reduced as students begin to prepare for the four qualifying examinations. Admission is highly competitive. Students are frequently admitted into the PhD program after strong undergraduate majors in religious studies; but in the fields of Buddhism and scriptural study, especially, most successful applicants offer several years of study beyond the BA, especially in the relevant languages. Applicants must submit, by January 2, their statement of intentions for graduate study, letters of reference, GRE aptitude scores, and transcripts. Tuition for the doctoral program in 1995-96 was $19,000. Most doctoral candidates in residence receive financial assistance in some form each year, usually equivalent to the amount of tuition plus stipend. Advanced graduate students may become teaching assistants in undergraduate and Divinity School courses. Most students desiring teaching assistantships are able to obtain them.

FACULTY:

Adams, Marilyn McCord, PhD, Cornell (1967), 1993, Professor—historical theology

Adams, Robert, PhD, Cornell (1969), Professor—moral philosophy and metaphysics

Bowering, Gerhard, PhD, McGill (1975), 1984, Professor—Islamic studies

Butler, Jon, PhD, University of Minnesota (1972), 1985, Professor—American religious history

Dittes, James E., PhD, Yale (1958), 1956, Professor—pastoral theology and psychology

Eire, Carlos, PhD, Yale (1979), Professor—Reformation history

Fraade, Steven, PhD, Pennsylvania (1980), 1979, Taper Professor—Judaic studies

Hayes, Christine, PhD, University of California, Berkeley (1992), 1996, Weis Assistant Professor—classical Judaica

Hyman, Paula, PhD, Columbia (1975), 1986, Moses Professor—Judaic studies

Layton, Bentley, PhD, Harvard (1971), 1976, Professor—ancient church history, gnosticism, Coptic

Marcus, Ivan G., PhD, Jewish Theological Seminary (1975), 1994, Rose Professor—Jewish History

Martin, Dale, PhD, Yale (1988), Professor—New Testament

Outka, Gene, PhD, Yale (1967), 1975, Dwight Professor—religious ethics

Silk, Jonathan A., PhD, University of Michigan (1994), Assistant Professor—Buddhist studies and religions of India

Stout, Harry S., PhD, Kent State (1974), 1986, Edwards Professor—American religious history

Weaver, Jace, PhD, Union Theological Seminary (1996) Associate Professor—Native American religion

Weinstein, Stanley, PhD, Harvard (1965), 1968, Professor—Buddhist studies

Wilson, Robert, PhD, Yale (1972), 1985, Hoober Professor—Old Testament and religious studies.

In addition, many other members of the Yale faculty instruct in the graduate program, especially:

Attridge, Harold W., PhD, Harvard University (1974), Professor—New Testament
Farley, Margaret, PhD, Yale (1973), 1987, Stark Professor—Christian ethics
Jones, L. Serene, PhD, Yale University (1991), Associate Professor—theology
Kelsey, David, PhD, Yale (1964), 1965, Weigle Professor—theology
Ogletree, Thomas W., PhD, Vanderbilt University (1963), Professor—theological ethics
Wolterstorff, Nicholas, PhD, Harvard (1957), 1990, Porter Professor—philosophical theology

Yale University Divinity School
409 Prospect St, New Haven CT 06510

Yellowstone Baptist College
1515 Shiloh Rd, Billings MT 59106

Yeshiva University
500 W 185 St, New York NY 10033

Yeshiva Bais Yisroel
1719 Avenue P, Brooklyn NY 11229

Yeshiva Bnei Torah
737 Elvire Ave, Far Rockaway NY 11691

Yeshiva Derech Chaim
1573-39th St, Brooklyn NY 11218

Yeshiva Gedolah of Greater Miami
1140 Alton Rd, Miami Beach FL 33139

Yeshiva Gedolah Rabbinical College
24600 Greenfield Rd, Oak Park MI 48237

Yeshiva Karlin Stolin

1818 54th St, Brooklyn NY 11204-9961

Yeshiva University of Los Angeles

9760 W Pico Blvd, Los Angeles CA 90035

Yeshiva of Mikdash Melech

1326 Ocean Pkwy, Brooklyn NY 11230

Yeshiva of Nitra Rabbinical College

194 Division Ave, Brooklyn NY 11211

Yeshiva Ohel Shmuel

165 Haines Rd, Bedford Mills NY 10507

Yeshiva Ohr Elchonon Chanad West Coast

7215 Waring Ave, Los Angeles CA 90046

Yeshiva Shaar Hatorah

83-96 117th St, Kew Gardens NY 11418

Yeshiva Toras Chaim Talmudical Seminary

1555 Stuart Street   Phone: 303-629-8200
PO Box 40067   Fax: 303-623-5949
Denver CO 80204
TYPE OF INSTITUTION: Private, Jewish
EXECUTIVE OFFICERS: Isaac Wasserman, Dean; Israel Kagan, Dean; Yehoshua Gutman, Principal
UNDERGRADUATE ENROLLMENT: 20

Yeshivath Zichron Moshe

PO Box 580, South Fallsburg NY 12779

York College

912 Kiplinger
York NE 68467

Phone: 402-362-4441
Fax: 402-363-5623

TYPE OF INSTITUTION: Denominational: Church of Christ
EXECUTIVE OFFICER: Wayne Baker, President
CHAIRPERSON: Frank Wheeler
UNDERGRADUATE ENROLLMENT: 500

York University

4700 Keele St
North York ON M3J 1P3 Canada

Phone: 416-736-2100 ext 77097
Fax: 416-736-5460
E-mail: ehrlich@yorku.ca
URL: www.yorku.ca

TYPE OF INSTITUTION: Public
COORDINATOR: Carl S. Ehrlich
UNDERGRADUATE ENROLLMENT: 25,000
GRADUATE ENROLLMENT: 5,000

Youngstown State University

One University Plaza
Youngstown OH 44555-0001

Phone: 330-742-3448
Fax: 330-742-1600 or 330-742-2304
E-mail: tashipka@cc.ysu.edu
URL: www.as.ysu.edu/~philrel/

TYPE OF INSTITUTION: Public
CHAIRPERSON: Thomas A. Shipka
UNDERGRADUATE ENROLLMENT: 43

Yukon College

Box 2799, Whitehorse, Yukon Y1A 5K4 Canada

Y

Zoe College Inc

PO Box 8435, Jacksonville FL 32239

Z

Theological Schools and Seminaries in North America

Members of the Council on Graduate Studies in Religion

Geographical Listing

United States:

Michigan

Minnesota

Oklahoma

FACULTY MEMBERS AT PARTICIPATING SCHOOLS

Faculty Index

Faculty Index

New from Trinity Press International

Reclaiming Our Roots, Volume 1
The Late First Century to the Eve of the Reformation
by Mark Ellingsen
336 pages, $27.00

The perfect text for church history courses, *Reclaiming Our Roots* is the most inclusive one on the market today. It pays special attention to such matters as Christianity in the southern hemisphere, Eastern Orthodoxy, the church among minority cultures in North America, and the role of women in church history. Volume 2 due Nov. '99.

Jesus and the Heritage of Israel
Vol. 1 – Luke's Narrative Claim upon Israel's Legacy
edited by David P. Moessner and David L. Tiede
400 pages, $40.00

Essays from seventeen leading international scholars that present an amazing "sea change" of opinion that Luke is indeed the interpreter of Israel.

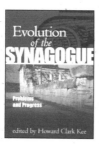

Evolution of the Synagogue
Problems and Progress
edited by Howard Clark Kee
192 pages, $22.00

Using literary and archaeological evidence, nine prominent rabbinic Judaism and early Christianity scholars trace the evolution of the synagogue.

God, Humanity and the Cosmos
A Textbook in Science and Religion
edited by Christopher Southgate
480 pages, $35.00

"A textbook on the current theology and science dialogue that is directly addressed to teachers and students, and as such, manages to be remarkably accessible... carefully addresses all the contemporary issues in the field in such a way that it moves the theology and science debate to the cutting edge of the current conversation."
    — J. Wentzel van Huyssteen,
        Princeton Theological Seminary

TRINITY PRESS INTERNATIONAL
HARRISBURG • PENNSYLVANIA

To order: 800-877-0012 • fax 717-541-8128 • www.trinitypressintl.com

NEW PUBLICATION
WELFARE REFORM AND FAITH-BASED ORGANIZATIONS
Edited by Derek Davis and Barry Hankins

The essays in this volume consider the potential problems and benefits of allowing churches and religious charitable organizations to receive government funds in order to operate private welfare programs. Pursuant to the "Charitable Choice" provisions of the Welfare Reform Act of 1996, faith-based organizations are now applying for government funding of social service programs. Whether this legislation amounts to a creative solution to the dilemma of welfare and poverty or a violation of church-state separation is but one of many questions raised by this important volume.

The authors offer diverse views on Charitable Choice, due in no small part to the range of their disciplines. In addition to constitutional scholars, this work includes contributions from theologians, public policy analysts, religious liberty lobbyists, and social service practitioners. The result is a vigorous but balanced presentation of Charitable Choice, its constitutionality, its impact upon religious liberty, and its potential for improving social conditions in America.

Essays include: "A 'Holy Mistaken Zeal': The Legislative History and Future of Charitable Choice," by Julie A. Segal of Americans United for the Separation of Church and State; "Faith-based Institutions Cooperating with Public Welfare: The Promise of the Charitable Choice Provision," by Stanley Carlson-Thies of the Center for Public Justice; "The Wrong Way to Do Right: Charitable Choice and Churches," by Melissa Rogers of the Baptist Joint Committee; "An (Ana)Baptist Theological Perspective on Church-State Cooperation: Evaluating 'Charitable Choice,'" by Ronald J. Sider and Heidi Rolland Unruh of Evangelicals for Social Action; "Common Sense and the Common Good: Helping the Poor and Protecting Religious Liberty," by Sharon Daly of Catholic Charities USA; "Overcoming Poverty: A New Era of Partnership," by Jim Wallis of Sojourners; "The Neutral Treatment of Religion and Faith-based Social Service Providers: Charitable Choice and Its Critics," by Carl H. Esbeck of the University of Missouri at Columbia; "Constitutional Questions About Charitable Choice," by Alan Brownstein of the University of California at Davis; and "Right Motive, Wrong Method: Thoughts on the Constitutionality of Charitable Choice," by Derek Davis of Baylor University.

Pp. vii + 312 pages, notes, index; Paper ISBN 929182-55-3 $13.95; Cloth ISBN 929182-54-5 $27.95.

Add $2.00 shipping and handling. Texas residents add 8.25% sales tax.

Send order and payment to
J.M. Dawson Institute of Church-State Studies
Baylor University, P.O. Box 97308 Waco, TX 76798-7308

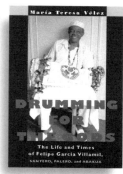

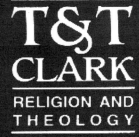

RELIGIOUS STUDIES
FROM ·ROUTLEDGE

Apocalyptic Bodies
The Biblical End of the World
in Text and Image
Tina Pippin

**Asceticism and the
New Testament**
*Edited by Leif E. Vaage and
Vincent L. Wimbush*

**Comparing Religions
Through Law**
Judaism and Islam
*Jacob Neusner and
Tamara Sonn*

**Four Stages of
Rabbinic Judaism**
Jacob Neusner

God and Goodness
A Natural Theological
Perspective
Mark Wynn

**God and the Creative
Imagination**
Metaphor, Symbol and Myth
in Religion and Theology
Paul Avis

The Israelites
An Introduction
Antony Kamm

**Jewish and Christian
Doctrines**
The Classics Compared
*Bruce Chilton and Jacob
Neusner*

**Jews, Christians and
Polytheists in the Ancient
Synagogue**
Edited by Steven Fine

**Knockin' on
Heaven's Door**
The Hebrew Bible and
Cultural Criticism
Roland Boer

Matthew's Gospel
David Graham

**Meanings of Death in
Rabbinic Judaism**
David Kraemer

**Miracles in Greco-Roman
Antiquity**
A Sourcebook for the Study
of New Testament Miracle
Stories
Wendy Cotter

The Multicultural Riddle
Rethinking National, Ethnic
and Religious Identities
Gerd Baumann

New Religious Movements
Challenge and Response
*Edited by Bryan Wilson and
Jamie Cresswell*

The Postzionism Debates
Knowledge and Power in
Israeli Culture
Laurence J. Silberstein

Religion and Culture
Michel Foucault
*Edited by
Jeremy Carrette*

**Sacred Languages
and Sacred Texts**
John Sawyer

Sikh Art and Literature
Edited by Kerry Brown

**Types of Authority in
Formative Christianity
and Judaism**
*Jacob Neusner and
Bruce Chilton*

Why Gods Persist
A Scientific Approach
to Religion
Robert Hinde

**Zionism and the
State of Israel**
A Moral Inquiry
Michael Prior

Expecting Armageddon
Edited by Jon R. Stone

Foucault and Religion
Spiritual Corporality and
Political Spirituality
Jeremy Carrette

God and Modernity
A New and Better Way to Do
Theology
Andrew Shanks

**Judaism and Islam
in Practice**
A Sourcebook
*Jacob Neusner, Tamara
Sonn, and Jonathan E.
Brockopp*

Psychology and Religion
An Introduction
Michael Argyle

One Nation Under God?
Religion and American
Culture
*Edited by Marjorie Garber
and Rebecca Walkowitz*

**The Concise Routledge
Encyclopedia of
Philosophy**

29 West 35th Street, New York, NY 10001-2299
AT BOOKSTORES, or call 1-800-634-7064
FAX 1-800-248-4724
www.routledge-ny.com

ROUTLEDGE

Society of Biblical Literature

The Dead Sea Scrolls at Fifty
Proceedings of the 1997 Society of Biblical Literature Qumran Section Meetings
Robert A. Kugler and Eileen M. Schuller, editors

Hidden untouched in caves for two millennia, the Dead Sea Scrolls now for fifty years have been poked and prodded to yield their treasure of knowledge about the history of early Jews and Christians. This veritable "who's  who" of international Scrolls research commemorates the fiftieth anniversary of the discovery of the Dead Sea Scrolls with essays focused on:
- The History of Dead Sea Scrolls Research
- The Scrolls and the Hebrew Bible/Old Testament, Early Judaism and the New Testament
- The Damascus Document
- The Future of Dead Sea Scrolls Research

The book includes 12 photographs, several recently released to the public for the first time.

Authors include George J. Brooke and Lawrence H. Schiffman; Emanuel Tov; Eugene Ulrich; Devorah Dimant; George J. Brooke; George W. E. Nickelsburg; John J. Collins; James H. Charlesworth; Carol A. Newsom; Florentino García Martínez and Julio Trebolle Barrera; Joseph Baumgarten; Philip R. Davies; Menahem Kister; John Kampen; Lawrence H. Schiffman and Marlene Schiffman.

Code: 063515   227 pages   (1999)
Paper: $49.95   ISBN: 0-7885-0543-2

Building Your New Testament Greek Vocabulary
Second Edition
Robert E. Van Voorst

Newly revised for this SBL edition, *Building Your New Testament Greek Vocabulary* provides students a user-friendly introduction to the vocabulary of New Testament Greek. Van Voorst helps the student to move away from rote  memorization toward better long-term vocabulary learning based on how Greek words are built and related to each other. He provides students with easy-to-remember English derivatives, lists the number of occurrences for each word learned, provides lists that are easily learned in a single vocabulary-learning session and, most importantly, organizes the book on the basis of word frequency and word families. New to this edition are helpful lists of verbs, prepositions, and particles.

Code: 060340   107 pages   (1999)
Paper: $7.50   ISBN: 0-7885-0552-1

Old Testament Exegesis
A Guide to the Methodology
Second Edition
Odil Hannes Steck
Translated by
James D. Nogalski

Code: 060339
207 pages
(1998)
Paper: $19.95
ISBN: 0-7885-0465-7

Customer Service • P.O. Box 116789, Atlanta, GA 30368-6789
Phone: 888-747-2354 (toll-free) or 404-727-2354 • Fax: 404-727-2348

Das Alte Testament Deutsch
Apokryphen

Neues Göttinger Bibelwerk.
In Verbindung mit Hans Hübner,
Ingo Kottsieper, Reinhard G. Kratz,
Hermann Lichtenberger, Karl Löning,
Manfred Oeming, Georg Sauer,
Odil Hannes Steck und Erich Zenger
herausgegeben von Otto Kaiser
und Lothar Perlitt.

This new series covers all OT
Apocrypha. It is the most detailed
commentary in German.

In preparation:
Band 1: Georg Sauer, **Jesus Sirach**

Band 2: Hermann Lichtenberger
Die Makkabäerbücher

Band 3: Erich Zenger / Karl Löning /
Manfred Oeming, **Judit und Tobit**

The complete works cover 5 volumes.
Subscription price 10% reduced.

Vol 4: Hans Hübner
Die Weisheit Salomons
Liber Sapientiae Salomonis
1999. 227 pp, Pb. $ 23,–
for subscribers of the series $ 21,–
ISBN 3-525-51404-2

After many years the first scholarly
Protestant commentary of the Book
of Wisdom for a wider audience.

Vol 5: Odil Hannes Steck /
Reinhard G. Kratz /
Ingo Kottsieper
Das Buch Baruch
Der Brief des Jeremia
Zusätze zu Ester und
Daniel
1998. 328 pp, Pb. $ 37,–
for subscribers of the series $ 34,–
ISBN 3-525-51405-0

The interpretation emphasizes the
relation of the apocrypha to the
canonical books of the Old Testament.

Prices vary according to exchange rates and do not
include postage.

For your order of for further information please
contact:
Vandenhoeck & Ruprecht, D-37070 Göttingen,
Fax: 0049-551-6959-17
E-mail: info@vandenhoeck-ruprecht.de
http://www.vandenhoeck-ruprecht.de

V&R
Vandenhoeck
& Ruprecht

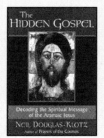

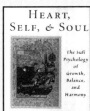

ALL

THE

HISTORY

OF

AMERICAN

RELIGION

CAN BE

FOUND

IN

ILLINOIS